MATHS IN ACTION

Advanced Higher Mathematics

Second Edition

E Mullan
C Chambers
W Richardson
P Westwood

OXFORD
UNIVERSITY PRESS

Great Clarendon Street, Oxford, OX2 6DP,
United Kingdom

Oxford University Press is a department of the University of Oxford.

It furthers the University's objective of excellence in research, scholarship, and education by publishing worldwide. Oxford is a registered trade mark of Oxford University Press in the UK and in certain other countries.

First published in 2015

British Library Cataloguing in Publication Data

Data available

ISBN 978-019-836421-4

10 9 8 7 6 5 4 3 2

Printed and bound in Great Britain by Ashford Colour Press Ltd, Gosport, Hampshire

Paper used in the production of this book is a natural, recyclable product made from wood grown in sustainable forests. The manufacturing process conforms to the environmental regulations of the country of origin.

The publisher would like to thank the following for permission to use their photographs:

p1: Sheila Terry/Science Photo Library; **p28:** GeorgiosArt/iStock; **p35:** Mariuszks/Dreamstime; **p42l&r:** Georgios Kollidas/Dreamstime; **p63:** Georgios Kollidas/Shutterstock; **p81:** Georgios Kollidas/Shutterstock; **p99:** Stefan Zachow/International Mathematical Union; **p126:** ZU_09/iStock; **p149:** Kamira/Shutterstock; **p152:** Georgios Kollidas/Dreamstime; **p166:** Georgios Kollidas/Shutterstock; **p175:** NYPL/Science Source/Science Photo Library; **p185:** Tinamou/Dreamstime; **p189:** Anthony Baggett/Dreamstime; **p206:** Sailko; **p216:** Institute of Astronomy Library/University of Cambridge; **p225:** School of Mathematics and Statistics/University of St. Andrews, Scotland; **p228l&r:** School of Mathematics and Statistics/University of St. Andrews, Scotland; **p265:** Georgios Kollidas/Dreamstime: **p279:** Mary Evans Picture Library; **p310:** ZU_09/iStock;

Contents

1 Formal proof

Historical note

Many mathematicians contributed to Number Theory. One of the most noted is Sophie Germain (1776–1831).

She wrote several papers and letters to other mathematicians of her time under the pseudonym M. LeBlanc because she feared that, being a woman, she would be ignored.

Her most famous correspondence was with Gauss who, without knowing her, gave her proofs on number theory a lot of praise. He only came to know her true identity after she intervened on his behalf during the French occupation of his town.

She did a lot of important work on Fermat's Last Theorem.

1.1 Some definitions

A **statement** is any sentence which is either true or false but not both. For example

a	$3 + 5 = 4$	False
b	$4 + 5 > 10$	False
c	$2x + 3x = 5x$	True

The **negation** of a statement can usually be constructed by putting '*not*' after the verb of the sentence. Where a statement is true its negation will be false and vice versa. For example

negation of a	$3 + 5 \neq 4$	True
negation of b	$4 + 5 \leqslant 10$	True
negation of c	$2x + 3x \neq 5x$	False

Compound statements

A **compound** statement can be formed from given statements by combining them in various ways. For example

By using AND	$(3 + 5 = 4)$ AND $(4 + 5 > 10)$	False
By using OR	$(3 + 5 = 4)$ OR $(4 + 5 > 10)$	False
By using IF...THEN	IF $(3 + 5 = 4)$ THEN $(4 + 5 > 10)$	True

When AND joins two statements, the compound statement is only true when both simple statements are true.

When OR joins two statements, the compound statement is true when at least one of the simple statements is true[1].

When IF ... THEN joins two statements, the compound statement is only false when the first simple statement is true and the second is false.

Truth tables

These statements can be summarised in 'truth tables'.

[1] In logic and in computing, a variation of the OR statement is also used. Called the *Exclusive Or* [XOR], it is only true when exactly one of the statements is true. That is, it is false when both statements are true.

For example the first compound table gives the truth values of A AND B for the different possible truth values of A and B.

A	B	Not A	Not B	A AND B	A OR B	IF A THEN B
T	T	F	F	T	T	T
T	F	F	T	F	T	F
F	T	T	F	F	T	T
F	F	T	T	F	F	T

If two statements have the same truth table then the statements are logically equivalent.

A **universal** statement refers to *all* items in a set.

Example 1 $2x + 3x = 5x$, for all $x \in R$.
Example 2 $x^2 + 1$ is odd for all $x \in Z$.

If a universal statement is false, this can be proved by citing *one* **counterexample**.

Example $x^2 + 1$ is odd for all x is false since for $x = 1, x^2 + 1 = 2$ which is even.

An **existential** statement states that there exists *at least one* item in a set that has a special property.

Example 1 There exists an x such that $2x + 3x \neq 5x$.
Example 2 There exists an x such that $x^2 + 1$ *is odd*.

If an existential statement is true, this can be proved by citing *one* example.

'For all x' is often denoted by '$\forall x$' and 'There exists an x' is often denoted by '$\exists x$'.

For all x, $2x + 3x = 5x$ is the same as $\forall x, 2x + 3x = 5x$.
There exists an x such that $2x + 3x \neq 5x$ is the same as
$\exists x$ such that (s.t.) $2x + 3x \neq 5x$ *or* $\exists x, 2x + 3x \neq 5x$.

Related implications

The *IF ... THEN* statement is often referred to as an **implication**.

For example, the theorem of Pythagoras is an implication.

IF the triangle ABC is right-angled at C THEN $c^2 = a^2 + b^2$.

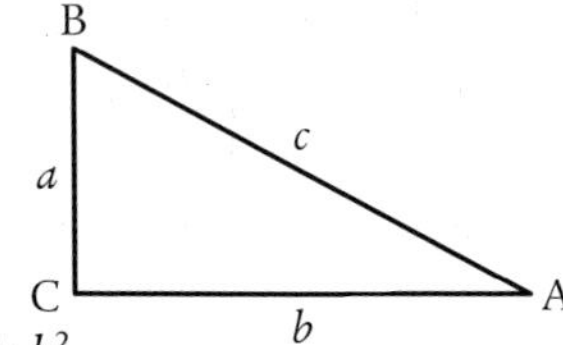

There are three related implications.

Its **inverse** is IF the triangle ABC is not right-angled at C THEN $c^2 \neq a^2 + b^2$.
Its **converse** is IF $c^2 = a^2 + b^2$ THEN the triangle ABC is right-angled at C.
Its **contrapositive** is IF $c^2 \neq a^2 + b^2$ THEN the triangle ABC is not right-angled at C.

Example 1

Write the inverse, converse and contrapositive of the statement
'IF the shape is a square THEN it has four sides.'

Its inverse is IF the shape is not a square THEN it does not have four sides.
Its converse is IF it has four sides THEN the shape is a square.
Its contrapositive is IF it does not have four sides THEN the shape is not a square.

The truth tables look like this.

A	B	Not A	Not B	implication: IF A THEN B	inverse: IF not A THEN not B	converse: IF B THEN A	contrapositive: IF not B THEN not A
T	T	F	F	T	T	T	T
T	F	F	T	F	T	T	F
F	T	T	F	T	F	F	T
F	F	T	T	T	T	T	T
				$A \Rightarrow B$	not $A \Rightarrow$ not B	$B \Rightarrow A$	not $B \Rightarrow$ not A

Notes
- In each case only 'True ⇒ False' is False.
- The truth tables for the original implication and the contrapositive are the same. That means they are logically equivalent.

  The original implication is true if and only if the contrapositive is true.
- If the original implication is true the inverse and converse need not be true.

Necessary and sufficient

The symbol '⇒' is used for '*implies*', for example
The triangle ABC is right-angled at C $\Rightarrow c^2 = a^2 + b^2$ is the same as 'IF the triangle ABC is right-angled at C THEN $c^2 = a^2 + b^2$'.

When the converse is also true
that is, $c^2 = a^2 + b^2 \Rightarrow$ the triangle ABC is right-angled at C
then we use the symbol '⇔' and write
the triangle ABC is right-angled at C $\Leftrightarrow c^2 = a^2 + b^2$.

The symbol '⇔' is often read as **'if and only if'**.
This is referred to as **two-way implication** or **equivalence**.

Consider the two statements

1 For n to be divisible by 4 it is **necessary** that it is divisible by 2.
2 For n to be divisible by 4 it is **sufficient** that it is divisible by 2.

Statement 1 is true: if $n = 4m \in Z$ then $n = 2(2m)$ and so it is divisible by 2.
Statement 2 is false: 6 is divisible by 2 but not by 4. A counterexample proves it false.

The two statements can be combined as

3 n is divisible by 4 if and only if it is divisible by 2.

Mathematically the statements can be written

1 $4|n \Rightarrow 2|n$ [The *necessary* statement]
2 $4|n \Leftarrow 2|n$ [The *sufficient* statement]
3 $4|n \Leftrightarrow 2|n$ [The *if and only if* statement]

Note that
- 1 is the converse of 2 (and vice versa).
- 3 is only true if both 1 and 2 are true.
- The truth table of 'equivalence' is

A	B	Not A	Not B
T	T	F	F
T	F	F	T
F	T	T	F
F	F	T	T

IF A THEN B
T
F
T
T

IF B THEN A
T
T
F
T

A if and only if B
T
F
F
T

Exercise 1.1

1 i Write the negation of each of these statements.
ii State whether the negation is true or false.

a $3x + 5x = 7x$ b $3 + 6 > 7$ c $4^3 \geqslant 3^4$

d $-1 \leqslant \sin x \leqslant 1$ e $\frac{\mathrm{d}}{\mathrm{d}x}\sin x = \cos x$ f $2x + 1$ is odd given $x \in W$

2 The negation of the statement 'All grass is green' is 'Not all grass is green' or 'There exists grass that is not green'. Write the negation of these statements.

a For all whole numbers $2x + 1 > 5$.

b For all x, $\frac{1}{x}$ exists.

c $\forall x,\ x^2 > 0$

d $\forall n,\ 2^n + 1$ is prime.

3 The negation of the statement 'There exists grass that is green' is 'All grass is not green'. State the negation of each of these statements and say whether it is true or false.

a Some numbers of the form $2x + 1$ are even.

b For some x, $2^x > 3^x$.

c There exists a natural number less than 1.

d There exists an even prime number.

e $\exists\ x$ such that $\ln x > \ln(x + 1)$.

f $\exists\ x$ such that $\sqrt{x} \notin R$.

4 For each implication, state its **i** inverse **ii** converse **iii** contrapositive.

a IF a shape is an isosceles triangle THEN it will have two equal sides.

b IF a whole number can be divided by 2 without remainder THEN it is even.

c IF $2x + 4 > 12$ THEN $x > 4$

d $\sqrt{x} > 1 \Rightarrow x > 1$

5 The converse of an implication can be written using the symbol '$\Leftarrow$'.
Example: $2x + 1 = 5 \Rightarrow x = 2$ has a converse $2x + 1 = 5 \Leftarrow x = 2$.
For these implications
i state the converse using '$\Leftarrow$'
ii say whether the implication and/or its converse is true
iii hence say whether the implication is two-way.

a $2x + 1 = 5 \Rightarrow x = 2$

b $x = y \Rightarrow x + z = y + z$

c $x = y \Rightarrow xz = yz$

d $x = y \Rightarrow \frac{x}{z} = \frac{y}{z},\ z \in N$

e $x = \frac{\pi}{6} \Rightarrow \sin x = \frac{1}{2}$

f $x = 1 \Rightarrow \ln x = 0$

g $x = 1 \Rightarrow x^2 = 1$

h x is even $\Rightarrow x^2$ is even

i $y = x^3 \Rightarrow \frac{dy}{dx} = 3x^2$

6 From each of these equivalences
i form two statements: the *necessary* and the *sufficient*
ii by finding a counterexample to either the necessary or the sufficient statement, show that each of these equivalences is false.

a $a = 6 \Leftrightarrow a^2 = 36$

b A shape is a square $\Leftrightarrow$ the shape has four equal sides.

c A team is to play football $\Leftrightarrow$ it has 11 players at the start.

d $t = 30$ if and only if $\sin t^\circ = 0.5$

e For integers a, b and c, $a|b$ and $b|c$ if and only if $a|c$.
[a|b means a divides b exactly]

f For integers a and b, $a^2|b^3 \Leftrightarrow a|b$.

7 Identify which of these pairs of statements form true equivalences and write them down using the symbol '$\Leftrightarrow$'.

a The shape is a triangle; the shape's internal angles sum to 180°.

b The shape is an isosceles triangle; the shape has one axis of symmetry.

c $2x^2 + 1 = 19;\ x = 3$

d $a \geqslant b;\ \ln a \geqslant \ln b$

e $a \geqslant b;\ \sin a \geqslant \sin b$

f $a \geqslant b;\ ac \geqslant bc,\ c \in W$

g $a \geqslant b;\ ac \geqslant bc,\ c \in R$

h $a \neq 0$ and $b \neq 0;\ ab \neq 0$

i $a = 0$ or $b = 0;\ ab = 0$

j $a = -b$ and $c = 0;\ a + b + c = 0$

8 Find a counterexample to disprove each of these universal statements.

a $\forall x \in W, 5x > 4x$

b $\forall x \in R, 2x \neq 2^x$

c $\forall x \in R, ax = bx \Rightarrow a = b$

d $\forall x \in Z, \sqrt{x^2} = x$

e $\forall x \in R, \sqrt{1 - \sin^2 x} = \cos x$

f $\forall a, b \in R, |a| + |b| \leqslant |a + b|$ where $|x| = \sqrt{x^2}$

g $\forall x \in W, e^{\ln x} = x$

9 Find an example to prove each of these existential statements.

a $\exists x \in W, 5x \leqslant 4x$

b $\exists x \in R, 2x = 2^x$

c $\exists a, b \in R, (a + b)^2 = a^2 + b^2$

d $\exists a, b \in R, \sin(a + b) = \sin a + \sin b$

e $\exists x \in R, \frac{x}{x} \neq 1$

f $\exists a, b \in R, |a| + |b| \leqslant |a + b|$ where $|x| = \sqrt{x^2}$

g $\exists x \in W, \tan^{-1}(\tan x) \neq x$

1.2 Direct proof

What is a proof?

A proof is an argument in which the truth of a statement is established, in a logical set of steps, from the truth of a given statement or set of statements.

The given statement is either a statement whose truth is to be taken for granted (an **axiom**), or a statement whose truth has been established by a previous proof (a **theorem**).

In a **direct proof** we move directly from statements whose truth is given, by a series of implications, to the truth of another statement.

Example 2

Given that $5x - 6 = 2x$ prove that $x = 2$.

	$5x - 6 = 2x$	$\Rightarrow$	$3x - 6 = 0$
	$3x - 6 = 0$	$\Rightarrow$	$3x = 6$
	$3x = 6$	$\Rightarrow$	$x = 2$
Thus	$5x - 6 = 2x$	$\Rightarrow$	$x = 2$
	$5x - 6 = 2x$ is true (given)		
Thus	$x = 2$ is true		which is what we wanted to prove.

If we represent the statement $5x - 6 = 2x$ by a, the statement $3x - 6 = 0$ by b, the statement $3x = 6$ by c and the statement $x = 2$ by d, we see that the proof takes the form

Given a prove d.		Given statement and declared goal
	$a \Rightarrow b$ $b \Rightarrow c$ $c \Rightarrow d$	Steps: a sequence of true implications
Thus	$a \Rightarrow d$	
	a is true (given)	
Thus	d is true.	Goal achieved.

This then is the shape of any direct proof:

Any number of linked implications leading to
given implies *goal*
and if *given* is true
this proves *goal* is true.

Care must be taken to ensure the linkage of the implications is as shown, namely $a \Rightarrow b, b \Rightarrow c, c \Rightarrow d$ etc.
The false linkage $a \Rightarrow b, c \Rightarrow b$ does not generally mean that $a \Rightarrow c$. For example, '$x = 10 \Rightarrow x$ is even', '$x = 20 \Rightarrow x$ is even' does not mean '$x = 10 \Rightarrow x = 20$'.
Each implication in the set of steps must be true or the proof fails. For example, if the implication $x^2 = 49 \Rightarrow x = 7$ occurs, then the conclusions reached will only be valid for, say, $x \in W$.

Example 3

This argument contains two errors. Find the steps that contain the errors.

Given $t \in R, t = \sqrt{3 - 2x + 4 + x}$, prove $x > 7$.

$$t = \sqrt{3 - 2x + 4 + x} \Rightarrow t = \sqrt{7 - x} \qquad 1$$

$$t = \sqrt{7 - x} \Rightarrow 7 - x > 0 \qquad 2$$

$$7 - x > 0 \Rightarrow x > 7 \qquad 3$$

Given $t \in R, t = \sqrt{3 - 2x + 4 + x}$ is true then $x > 7$ is true.

The first error occurs in line 2 where the true implication is $t = \sqrt{7 - x} \Rightarrow 7 - x \geqslant 0$.
The second error occurs in line 3 where the implication should be $7 - x \geqslant 0 \Rightarrow x \leqslant 7$.
The corrected proof for convenience can be written as

Given $t \in R, t = \sqrt{3 - 2x + 4 + x}$, prove $x \leqslant 7$.

$$t = \sqrt{3 - 2x + 4 + x} \Rightarrow t = \sqrt{7 - x} \qquad 1$$

$$t = \sqrt{7 - x} \Rightarrow 7 - x \geqslant 0 \qquad 2$$

$$7 - x \geqslant 0 \Rightarrow x \leqslant 7 \qquad 3$$

Given $t \in R, t = \sqrt{3 - 2x + 4 + x}$ is true then $x \leqslant 7$ is true.

Exercise 1.2

1 Here are two well-known false arguments.
Find the steps which contain errors.

a Given $x = y$, prove that $1 = 2$.

$x = y \Rightarrow x^2 = y^2 = xy$
$\Rightarrow x^2 - xy = x^2 - y^2$
$\Rightarrow x(x - y) = (x - y)(x + y)$
$\Rightarrow x = x + y$
$\Rightarrow x = 2x$ (since $x = y$)
$\Rightarrow 1 = 2$

Given $x = y$ is true, then $1 = 2$ is true.

b Given $\frac{1}{2} > \frac{1}{4}$, prove that $1 > 2$.

$\frac{1}{2} > \frac{1}{4}, \Rightarrow \ln\left(\frac{1}{2}\right) > \ln\left(\frac{1}{4}\right)$

$\Rightarrow \ln\left(\frac{1}{2}\right) > \ln\left(\left(\frac{1}{2}\right)^2\right)$

$\Rightarrow \ln\left(\frac{1}{2}\right) > 2\ln\left(\frac{1}{2}\right)$

$\Rightarrow 1 > 2$

Given $\frac{1}{2} > \frac{1}{4}$ is true then $1 > 2$ is true.

2 Read through each of these short proofs.
If you think there is a fault, state the line number and why it is wrong.

a Given $x \in Z$ and $x^2 + 3x = 3x + 16$ prove $x = 4$.

$x^2 + 3x = 3x + 16$	1
$\Rightarrow x^2 = 16$	2
$\Rightarrow x = 4$	3
If the given statements are true then $x = 4$ is true.	4

b Given that ABCD is a parallelogram and BC = 7, CD = 6, BD = 11 prove AC = 11.

ABCD is a parallelogram	$\Rightarrow$ AC = BD	1
	$\Rightarrow$ AC = 11 (since BD = 11)	2
If the given statements are true then AC = 11 is true.		3

c Given PQ = 12, PR = 5, QR = 13 prove triangle PQR is right-angled.

$12^2 = 144$ and $5^2 = 25$	1
$\Rightarrow 12^2 + 5^2 = 169$	2
$\Rightarrow PR^2 + PQ^2 = QR^2$ (since $13^2 = 169$)	3
$\Rightarrow$ triangle is right-angled at Q (By the converse of the theorem of Pythagoras)	4
If the given statements are true then triangle PQR is right-angled is true.	5

d Given $4 - 7(x - 3) < 2x + 5$, prove $x > -4$.

$4 - 7(x - 3) < 2x + 5$

$\Rightarrow \quad 4 - 7x + 21 < 2x + 5$	1
$\Rightarrow \quad -5x < 20$	2
$\Rightarrow \quad x > -4$	3
If the given statements are true then $x > -4$ is true.	4

e Given ln 8 and ln 3 are irrational and that $3^x = 8$, prove x is irrational.

$3^x = 8$

$\Rightarrow x\ln 3 = \ln 8$	1
$\Rightarrow x = \frac{\ln 3}{\ln 8}$	2
$\Rightarrow x = \frac{\text{an irrational number}}{\text{an irrational number}}$	3
$\Rightarrow x$ is an irrational number	4
If the given statements are true then x is irrational is true.	5

3 Look at the short proofs below, and for each write the line number(s) where you would insert the implication sign. ($\Rightarrow$)

a Given that $x^2 + 4x - 2 = 0$, prove $x = -2 \pm \sqrt{6}$

$x^2 + 4x - 2 = 0$	1
$(x + 2)^2 - 4 - 2 = 0$	2

$(x + 2)^2 = 6$ 3

$x + 2 = \pm \sqrt{6}$ 4

$x = -2 \pm \sqrt{6}$ 5

If the given statement is true then it is true that $x = -2 \pm \sqrt{6}$.

b Given x is an even number, prove x^2 is an even number.

x is an even number

$x = 2k$ where $k \in W$ 1

$x^2 = (2k)^2$ 2

$x^2 = 4k^2$ 3

$x^2 = 2(2k^2)$ 4

x^2 is an even number 5

If the given statement is true then it is true that x^2 is an even number.

c Given that AC = 15, AD = 9 and ABCD is a rectangle, prove DC = 12.

$AC^2 = 225$ 1

$AD^2 = 81$ 2

$DC^2 = AC^2 - AD^2$ 3

$DC^2 = 225 - 81$ 4

$DC^2 = 144$ 5

$DC = 12$ 6

If the given statements are true then it is true that DC = 12.

d Given $t = \dfrac{1}{2 - \sqrt{3}} - \sqrt{3}$, prove t is rational ($t \in Z$).

$t = \dfrac{1}{2 - \sqrt{3}} - \sqrt{3}$ 1

$t = \dfrac{1}{2 - \sqrt{3}} \times \dfrac{2 + \sqrt{3}}{2 + \sqrt{3}} - \sqrt{3}$ 2

$t = \dfrac{2 + \sqrt{3}}{4 - 3} - \sqrt{3}$ 3

$t = 2 + \sqrt{3} - \sqrt{3}$ 4

$t = 2$ 5

t is rational since $2 \in Z$. 6

If the given statement is true then it is true that t is rational.

4 Each part below consists of two implications (either of which may be true or false). If each pair of statements is true, then they may be replaced by a single equivalence. Either write the equivalence or give a counterexample to prove one of the statements false.

a $x = 7 \Rightarrow x^2 = 49$; $x^2 = 49, x \in N \Rightarrow x = 7$

b $x = 7 \Rightarrow x^2 = 49$ $x^2 = 49, x \in R \Rightarrow x = 7$

c A, B, C are collinear $\Rightarrow \overrightarrow{AC} = \overrightarrow{AB} + \overrightarrow{BC}$;

$\overrightarrow{AC} = \overrightarrow{AB} + \overrightarrow{BC} \Rightarrow$ A, B, C are collinear.

d a and $b \notin Z \Rightarrow a + b \notin Z$; $a + b \notin Z \Rightarrow a$ and $b \notin Z$

e a and $b \notin Z \Rightarrow ab \notin Z$; $ab \notin Z \Rightarrow a$ and $b \notin Z$

f $3x + 5 = 15 \Rightarrow x = 4$; $x = 4 \Rightarrow 3x + 5 = 15$

5 By finding a counterexample, prove that each of these conjectures is false.

a $u_n = n^3 - 6n^2 + 13n - 7, n \in N$, gives the sequence of odd numbers 1, 3, 5, ...

b Diagonals of a quadrilateral are equal $\Rightarrow$ the quadrilateral is a square.

c June has five Thursdays $\Rightarrow$ the first of June is a Thursday.

d (Note: $p \mid a$ reads as 'p divides a' and means p is a factor of a)
$p \mid (a + b)$ and $p \mid (b + c) \Rightarrow p \mid (a + c)$

e $\int x^n \, dx = \frac{1}{n+1} x^{n+1} + c, \quad \forall n \in Z$

f $S(n)$ is defined as the sum of the divisors of n other than n itself. For example, $S(10) = 1 + 2 + 5 = 8$.
Conjecture: $S(n) < n$ for all $n \in$ N.

6 A famous conjecture states that $2^k - 1$ is prime whenever k is prime.
Show that $k = 11$ is the smallest counterexample to this conjecture.

1.3 Constructing a direct proof

Looking for the right steps

Study the given statements and data.

- They may suggest some standard algorithm such as Pythagoras' Theorem, trigonometric rules, etc.
- If the number x is known to be even, it often helps to express it as $x = 2k, k \in W$.
  Likewise, if the number x is odd, it can help to express it as $x = 2k + 1, k \in W$.
- If $b \mid a$ then we can write $a = kb, k \in W$.

Study the required goal.

- It may be similar to other problems.
- Its form may be reminiscent of known formulae.
- Consider intermediate goals.
- Can the goal be expressed in another fashion?

Sometimes the steps come as a moment of *inspiration*. It is said that Gauss, at the age of 10, produced the following proof without instruction. He had been asked to find the sum of the numbers 1 to 100.

Example 4

Prove that if $S(n)$ is the sum of the first n natural numbers then $S(n) = \frac{1}{2}n(n + 1)$.

$S(n) = 1 + 2 + 3 + ... + (n - 1) + n$ (Given)

$\Rightarrow S(n) = n + (n - 1) + ... + 3 + 2 + 1$ (Reversing the order of terms)

Adding, we get $2S(n) = (n + 1) + (n + 1) + ... + (n + 1) + (n + 1)$ for n terms

$\Rightarrow 2S(n) = n(n + 1)$

$\Rightarrow S(n) = \frac{1}{2}n(n + 1)$

The inspiration is to a find a strategy which will eradicate the 'non-specific' part of the sequence represented by '...'. The formula then becomes apparent.

Proof by exhaustion

Example 5

Prove that $n^2 + 3n$ is divisible by 2 for all $n \in N$.

When something is divisible by 2 it can be expressed as $2k$ for some $k \in N$.
The question suggests we want to prove $\forall n, (n^2 + 3n) = 2a$, for some $a \in N$.
When we wish to consider divisibility by 2, it can often be useful to consider the only two cases possible, namely $n = 2k$ (n even) and $n = 2k + 1$(n odd).

Case 1 n is even $\Rightarrow n = 2k, k \in N$

$\Rightarrow n^2 + 3n = (2k)^2 + 3(2k)$

$\Rightarrow \quad = \mathbf{2}(2k^2 + 3k)$ (Deliberately identifying the factor 2)

$\Rightarrow \quad = 2a, a \in N$ (Since $(2k^2 + 3k) \in N$)

$\Rightarrow (n^2 + 3n)$ is divisible by 2 $\forall$ even n

Case 2 n is odd $\Rightarrow n = 2k - 1, k \in N$
$\Rightarrow n^2 + 3n = (2k - 1)^2 + 3(2k - 1)$
$\Rightarrow = \mathbf{2}(2k^2 + k - 1)$
$\Rightarrow = 2a, a \in N$ (since $(2k^2 + k - 1) \in N$)
$\Rightarrow (n^2 + 3n)$ is divisible by 2 $\forall$ odd n

$(n^2 + 3n)$ is divisible by 2 $\forall$ even n and $(n^2 + 3n)$ is divisible by 2 $\forall$ odd n
$\Rightarrow (n^2 + 3n)$ is divisible by 2 $\forall n \in N$.

This sort of proof is often called 'proof by exhaustion' where all cases are proved separately. If, say, we wish to prove $n^3 - 7n$ is divisible by 3 $\forall n \in N$ then there are only three cases to consider: $n = 3k$, $n = 3k + 1$ and $n = 3k + 2$. [That is, when we divide by 3, we must get a remainder of 0, 1, or 2.]

Example 6

Prove that $S = 4 + 16 + 64 + ... + 4^n = \frac{4}{3}(4^n - 1)$.

[As with Example 4, we desire a strategy for handling the sections denoted by '...'.
Here, spotting that the terms increase by a factor of 4 as the sum progresses, we could multiply throughout by 4. See what happens.]

$S = 4 + 16 + 64 + ... + 4^n$
$\Rightarrow 4S = 16 + 64 + ... + 4^n + 4^{n+1}$ (Multiplying throughout by 4)
$\Rightarrow 3S = 4^{n+1} - 4 = 4(4^n - 1)$ (Subtracting line 1 from line 2)
$\Rightarrow S = \frac{4}{3}(4^n - 1)$

Exercise 1.3

1 Use the method of Example 3 above to prove these statements.

a $2 + 4 + 6 + ... + 2n = n(n + 1)$ where $n \in W$.

b $1 + 3 + 5 + ... + (2n - 1) = n^2$ where $n \in W$.

2 Use the method of Example 5 to prove these statements.

a $3 + 9 + 27 + 81 + ... + 3^n = \frac{3}{2}(3^n - 1)$ where $n \in W$.

b $4 + 12 + 36 + ... + 4 \times 3^{n-1} = 2(3^n - 1)$ where $n \in W$.

3 When a whole number is divided by 2 there are only two possibilities: either it divides exactly or there is a remainder of 1. [See Example 4]
So any whole number can be written in the form $2k$ or $2k + 1$ where $k \in$ W.

a If $k \in$ N then these forms would look slightly different.
How would they look?

b Prove that $n(n + 1)$ is always divisible by 2 where $n \in N$.

c Prove that $n^3 - 7n$ is divisible by 3 where $n \in W$.

d Prove that the product of three consecutive numbers is divisible by 6.
[Hint: express the three numbers as n, $(n + 1)$ and $(n + 2)$.]

4 Prove by exhaustion that $2n^2 + 6n$ is divisible by 4, $\forall n \in N$.

5 Three edges of a tetrahedron meet at a vertex so that a right-angle is formed between each pair of edges. Prove that the base triangle cannot be right-angled.

6 This is an example of a classic problem: the stamp problem.
In my stamp box I only have 2p stamps and 5p stamps.

By considering even amounts and odd amounts prove that I can post packages which require stamps of any total value of 4p or more.

7 Conjecture: 'If n is odd, then $n^2 + 1$ is even'.

Give a direct proof of this conjecture.

8 Prove that $\sin x = k\sin(x + 2y) \Rightarrow \tan(x + y) = \frac{1 + k}{1 - k}\tan y$,

where $k \neq 1$ and $x, y, k, \in R$.

[Hints: **i** Start with left-hand side of implication.

ii Express $(x + 2y)$ as $((x + y) + y)$ and x as $((x + y) - y)$.

iii Expand using $\sin(A \pm B) = \sin A\cos B \pm \cos A\sin B$.

iv Divide throughout by $\cos(x + y)\cos y$ and make use of $\tan A = \frac{\sin A}{\cos A}$.

v Tidy up to get required result.]

9 By considering the *units digit* of the powers of 6, prove that $6^n + 4$, $n \in N$, is always divisible by 10.

10 **a** Prove the product of two consecutive even numbers is divisible by 8.

b By considering the factors of $3^{2n} - 1$, prove that it is divisible by 8.

c Prove that $3^{2n} + 7$ is divisible by 8 for all $n \in N$.

11 **a** $9 \times 11 = (10 - 1)(10 + 1) = 100 - 1 = 99$
$9 \times 110 = (10 - 1)(10 + 1)10 = (100 - 1)10 = 1000 - 10 = 990$
Use this arithmetic algorithm to calculate 9×1089.

b Prove that $9 \times 1\,099\,999\,989 = (100 - 1)(100\,000\,000 - 1)$.

12 Prove that the sum of the squares of three consecutive integers cannot end in a 1, 3, 6 or 8.
[Hint: let the three consecutive integers be $x - 1$, x and $x + 1$,
and try all 10 cases, namely when the units digit of x, $u = 1, 2, 3$, etc.
For example, if x has a units digit of 2 then $5x^2 + 1$ will have a units digit of 1.]

13 If n is an odd integer, prove that $n^2 - 1$ is divisible by 8.

14 Prove that the product of three consecutive numbers plus the middle number is always a perfect cube.

15 The arithmetic mean of two numbers $a, b \geqslant 0$ is defined as $\frac{a + b}{2}$.

The geometric mean of two numbers $a, b \geqslant 0$ is defined as $\sqrt{ab}$.

Prove that $\forall a, b \geqslant 0, \frac{a + b}{2} \geqslant \sqrt{ab}$.

[Hint: **i** Consider the fact that $(a - b)^2 \geqslant 0$.

ii Find a substitute for $a^2 + b^2$ using the expansion of $(a + b)^2$.]

16 **a** Prove by exhaustion that $k(k^2 + 5)$ is divisible by 6.

b Hence prove that, if n is even, $n(n^2 + 20)$ is divisible by 48.

1.4 Indirect proof

Proof by contradiction

Proof by contradiction is an **indirect proof** which is often referred to by the Latin expression, *reductio ad absurdum* (reduce to an absurdity), because it has this structure.

- Whatever statement we wish to prove, we assume its *negation* to be true.
- By a series of steps (valid implications) we arrive at some contradiction.
- Since all the steps are valid, it can only be the assumption which is false.
- If the negation is false, the original statement must be true.

Example 7

The 10 digits 0 to 9 can be arranged to form numbers which can then be summed.
Each digit should be used once and only once in the formation of the numbers, for example

$$10 + 23 + 45 + 6 + 7 + 8 + 9 = 108$$

or $$20 + 38 + 19 + 4 + 5 + 6 + 7 = 99$$

Prove that it is impossible to arrange the 10 digits into numbers whose sum is 100.

Proof
Assume there exists an arrangement of the digits which results in the sum of 100.
The sum of the digits is $0 + 1 + 2 + 3 + \dots + 8 + 9 = 45$.
Some of the digits will be used as *units* and the rest will be used as *tens*.
Let the whole number u represent the sum of the units digits. (Note: $u \in W$.)
Then $45 - u$ is the sum of the tens digits.

Assume there exists an arrangement of the digits which results in a sum of 100

$\Rightarrow \quad 100 = u + 10(45 - u)$
$\Rightarrow \quad 9u = 350$
$\Rightarrow \quad u = \dfrac{350}{9}$
$\Rightarrow \quad u \notin W$ a contradiction.
$\Rightarrow$ The assumption is false
$\Rightarrow$ It is impossible to arrange the 10 digits into numbers whose sum is 100.

Example 8

Prove $\dfrac{a+b}{2} \geqslant \sqrt{ab}, \forall a, b \in N$.

Assume $\dfrac{a+b}{2} < \sqrt{ab}$ for some $a, b \in N$
$\Rightarrow \quad a + b < 2\sqrt{ab}$
$\Rightarrow \quad (a + b)^2 < 4ab$ (Valid while $a, b \in N$)
$\Rightarrow \quad a^2 + 2ab + b^2 < 4ab$
$\Rightarrow \quad a^2 - 2ab + b^2 < 0$
$\Rightarrow \quad (a - b)^2 < 0$
$\Rightarrow \quad a, b \notin N$
$\Rightarrow$ The assumption is false.
$\Rightarrow \quad \dfrac{a+b}{2} \geqslant \sqrt{ab}, \forall a, b \in N$

Example 9

Prove that $\sqrt{2}$ is not rational, that is, $\sqrt{2} \notin Q$.

Assume that $\sqrt{2} \in Q$

$\Rightarrow \quad \exists\, a, b \in N$, where a and b have no common factors, such that $\sqrt{2} = \frac{a}{b}$

$\Rightarrow \quad a = b\sqrt{2}$

$\Rightarrow \quad a^2 = 2b^2$

$\Rightarrow \quad a^2$ is even

$\Rightarrow \quad a$ is even, so a has a factor of 2

Let $a = 2k$ where $k \in N$

Then $4k^2 = 2b^2$ (Since $a^2 = 2b^2$)

$\Rightarrow \quad b^2 = 2k^2$

$\Rightarrow \quad b^2$ is even

$\Rightarrow \quad b$ is even, so b has a factor of 2

Both a and b are even

$\Rightarrow \quad a$ and b have a common factor of 2.

We have a contradiction.

Thus $\sqrt{2}$ is not rational.

Proof by contrapositive

This type of proof depends on the fact that an implication and its contrapositive are logically equivalent. It can be better than proof by contradiction by virtue of the fact that the 'goal' is easier to see: in proof by contradiction we cannot always see ahead where the contradiction is going to appear.

Example 10

Prove that given $x, y \in N$, if their sum is even then they are either both odd or both even.

The contrapositive of this implication is 'If only one of x, y is odd then their sum is not even'.

Let x be odd and y be even. [The same argument will apply if we make x even and y odd.]

$\Rightarrow \exists k_1, k_2 \in N$ such that $x = 2k_1 + 1$ and $y = 2k_2$

$\Rightarrow x + y = 2k_1 + 1 + 2k_2 = 2(k_1 + k_2) + 1$

$\Rightarrow x + y$ is not even

So the contrapositive is true.

So the original implication is true.

Example 11

Prove that if $5x + 3$ is even then x is odd.

The contrapositive is 'If x is not odd then $5x + 3$ is not even'.

This can be written 'If x is even then $5x + 3$ is odd'.

x even $\Rightarrow \exists\, k \in N$ such that $x = 2k$

$\Rightarrow 5x + 3 = 5(2k) + 3 = 10k + 2 + 1 = 2(5k + 1) + 1$

$\Rightarrow 5x + 3$ is odd

So the contrapositive is true.

So the original implication is true.

Exercise 1.4

1 Prove by contradiction that $\sqrt{3}$ is irrational (that is, $\sqrt{3} \notin Q$).

2 Prove by contradiction that $\sqrt{7}$ is irrational.

3 Prove that $\frac{1}{2}(6\sqrt{3} - 1)$ is irrational.

4 Prove that no integers m and n can be found to satisfy the equation
$14m + 20n = 101$.
[Hint: assume that they do exist and consider factors of both sides.]

5 Prove that no integers m and n can be found to satisfy the equation $14m + 21n = 100$.

6 a i Prove by contradiction 'If n is odd, then $n^2 + 1$ is even'.
[Hint: start with 'If n is odd, then $n^2 + 1$ is not even'.]
ii Compare this with a direct proof.

b i Use proof by contrapositive to show that if $n^2 + 1$ is even then n is odd.
ii Compare this with a direct proof if you can.
iii Compare it with a proof by contradiction.

7 Use proof by contrapositive to show that if $6x + 1$ is even then x is odd.

8 a Prove by contrapositive that if x^2 is even then x is even.
[This fact is needed for the above proof that $\sqrt{2}$ is irrational.]

b Prove by contrapositive that if $x^2 + 5x - 3$ is even then x is odd.

9 Use an indirect proof to show that $n^2 + n$ is even, $\forall n \in Z$.

10 Given $a, b \in N$, if $a + b\sqrt{2} = 3 + 4\sqrt{2}$ then $a = 3$ and $b = 4$.
Give a proof by contradiction of this conjecture.
[Note: the negation of '$a = 3$ AND $b = 4$' is '$a \neq 3$ OR $b \neq 4$'.]

11 Prove by contrapositive that if the sum of two real numbers is irrational then at least one of the numbers must be irrational. [$a + b \notin Q \Rightarrow a \notin Q$ or $b \notin Q$]

[Note: the negation of $a \notin Q$ OR $b \notin Q$ is $a \in Q$ AND $b \in Q$.]

12 Given $a, b \in Z$, if ab is even then at least one of a or b is even.
a Prove this **i** directly **ii** by contradiction **iii** by contrapositive.
b Compare methods.
c Prove that if ab is odd then a, b are both odd.

13 Conjecture: if we divide a number by 4 and get a remainder of 2 or 3 then the number is not a perfect square.
a State the contrapositive of the conjecture as simply as you can.
b Use proof by exhaustion to prove the contrapositive, and hence the original conjecture, is true.

14 Prove that if ab is irrational then one of a or b is irrational.

1.5 Proof by induction

You may have seen this curio at Higher.
A student worked in a pizza shop.
Using a blank pizza base, he put an olive on the circumference.
He then decided to add more olives, placing them one at a time on the circumference.
As he added an olive, he made a cut from that olive to every other already there.

He always made sure to detour to avoid going through any existing intersection.
He then counted the pieces of pizza he had made.
Here we see the state of the pizza after one, two, three, four and five olives have been placed.

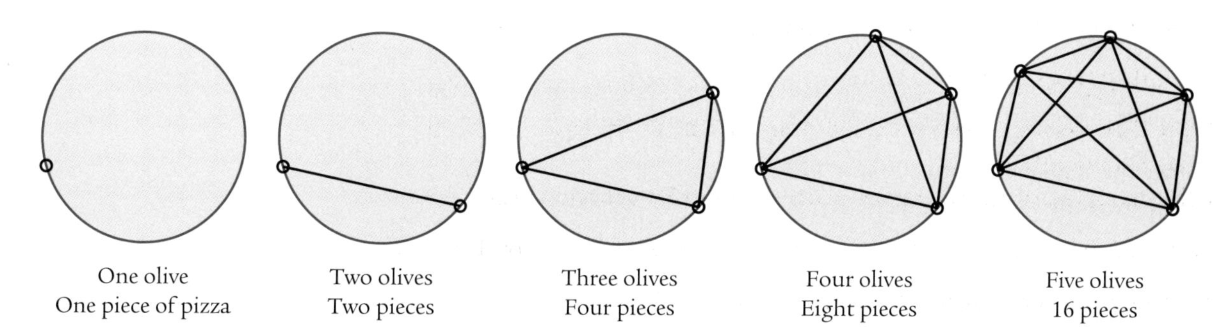

One olive One piece of pizza	Two olives Two pieces	Three olives Four pieces	Four olives Eight pieces	Five olives 16 pieces

If you were to make a conjecture after four olives had been placed you might be forgiven for suggesting $y = 2^{x-1}$ where y is the number of pieces made using x olives.
The case when $x = 5$ would seem to support your conjecture.
However, try $x = 6$. Where you expect $y = 32$, you get $y = 31$.

No matter how many cases are considered, the next case could well be the counterexample to prove the conjecture false.

A list of special cases, no matter how long, does not constitute a proof.

Using the same context, consider the number of cuts, c, made at each step:
0, 1, 3, 6, 10, 15, ... Given the storyline we can say that case $n + 1$ can be created from case n by adding n cuts.
That is, $c_{n+1} = c_n + n$, $c_1 = 0$.
It is conjectured that the nth case is described by $c_n = \frac{1}{2}n(n - 1)$.
Can we prove it?

The **principle of induction** provides a method to prove such a conjecture.

1 A general statement is made about $n \in \mathbb{Z}$, and demonstrated to be true for some value $n = a$.

2 It is then proved that if the statement is true for $n = k$ then it is true for $n = k + 1$.

3 We can conclude that since it is true for $n = a$ (By step 1)
then it is true for $n = a + 1$ (By step 2)
and it is true for $n = a + 2$ (By step 2)
etc.
and thus by induction it is true for all $n \geqslant a,\ n \in \mathbb{Z}$.

Example 12

Consider the sequence generated by the pizza problem.
Prove that $c_n = \frac{1}{2}n(n - 1)$ when $c_{n+1} = c_n + n$, $c_1 = 0$ for all $n \in \mathbb{N}$.

1 We can see that the statement is true for $n = 1$: $c_1 = \frac{1}{2} \cdot 1 \cdot (1 - 1) = 0$.

2 Assume that it is true for some value $n = k$.
So $c_k = \frac{1}{2}k(k - 1)$ (A)
Now consider when $n = k + 1$
in this case by referring to the recurrence relation
$$c_{k+1} = c_k + k$$

$\Rightarrow \quad c_{k+1} = \frac{1}{2}k(k-1) + k$ (Making use of the assumption at (A))
$\Rightarrow \quad c_{k+1} = \frac{1}{2}k(k-1+2)$
$\Rightarrow \quad c_{k+1} = \frac{1}{2}(k-1+1)(k+1)$
$\Rightarrow \quad c_{k+1} = \frac{1}{2}(k+1)(k+1-1)$
$\Rightarrow$ statement true for $n = k + 1$

Note: when we made the assumption at (A) we knew our target was to get $c_{k+1} = \frac{1}{2}(k+1)(k+1-1)$, the equivalent expression with $k + 1$ replacing k.

3 Since the statement is true for $n = 1$ and
since (true for $n = k$) $\Rightarrow$ (true for $n = k + 1$)
then by induction, it is true for $\forall n \geqslant 1, n \in N$.

Example 13

Prove that $n^3 + 2n$ is divisible by 3 $\forall n \geqslant 1, n \in N$.

1 It is true for the lowest required value, namely 1, since $1^3 + 2 \cdot 1 = 3$ which is divisible by 3.

2 Assume that it is true for $n = k$.

Thus $k^3 + 2k$ is divisible by $3 \Rightarrow k^3 + 2k = 3m, m \in N$. (B)

Consider when $n = k + 1$

$$\begin{aligned}(k+1)^3 + 2(k+1) &= k^3 + 3k^2 + 3k + 1 + 2k + 2\\ &= k^3 + 3k^2 + 5k + 3\\ &= k^3 + 2k + 3k^2 + 3k + 3\\ &= 3m + 3(k^2 + k + 1) \quad \text{(Making use of (B))}\\ &= 3m_1, m_1 \in N\end{aligned}$$

$\Rightarrow$ statement true for $n = k + 1$

3 Since the statement is true for $n = 1$ and
since (true for $n = k$) $\Rightarrow$ (true for $n = k + 1$)
then by induction, it is true for $\forall n \geqslant 1, n \in N$.

Example 14

Prove that $2^n > n, \forall n \in N$.

1 The statement is true for $n = 1$, since $2^1 > 1$.

2 Assume it is true for $n = k$.
So $2^k > k$ (C)
Consider when $n = k + 1$
$\Rightarrow 2^{k+1} = 2 \cdot 2^k$
$\Rightarrow 2^{k+1} > 2k$ (Making use of (C))
$\Rightarrow 2^{k+1} > k + k$
$\Rightarrow 2^{k+1} > k + 1$
$\Rightarrow$ statement true for $n = k + 1$.

3 Since the statement is true for $n = 1$ and

since (true for $n = k$) $\Rightarrow$ (true for $n = k + 1$)

then by induction, it is true for $\forall n \geqslant 1, n \in N$.

Exercise 1.5

1 A recurrence relation, $u_{n+1} = u_n + 2n + 2$, $u_1 = 1$, generates the sequence 1, 5, 11, ...

Prove by induction that the nth term of the sequence is $u_n = n^2 + n - 1$.

2 Prove that the recurrence relation defined by $u_{n+1} = u_n + 4n + 4$, $u_1 = 4$, has an nth term, $u_n = 2n(n + 1)$.

3 A particular linear recurrence relation is defined by $u_{n+1} = 2u_n + 1$, $u_1 = 2$. Prove that $u_n = 3 \times 2^{n-1} - 1$.

4 Examine the number pattern being generated.

$1 = 1^2$

$1 + 3 = 2^2$

$1 + 3 + 5 = 3^2$

$1 + 3 + 5 + 7 = 4^2$

a Make a conjecture about the sum of the first n odd numbers.

b Prove your conjecture by induction.

5 The pentagonal number pattern is generated by considering the number of points generated in a diagram similar to that shown as the number of pentagons increases. Note the number of points per side increases by one each time.

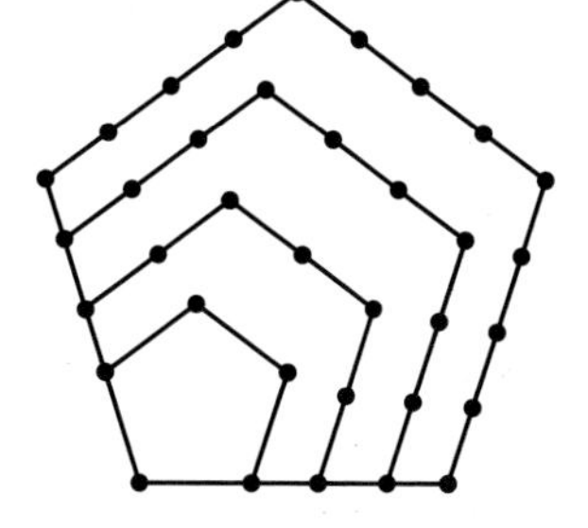

We get 1, 5, 12, 22, ...

It is easy to see that the addition of the nth pentagon will add $3(n - 1) + 1$ points to the total.

a Write the recurrence relation which generates the sequence.

b It has been conjectured that the formula for the nth pentagonal number is $u_n = \frac{n(3n - 1)}{2}$. Prove this by induction.

c Hexagonal numbers are generated in a similar fashion by considering hexagons. Prove that the nth hexagonal number is $n(2n - 1)$.

6 Prove by induction that

a $2^n > n, \forall\, n \in N$

b $3^n > 2^n, \forall\, n \in N$

c $2^n > n^2, \forall\, n > 4 \in N$

7 **a** Prove by induction that

$5 + 7 + 9 + ... + (2n - 1) = n^2 - 4, \forall n \geqslant 3, n \in N$

b Try forming a direct proof. Note that the sum has $(n - 2)$ terms.

8 Prove by induction that $2^{3n} - 1$ is divisible by 7, $\forall n \in N$.

9 **a** Prove by induction that $3^{2n} - 5$ is divisible by 4 $\forall n \in N$.

b Form a direct proof that 9^n is one more than a multiple of 8, that is, $9^n = 8k + 1$, $n, k \in N$

c **i** Hence prove directly that $3^{2n} - 5$, $n \in N$ is always divisible by 4.

ii Compare the amount of working needed here with that of part **a**.

10 The sequence 1, 1, 2, 3, 5, 8, 13, ... is called the Fibonacci sequence and is defined by the recurrence relation $F_{n+2} = F_{n+1} + F_n$, $F_1 = F_2 = 1$. The sequence first appeared in a problem in the book *Liber Abaci*, written by Leonardo De Pisa, also known as Fibonacci, in 1202.
It was the Frenchman Edouard Lucas who attached Fibonacci's name to the sequence over 600 years later. The sequence can be found in many contexts: Pascal's triangle and the Golden Ratio to name but two.

Prove these results by induction.

a Sum of n terms $F_1 + F_2 + F_3 + \ldots + F_n = F_{n+2} - 1$

b Sum of n even terms $F_2 + F_4 + F_6 + \ldots + F_{2n} = F_{2n+1} - 1$

c Sum of n odd terms $F_1 + F_3 + F_5 + \ldots + F_{2n-1} = F_{2n}$

d Sum of the squares of the terms $F_1^2 + F_2^2 + F_3^2 + \ldots + F_n^2 = F_n \times F_{n+1}$

11 a Prove that $\frac{d}{dx}(x^n) = nx^{n-1}, \forall n \in N$.
[Hint: use the product rule.]

b Why, in this context, would proof by induction not be appropriate to show
i $\frac{d}{dx}(x^n) = nx^{n-1}, \forall n \in Z$ ii $\frac{d}{dx}(x^n) = nx^{n-1}, \forall n \in Q$

12 Prove that, for all n greater than a particular value, $n! > 2^n$.
The particular value has to be stated in the first part of the proof.

13 Prove by induction that, with unlimited supplies of 4p and 7p stamps, you can make up postage to any value of 18p or more.

14 The fundamental theorem of arithmetic states that every natural number greater than 1 is either prime or can be expressed uniquely as the product of primes (See Section **16.2**).
Prove by induction the lesser result that every natural number greater than 1 is either prime or can be expressed as the product of primes.
[Hint: the assumption to make is that every number up to $n = k$ is either prime or can be expressed as a product of primes.]

1.6 Harder mixed examples

These examples require you to use a variety of forms of proof.

Exercise 1.6

1 a Form a direct proof that 16^n can be expressed in the form $15k + 1$ where $n, k \in N$.

b Hence prove by contradiction that $4^{2n} + 5$ is never divisible by 15.

2 The Arithmetic/Geometric Mean (A/GM) Inequality with three terms looks like this: $\frac{a_1 + a_2 + a_3}{3} \geqslant \sqrt[3]{a_1 a_2 a_3}$
where $\frac{a_1 + a_2 + a_3}{3}$ is the arithmetic mean and $\sqrt[3]{a_1 a_2 a_3}$ is the geometric mean of the three numbers a_1, a_2, a_3.
You are given that p, q and r are three non-negative real numbers such that $(1 + p)(1 + q)(1 + r) = 8$.

a Show that the given statement is equivalent to $1 + (p + q + r) + (pq + qr + rp) + pqr = 8$.

b Use the A/GM inequality with $a_1 = p$, $a_2 = q$, $a_3 = r$ to form a useful inequality.

c Use the A/GM inequality with $a_1 = pq$, $a_2 = qr$, $a_3 = rp$ to form another useful inequality.

d Combine the above three parts to form a direct proof that $pqr \leq 1$.

3 Prove that $(a + b)^3 \geqslant \frac{27}{4}a^2b, \forall a, b \geqslant 0$.

[Hint: try a couple of values for a and b just to convince yourself that it is true and get a feel for the inequality. Use the A/GM inequality for three terms. How can you usefully express a and b as three terms? Find this and the proof takes only two or three lines.]

4 Give a direct proof of this statement.
Every square number S has the form $5n$ or $5n + 1$ or $5n - 1, n \in N$.

Review 1

1 Form a direct proof that $2 + 4 + 6 + ... + 2n = n(n + 1)$ where $n \in W$.

2 Prove directly that $[(a + b)^2 - (a - b)^2 > 0$ AND $a > 0] \Rightarrow b > 0$.

3 Give a counterexample to prove that this statement is false.
'If the diagonals of a quadrilateral intersect at 90° then the quadrilateral is a rhombus'.

4 Prove by contradiction that $\sqrt{11}$ is irrational.

5 Prove by contrapositive that if $x^2 + 4x - 1$ is odd then x is even.

6 Prove by induction that $2 + 5 + 8 + ... + (3n - 1) = \frac{1}{2}n(3n + 1)$, for all $n \geqslant 1, n \in N$.

7 a Prove by induction that $n(n^2 - 1)(3n + 2)$ is divisible by 24.

b i Prove directly that the product of two consecutive numbers is divisible by 2.
ii Prove directly that the product of three consecutive numbers is divisible by 6.
iii Hence prove directly that $n(n^2 - 1)(3n + 2)$ is divisible by 24.

Summary 1

1 a Let a, b, c represent **statements** which can be either true or false but not both.

b The **negation** of a, *not a*, is true when a is false and false when a is true.

c Statements can be combined to form compound statements.

a AND b	[true when both a and b are true]
a OR b	[false only when both a and b are false]
IF a THEN b	[false only when 'a is true' implies 'b is false']

d A **universal** statement refers to all items in a set: 'for all x' is written $\forall x$.

A universal statement can be disproved if one **counterexample** can be cited.

e An **existential** statement refers to the existence of an item in a set:
'there exists an x' is written $\exists x$.

An existential statement can be proved if one example can be cited.

2 a 'IF a THEN b' is an implication. ($a \Rightarrow b$)

b 'IF *not a* THEN *not b*' is the **inverse** of 'IF a THEN b'.

c 'IF b THEN a' is the **converse** of 'IF a THEN b'. ($b \Rightarrow a$)

d 'IF *not b* THEN *not a*' is the **contrapositive** of 'IF a THEN b'.

e If both the implication and its converse are true the statements are said to be **equivalent**. ($a \Leftrightarrow b$)

f An implication and its contrapositive are logically equivalent.

3 a In **direct proof** we move directly from a statement whose truth is given, by a series of implications, to the truth of another statement.
Given a true, $a \Rightarrow b$, $b \Rightarrow c$, $c \Rightarrow d$, proves d true.

b **Indirect** proof – **proof by contradiction**.
The negation of that which we wish to prove is assumed and a contradiction is reached, which implies the assumption is false.

c Indirect proof – **proof by contrapositive**.
Rather than prove $a \Rightarrow b$ it can be easier to prove *not* $b \Rightarrow$ *not* a, which is equivalent to it.

d **Proof by induction**.
Wishing to prove some statement involving natural numbers, n

i We demonstrate its truth when $n = a$, some particular value of n.

ii We prove that 'true for $n = k$' implies 'true for $n = k + 1$'.

iii i and ii combine to prove by induction that the statement is true $\forall n \geqslant a$, $n \in N$.

2 Partial fractions

2.1 Proper and improper rational functions

A rational function is one expressed in fractional form whose numerator and denominator are polynomials.

A rational function is termed **proper** when the degree of the numerator is less than the degree of the denominator.

It is termed **improper** otherwise.

For example $\frac{x+1}{x^2+2}$, $\frac{x}{(x+1)(x+2)}$ and $\frac{2}{x^2+3x+1}$ are all proper rational functions

whereas $\frac{x^3+1}{x^2+2}$, $\frac{x}{x+2}$ and $\frac{x^2}{(x+1)(x+2)}$ are all improper rational functions.

Improper rational functions can be simplified by algebraic division.

Example 1

Simplify $\frac{x^3+4x^2-x+2}{x^2+x} = (x^3+4x^2-x+2) \div (x^2+x)$

$$\begin{array}{r|l} & x \\ \hline x^2+x & x^3+4x^2-x+2 \\ & x^3+x^2 \\ \hline & 3x^2-x+2 \end{array}$$

By what do we multiply x^2 to make x^3?
Answer: x

Multiply divisor by x.

Subtract result from dividend to find the remainder.

$$\begin{array}{r|l} & x+3 \\ \hline x^2+x & x^3+4x^2-x+2 \\ & x^3+x^2 \\ \hline & 3x^2-x+2 \\ & 3x^2+3x \\ \hline & -4x+2 \end{array}$$

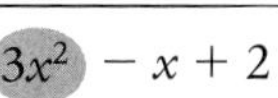

By what do we multiply x^2 to make $3x^2$?
Answer: 3

Multiply divisor by 3.

Subtract to find remainder.

The remainder is now a lower order than the divisor, so
$\frac{x^3+4x^2-x+2}{x^2+x} = x+3+\frac{-4x+2}{x^2+x}$; the fractional part is now a proper rational function.

Exercise 2.1

Simplify these rational functions by algebraic division.

1 $\frac{x^2+3x+5}{x+2}$

2 $\frac{x^2-2x+4}{x+3}$

3 $\frac{x^2+3x-5}{x-2}$

4 $\frac{3x^2-5x+1}{x-4}$

5 $\frac{3x^2-4x+5}{x^2+x+1}$

6 $\frac{x^2-x+1}{x^2+x-2}$

7 $\frac{x^2}{x^2-x+2}$

8 $\frac{x^3+3x^2+4x-5}{x^2+1}$

9 $\dfrac{x^3+1}{x^2-4}$ [Hint: express the numerator as $x^3 + 0x^2 + 0x + 1$.]

10 $\dfrac{3x^2-2x+4}{x-4}$

11 $\dfrac{x^2+3}{x^2-4}$

12 $\dfrac{x^4+3x^3+2x^2-3}{x^2+2x}$

13 $\dfrac{x^5+1}{x^3-x+1}$

14 $\dfrac{3x^3+7x-1}{x^2+3}$

General Forms

In the general form of a proper rational function the numerator is of an order one less than the denominator. For example, if the denominator is linear then the general form is

$\dfrac{a}{bx+c}$ where a and c take any integer values; $b \neq 0$; $bx + c \neq 0$.

If the denominator is a quadratic then the general form is

$\dfrac{ax+b}{cx^2+dx+e}$ where a, b, d and e take any integer values; $c \neq 0$; $cx^2 + dx + e \neq 0$.

2.2 Distinct linear factors in the denominator

When we encounter a rational function whose denominator is the product of two factors it is often of great help to decompose the function into the sum of two simpler rational functions.

These simpler functions are referred to as **partial fractions**.

Their denominators will be the factors of the denominator of the original function.

The simplest case to study is when the factors of the denominator are linear and distinct.

Example 2

Decompose $\dfrac{4x+1}{(x+1)(x-2)}$ into partial fractions.

We should be able to find two numbers A and B such that

$$\frac{4x+1}{(x+1)(x-2)} = \frac{A}{x+1} + \frac{B}{x-2}$$

$$= \frac{A}{x+1} + \frac{B}{x-2} = \frac{A(x-2)+B(x+1)}{(x+1)(x-2)} = \frac{(A+B)x-2A+B}{(x+1)(x-2)}$$

We wish $4x + 1 = (A + B)x - 2A + B$ for all values of x.

This can be achieved by equating coefficients.

$A + B = 4$

$-2A + B = 1$

Solving the system of equations gives $A = 1$ and $B = 3$.

Thus $\dfrac{4x+1}{(x+1)(x-2)} = \dfrac{1}{x+1} + \dfrac{3}{x-2}$

Alternative method: strictly speaking, the function is only defined when $x \neq -1$ and $x \neq 2$.

However, examining $4x + 1 = A(x - 2) + B(x + 1)$, we see that

- Letting $x = 2$, the equation becomes $9 = 3B$. Thus $B = 3$.
- Letting $x = -1$ the equation becomes $-3 = -3A$. Thus $A = 1$.

Exercise 2.2

Resolve each of these rational functions into its partial fractions.

1 $\frac{2x}{(x-1)(x+1)}$ **2** $\frac{10x}{(x-2)(x+3)}$ **3** $\frac{4x}{(x+1)(x+5)}$ **4** $\frac{20}{(x-3)(x+2)}$

5 $\frac{3}{(x-1)(x+2)}$ **6** $\frac{5}{(x+2)(x+3)}$ **7** $\frac{5x-14}{(x-2)(x-3)}$ **8** $\frac{3x-2}{(x+2)(x-2)}$

9 $\frac{15-2x}{(2x-1)(x+3)}$ **10** $\frac{7x+5}{(x-1)(x+3)}$ **11** $\frac{-x-7}{(x-3)(x+1)}$ **12** $\frac{6x-15}{x(x+3)}$

13 $\frac{3x+4}{x(x+2)}$ **14** $\frac{-3x-12}{x(x+6)}$ **15** $\frac{4-6x}{x(x+4)}$ **16** $\frac{7x-11}{(5-x)(x+1)}$

17 $\frac{11x+6}{(3x+1)(2x+3)}$ **18** $\frac{2x+7}{(2x-3)(4x-1)}$ **19** $\frac{5x-3}{x^2+x-30}$ **20** $\frac{5x-11}{x^2+4x+3}$

21 $\frac{4x+5}{x^2+3x+2}$ **22** $\frac{4x-10}{x^2-3x}$ **23** $\frac{6x-1}{4x^2-1}$ **24** $\frac{4x+1}{2x^2+3x+1}$

25 $\frac{2x^2-2x-6}{(x+1)(x+2)(x-1)}$ [Hint: three partial fractions.] **26** $\frac{6x^2-10x+2}{x^3-3x^2+2x}$

2.3 A repeated linear factor in the denominator

When a factor of the form $(ax+b)^2$ appears in the denominator, we would expect the general form to be $\frac{cx+d}{(ax+b)^2}$ that is with the numerator of order 1 given that the denominator is order 2. However, notice that

$$\begin{aligned}\frac{cx+d}{(ax+b)^2} &= \frac{\frac{c}{a}(ax+b)-\frac{cb}{a}+d}{(ax+b)^2}\\ &= \frac{\frac{c}{a}(ax+b)+\left(d-\frac{cb}{a}\right)}{(ax+b)^2}\\ &= \frac{\frac{c}{a}}{(ax+b)}+\frac{\left(d-\frac{cb}{a}\right)}{(ax+b)^2}\end{aligned}$$

Since a, b, c and d are constants, we see the general form in this case has constant numerators.

$$\frac{cx+d}{(ax+b)^2}=\frac{A}{(ax+b)}+\frac{B}{(ax+b)^2}$$

Example 3

Reduce $\frac{x^2-7x+9}{(x+2)(x-1)^2}$ to its partial fractions.

$$\begin{aligned}\frac{x^2-7x+9}{(x+2)(x-1)^2} &= \frac{A}{x+2}+\frac{B}{x-1}+\frac{C}{(x-1)^2}\\ &= \frac{A(x-1)^2+B(x+2)(x-1)+C(x+2)}{(x+2)(x-1)^2}\\ &= \frac{Ax^2-2Ax+A+Bx^2+Bx-2B+Cx+2C}{(x+2)(x-1)^2}\end{aligned}$$

We wish the numerators to be equal for all values of x.

$x^2-7x+9=(A+B)x^2+(-2A+B+C)x+(A-2B+2C)$

This can be achieved by equating the coefficients

of x^2 $\quad A+B=1 \quad (1)$

of x $\quad -2A+B+C=-7 \quad (2)$

of the constants. $\quad A-2B+2C=9 \quad (3)$

$2 \times (1) + (2)$	$3B + C = -5$	(4)	Eliminate A from (1) & (2)
$(1) - (3)$	$3B - 2C = -8$	(5)	Eliminate A from (1) & (3)
$(4) - (5)$	$3C = 3$	$\Rightarrow$ $C = 1$	Eliminate B
Substitute in (4)	$3B + 1 = -5$	$\Rightarrow$ $B = -2$	
Substitute in (1)	$A + (-2) = 1$	$\Rightarrow$ $A = 3$	

$$\frac{x^2 - 7x + 9}{(x+2)(x-1)^2} = \frac{3}{(x+2)} - \frac{2}{x-1} + \frac{1}{(x-1)^2}$$

Alternative method: strictly speaking, the function is only defined when $x \neq -2$ and $x \neq 1$.

However, examining $x^2 - 7x + 9 = A(x-1)^2 + B(x+2)(x-1) + C(x+2)$

- Letting $x = -2$, $(-2)^2 - 7 \cdot (-2) + 9 = A \cdot (-3)^2$ which gives $A = 3$.
- Letting $x = 1$, $(1)^2 - 7 \cdot (1) + 9 = C \cdot 3$ which gives $C = 1$.
- Letting $x = 0$, $(0)2 - 7 \cdot (0) + 9 = A + B \cdot (-2) + C \cdot 2$.

  Substituting $A = 3$ and $C = 1$ gives $B = 2$.

Exercise 2.3

Express each of these rational functions in partial fractions.

1 $\frac{3x^2 - 11x + 5}{(x-2)(x-1)^2}$ **2** $\frac{6x^2 + x - 7}{(x+2)^2(x-3)}$ **3** $\frac{4x^2 - 8x + 15}{(x-2)^2(x+1)}$ **4** $\frac{x^2 - x - 1}{x^2(x-1)}$

5 $\frac{x^2 + 6x - 3}{x(x-1)^2}$ **6** $\frac{4x^2 + 19x + 13}{(x-1)(x+2)^2}$ **7** $\frac{2x + 5}{(1-x)(x+2)^2}$ **8** $\frac{25}{(2-x)(2x+1)^2}$

9 $\frac{5x + 1}{x(2x+1)^2}$ **10** $\frac{x - 2}{x^2(3x-2)}$ **11** $\frac{1}{x^2 - 3x^3}$ **12** $\frac{16}{(x^2 - 2x - 3)(x-3)}$

13 $\frac{-x^2 + 7x - 6}{x^3 - 2x^2}$ **14** $\frac{3x^3 - 26x + 77}{(2x+1)(x-5)^2}$ **15** $\frac{3x^2 - 14x - 1}{(x^2 + 4x - 5)(x-1)}$ **16** $\frac{7x^2 + 1}{x^3 - x^2}$

17 $\frac{x^2 - 9x - 2}{(x-1)(x^2-1)}$ **18** $\frac{2x^2 + 7x + 3}{x^3 + 2x^2 + x}$

2.4 An irreducible quadratic factor in the denominator

Consider the function $f(x) = x^2 + 2x + 2$.

Its discriminant is $2^2 - 4 \times 1 \times 2 = -4$.

As this is less than zero, the function has no real roots

and thus the expression $x^2 + 2x + 2$ has no real factors (it is irreducible).

If an irreducible expression appears as a factor in the denominator of a rational function which has to be decomposed into its partial fractions then the general form $\frac{ax + b}{cx^2 + dx + e}$ has to be considered.

Example 4

Reduce $\frac{3x^2 + 2x + 1}{(x+1)(x^2 + 2x + 2)}$ into its partial fractions.

$$\frac{3x^2 + 2x + 1}{(x+1)(x^2 + 2x + 2)} = \frac{A}{x+1} + \frac{Bx + C}{x^2 + 2x + 2}$$

$$= \frac{A(x^2 + 2x + 2) + (Bx + C)(x+1)}{(x+1)(x^2 + 2x + 2)}$$

We wish the numerators to be equal for all values of x.

$$3x^2 + 2x + 1 = A(x^2 + 2x + 2) + (Bx + C)(x + 1)$$
$$= (A + B)x^2 + (2A + B + C)x + (2A + C)$$

This can be achieved by equating the coefficients

of x^2	$A + B = 3$	(1)	
of x	$2A + B + C = 2$	(2)	
of the constants	$2A + C = 1$	(3)	
(2) − (1)	$A + C = -1$	(4)	Eliminating B
(3) − (2)	$A = 2$		
Substitute in (4)	$2 + C = -1 \Rightarrow C = -3$		
Substitute in (1)	$2 + B = 3 \quad \Rightarrow B = 1$		

Thus $\dfrac{3x^2 + 2x + 1}{(x + 1)(x^2 + 2x + 2)} = \dfrac{2}{x + 1} + \dfrac{x - 3}{x^2 + 2x + 2}$

Alternative method: strictly speaking, the function is only defined when $x \neq -1$.

However, examining $3x^2 + 2x + 1 = A(x^2 + 2x + 2) + (Bx + C)(x + 1)$

- Letting $x = -1$, $\quad 3 - 2 + 1 = A(1 - 2 + 2) \Rightarrow A = 2$.
- Letting $x = 0$, $\quad 1 = 2A + C \Rightarrow 1 = 4 + C \Rightarrow C = -3$.
- Letting $x = 1$, $\quad 3 + 2 + 1 = 5A + 2(B + C) \Rightarrow 6 = 10 + 2B - 6 \Rightarrow B = 1$.

Exercise 2.4

Express each of these rational functions in partial fractions.

1 $\dfrac{3}{(x + 1)(x^2 - x + 1)}$

2 $\dfrac{8}{(1 - x)(x^2 + 2x + 5)}$

3 $\dfrac{16x^2}{(x - 3)(2x^2 - x + 1)}$

4 $\dfrac{2x^2 + 3x + 1}{(x - 1)(x^2 + x + 1)}$

5 $\dfrac{2x^2 - 11}{(x - 3)(x^2 - x + 1)}$

6 $\dfrac{3x - 2}{x^3 + 2x}$

7 $\dfrac{x^2 + 2x + 9}{(x^2 + 3)(x - 1)}$

8 $\dfrac{4x^2 + 5x + 13}{(x^2 + x + 3)(x + 1)}$

9 $\dfrac{4x^2 - 4x + 1}{(x^2 - x + 1)(x - 2)}$

10 $\dfrac{x^2 + 3x + 3}{(2x + 1)(x^2 + x + 2)}$

11 $\dfrac{x^2 + x}{x^3 - 2x^2 + 2x - 1}$

12 $\dfrac{8x^2 - 5x + 6}{x^3 + x^2 + 4}$

13 $\dfrac{x^2 - 2x + 2}{x^3 - 1}$

14 $\dfrac{x^2 - 10x - 8}{x^3 - 8}$

15 $\dfrac{4x^2 - 3x + 2}{x^3 - 1}$

Before attempting to resolve a proper rational function into its partial fractions the denominator should be carefully examined to see what general forms are to be used.

Resolve each proper rational function into its partial fractions.

16 $\dfrac{x}{(1 - x)(2 + x)}$

17 $\dfrac{2x - 1}{(2x + 1)(x - 3)}$

18 $\dfrac{3x}{(x - 2)(x + 1)}$

19 $\dfrac{2}{(x - 1)^2(x + 1)}$

20 $\dfrac{3x^2 - 4}{x(x^2 + 1)}$

21 $\dfrac{3}{x(x - 2)^2}$

22 $\dfrac{1}{x(x^2 + 4)}$

23 $\dfrac{4x - 3}{x^3(x + 1)}$

24 $\dfrac{5x - 3}{(x + 2)(x - 3)^2}$

25 $\dfrac{3x^2 + 2x}{(x + 2)(x^2 + 3)}$

26 $\dfrac{3}{1 - x^3}$

27 $\dfrac{x^2 + 1}{x(x^2 - 1)}$

28 $\dfrac{2x-1}{(x-2)(x+1)(x+3)}$ **29** $\dfrac{4x-1}{x^2(x^2-4)}$ **30** $\dfrac{1}{x^2-2}$

31 $\dfrac{x^2}{(x-3)^2}$ **32** $\dfrac{(x+13)^2}{(x-3)^2(x+5)}$ **33** $\dfrac{1-2x}{x^3+1}$

34 $\dfrac{x}{x^4-16}$ **35** $\dfrac{2x-1}{(x-3)^2(x+5)}$ **36** $\dfrac{3x}{(x+1)(3-x^2)}$

37 $\dfrac{2x^2-5x}{(x^2-1)(x^2-4)}$ **38** $\dfrac{1}{x^3(1-2x)}$ **39** $\dfrac{2x-7}{(x^2+4)(x-1)^2}$

40 $\dfrac{1}{x(x^2-1)^2}$ **41** $\dfrac{1}{x(x^2+4)^2}$

2.5 Improper rational functions

As demonstrated at the beginning of this section on partial fractions, an improper rational function can be reduced, by algebraic division, to the sum of a polynomial function and a *proper* rational function.

This proper rational function can then be resolved into its partial fractions.

Example 5

Resolve $\dfrac{x^3+4x^2-x+2}{x^2+x}$ into a polynomial function plus partial fractions.

$$\begin{array}{r|l} & \quad x+3 \\ \hline x^2+x & x^3+4x^2-x+2 \\ & x^3+x^2 \\ \hline & \quad 3x^2-x+2 \\ & \quad 3x^2+3x \\ \hline & \qquad -4x+2 \end{array}$$

The division gives us $\dfrac{x^3+4x^2-x+2}{x^2+x} = x+3+\dfrac{-4x+2}{x^2+x}$.

Resolving the rational portion into partial fractions.

$\dfrac{-4x+2}{x^2+x} = \dfrac{-4x+2}{x(x+1)} = \dfrac{A}{x} + \dfrac{B}{x+1}$

$\Rightarrow -4x+2 = A(x+1)+Bx$

Letting $x = 0$ $\quad A = 2$

Letting $x = -1$ $\quad B = -6$

Thus $\dfrac{x^3+4x^2-x+2}{x^2+x} = x+3+\dfrac{2}{x}-\dfrac{6}{x+1}$

Exercise 2.5

1 Resolve each of the improper rational functions into a polynomial function plus partial fractions.

a $\dfrac{x^2-x+6}{x^2+x-2}$ b $\dfrac{x^3-x^2-5x-7}{x^2-2x-3}$ c $\dfrac{x^3-5x^2+11x-12}{x^2-5x+6}$

d $\dfrac{2x^2-7}{x^2-4}$ e $\dfrac{x^3-3x}{x^2-x-2}$ f $\dfrac{x^2}{(x-1)^2}$

g $\dfrac{x^3 + 2}{x(x^2 - 3)}$ h $\dfrac{x^4 + 1}{x^3 + 2x}$ i $\dfrac{3x^4 + 4x^3 + 6x^2 + 2x - 1}{x^3 + x^2}$

j $\dfrac{(x + 2)(x - 2)}{(x + 1)(x - 1)}$ k $\dfrac{(x + 3)(x - 1)}{(x + 2)(x + 1)}$ l $\dfrac{(x + 1)(x - 2)(x + 3)}{(x - 1)(x - 3)}$

2 Assuming $\dfrac{x^2}{(x + a)(x + b)}$ can be expressed in the form $A + \dfrac{B}{x + a} + \dfrac{C}{x + b}$ find expressions for A, B and C in terms of a and b.

Review 2

1 Resolve these rational functions into partial fractions.

a $\dfrac{x + 14}{(x - 4)(x + 2)}$ b $\dfrac{1 + x - 3x^2}{(x - 2)(x + 1)^2}$ c $\dfrac{5x^2 + 6x + 7}{(x - 1)(x^2 + 2x + 3)}$

2 Factorise the denominator and then resolve these rational functions into partial fractions.

a $\dfrac{x + 3}{x^3 - x}$ b $\dfrac{x^2 - 3x + 3}{x^2 - x^3}$ c $\dfrac{1 - 2x - x^2}{x^3 + x^2 + x}$

3 Express each improper rational function as the sum of a polynomial function and partial fractions.

a $\dfrac{x^2 + 2}{(x - 1)(x + 2)}$ b $\dfrac{x^4 + 2x^2 - 2x + 1}{x^3 + x}$

Summary 2

1 A **proper** rational function can be resolved into **partial fractions**.

There are three basic cases.

a The factors of the denominator are distinct linear functions.

$$\frac{ax + b}{(cx + d)(ex + f)} = \frac{A}{cx + d} + \frac{B}{ex + f}$$

b The denominator contains a repeated linear factor.

$$\frac{ax^2 + bx + c}{(dx + e)(fx + g)^2} = \frac{A}{dx + e} + \frac{B}{fx + g} + \frac{C}{(fx + g)^2}$$

c The denominator contains an irreducible quadratic factor.

$$\frac{ax^2 + bx + c}{(dx + e)(fx^2 + gx + h)^2} = \frac{A}{dx + e} + \frac{Bx + C}{fx^2 + gx + h}$$

2 In particular examples the values of the upper-case constants can be ascertained by suitable selection of convenient values of x.

3 An **improper** rational function can be reduced to a polynomial and a proper rational function by the process of algebraic division.

3 The binomial theorem

Historical note

Blaise Pascal was a French mathematician born in 1623. He lived through the French Revolution, invented one of the earliest calculating machines and developed much new material.

In 1654 an expert gambler, the Chevalier de Méré, consulted him about certain problems to do with games of chance.

Pascal wrote to his friend, Pierre De Fermat, about the problems and between them they produced what was to become the Theory of Probability. It was while working on this that he produced a treatise called *Traité du triangle arithmétique* in which he discussed a number pattern which now bears his name.

3.1 Introduction

This exercise introduces **Pascal's triangle** and explores some of its properties.

Exercise 3.1

1 When two coins are tossed, we can use a tree diagram to help us enumerate the possible outcomes.

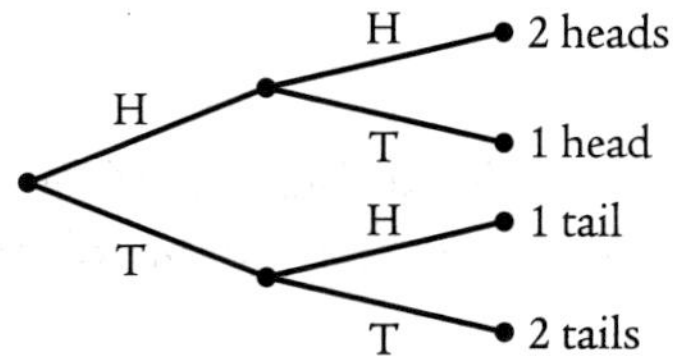

Summary of the four outcomes			
Number of heads	0	1	2
Frequency	1	2	1

a Construct a tree diagram to help you complete the table which summarises the eight possible outcomes when three coins are tossed.

Summary of the eight outcomes				
Number of heads	0	1	2	3
Frequency	1			

b Copy and complete the table which summarises the 16 possible outcomes when four coins are tossed.

Summary of the 16 outcomes					
Number of heads	0	1	2	3	4
Frequency	1				

2 $(x+y)^2 = x^2 + 2xy + y^2$

This multiplication can be represented in tabular form as in Table 1, or more compactly, using coefficients only, as in Table 2.

Table 1

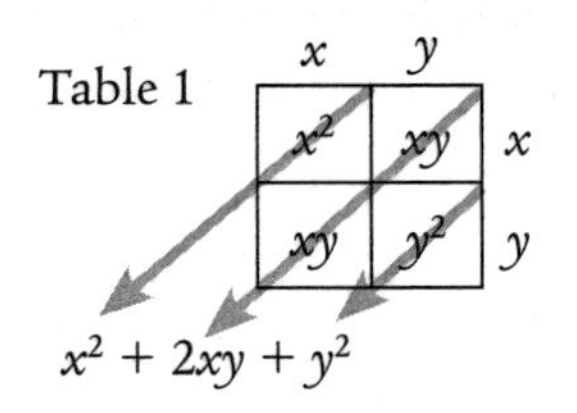

Table 2

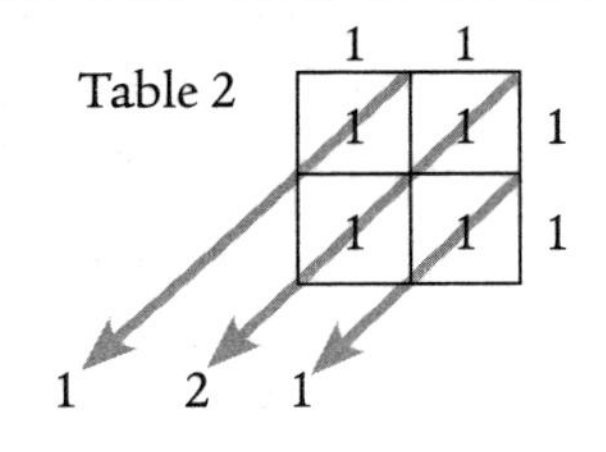

For $(x+y)^3 = (x+y)(x+y)^2 = (x+y)(x^2 + 2xy + y^2)$ a similar compact table produces

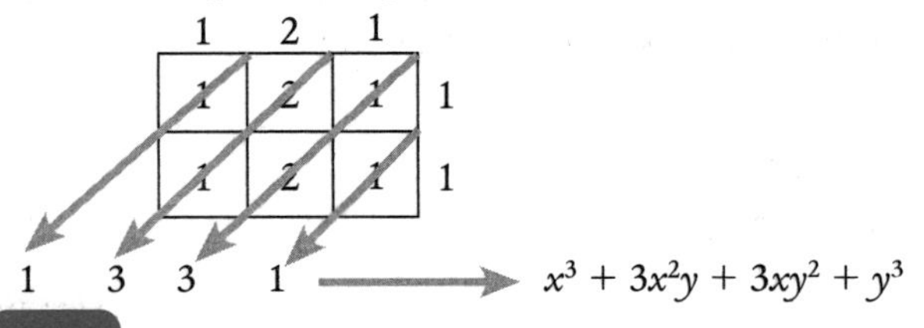

Note
- the descending powers of x
- the ascending powers of y

a Use this technique to expand **i** $(x + y)^4$ **ii** $(x + y)^5$ **iii** $(x + y)^6$

b Compare these results with the tables of question 1.

3 The coefficients of these expansions, arranged in order, form the number pattern known as Pascal's triangle.

	A	B	C	D	E	F	G	H	I	J
1		0	1	2	3	4	5	6	7	8
2	0	1								
3	1	1	1							
4	2	1	2	1						
5	3	1	3	3	1					
6	4	1	4	6	4	1				
7	5	1	5	10	10	5	1			
8	6	1	6	15	20	15	6	1		
9	7	1	7	21	35	35	21	7	1	
10	8	1	8	28	56	70	56	28	8	1
11	9	1	9	36	84	126	126	84	36	9
12	10	1	10	45	120	210	252	210	120	45
13	11	1	11	55	165	330	462	462	330	165
14	12	1	12	66	220	495	792	924	792	495

Each entry in the triangle is the sum of two entries, the one immediately above it and the one above it and to the left.

This spreadsheet has been created to build Pascal's triangle.

1
- In B1 enter 0.
- In C1 enter the formula '=B1 + 1'.
- Fill right [to column J for the moment].

2
- In A2 enter 0.
- In A3 enter the formula '=A2 + 1'.
- Fill down [to row 14 for the moment].

The row and column thus created are to be used as a coordinate reference system and do not form part of the triangle. Give them a grey background to emphasise this. Note that the system makes use of a row 0 and column 0. Now we find the triangle entries.

3
- In B2 enter 1.
- Fill down.

4
- In C3 enter the formula '= B2 + C2'.
- Fill down.
- Highlight all of C3 to J14 and 'Fill right'.

5
- Delete zero entries to highlight the triangular pattern.

a The formula for the entry in row n in column 0 is $u_n = 1$.
The formula for the entry in row n in column 1 is $u_n = n$.
Find similar formulae for **i** column 2 **ii** column 3.

b The coefficients of the expansion $(x + y)^n$ are to be found in row n.
By examining the symmetry in the rows, write the expansion of
i $(x + y)^8$ **ii** $(x + y)^9$ **iii** $(x + y)^{10}$

c Each entry can be referenced using a number pair given in the format (row, column), for example (5, 3) is the entry 10 in the 5th row, 3rd column; (4, 2) is the entry 6 in the 4th row, 2nd column.
Traditionally we refer to row n and column r as (n, r).

i Identify the entries in (5, 0), (5, 1), (5, 2), (5, 3), (5, 4) and (5, 5).
Comment on the symmetry by completing the equation $(n, r) = \dots$

ii In general, is entry $(a, b) = (b, a)$?
Note that the property used to build the triangle is that
$(n, r-1) + (n, r) = (n+1, r)$

d There are many patterns to be found in the triangle.
i Why should the sum of any two adjacent numbers in column 2 always be a perfect square?
ii Diagonals which slope up to the right can be identified by giving the row reference in which they start. Explore the sum of their entries.

For example Diagonal 1: 1 $= 1$
Diagonal 2: 1 $= 1$
Diagonal 3: $1 + 1 = 2$
Diagonal 4: $1 + 2 = 3$
Diagonal 5: $1 + 3 + 1 = 5$
Diagonal 6: $1 + 4 + 3 = 8$

These are known as the Fibonacci numbers. If F_n is the nth Fibonacci number, investigate the quotient $F_{n+1} \div F_n$.

Look for more patterns!

e Isaac Newton explored the development of the triangle *upwards* to study the expansion of expressions of the form $(x + y)^{-n}$. Investigate such an upward development.

3.2 The factorial function

Example 1

Six cyclists enter a race. All six finish at different times.
There is a first and a second prize.

a How many different ways can the cyclists finish the race?

b How many different ways can the prizes be awarded?

a There are six different possible winners.
For each possibility there are five possible seconds $6 \times 5 = 30$ ways of getting a first and a second
For each of these, there are four possible thirds $6 \times 5 \times 4 = 120$ ways of getting a first, second and third
For each of these, there are three possible fourths $6 \times 5 \times 4 \times 3 = 360$
For each of these, there are two possible fifths $6 \times 5 \times 4 \times 3 \times 2 = 720$
For each of these, there is only one possible last $6 \times 5 \times 4 \times 3 \times 2 \times 1 = 720$

b Looking at the working above we see that there are
$6 \times 5 = 30$ ways of getting a first and second prize.

Calculations similar to $6 \times 5 \times 4 \times 3 \times 2 \times 1 = 720$ appear often enough for there to be a special function created to represent them.

$n!$, read as n factorial, is defined as $n \times (n-1) \times (n-2) \times \ldots \times 3 \times 2 \times 1, n \in W$
For example $6! = 6 \times 5 \times 4 \times 3 \times 2 \times 1 = 720$

Most calculators carry this function. $n!$

Part **b** of Example **1** can be answered using factorials when you note that

$$6 \times 5 = \frac{6 \times 5 \times 4 \times 3 \times 2 \times 1}{4 \times 3 \times 2 \times 1} = \frac{6!}{4!}$$

This calculation is also supported by most calculators: look for ${}^nP_r$

It calculates the number of ways of arranging r objects when they are first to be selected from a pool of n objects.

The cycling example required the number of ways of arranging two cyclists when they are first to be selected from a pool of six cyclists.

$${}^nP_r = \frac{n!}{(n-r)!}$$

${}^6P_2 = 6! \div (6-2)! = 30$

P refers to the word **permutation**, which means **arrangement**.

Example 2

From a palette of seven colours you can pick four to blend.
How many ways can this be done?

The order in which the colours get blended does not matter.
Red, blue, yellow, green is the same choice as *red, blue, green, yellow*.

There are $4 \times 3 \times 2 \times 1 = 4! = 24$ ways of arranging four colours, so ${}^7P_4$, which includes all of these ways, will be 24 times too big.

We get our desired answer by performing the calculation ${}^7P_4 \div 4! = 35$.

This also is a very common type of problem and this calculation has a special function ${}^nC_r$ supported by most calculators: look for ${}^nC_r$

C refers to the word **combination**, which means selection *without* arrangement.

$${}^nC_r = \frac{n!}{r!(n-r)!}$$

Example 3

Hobson's choice

Hobson hired out horses. You paid your money and got the horse of your choice – as long as you chose the horse he offered you.

How many ways can you pick one horse when there is only one horse from which to pick?

$${}^1C_1 = \frac{1!}{1!(1-1)!} = \frac{1!}{1! \times 0!}$$

We know the answer is that there is only one way.
For this to make sense we must give a value of 1 to 0!.

As a definition we have $0! = 1$

Notes
- The domain of the factorial function is W, the set of whole numbers.
- The functions can be found in the maths menu of most graphic calculators.
- On a spreadsheet they can be found as

  = FACT(n), = PERMUT(n, r), = COMBIN(n, r)

Exercise 3.2

1 a Use your calculator/spreadsheet to obtain values for
  i 4! ii 6! iii 0!

  b Describe what happens when you attempt to get i $-4!$ ii $(-4)!$ iii 4.2!

2 a The combination on the lock on my case uses the four digits 1, 2, 3 and 4. I have forgotten the order in which they appear.
  How many different ways can they be arranged?

  b In a game of Scrabble a player has seven different letters.
  He rearranges them, looking for words.
  How many different arrangements can he make of the seven letters?

  c A pack of cards has 52 different cards.
  Calculate the number of ways these can be arranged, giving your answer correct to 3 significant figures.

3 a Evaluate i $\frac{7!}{3!}$ ii $\frac{10!}{6!}$ iii $\frac{12!}{11!}$

  b Can you account for the fact that the values of these divisions are all whole numbers?

c Use the ^nP_r facility on your calculator to evaluate the same expressions.
[Hint: the first one will require $^7P_{7-3}$]

4 a From a class of 23 students, three have to be selected to be class representative, secretary and treasurer of the newly formed student committee.
In how many different ways can this be done?

b At the bank, a customer invents her own personal identification number (PIN) by choosing four digits.
Given that there are 10 different digits, how many arrangements of four different digits can be made?
An arrangement may start with zero.

c A driver has five tyres on his car: the four on the road and one in the boot.
He rotates them regularly so that they wear evenly.
i How many different ways of picking four tyres for the road are there assuming position matters?
ii How many different ways of picking one tyre for the boot are there?
iii Comment on your answers.

5 a Evaluate i $\frac{7!}{4!3!}$ ii $\frac{10!}{6!4!}$ iii $\frac{12!}{11!1!}$ iv $\frac{7!}{3!4!}$ v $\frac{10!}{4!6!}$

b The answers are all integers. Can you explain this?

c Each expression in **a** is the expansion of a function of the form ^nC_r.
Express each expansion in this form.

d Explain why $^nC_r = {^nC_{n-r}}$.

6 a i In the card game *Brag* players are given three cards. Assuming the pack is made up of 52 different cards, how many different hands are possible?

ii In the game *Bridge* players are given 13 cards.
How many different hands are possible?
Give your answer to 3 significant figures.

iii In the game *Solitaire* players are given 52 cards.
How many different hands are possible?

b In the national lottery there are 49 numbers from which to pick a set of six numbers.
How many different sets of six numbers can be picked?

c There were 12 people at a meeting. I sat between two.
What is the probability that you can pick the two people out correctly from a list of the 12 names?

7 A manufacturer of soup has six basic ingredients from which he can pick and mix to make varieties of soup.
He has to use at least two ingredients before he can call it a soup.
How many varieties of soup can he make?

3.3 A factorial function spreadsheet

	A	B	C	D	E	F	G	H	I	J
1		0	1	2	3	4	5	6	7	8
2	0	1								
3	1	1	1							
4	2	1	2	1						
5	3	1	3	3	1					
6	4	1	4	6	4	1				
7	5	1	5	10	10	5	1			
8	6	1	6	15	20	15	6	1		
9	7	1	7	21	35	35	21	7	1	
10	8	1	8	28	56	70	56	28	8	1
11	9	1	9	36	84	126	126	84	36	9
12	10	1	10	45	120	210	252	210	120	45

1
- In B1 enter 0.
- In C1 enter '= B1 + 1'.
- Fill right to column J, say.

2
- In A2 enter 0.
- In A3 enter '= A2 + 1'.
- Fill down to row 12, say.

3
- In B2 enter =FACT($A2)/(FACT(B$1)*FACT($A2-B$1)).
- Fill down.
- Highlight B2 to J12 and fill right.
- Error messages appear in some upper cells: highlight and delete.

Notes
- FACT(n) is the function $n!$
- Steps 1 and 2 create row and column coordinate references.
- Step 3 puts ${}^nC_r$ into the cell with reference (n, r).
- The formula may be more recognisable as $\frac{\text{FACT}(n)}{\text{FACT}(r)\cdot\text{FACT}(n-r)}$.
- This is just Pascal's triangle again.

Remember the rule used to build the triangle is $(n, r-1) + (n, r) = (n+1, r)$.
This can now be re-expressed as

$${}^nC_{r-1} + {}^nC_r = {}^{n+1}C_r$$

${}^nC_r$ notation can get quite cumbersome and a more compact notation has been devised, namely ${}^nC_r = \binom{n}{r}$.

In this notation the rule becomes $\binom{n}{r-1} + \binom{n}{r} = \binom{n+1}{r}$.

Proof

$$\begin{aligned}
\binom{n}{r-1} + \binom{n}{r} &= \frac{n!}{(r-1)!(n-(r-1))!} + \frac{n!}{r!(n-r)!} \\
&= \frac{n!}{(r-1)!(n-r+1)!} + \frac{n!}{r!(n-r)!} \\
&= \frac{n!r}{r(r-1)!(n-r+1)!} + \frac{n!(n-r+1)}{r!(n-r+1)(n-r)!} \\
&= \frac{n!r}{r!(n-r+1)!} + \frac{n!(n-r+1)}{r!(n-r+1)!} \\
&= \frac{n!r + n!(n-r+1)}{r!(n-r+1)!} \\
&= \frac{n!(n+1)}{r!(n-r+1)!} \\
&= \frac{(n+1)!}{r!(n-r+1)!} \\
&= \binom{n+1}{r}
\end{aligned}$$

Note

$r \times (r-1)! = r!$

$(n-r+1) \times (n-r)! = (n-r+1)!$

Exercise 3.3

1 Given that ${}^{10}C_2 = 45$, ${}^{10}C_7 = 120$ and ${}^{10}C_4 = 210$
write the values of

a ${}^{10}C_6$ b ${}^{10}C_8$ c ${}^{10}C_3$

2 a From a team of 11 cricketers, two are selected to bat first.
How many different ways can this be done?

b From a team of 11 cricketers, nine are selected not to bat first.
How many different ways can this be done?

c Complete the statement $^{11}C_2 = {}^{11}C$.

3 a A pentagon with diagonals is drawn by joining five points on a plane two at a time.

i How many ways can two points be selected from five?

ii How many of these joins will be sides of the pentagon?

iii How many of these joins will be diagonals?

b Prove that an n-sided polygon will have $\binom{n}{2} - n$ diagonals.

c Counting both sides and diagonals, a polygon is made up of 15 line segments. By solving the equation $\binom{n}{2} = 15$, identify the type of polygon. (Do not use trial and error.)

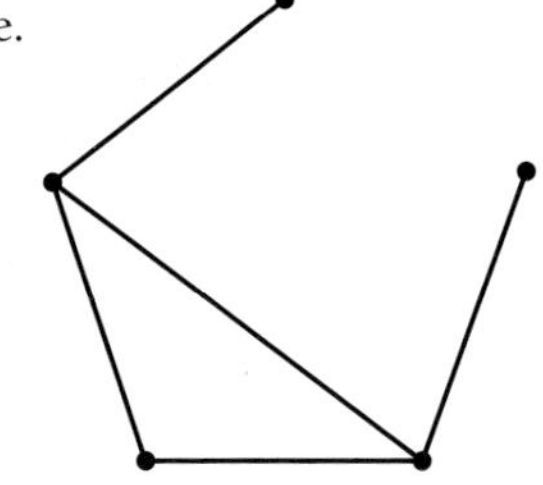

4 Solve these equations.

a $\binom{n}{2} = 6$ b $\binom{n}{2} = 45$ c $\binom{n}{2} = 28$ d $\binom{n}{2} = 120$

e $\binom{2n}{2} = 15$ f $\binom{2n}{2} = 45$ g $\binom{2n}{2} = 66$ h $\binom{2n}{2} = 276$

5 Find a value of n which satisfies these equations.

a $\binom{n}{3} = 4$ b $\binom{n}{3} = 10$ c $\binom{n}{3} = 35$ d $\binom{n}{3} = 120$

6 Make use of the fact that $\binom{n}{n-r} = \binom{n}{r}$ to help you solve these equations.

a $\binom{n}{n-2} = 15$ b $\binom{n}{n-2} = 55$ c $\binom{n}{n-3} = 84$

7 Using the identity $\binom{n}{r-1} + \binom{n}{r} = \binom{n+1}{r}$ find a value of n which satisfies each of these equations.

a $\binom{n}{1} + \binom{n}{2} = 28$ b $\binom{n+1}{1} + \binom{n+1}{2} = 66$

c $\binom{4}{n-1} + \binom{4}{n} = 5$ d $\binom{n+1}{2} - \binom{n}{1} = 36$ [careful]

3.4 The binomial theorem

At the beginning of the chapter we saw how row n of Pascal's triangle gave us the coefficients of expansions of the form $(x + y)^n$, for example

$(x + y)^4 = \mathbf{1}x^4 + \mathbf{4}x^3y + \mathbf{6}x^2y^2 + \mathbf{4}xy^3 + \mathbf{1}y^4$

Using the $\binom{n}{r}$ notation, this could have been written as

$$(x + y)^4 = \binom{4}{0}x^4 + \binom{4}{1}x^3y + \binom{4}{2}x^2y^2 + \binom{4}{3}xy^3 + \binom{4}{4}y^4$$

When this is generalised for any whole number n, we get

$$(x + y)^n = \binom{n}{0}x^n + \binom{n}{1}x^{n-1}y + \binom{n}{2}x^{n-2}y^2 + \ldots + \binom{n}{r}x^{n-r}y^r + \ldots + \binom{n}{n}y^n$$

This expansion is known as the **binomial theorem**.
We can use induction to prove the theorem true for positive integers.

Proof

1 Consider when $n = 1$: $(x+y)^1 = x + y$ and $\binom{1}{0}x^1 + \binom{1}{1}y^1 = x + y$.

The theorem is true for $n = 1$.

2 Assume the theorem is true for some value $n = k, k \in \mathbb{N}$.

$(x+y)^k = \binom{k}{0}x^k + \binom{k}{1}x^{k-1}y + \binom{k}{2}x^{k-2}y^2 + \ldots + \binom{k}{r}x^{k-r}y^r + \ldots + \binom{k}{k}y^k$

Consider when $n = k + 1$

$$(x+y)^{k+1} = (x+y)(x+y)^k$$

$$= (x+y)\left(\binom{k}{0}x^k + \binom{k}{1}x^{k-1}y + \binom{k}{2}x^{k-2}y^2 + \ldots + \binom{k}{r}x^{k-r}y^r + \ldots + \binom{k}{k}y^k\right)$$

$$= \binom{k}{0}x^{k+1} + \binom{k}{1}x^k y + \binom{k}{2}x^{k-1}y^2 + \ldots + \binom{k}{r}x^{k-r+1}y^r + \ldots + \binom{k}{k}xy^k$$

$$+ \binom{k}{0}x^k y + \binom{k}{1}x^{k-1}y^2 + \ldots + \binom{k}{r-1}x^{k-r+1}y^r + \binom{k}{r}x^{k-r}y^{r+1} + \ldots + \binom{k}{k}y^{k+1}$$

$$= \binom{k}{0}x^{k+1} + \left(\binom{k}{1} + \binom{k}{0}\right)x^k y + \left(\binom{k}{2} + \binom{k}{1}\right)x^{k-1}y^2 + \ldots$$

$$\ldots + \left(\binom{k}{r} + \binom{k}{r-1}\right)x^{k-r+1}y^r + \ldots + \binom{k}{k}y^{k+1}$$

Now, remembering that $\binom{n}{r-1} + \binom{n}{r} = \binom{n+1}{r}$

$$(x+y)^{k+1} = \binom{k+1}{0}x^{k+1} + \binom{k+1}{1}x^{k+1-1}y + \binom{k+1}{2}x^{k+1-2}y^2 + \ldots + \binom{k+1}{r}x^{k+1-r}y^r + \ldots + \binom{k+1}{k+1}y^{k+1}$$

This is the stated theorem with $n = k + 1$.

Thus if the theorem is true for $n = k$ then the theorem is true for $n = k + 1$.

Since it is true for $n = 1$, by induction it is true $\forall n \geqslant 1, n \in N$.

Alternative notation

The theorem can be expressed in a 'condensed' form using what is called 'sigma notation'.

$$(x+y)^n = \sum_{r=0}^{n} \binom{n}{r}x^{n-r}y^r$$

$\sum$ (Sigma) is the Greek capital letter 'S': it stands for 'sum'. We want to sum all the terms generated as we substitute $r = 0, r = 1, r = 2, \ldots, r = n - 1, r = n$ into the formula appearing after the symbol.

It can be read as 'For $r = 0$ up to n, sum the values of $\binom{n}{r}x^{n-r}y^r$'.

Sigma notation will be explored more fully in chapter **10**.

Historical note

The binomial theorem where n is a positive integer was known to the Chinese in the 14th century.

It was developed by Newton in the 17th century to include any rational number.

The proof, where n takes any value, was completed by the Norwegian mathematician Niels Abel in the 19th century.

Example 4

Expand $(1 + x)^5$ using the binomial theorem.

$$(1 + x)^5 = \sum_{r=0}^{5} \binom{5}{r} 1^{5-r} x^r$$

$$= \binom{5}{0}1^5 x^0 + \binom{5}{1}1^4 x^1 + \binom{5}{2}1^3 x^2 + \binom{5}{3}1^2 x^3 + \binom{5}{4}1^1 x^4 + \binom{5}{5}1^0 x^5$$

$$= 1 + 5x + 10x^2 + 10x^3 + 5x^4 + x^5$$

Example 5

Expand $(1 - 3p)^3$ using the binomial theorem.

$$(1 - 3p)^3 = \sum_{r=0}^{3} \binom{3}{r} 1^{3-r} (-3p)^r$$

$$= \binom{3}{0}1^3 (-3p)^0 + \binom{3}{1}1^2 (-3p)^1 + \binom{3}{2}1^1 (-3p)^2 + \binom{3}{3}1^0 (-3p)^3$$

$$= 1 + 3(-3p) + 3(9p^2) + (-27p^3)$$

$$= 1 - 9p + 27p^2 - 27p^3$$

Exercise 3.4

1 Use the binomial theorem to expand these expressions.

a $(a + b)^5$ **b** $(1 + 2x)^3$ **c** $(2 + 3b)^4$ **d** $(3a + 2b)^3$

e $(a - b)^4$ **f** $(1 - p)^3$ **g** $(3 - x)^4$ **h** $(2a - 3b)^3$

2 **a** Expand these expressing your answer as positive powers of x.

i $\left(x + \frac{1}{x}\right)^3$ **ii** $\left(x + \frac{1}{x}\right)^4$ **iii** $\left(x - \frac{1}{x}\right)^5$ **iv** $\left(x - \frac{1}{x}\right)^6$

b Which of these expressions produced a term independent of x?

3 Work out

a the third term in the expansion of $(x + y)^{12}$, that is, the term containing x^{10}

b the fourth term in the expansion of $(3 + a)^8$

c the seventh term in the expansion of $(2x + 3y)^9$

d the second term in the expansion of $(2x + 5)^7$

e the seventh term in the expansion of $(x - y)^6$

f the fifth term in the expansion of $(3x - 4y)^5$.

4 Calculate the term

a containing x^4 in the expansion of $(x + y)^8$

b containing a^3 in the expansion of $(3 + 2a)^5$

c whose coefficient is 64 in the expansion of $(2 + x)^6$

d containing x^3 in the expansion of $(x - 7)^5$

e containing a^4 term in the expansion of $(1 - 3a)^6$

f independent of x in the expansion of $\left(x + \frac{1}{x}\right)^8$.

5 **a** Expand $(1 + x + y)^3$ by first expressing it as $[(1 + x) + y]^3$.

b In a similar fashion expand

i $(2 + a + 2b)^3$ **ii** $(1 - x + y)^5$ **iii** $(1 + x - y)^4$

6 By considering $(1 + x)^n$, prove that $2^n = {}^nC_0 + {}^nC_1 + {}^nC_2 + \dots + {}^nC_n$.

7 Every quadratic expression can be written in the form $a(x + b)^2 + c$ by the process known as **completing the square**.
By considering a similar process write $x^3 + 6x^2 + 10x + 4$ in the form $(x + a)^3 + bx + c$.

8 How did Pascal use the binomial theorem for probability?
Consider driving down a road with three sets of traffic lights.
If p is the probability of being stopped at any set of lights and q is the probability of not being stopped, then the terms of the expansion $(p + q)^3$ provide formulae for the probability of being stopped by three, two, one and zero sets of lights.

$(p + q)^3 = p^3 + 3p^2q + 3pq^2 + q^3$

$P(3) = p^3$ $P(2) = 3p^2q$ $P(1) = 3pq^2$ $P(0) = q^3$

a If $p = 0.8$ and $q = 0.2$ calculate the probability of being

i stopped by two sets of lights **ii** stopped by all three.

b By expanding $(p + q)^4$, find the probability of being stopped at two out of four sets of lights

9 The probability that it will rain on any day is 0.4, and that it will not rain is 0.6.
By considering the expansion $(p + q)^7$, calculate the probability that

a it will rain twice in a seven-day week

b that it will not rain in the week.

3.5 Harder examples

These examples illustrate how to apply the binomial theorem in more complicated situations.

Example 6

What is the coefficient of x^5 in the expansion of $(1 + x)^4(1 - 2x)^3$?

Terms in x^5 are obtained by multiplying certain terms together, namely
the term containing x^2 in the first expansion with the term containing x^3 in the second,
the term containing x^3 in the first expansion with the term containing x^2 in the second,
the term containing x^4 in the first expansion with the term containing x in the second.

$$\binom{4}{2}x^2\binom{3}{0}x^3 + \binom{4}{1}x^3\binom{3}{1}x^2 + \binom{4}{0}x^4\binom{3}{2}x$$

$$= 6x^2 \cdot x^3 + 4x^3 \cdot 3x^2 + x^4 \cdot 3x$$

$$= 21x^5$$

The required coefficient is therefore 21.

Example 7

Expand $(x+1)^2(1+2x+x^2)^3$.

Consider each set of brackets separately.

$(x+1)^2 = \binom{2}{0}x^2 + \binom{2}{1}x + \binom{2}{2}1 = x^2+2x+1$

$(1+2x+x^2)^3 = ((1+2x)+x^2)^3$

$= \binom{3}{0}(1+2x)^3 + \binom{3}{1}(1+2x)^2(x^2) + \binom{3}{2}(1+2x)(x^2)^2 + \binom{3}{3}(x^2)^3$

$= (1+6x+12x^2+8x^3) + 3(1+4x+4x^2)x^2 + 3(1+2x)x^4 + x^6$

$= 1+6x+15x^2+20x^3+15x^4+6x^5+x^6$

$(x+1)^2(1+2x+x^2)^3 = (x^2+2x+1)(1+6x+15x^2+20x^3+15x^4+6x^5+x^6)$

The expansion can be made clearer by a tabular layout

Multiplying by x^2	$x^2 + 6x^3 + 15x^4 + 20x^5 + 15x^6 + 6x^7 + x^8$
Multiplying by $2x$	$2x + 12x^2 + 30x^3 + 40x^4 + 30x^5 + 12x^6 + 2x^7$
Multiplying by 1	$1 + 6x + 15x^2 + 20x^3 + 15x^4 + 6x^5 + x^6$
Total	$1 + 8x + 28x^2 + 56x^3 + 70x^4 + 56x^5 + 28x^6 + 8x^7 + x^8$

Therefore

$(x+1)^2(1+2x+x^2)^3 = 1+8x+28x^2+56x^3+70x^4+56x^5+28x^6+8x^7+x^8$

Example 8

Find the term independent of x in $\left(2x^2 + \frac{1}{3x}\right)^6$.

The general term in the expansion is $\binom{6}{r}(2x^2)^{6-r}\left(\frac{1}{3x}\right)^r$

$= \binom{6}{r}2^{6-r}3^{-r}x^{12-2r-r}$

For this to be independent of x we must have $x^{12-3r} = x^0$

$\Rightarrow 12-3r=0 \Rightarrow r=4$

So the term independent of x is $\binom{6}{4}2^{6-4}3^{-4}x^0 = \frac{15\cdot 4}{81} = \frac{20}{27}$.

Exercise 3.5

1 What is the coefficient of

a x^4 in the expansion $(1+x)^2(1+2x)^3$

b x^5 in the expansion $(1-x)^3(2+x)^4$

c x^7 in the expansion $(1+2x)^4(1-2x)^6$?

2 Find the coefficients of x^3 and x^5 in the expansion of $(1+x+x^2)^5$.

3 What are the terms in x^3 and x^{10} in $(1+x)^5(1-x+x^2)^4$?

4 Expand

a $(1 + x)^2(1 + x + x^2)^3$

b $(1 - 3x)^3 (1 + 2x + x^2)^2$

c $(3 + 2x)^2 (1 - x + x^2)^4$

d $(1 - 2x)^4 (1 + 2x + 4x^2)^3$

5 a Expand $\left(x + \frac{1}{x}\right)^2 \left(x - \frac{1}{x}\right)^3$.

b Expand $\left(x + \frac{1}{x}\right)^2 \left(x - \frac{1}{x}\right)^4$.

c Under what circumstances do you get terms independent of x?

d Find the term independent of x in the expansion of $\left(x + \frac{1}{x}\right)^6 \left(x - \frac{1}{x}\right)^8$.

6 Find the terms in a^5 and a^6 in $\left(3a^2 - \frac{1}{a}\right)^6 \left(a - \frac{1}{a}\right)^4$.

7 Find the term independent of a in $\left(\frac{3}{2}a^2 - \frac{1}{3a}\right)^9$.

8 a Use the binomial theorem to help you write expressions for the coefficients of x^r and x^{r+1} in the expansion of $(3x + 2)^{19}$.

b Find the value of r if these coefficients are equal.

9 If $x = \frac{1}{4}$, find the ratio of the eighth term to the seventh term in the expansion of $(1 + 2x)^{15}$.

10 Find the greatest terms in these expansions.

[Hint: find where the ratio of the $(r + 1)$th term to the rth term is less than 1.]

a $(1 + 3x)^{18}$ when $x = \frac{1}{4}$ b $(1 + \frac{1}{2}x)^{12}$ when $x = \frac{1}{2}$

c $(4 + x)^8$ when $x = 3$ d $(x + y)^n$ when $n = 14, x = 2, y = \frac{1}{2}$

11 Find the numerically greatest terms, positive or negative, in these expansions.

a $(2 - x)^{12}$ when $x = \frac{2}{3}$ b $(3a + 2b)^n$ when $n = 16, a = 1, b = \frac{1}{2}$

12 Find which terms have the greatest coefficients in

a $(1 + x)^{10}$ b $(2 + x)^{11}$ c $(1 + x)^{2n+1}$

13 In this expansion, show that there are two greatest terms and find their values.

$(a + x)^n$ when $n = 9, a = \frac{1}{2}, x = \frac{1}{3}$

3.6 Approximation

For $-1 < a < 1$ as $n \to \infty$ then $a^n \to 0$.

Using this fact and the binomial theorem allows us to make useful approximations.

Example 9

Calculate 1.02^3 correct to 3 decimal places.

$$1.02^3 = (1 + 0.02)^3 = 1 + 3 \times 0.02 + 3 \times 0.02^2 + 0.02^3$$
$$= 1 + 0.06 + 0.0012 + 0.000008$$
$$= 1.061 \text{ (3 dp)}$$

Note that the term 0.02^3 does not contribute to the rounded result.

Example 10

Calculate 0.9^7 correct to 2 decimal places.

$$0.9^7 = (1 - 0.1)^7 = 1 - 7 \times 0.1 + 21 \times 0.1^2 - 35 \times 0.1^3 + 35 \times 0.1^4 \ldots$$
$$= 1 - 0.7 + 0.21 - 0.035 + 0.0035 \ldots$$
$$= 0.48 \text{ (2 dp)}$$

Note that the terms in 0.1^4 and higher do not contribute to the rounded result.

Exercise 3.6

1 Calculate these powers correct to 3 significant figures.

a 1.01^5 b 1.04^6 c 0.94^7 d 12.01^5

e e^8 f π^7 g $\sin^6 30°$ h 199^4

2 When metal of length x is heated, it expands by the amount δx, where δx is so small that $(\delta x)^2$ and higher powers can be ignored. The new length is $x + \delta x$.

Write an expression for

a the increase in area when a square of metal of side x expands

b the increase in volume when a cube of metal of side x expands.

3 Given that a is so small that terms in a^3 are negligible, work out approximate expansions for

a $(1 + a)^6$ b $(2a - 1)^7$ c $(a^2 + 2)^8$

4 Given that x is so small that x^3 and higher powers can be neglected, show that

$$\left(1 - \frac{3}{2}x\right)^5 (2 + 3x)^6 = 64 + 96x - 720x^2$$

5 Assuming that $f'(x) = \frac{f(x + h) - f(x)}{h}$ where h is so small that h^2 and higher powers can be ignored, use the binomial theorem to find $f'(x)$ when $f(x) = x^n$.

6 a The value in pounds (£) of a car, n years old, can be computed from the formula $V_n = 0.9^n \times 10\,000$.

Use the binomial theorem to come up with a simplified formula which will be useful when only two significant figures are required.

b In a similar manner simplify this formula where V_n is the value of an investment after n years.

$V_n = 1.05^n \times 5000$

Review 3

1 Write out Pascal's triangle to the seventh row.

2 Consider the expansion of $(x + y)^{20}$.

a The term in x^5 is of the form $\binom{p}{q}x^5y^r$.

What are the values of p, q and r?

b For what values of s and t is $\binom{20}{14}$ the coefficient of x^sy^t?

c Evaluate i $\binom{20}{14}$ ii ${}^{20}C_{11}$

3 a For what value of $n \neq 3$ is $\binom{8}{n} = \binom{8}{3}$?

b For what values of p and q is $\binom{7}{3} + \binom{7}{4} = \binom{p}{q}$?

4 Use the binomial theorem to expand

a $(x - 4)^5$ b $(2y - 3)^3$

5 a Evaluate the term in x^7 in the expansion of $(1 + x)^{10}$.

b Evaluate the term in y^3 in the expansion of $\left(y - \frac{5}{y}\right)^7$.

6 Show that in the expansion of $\left(x - \frac{2}{x}\right)^{10}$, the term which is independent of x has the value -8064.

7 a Evaluate ${}^{11}C_0 + {}^{11}C_1 + {}^{11}C_2 + \ldots + {}^{11}C_{10} + {}^{11}C_{11}$

by considering the expansion of $(1 + x)^{11}$ when $x = 1$.

b Evaluate i ${}^{11}C_0 + {}^{11}C_2 + {}^{11}C_4 + \ldots + {}^{11}C_8 + {}^{11}C_{10}$

ii ${}^{11}C_1 + {}^{11}C_3 + {}^{11}C_5 + \ldots + {}^{11}C_9 + {}^{11}C_{11}$

by considering the expansion of $(1 + x)^{11}$ when $x = -1$.

8 Prove that $\binom{n}{r} + 2\binom{n}{r+1} + \binom{n}{r+2} = \binom{n+2}{r+2}$.

Summary 3

1 n factorial, $n!$, is the number of ways of arranging in order n distinct objects.

$n! = n \times (n-1) \times (n-2) \times \ldots \times 3 \times 2 \times 1;$ $0! = 1$ [By definition]

2 n choose r, ${}^nC_r$, is the number of ways of choosing r objects from n objects if the order does not matter.

$$\binom{n}{r} = {}^nC_r = \frac{n!}{r!(n-r)!}$$

3 $\binom{n}{r} = \binom{n}{n-r}$

4 $\binom{n}{r-1} + \binom{n}{r} = \binom{n+1}{r}$

5 **Pascal's triangle**

	A	B	C	D	E	F	G	H	I	J
1		0	1	2	3	4	5	6	7	8
2	0	1								
3	1	1	1							
4	2	1	2	1						
5	3	1	3	3	1					
6	4	1	4	6	4	1				
7	5	1	5	10	10	5	1			
8	6	1	6	15	20	15	6	1		
9	7	1	7	21	35	35	21	7	1	
10	8	1	8	28	56	70	56	28	8	1

- Each entry can be computed using ${}^{\text{row}}C_{\text{column}}$. [See summary point 2]
- Each row is symmetrical. [See summary point 3]
- Each entry is the sum of the entry above it and the entry above it and to the left. [See summary point 4]

6 The **binomial theorem** states

$$(x + y)^n = \sum_{r=0}^{n} \binom{n}{r} x^{n-r} y^r$$

which when expanded becomes

$$(x + y)^n = \binom{n}{0} x^n + \binom{n}{1} x^{n-1} y + \binom{n}{2} x^{n-2} y^2 + \ldots + \binom{n}{r} x^{n-r} y^r + \ldots + \binom{n}{n} y^n$$

7 The general term in the binomial expansion is $\binom{n}{r} x^{n-r} y^r$.

This can be used to find particular terms with particular properties.

4 Differential calculus 1

Historical note

Newton

Leibniz

Sir Isaac Newton invented infinitesimal calculus devising his method of fluxions in about 1665.

Gottfried Leibniz independently invented calculus publishing a paper on the subject in 1684.

A dispute arose as to who had invented it first.

A committee of inquiry in 1712 set up by the Royal Society found in favour of Newton. It is, however, the notation devised by Leibniz which is popularly used.

While Newton and Leibniz can share credit for the invention of calculus, Fermat had made critically important discoveries over 10 years before either of them was born. In particular he found the equations of tangents, located stationary points and found the areas under many different curves.

4.1 Differentiation

Reminders

Definition

The **derivative**, or derived function, of $f(x)$, denoted by $f'(x)$, is defined as

$$f'(x) = \lim_{h \to 0}\left(\frac{f(x+h) - f(x)}{h}\right)$$

Geometric Interpretation

Given the points P$(a, (f(a))$ and Q$(a+h, (f(a+h))$ the gradient of PQ is

$$m_{PQ} = \frac{f(a+h) - f(a)}{h}$$

As $h \to 0$, Q approaches P along the curve and the gradient of PQ approaches the gradient of PT, the tangent at P.

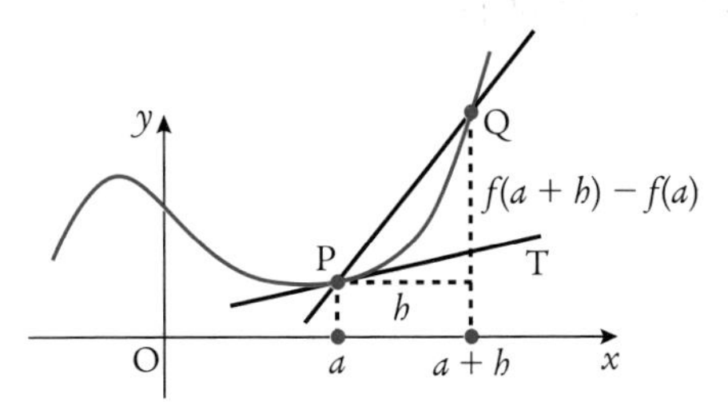

Thus the gradient of the tangent at P can be defined as

$$\lim_{h \to 0}\left(\frac{f(a+h) - f(a)}{h}\right)$$

which is, of course, the value of the derived function at $x = a$.

Leibniz notation

In the definition of $f(x)$, h represents a small change in x and is often referred to as the x-increment and denoted by δx.
$f(x + h) - f(x)$ denotes the corresponding change in y, the y-increment, which is denoted by δy.

Thus we have an alternative notation, Leibniz notation $f'(x) = \lim_{\delta x \to 0}\left(\frac{\delta y}{\delta x}\right) = \frac{dy}{dx}$.

Strictly speaking, as Q approaches P from the right, and the limit $f'(x)$ exists, we find only the *right* derivative.

Similarly if Q approaches P from the left, and the limit $f'(x)$ exists, we find the *left* derivative.

If both limits exist, and are the same, then we may conclude that the function is **differentiable**.

Differentiation from first principles

Example 1

$f(x) = x^2$ is differentiable. Use the definition of the derivative to find the value of $f'(x)$ when $x = 4$.

$$f'(x) = \lim_{h \to 0}\left(\frac{f(x+h) - f(x)}{h}\right)$$

$$\Rightarrow f'(4) = \lim_{h \to 0}\left(\frac{f(4+h) - f(4)}{h}\right) = \lim_{h \to 0}\left(\frac{(4+h)^2 - 4^2}{h}\right)$$

$$= \lim_{h \to 0}\left(\frac{16 + 8h + h^2 - 16}{h}\right) = \lim_{h \to 0}\left(\frac{8h + h^2}{h}\right) = \lim_{h \to 0}(8 + h)$$

$$= 8$$

This is referred to as 'finding the derivative from first principles'.

For each function we study, we initially find the derived function from first principles.

Thereafter we can simply exploit the result.

Example 2

Given $f(x) = x^n$ is differentiable, find the derived function, $f'(x)$, from first principles.

$$f'(x) = \lim_{h \to 0}\left(\frac{f(x+h) - f(x)}{h}\right)$$

$$\Rightarrow f'(x) = \lim_{h \to 0}\left(\frac{(x+h)^n - x^n}{h}\right) = \lim_{h \to 0}\left(\frac{\sum_{r=0}^{n}\binom{n}{r}x^{n-r}h^r - x^n}{h}\right)$$

$$= \lim_{h \to 0}\left(\frac{\binom{n}{0}x^n h^0 + \binom{n}{1}x^{n-1}h^1 + \sum_{r=2}^{n}\binom{n}{r}x^{n-r}h^r - x^n}{h}\right)$$

$$= \lim_{h \to 0} \left(\frac{x^n + nx^{n-1}h^1 + \sum_{r=2}^{n} \binom{n}{r} x^{n-r} h^r - x^n}{h} \right) = \lim_{h \to 0} \left(\frac{nx^{n-1}h + h^2 \sum_{r=2}^{n} \binom{n}{r} x^{n-r} h^{r-2}}{h} \right)$$

$$= \lim_{h \to 0} \left(nx^{n-1} + h \sum_{r=2}^{n} \binom{n}{r} x^{n-r} h^{r-2} \right) = nx^{n-1}$$

$\Rightarrow f'(x) = nx^{n-1}$

Warning

Not all functions can be differentiated everywhere, for example

- The tangent function has breaks in its graph at $\frac{\pi}{2} + n\pi, n \in Z$, where the derivative is undefined.
- $f(x) = \sqrt{x^2}$. The derivative of this function is undefined at $x = 0$ as the left derivative is -1 while the right derivative is 1. [See the graph.]
- $f(x) = \sqrt{x}$. Although the function is defined at $x = 0$, it is not defined for $x < 0$. So we cannot calculate a left derivative at $x = 0$. So $f(x) = \sqrt{x}$ is not differentiable at $x = 0$.

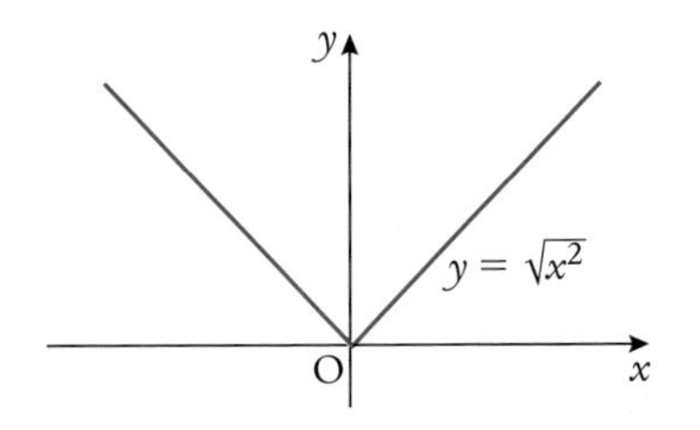

Limits

Many of the 'first principle' proofs require a knowledge of certain limits.

1 If $f(x) = k$, where k is a constant, then $\lim_{x \to a} f(x) = k$.

2 $\lim_{x \to a} kf(x) = k \times \lim_{x \to a} f(x)$, where k is a constant.

3 $\lim_{x \to a} [f(x) \pm g(x)] = \lim_{x \to a} f(x) \pm \lim_{x \to a} g(x)$

4 $\lim_{x \to a} [f(x) \cdot g(x)] = \lim_{x \to a} f(x) \cdot \lim_{x \to a} g(x)$

5 $\lim_{x \to a} \left[\frac{f(x)}{g(x)} \right] = \frac{\lim_{x \to a} f(x)}{\lim_{x \to a} g(x)}$, when $\lim_{x \to a} g(x) \neq 0$

6 $\lim_{\theta \to 0} \frac{\sin \theta}{\theta} = 1$, where θ is measured in radians.

7 $\lim_{\theta \to 0} \frac{\cos \theta - 1}{\theta} = 0$, where θ is measured in radians.

Proof of 6

ABD is the sector of a circle.

BD is a chord and BC is a tangent at B cutting AD extended at C.

Let the radius be r units long and $\angle CAB$ be θ radians.
So $AB = AD = r$ and $CB = r \tan \theta$.

From the diagram we see the area of the sector ABD lies between the area of the small triangle ABD and the large triangle ABC.

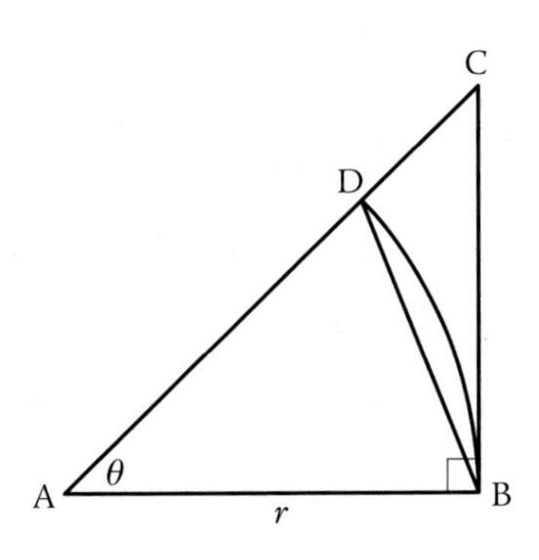

$$\Delta ABD \leq \text{sector } ABD \leq \Delta ABC$$

$$\Rightarrow \tfrac{1}{2} r \cdot r \cdot \sin\theta \leq \frac{\theta}{2\pi} \cdot \pi r^2 \leq \tfrac{1}{2} r \cdot r \cdot \tan\theta$$

$$\Rightarrow \sin\theta \leq \theta \leq \tan\theta$$

$$\Rightarrow 1 \leq \frac{\theta}{\sin\theta} \leq \frac{1}{\cos\theta}$$

$$\Rightarrow 1 \geq \frac{\sin\theta}{\theta} \geq \cos\theta$$

$$\Rightarrow \lim_{\theta\to 0} 1 \geq \lim_{\theta\to 0} \frac{\sin\theta}{\theta} \geq \lim_{\theta\to 0} \cos\theta$$

$$\Rightarrow 1 \geq \lim_{\theta\to 0} \frac{\sin\theta}{\theta} \geq 1$$

Thus $\lim\limits_{\theta\to 0} \dfrac{\sin\theta}{\theta} = 1$

Proof of 7

$$\lim_{\theta\to 0} \frac{(\cos\theta - 1)}{\theta} = \lim_{\theta\to 0} \frac{(\cos\theta - 1)(\cos\theta + 1)}{\theta(\cos\theta + 1)}$$

$$= \lim_{\theta\to 0} \frac{(\cos^2\theta - 1)}{\theta(\cos\theta + 1)} = \lim_{\theta\to 0} \frac{(1 - \sin^2\theta - 1)}{\theta(\cos\theta + 1)} = \lim_{\theta\to 0} \frac{(-\sin^2\theta)}{\theta(\cos\theta + 1)}$$

$$= \lim_{\theta\to 0}\left(-\sin\theta \cdot \frac{\sin\theta}{\theta} \frac{1}{(\cos\theta + 1)}\right) = 0 \times 1 \times \tfrac{1}{2} = 0$$

Thus $\lim\limits_{\theta\to 0} \dfrac{\cos\theta - 1}{\theta} = 0$

Note that these trigonometric limits only hold when radian measure is used.

Example 3

If $f(x) = \sin x$, where x is measured in radians, and $f(x)$ is differentiable, find the derivative $f'(x)$.

$$f'(x) = \lim_{h\to 0}\left(\frac{f(x+h) - f(x)}{h}\right) = \lim_{h\to 0}\left(\frac{\sin(x+h) - \sin(x)}{h}\right)$$

$$= \lim_{h\to 0}\left(\frac{\sin x \cos h + \cos x \sin h - \sin x}{h}\right) = \lim_{h\to 0}\left(\sin x\left(\frac{\cos h - 1}{h}\right) + \cos x \frac{\sin h}{h}\right)$$

$$= \sin x \cdot 0 + \cos x \cdot 1$$

$$= \cos x$$

Exercise 4.1

Find the derivative of each function from first principles.

1 $f(x) = 3x$

2 $f(x) = 4x + 5$

3 $f(x) = 5x^2$

4 $f(x) = 2x^2 - 1$

5 $f(x) = x^3$

6 $f(x) = 4x^3 + 5x$

7 $f(x) = \dfrac{1}{x}, x \neq 0$

8 $f(x) = \dfrac{3}{x^2}, x \neq 0$

9 $f(x) = \sin 2x$ **10** $f(x) = \cos x$ **11** $f(x) = \cos 3x$ **12** $f(x) = (3 - x)^2$

13 $f(x) = \dfrac{1}{x + 1}$ **14** $f(x) = \sin(3x + 1)$ **15** $f(x) = \dfrac{1}{(x + 1)^2}$

4.2 The basic rules of differentiation

Standard derivatives

1 $f(x) = ax^n \Rightarrow f'(x) = nax^{n-1}$ or $\dfrac{d}{dx}(ax^n) = nax^{n-1}$

2 $f(x) = \sin ax \Rightarrow f'(x) = a\cos ax$ or $\dfrac{d}{dx}(\sin ax) = a\cos ax$

3 $f(x) = \cos ax \Rightarrow f'(x) = -a\sin ax$ or $\dfrac{d}{dx}(\cos ax) = -a\sin ax$

Sum and difference rule

If f and g are differentiable then $\dfrac{d}{dx}(f(x) \pm g(x)) = \dfrac{d}{dx}f(x) \pm \dfrac{d}{dx}g(x)$.

Proof

Let $k(x) = f(x) + g(x)$.

$$k'(x) = \lim_{h\to 0}\left(\frac{k(x+h) - k(x)}{h}\right) = \lim_{h\to 0}\left(\frac{f(x+h) + g(x+h) - f(x) - g(x)}{h}\right)$$

$$= \lim_{h\to 0}\left(\frac{f(x+h) - f(x) + g(x+h) - g(x)}{h}\right) = \lim_{h\to 0}\left(\frac{f(x+h) - f(x)}{h} + \frac{g(x+h) - g(x)}{h}\right)$$

$$= \lim_{h\to 0}\left(\frac{f(x+h) - f(x)}{h}\right) + \lim_{h\to 0}\left(\frac{g(x+h) - g(x)}{h}\right)$$

$$k'(x) = f'(x) + g'(x)$$

Exercise 4.2

1 Find the derivatives of these functions.

a $x^4 - \sin x$ b $\sin 2x + \cos 2x$ c $x + \dfrac{1}{x}, x \neq 0$

2 Differentiate these functions.

a $x^2 + x^{-2}$ b $\dfrac{1}{x^3} + 3x^2$ c $\dfrac{2}{x^3} + \dfrac{x^2}{2}$ d $2\sin 3x - 3\cos 2x$

3 Use the identity $\dfrac{a+b}{c} = \dfrac{a}{c} + \dfrac{b}{c}$ to help solve these problems.

a Given $f(x) = \dfrac{x^3 - 2x}{x^2}$, find $f'(x)$.

b Given $f(x) = \dfrac{2x^2 + 5x}{x^4}$, find $f'(x)$.

4 Find $\frac{dy}{dx}$ given that

a $y = \frac{2x^5 - 3x^3}{x^3}$ b $y = \frac{2(x+1)^5 - 3(x+1)^3}{(x+1)^3}$

5 Calculate $f'(1)$ when

a $f(x) = \frac{1}{3x^3} + 4x^4$ b $f(x) = \cos\frac{x}{2} - \frac{2}{x^2}$

Note that in Questions **2** to **5** the functions are not differentiable for all values of x.

4.3 The chain rule

If g is differentiable at x, and f is differentiable at $g(x)$ and $y(x) = f(g(x))$, then y is differentiable and $y'(x) = f'(g(x)) \cdot g'(x)$.

Proof

We wish to find the derivative of $y(x) = f(g(x))$.

Let $u = g(x)$ and $t = g(x+h) - g(x)$.

Then $g(x+h) = g(x) + t = u + t$.

$$y'(x) = \lim_{h\to 0}\left[\frac{f(g(x+h)) - f(g(x))}{h}\right] = \lim_{h\to 0}\left[\frac{f(u+t) - f(u)}{h}\right]$$

$$= \lim_{h\to 0}\left[\frac{f(u+t) - f(u)}{t} \times \frac{t}{h}\right]$$

$$= \lim_{h\to 0}\left[\frac{f(u+t) - f(u)}{t}\right] \times \lim_{h\to 0}\left[\frac{t}{h}\right]$$

$$= \lim_{h\to 0}\left[\frac{f(u+t) - f(u)}{t}\right] \times \lim_{h\to 0}\left[\frac{g(x+h) - g(x)}{h}\right] \quad \text{[Note that as } h \to 0, t \to 0\text{]}$$

$$= f'(u) \times g'(x)$$

$y'(x) = f'(g(x)) \times g'(x)$ This is known as the **chain rule**.

Using Leibniz notation

Given $y = f(g(x))$,

let $u = g(x) \Rightarrow y = f(u)$

$$\Rightarrow \frac{du}{dx} = g'(x) \text{ and } \frac{dy}{dx} = f'(u)$$

$$\Rightarrow \frac{dy}{dx} = \frac{dy}{du} \times \frac{du}{dx}$$

Example 4

Find $\frac{d}{dx}(2x-3)^5$.

Let $2x - 3 = u$

$\Rightarrow f(u) = u^5$ and $g(x) = 2x - 3$

$\Rightarrow f'(u) = 5u^4$ and $g'(x) = 2$

$\Rightarrow \frac{d}{dx}(2x-3)^5 = f'(u) \cdot g'(x) = 5u^4 \cdot 2$

$\Rightarrow \frac{d}{dx}(2x-3)^5 = 5(2x-3)^4 \cdot 2 = 10(2x-3)^4$

Generally the notation you use is a matter of choice.

In Leibniz notation

Let $2x - 3 = u$

$\Rightarrow y = u^5$ and $u = 2x - 3$

$\Rightarrow \frac{dy}{du} = 5u^4$ and $\frac{du}{dx} = 2$

$\Rightarrow \frac{d}{dx}(2x-3)^5 = \frac{dy}{du} \times \frac{du}{dx} = 5u^4 \cdot 2$

$\Rightarrow \frac{d}{dx}(2x-3)^5 = 5(2x-3)^4 \cdot 2 = 10(2x-3)^4$

Example 5

Differentiate $\sin(x^2 + 3x)$.

Let $x^2 + 3x = u$

$\Rightarrow y = \sin u$ and $u = x^2 + 3x$

$\Rightarrow \frac{dy}{du} = \cos u$ and $\frac{du}{dx} = 2x + 3$

$\Rightarrow \frac{d}{dx}\sin(x^2 + 3x) = \frac{dy}{du} \times \frac{du}{dx} = \cos u \cdot (2x + 3)$

$\Rightarrow \frac{d}{dx}\sin(x^2 + 3x) = \cos(x^2 + 3x) \cdot (2x + 3) = (2x + 3)\cos(x^2 + 3x)$

After some practice you should be able to identify u mentally and go straight to the last line of the solution.

Exercise 4.3

1 Find the derivative of each of these expressions.

a $(3x + 4)^6$ b $3(2x - 5)^4$ c $(3x^2 + 2x - 1)^5$ d $\sin(x^3)$ e $\sin^3 x$

2 Find $f'(x)$ given

a $f(x) = \cos 7x$ b $f(x) = (2x^3 + 4x^2 - 1)^4$ c $f(x) = \sin(2x^2 - 5x)$

3 Find $\frac{dy}{dx}$ given that

a $y = \frac{1}{3x + 1}$ b $y = \frac{1}{(3x + 1)^2}$ c $y = \frac{3}{(3x + 2)^3}$ d $y = \frac{1}{\sin x}$ e $y = \frac{1}{\cos x}$

4 Use the fact that $x° = \frac{\pi}{180}x$ radians to help you differentiate these expressions.

a $\sin x°$ b $\cos x°$ c $\sin(2x + 30)°$

5 Differentiate these expressions.

a $\sin(\cos x)$ b $\cos(\cos x)$ c $\sin(\sin x)$ d $\cos(\sin x)$

6 a By expressing $y = x$ in the form $y = \sin(\sin^{-1} x)$ where $-\frac{\pi}{2} \leq x \leq \frac{\pi}{2}$, prove that $\frac{d}{dx}(\sin^{-1}(x)) = \frac{1}{\cos(\sin^{-1}(x))}$.

b Use the identity $\cos x = \sqrt{1 - \sin^2 x}$ to help you express $\cos(\sin^{-1} x)$ in terms of $\sin(\sin^{-1} x)$ and simplify.

c Hence express the derivative of $\sin^{-1} x$ in terms of x without the use of trigonometric functions.

d Differentiate $\cos^{-1} x$.

4.4 Further uses of the chain rule

The chain rule can be adapted to deal with more complicated functions.

For example, if $y = f(g(h(x)))$, then, using Leibniz notation, we have $y = f(u)$ where $u = g(t)$ where $t = h(x)$. This gives $\frac{dy}{dx} = \frac{dy}{du} \times \frac{du}{dt} \times \frac{dt}{dx}$.

Example 6

Differentiate $y = \cos^2 3x$.

Consider the function as $y = (\cos(3x))^2$.

Let $t = 3x \quad \Rightarrow \frac{dt}{dx} = 3 \quad$ and $y = (\cos t)^2$

Let $u = \cos t \quad \Rightarrow \frac{du}{dt} = -\sin t \quad$ and $y = u^2$

$$y = u^2 \Rightarrow \frac{dy}{du} = 2u$$

$$\begin{aligned}\frac{dy}{dx} = \frac{dy}{du} \times \frac{du}{dt} \times \frac{dt}{dx} &= 2u \times (-\sin t) \times 3 \\ &= 2\cos t \times (-\sin t) \times 3 \\ &= -6\cos 3x \sin 3x \\ &= -3\sin 6x\end{aligned}$$

Using the identity $\sin 2A = 2\sin A \cos A$

Exercise 4.4

1 Find $\frac{dy}{dx}$ for each of these.

a $y = \sin^2 3x$ **b** $y = \cos^2(\sin x)$ **c** $y = (x + \sin 3x)^2$ **d** $y = \cos(\sin^2 x)$

2 Differentiate

a $\cos^3(2x + 4)$ **b** $\frac{1}{\sin^2(3x + 1)}$ **c** $\cos\left(\frac{1}{x^2 + 2x + 1}\right)$

3 Find the derivative of

a $\frac{1}{\cos(x^2 + x)}$ **b** $\frac{1}{\sin(\cos x)}$ **c** $\frac{1}{\sqrt{\sin(3x + 2)}}$

4 a Express $\frac{\sin^3 x + \cos^2 x}{\sin^2 x}$ as sums or differences of powers of $\sin x$.

You will need the identity $\sin^2 x + \cos^2 x = 1$.

b Hence or otherwise differentiate $\frac{\sin^3 x + \cos^2 x}{\sin^2 x}$.

4.5 The product rule

Given that f and g are differentiable and $y(x) = f(x) \cdot g(x)$ then
$y'(x) = f'(x) \cdot g(x) + f(x) \cdot g'(x)$

Proof

$$y'(x) = \lim_{h \to 0}\left[\frac{y(x + h) - y(x)}{h}\right] = \lim_{h \to 0}\left[\frac{f(x + h) \cdot g(x + h) - f(x) \cdot g(x)}{h}\right]$$

Add and subtract $f(x) \cdot g(x+h)$ to the numerator for reasons that will become apparent.

$$y'(x) = \lim_{h \to 0} \left[\frac{f(x+h) \cdot g(x+h) - f(x) \cdot g(x+h) + f(x) \cdot g(x+h) - f(x) \cdot g(x)}{h} \right]$$

Rearrange using common factors.

$$y'(x) = \lim_{h \to 0} \left[\frac{[f(x+h) - f(x)]g(x+h) + f(x)[g(x+h) - g(x)]}{h} \right]$$

$$= \lim_{h \to 0} \left[\frac{f(x+h) - f(x)}{h} g(x+h) + f(x) \frac{g(x+h) - g(x)}{h} \right]$$

$$= \lim_{h \to 0} \left[\frac{f(x+h) - f(x)}{h} g(x+h) \right] + \lim_{h \to 0} \left[f(x) \frac{g(x+h) - g(x)}{h} \right]$$

$$y'(x) = f'(x) \cdot g(x) + f(x) \cdot g'(x)$$

In Leibniz notation: $y = f(x)\,g(x) \Rightarrow \frac{dy}{dx} = \frac{df}{dx}g + f\frac{dg}{dx}$

Example 7

Differentiate $x^2 \sin x$.

Identify the two factors forming the product: $f(x) = x^2$ and $g(x) = \sin x$.

Thus $f'(x) = 2x$; $g'(x) = \cos x$.

So $\frac{d}{dx} x^2 \sin x = 2x \sin x + x^2 \cos x$.

Example 8

Find the derivative of $(x+3)^4(x-3)^5$.

Identify the two factors forming the product: $f(x) = (x+3)^4$ and $g(x) = (x-3)^5$.

Thus $f'(x) = 4(x+3)^3$; $g'(x) = 5(x-3)^4$.

So $\frac{d}{dx}(x+3)^4(x-3)^5 = 4(x+3)^3(x-3)^5 + (x+3)^4 \cdot 5(x-3)^4$

At this line, the derivative has been found. However, it can be useful to simplify the expression. The terms contain common factors.

$$\frac{d}{dx}(x+3)^4(x-3)^5 = \left[(x+3)^3(x-3)^4\right](4(x-3) + 5(x+3))$$

$$= (x+3)^3(x-3)^4(9x+3) = 3(x+3)^3(x-3)^4(3x+1)$$

Example 9

Differentiate $x^2(x+1)^3 \sin x$.

Here we have the product of three functions. Initially treat the first two as one,

giving $f(x) = x^2(x+1)^3$ and $g(x) = \sin x$.

Thus $f'(x) = 2x(x+1)^3 + x^2 \cdot 3(x+1)^2$ (using the product rule) and $g'(x) = \cos x$.

So, $\frac{d}{dx} x^2(x+1)^3 \sin x = \left[2x(x+1)^3 + x^2 \cdot 3(x+1)^2\right] \sin x + \left[x^2(x+1)^3\right] \cos x$

Again, the process of differentiation is complete but simplifications can be made if

desired, say, $\frac{d}{dx} x^2(x+1)^3 \sin x = x(x+1)^2\left[2(x+1) + 3x\right] \sin x + \left[x^2(x+1)^3\right] \cos x$

$$= x(x+1)^2(5x+2) \sin x + (x^2(x+1)^3) \cos x$$

$$= x(x+1)^2\left[(5x+2) \sin x + x(x+1) \cos x\right]$$

Exercise 4.5

1 Find the derivative of each of these.

a $x^3 \sin x$ b $(x+1)^2 \cos x$ c $(2x+3)^2 \cos 3x$ d $(x+1)^4 (x-1)^3$

e $(3-x)^4 (x+2)^2$ f $x^{-2}(x+4)^3$ g $(x+1)^{-2} (x-1)^2$ h $(x+2)^{-1} (x-1)^{-1}$

2 a If $f(x) = x^3(x+1)^2$, find $f'(1)$.

b If $f(x) = (x-1)^2 \sin x$, find $f'\left(\frac{\pi}{2}\right)$.

3 Differentiate each of these.

a $(2x+1)^2 \cos x$ b $\sin 2x \cos 3x$ c $x^4 \sin 3x$ d $(2x+1)^2(3x-1)^4$

e $(x^2+x) \sin 2x$ f $(x^2-1)(x^3-1)$ g $\sin 2x \sin 3x$ h $x(x^2+3x)^3$

i $x^4(x^2+3x)$ j $\sin x \cos x$ k $\sin (2x+1) \sin (3x+2)$ l $\sin^2 x \cos^2 x$

4 Find the derivative of each of these.

a $(1-5x)^3 (1+5x)^2$ b $\sin 3x \cos 5x$

c $x(x+1)^3 \sin 2x$ d $(x+1)^{-2} (2x+1)^2$

5 Find $f'\left(\frac{\pi}{4}\right)$ given that a $f(x) = x \cos^2 x$ b $f(x) = x \cos x^2$

6 Find $f'\left(\frac{\pi}{3}\right)$ given that a $f(x) = (\cos x \sin x)^2$ b $f(x) = \cos x \sin^2 x$

7 If $f(x) = (3x^2+5)(2x^2+3x+1)$ find $f'(0)$.

8 $f(x) = \dfrac{x+1}{x-1}$

a By considering the function as $f(x) = (x+1)(x-1)^{-1}$, find $f'(x)$.

b Differentiate i $\dfrac{3x+1}{2x-1}$ ii $\dfrac{3-2x}{x+4}$ iii $\dfrac{\sin x}{\cos x}$

9 In 1630 Pierre De Fermat studied a curve called 'The Witch of Agnesi'.

Its equation is of the form $x^2 y = 4a^2(2a-y)$ where a is a constant.

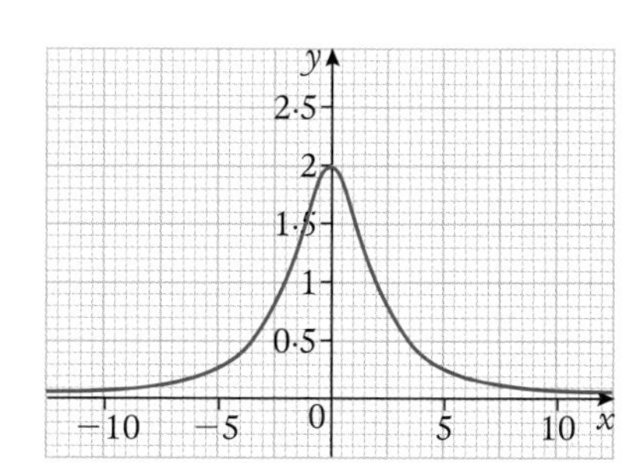

a In this example $a = 1$. Show that $y = \dfrac{8}{x^2+4}$.

b Find the gradient of the tangent to the curve at the point (2, 1).

4.6 The quotient rule

Given that f and g are differentiable and $y(x) = \dfrac{f(x)}{g(x)}$ then

$$y'(x) = \frac{f'(x) \cdot g(x) - f(x) \cdot g'(x)}{(g(x))^2}$$

Proof

Express the quotient as a product.

$y(x) = \dfrac{f(x)}{g(x)} = f(x) \times (g(x))^{-1}$

$\Rightarrow y(x) = f'(x) \times (g(x))^{-1} + f(x) \times \dfrac{d}{dx}(g(x))^{-1}$

Now, by the chain rule $\dfrac{d}{dx}(g(x))^{-1} = -(g(x))^{-2} \cdot g'(x)$.

Thus $y(x) = f'(x) \times (g(x))^{-1} + f(x) \times \left(-(g(x))^{-2}\right) \cdot g'(x)$

$= \dfrac{f'(x)}{g(x)} - \dfrac{f(x)g'(x)}{(g(x))^2}$

$= \dfrac{f'(x)g(x) - f(x)g'(x)}{(g(x))^2}$

In Leibniz notation: $y(x) = \dfrac{f(x)}{g(x)} \Rightarrow \dfrac{dy}{dx} = \dfrac{\dfrac{df}{dx}g - f\dfrac{dg}{dx}}{g^2}$

Example 10

Find $\dfrac{d}{dx}\left(\dfrac{x^3}{\sin x}\right)$.

Identify the two factors forming the quotient, $f(x) = x^3$ and $g(x) = \sin x$.

Thus $f'(x) = 3x^2$; $g'(x) = \cos x$.

So $\dfrac{d}{dx}\left(\dfrac{x^3}{\sin x}\right) = \dfrac{3x^2 \sin x - x^3 \cos x}{(\sin x)^2}$.

Example 11

Find the derivative of $\tan x$.

$y = \tan x = \dfrac{\sin x}{\cos x}$

$f(x) = \sin x$ and $g(x) = \cos x$

Thus $f'(x) = \cos x$; $g'(x) = -\sin x$

So $\dfrac{d}{dx}(\tan x) = \dfrac{\cos x \cos x - (-\sin x) \sin x}{(\cos x)^2} = \dfrac{\cos^2 x + \sin^2 x}{\cos^2 x} = \dfrac{1}{\cos^2 x}$

Exercise 4.6

1 Differentiate these.

a $\dfrac{x^3}{2x + 1}$ b $\dfrac{\cos x}{\sin x}$ c $\dfrac{1 - x}{1 + x^2}$ d $\dfrac{\sin x}{x}$

2 Find the derivative of

a $\dfrac{x^2}{\sin x}$ b $\dfrac{2x}{\sqrt{x} + 5}$ c $\dfrac{x + 2}{\sqrt{\sin x}}$ d $\dfrac{\sqrt{x} + 1}{2x}$ e $\dfrac{3x + 4}{x^{\frac{3}{2}}}$

3 Use the quotient rule to differentiate

a $\dfrac{1}{\sin x}$ b $\dfrac{1}{\cos x}$ c $\dfrac{\sin x}{\cos^2 x}$ d $\dfrac{\sin x}{\cos 2x}$

4 a If $f(x) = \dfrac{x + 1}{x^2 + 2}$ find $f'(0)$. b If $f(x) = \dfrac{x^2}{\sqrt{x} - 1}$ find $f'(2)$.

5 Solve $\dfrac{dy}{dx} = 0$ where $y = \dfrac{2x^2 + 3x - 6}{x - 2}$.

6 a Find $\frac{dy}{dx}$ where $y = \frac{4}{(x-3)(x+1)}$.

b i Express y in partial fractions.

ii Now find $\frac{dy}{dx}$.

c Compare the methods.

7 The graph shows $y = \frac{1}{\sin x + \cos x}$; $-0.5 \leqslant x \leqslant 2$.

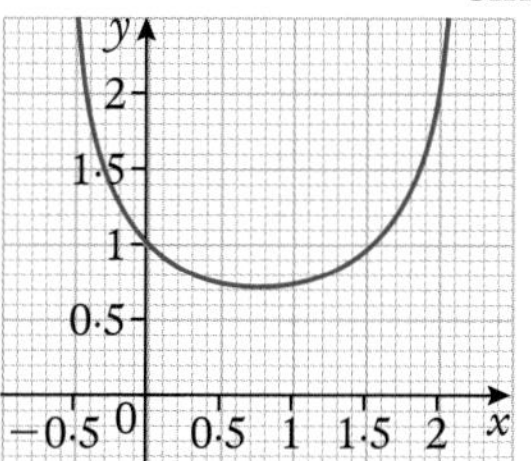

a Find $\frac{dy}{dx}$.

b Show that $\frac{dy}{dx} = \frac{\sin x - \cos x}{1 + \sin 2x}$.

c Find the gradient of the curve

i where it cuts the y-axis

ii where $x = \frac{\pi}{2}$.

4.7 A short summary so far

Standard functions $\quad \frac{d}{dx}(x^n) = nx^{n-1}$; $\frac{d}{dx}(\sin ax) = a\cos ax$; $\frac{d}{dx}(\cos ax) = -a\sin ax$

Chain rule $\quad \frac{d}{dx}(f(g(x))) = f'(g(x)) \cdot g'(x)$

$$y = f(g(x)) \Rightarrow \frac{dy}{dx} = \frac{dy}{du} \times \frac{du}{dx} \text{ where } u = g(x)$$

Sums/differences $\quad \frac{d}{dx}(f(x) \pm g(x)) = f'(x) \pm g'(x)$

$$y(x) = f(x) \pm g(x) \Rightarrow \frac{dy}{dx} = \frac{df}{dx} \pm \frac{dg}{dx}$$

Product rule $\quad \frac{d}{dx}(f(x) \cdot g(x)) = f'(x)g(x) + f(x)g'(x)$

$$y(x) = f(x) \times g(x) \Rightarrow \frac{dy}{dx} = \frac{df}{dx}g + f\frac{dg}{dx}$$

Quotient rule $\quad \frac{d}{dx}\left(\frac{f(x)}{g(x)}\right) = \frac{f'(x)g(x) - f(x)g'(x)}{[g(x)]^2}$

$$y(x) = \frac{f(x)}{g(x)} \Rightarrow \frac{dy}{dx} = \frac{\frac{df}{dx}g - f\frac{dg}{dx}}{g^2}$$

Exercise 4.7

1 Find the derivative of each of these.

a $\frac{x+1}{x^2+3}$ b $\frac{1}{\sin 2x}$ c $\sin^2 3x$ d $(x+1)^3(x^3+1)$

2 If $y = \sin(\sin x)$, find $\frac{dy}{dx}$.

3 Find $f'(x)$ when $f(x) = (x+1)^2 \cos 2x$.

4 $y = \dfrac{\cos x}{\cos x + \sin x}$. Show that $\dfrac{dy}{dx} = -\dfrac{1}{1 + \sin 2x}$ and hence find the gradient of the tangent at $x = \dfrac{\pi}{4}$.

5 Differentiate $\dfrac{(2x + 3)^3}{x^2 + 3x - 1}$.

6 The diagram shows a classic curve, the serpentine curve, whose equation is

$x^2 y = ax - a^2 y$ where a is a constant.

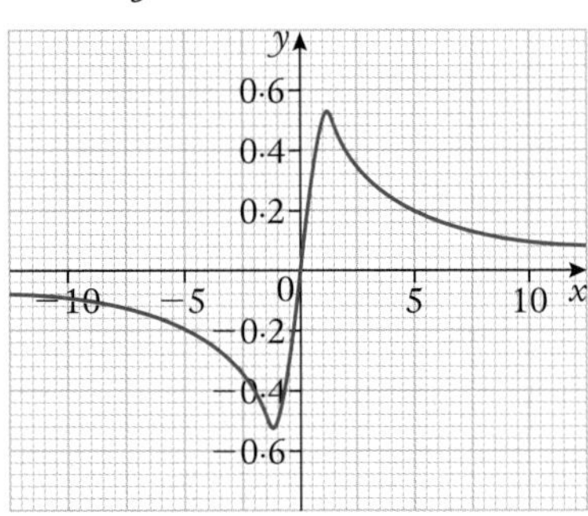

a Make y the subject of the equation.

b Show that $\dfrac{dy}{dx} = \dfrac{a(a^2 - x^2)}{(a^2 + x^2)^2}$.

c The diagram shows the case where $a = 1$.
What is the gradient at $x = 0$ in this case?

d Let m_1, m_2, m_3 be the gradients of the tangents at $x = \dfrac{a}{2}$, $x = a$ and $x = 2a$ respectively. Show that $m_1 + m_2 + 4m_3 = 0$.

4.8 Further trigonometric functions

Currently you have been introduced to the functions sine, cosine and tangent of x.
Let us now introduce three new related functions.

1 The **secant** of x: $f(x) = \sec x = \dfrac{1}{\cos x}$, where $\cos x \neq 0 \Rightarrow x \neq \dfrac{\pi}{2} + n\pi, n \in Z$.

2 The **cosecant** of x: $f(x) = \operatorname{cosec} x = \dfrac{1}{\sin x}$, where $\sin x \neq 0 \Rightarrow x \neq n\pi, n \in Z$.

3 The **cotangent** of x: $f(x) = \cot x = \dfrac{1}{\tan x}$, where $\sin x \neq 0 \Rightarrow x \neq n\pi, n \in Z$.

Note that $\tan x$ is not defined where $\cos x = 0$; $\cot x$ is not defined where $\sin x = 0$.
You should explore the graphs of these functions using a calculator or spreadsheet.

Drawing y = sec x

In A1 type: 0

In A2 type: = A1 + PI()/12 [Note that PI() = π]

Select A2 and Fill down to A25.

In B1 type: = 1/COS(A1) [Note that spreadsheets do not carry SEC as a function]

Select B1 and Fill down to B25.

Delete the contents of B7 and B19. [These represent $\pm\infty$ and distort the vertical scale]

Select A1 to B25 then Charts > Scatter > Smooth Lined Scatter.

A graph of $y = \sec x$ appears. This can be formatted to tighten the domain and range, to add a title, to add axes and to indicate where the function is undefined.

Drawing y = cosec x

The instructions are as above except

i In B1 type: = 1/SIN(A1).

ii Delete the contents of B1, B13 and B25.

Drawing y = cot x

The instructions are as above except

i In B1 type: = 1/TAN(A1).

ii Delete the contents of B1, B13 and B25.

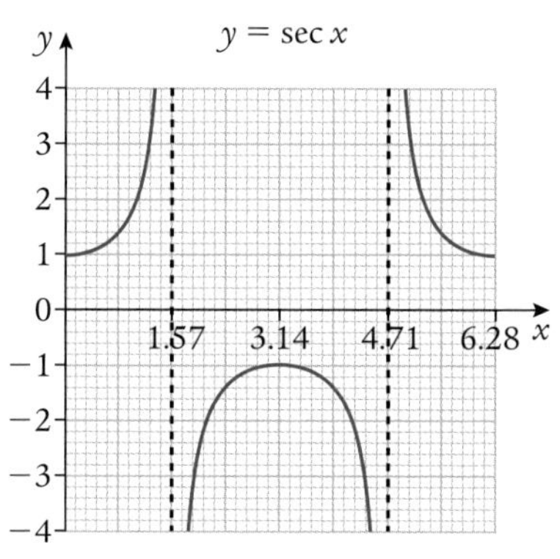

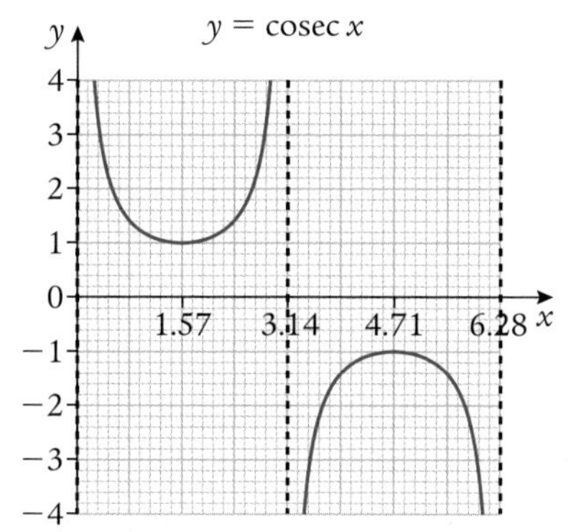

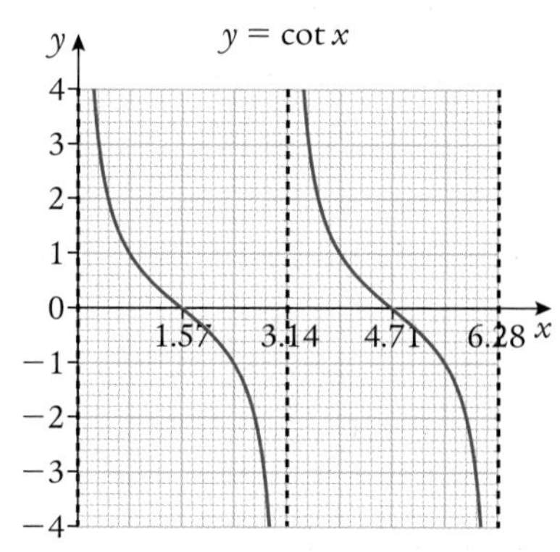

In Example 2 before Exercise 4.6 we found that $y = \tan x \Rightarrow \dfrac{dy}{dx} = \dfrac{1}{\cos^2 x}$.

We can now formally state that $y = \tan x \Rightarrow \dfrac{dy}{dx} = \sec^2 x$.

Example 12

Prove that $\sec^2 x = \tan^2 x + 1$.

We know $\sin^2 x + \cos^2 x = 1$

$\Rightarrow \dfrac{\sin^2 x}{\cos^2 x} + \dfrac{\cos^2 x}{\cos^2 x} = \dfrac{1}{\cos^2 x}$

$\Rightarrow \tan^2 x + 1 = \sec^2 x$

Example 13

Differentiate $\sec x$.

$$\frac{d}{dx}\sec x = \frac{d}{dx}\left(\frac{1}{\cos x}\right) = \frac{0 \cdot \cos x - 1 \cdot (-\sin x)}{\cos^2 x} = \frac{\sin x}{\cos^2 x}$$

This can be simplified in various ways, for example $\dfrac{\sin x}{\cos^2 x} = \tan x \sec x = \sin x \sec^2 x$.

Exercise 4.8

1 Differentiate and simplify **a** $\operatorname{cosec} x$ **b** $\cot x$

2 Find the derivative of each of these.

a $\sec 2x$ **b** $\tan 2x$ **c** $\operatorname{cosec} 2x$ **d** $\operatorname{cosec}(2x + 3)$

e $\sec(4 - 3x^2)$ **f** $\cot 5x$ **g** $\cot(x^2)$ **h** $\tan(1 - 17x)$

3 Calculate $\frac{dy}{dx}$ in each case.

a $y = \sec x \tan x$ b $y = \cot(\tan x)$ c $y = \text{cosec}(\sin x)$

d $y = \text{cosec}^2 3x$ e $y = \sec^2 x$ f $y = \tan^2 4x$

g $y = \sqrt{\sec x}$ h $y = \frac{1}{\sqrt{1 + \text{cosec}\, x}}$

4 Find $f'(x)$ when

a $f(x) = \frac{x^2 + x}{1 + \cot x}$ b $f(x) = \frac{\cot x + \sec x}{\cot x - \sec x}$ c $f(x) = \frac{\sec x + \cot x}{x^2 + 2x + 1}$

5 Given that $f(x) = \sin^2 x \tan x$, show that $f'\left(\frac{\pi}{4}\right) = 2$.

6 a If $f(x) = \sin x \sec x$, show that $f'\left(\frac{\pi}{3}\right) = 4$.

b How might $f(x)$ have been simplified to make the problem easier?

4.9 Exponential and logarithmic functions

A function of the form $f(x) = a^x$, $a \in R$, is an exponential function.

Given that $a^0 = 1$ then every function of the form $f(x) = a^x$ passes through (0, 1).

The graph shows a select few for different values of a including $a = 1$.
Though they all pass through (0, 1), each curve has a different gradient at this point.
These gradients vary from 0, at $a = 1$, to infinity as a increases.

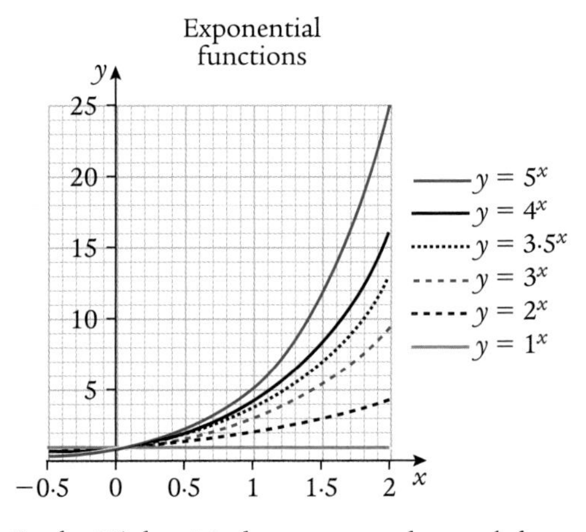

In the Higher Maths course we learned that one particular base is used more than others. The number represented by $e = 2.71828182845904523...$ takes this role.

The function $f(x) = e^x$ is called the exponential function. [sometimes written as $f(x) = \exp(x)$]

Why should e be used in preference to other numbers?

Differentiating exponential functions

Let $f(x) = a^x$.

$$f'(x) = \lim_{h\to 0}\left[\frac{f(x+h) - f(x)}{h}\right]$$

$$= \lim_{h\to 0}\left[\frac{a^{x+h} - a^x}{h}\right]$$

$$= \lim_{h\to 0}\left[\frac{a^x(a^h - 1)}{h}\right]$$

$$= \lim_{h\to 0}[a^x] \times \lim_{h\to 0}\left[\frac{a^h - 1}{h}\right]$$

$$= a^x \times \lim_{h\to 0}\left[\frac{a^h - 1}{h}\right]$$

The value of this limit is dependent on the value of a.

Note that, when $x = 0$, the limit gives the gradient at $(0, 1)$, $f'(0) = \lim_{h \to 0}\left[\frac{a^h - 1}{h}\right]$.

This gradient varies from 0 to infinity.

The number e is defined as the value of a which makes this gradient 1.

That is, $\lim_{h \to 0}\left[\frac{e^h - 1}{h}\right] = 1$

So $f(x) = e^x \Rightarrow f'(x) = e^x \times \lim_{h \to 0}\left[\frac{e^h - 1}{h}\right] = e^x \times 1 = e^x$

Example 14

Find $\frac{dy}{dx}$ when $y = 2e^{3x}$.

Use the chain rule:

let $u = 3x \Rightarrow y = 2e^u$

$\Rightarrow \frac{du}{dx} = 3$ and $\frac{dy}{du} = 2e^u$

$\Rightarrow \frac{dy}{dx} = \frac{dy}{du} \times \frac{du}{dx} = 2e^u \times 3 = 6e^u$

$= 6e^{3x}$

The working has been 'expanded' for the sake of explanation.

In practice, the problem can be tackled in one line: $\frac{dy}{dx} = 2e^{3x} \times 3 = 6e^{3x}$.

Example 15

Find the derivative of xe^x.

Using the product rule, $\frac{d}{dx}xe^x = \frac{d}{dx}x \cdot e^x + x\frac{d}{dx}e^x = 1 \cdot e^x + x \cdot e^x = e^x + xe^x$.

Differentiating the logarithmic function

The natural logarithm function is the inverse of the exponential function.

$y = e^x \Leftrightarrow x = \ln y$

So $e^{\ln x} = x$

Differentiating with respect to x,

$\frac{d}{dx}e^{\ln x} = \frac{d}{dx}x$

Using the chain rule,

$e^{\ln x} \times \frac{d}{dx}(\ln x) = 1$

$\frac{d}{dx}(\ln x) = \frac{1}{e^{\ln x}}$

giving us our final result, $\frac{d}{dx}(\ln x) = \frac{1}{x}$

Example 16

Find the derivative of $\ln 3x$.

By the chain rule, $\frac{d}{dx}(\ln 3x) = \frac{1}{3x} \times 3 = \frac{1}{x}$.

Example 17

Differentiate $\frac{\ln x}{x^2}$.

By the quotient rule, $\frac{d}{dx}\left(\frac{\ln x}{x^2}\right) = \frac{\frac{1}{x}x^2 - \ln x \cdot 2x}{(x^2)^2} = \frac{x - 2x\ln x}{x^4} = \frac{1 - 2\ln x}{x^3}$.

Example 18

Given that $y = a^x$, $a > 0$, calculate $\frac{dy}{dx}$.

$\ln y = \ln a^x = x \ln a$

$\Rightarrow y = e^{x \ln a}$ [These two steps make e the base.]

By the chain rule, $\frac{dy}{dx} = e^{x\ln a} \times \frac{d}{dx} x \ln a = e^{x \ln a} \cdot \ln a$.

By the laws of logs, $= \ln a \times a^x$.

Example 19

Given that $y = \log_{10} x$, calculate $\frac{dy}{dx}$.

$y = \log_{10} x \Leftrightarrow x = 10^y$

$x = 10^y \Rightarrow \ln x = \ln(10^y)$

$\Rightarrow \ln x = y \ln 10$

$\Rightarrow y = \frac{\ln x}{\ln 10} = \ln x \frac{1}{\ln 10}$

$\Rightarrow \frac{dy}{dx} = \frac{1}{\ln 10} \cdot \frac{1}{x} = \frac{1}{x \ln 10}$

Remember that $\frac{1}{\ln 10}$ is a constant.

Exercise 4.9

1 Find the derivative of each of these.

a e^{4x} b e^{4x+1} c e^{x^2} d e^{1-x^2} e $e^{\cos x}$

f $2e^{3x+4}$ g $3e^{\frac{x}{3}}$ h $4e^{x^3-2x}$ i $5e^{\sin x}$ j $-e^{2\cos x}$

k $\ln(x+3)$ l $\ln(3x-1)$ m $3\ln(1-2x)$ n $\ln(2x^3+5)$ o $\ln(\sin x)$

p $\ln(x+3)^2$ q $\ln\left(\frac{1}{x}\right)$ r $\sin(\ln x)$ s $(\ln(x))^3$ t $\frac{1}{\ln x}$

2 Differentiate

a $e^{\frac{1}{2x}}$ b $e^{\sin^2 x}$ c $e^{\frac{x+1}{x-1}}$ d $e^{\sin x \cos x}$ e $e^{\sec x}$

f $\ln\left(\frac{1}{x^2}\right)$ g $\ln(\sin^2 x)$ h $e^x \ln x$ i $\ln x^2 \ln(x+2)$ j $\ln(\sec x)$

3 Calculate $f'(x)$ when $f(x)$ is

a $\ln(\cos 3x)$ b $\ln(\ln(x))$ c $e^{2x+1}\ln(2x+1)$ d $3e^{\sec x}$ e e^{e^x}

4 Find $\frac{dy}{dx}$ when y is

a $(3x+1)e^{3x}$ b $\cos x e^{\cos x}$ c $e^{1-3x}\tan 2x$ d $e^{(1-\ln x)}$ e $4e^x \cot x$

5 Differentiate

a $\frac{2x}{3e^x}$ b $\frac{x+e^x}{x-e^x}$ c $\frac{e^x+e^{-x}}{e^x-e^{-x}}$ d $\frac{\ln x + \ln 2x}{e^{x-1}}$ e $\frac{(x-1)(x+2)}{e^{x-1}}$

f $\frac{\ln(x+1)}{e^x+\ln x}$ g $\frac{e^x}{\sqrt{\ln x}}$ h $\frac{\ln(x^2+2x-1)}{\sqrt{e^x}}$ i $\cos\left(\frac{\ln x}{e^x}\right)$

6 Check Example 18 to help you find the derivative of:

a 3^x b 4^x c 5^x d $2a^x$ e 5^{3x} f 6^{2x+3}

7 Show that if $f(x) = x^x$ then $f'(x) = (1 + \ln x)x^x$.

8 Check Example 19 above to help you find the derivative of

a $\log_3 x$ b $\log_{10} 3x$ c $\log_8(2x - 1)$ d $\log_2\left(\frac{1}{x}\right)$

4.10 Higher derivatives

A function f has a derivative f'.

If f' is also differentiable, its derivative is denoted by f''; it is called the second derivative of f.
In a similar way third, fourth and higher derivatives can be defined.

In Leibniz notation

$$f(x) = y \Rightarrow f'(x) = \frac{dy}{dx} \Rightarrow f''(x) = \frac{d}{dx}\left(\frac{dy}{dx}\right) = \frac{d^2y}{dx^2} \Rightarrow f'''(x) = \frac{d^3y}{dx^3} \Rightarrow f^{(4)}(x) = \frac{d^4y}{dx^4}$$

The nth derivative would be denoted by $f^{(n)}(x) = \frac{d^ny}{dx^n}$.

Example 20

Given $y = 3x^4$ find the fifth derivative, $\frac{d^5y}{dx^5}$.

$$y = 3x^4 \Rightarrow \frac{dy}{dx} = 12x^3 \Rightarrow \frac{d^2y}{dx^2} = 36x^2 \Rightarrow \frac{d^3y}{dx^3} = 72x \Rightarrow \frac{d^4y}{dx^4} = 72 \Rightarrow \frac{d^5y}{dx^5} = 0$$

Example 21

a Find the nth derivative of $\sin x$ for $n = 1$ to 4.

b Prove by induction that $\frac{d^n}{dx^n}\sin x = \sin\left(x + \frac{n\pi}{2}\right)$.

a $y = \sin x \Rightarrow \frac{dy}{dx} = \cos x \Rightarrow \frac{d^2y}{dx^2} = -\sin x \Rightarrow \frac{d^3y}{dx^3} = -\cos x \Rightarrow \frac{d^4y}{dx^4} = \sin x$

b Before we start we need to know that

$$\sin\left(x + \frac{\pi}{2}\right) = \sin x \cos\left(\frac{\pi}{2}\right) + \cos x \sin\left(\frac{\pi}{2}\right) = \sin x \cdot 0 + \cos x \cdot 1 = \cos x \qquad \text{(A)}$$

Now we can see that the conjecture is true when $n = 1$

$$\frac{dy}{dx} = \cos x = \sin\left(x + \frac{1 \cdot \pi}{2}\right)$$

Assume the conjecture is true for $n = k$.

$$\text{Thus } \frac{d^ky}{dx^k} = \sin\left(x + \frac{k \cdot \pi}{2}\right) \qquad \text{(B)}$$

$$\Rightarrow \frac{d^{k+1}y}{dx^{k+1}} = \frac{d}{dx}\left(\frac{d^ky}{dx^k}\right) = \frac{d}{dx}\left(\sin\left(x + \frac{k \cdot \pi}{2}\right)\right) \qquad \text{Using assumption (B)}$$

$$= \cos\left(x + \frac{k \cdot \pi}{2}\right) = \sin\left(x + \frac{k \cdot \pi}{2} + \frac{\pi}{2}\right) \qquad \text{Using (A)}$$

$$= \sin\left(x + \frac{(k + 1) \cdot \pi}{2}\right)$$

Thus if the conjecture is true for $n = k$ then it is true for $n = k + 1$.

We know it is true for $n = 1$, so by induction it is true for all $n \geqslant 1, n \in \mathbb{N}$.

Exercise 4.10

1 a For each of these functions find the value of n for which $\frac{d^n y}{dx^n} = c_n$, where c_n is a constant.

i x ii x^2 iii x^3 iv x^4 v x^5

b Express c_n as a function of n.

2 a Find i $\frac{d}{dx}(2x+1)^3$ ii $\frac{d^2}{dx^2}(2x+1)^3$ iii $\frac{d^3}{dx^3}(2x+1)^3$

b What is the lowest value of n for which $\frac{d^n}{dx^n}(2x+1)^3 = 0$?

3 Find the derivatives which do not equal zero for $(2x+3)^4$.

4 For each of these functions

i write its first, second and third derivative

ii make a conjecture about its nth derivative

iii prove your conjecture true using induction.

a $\cos x$ [Hint: express $\cos x$ as $\sin\left(x + \frac{\pi}{2}\right)$.] b $\sin 2x$

c $\frac{1}{x}$ [Hint: $(-1)^n = 1$ when n is even; $(-1)^n = -1$ when n is odd.]

d $\ln x$ e e^{3x} f $\sqrt{x}$ g xe^x

5 a Given $y_1 = \tan x$, find $\frac{dy}{dx}$ and $\frac{d^2y}{dx^2}$.

b Given $y_2 = \ln(\cos x)$, find $\frac{dy}{dx}$ and $\frac{d^2y}{dx^2}$.

c Write a connection between the derivatives of $y_2 = \ln(\cos x)$ and $y_1 = \tan x$.

6 Given $y = be^{ax}$ where a and b are constants, make a conjecture about $\frac{d^n y}{dx^n}$ and prove it by induction.

7 Given that $y = \frac{x}{2x+1}$

a show that $\frac{dy}{dx} = \frac{y^2}{x^2}$

b show that $\frac{d^2y}{dx^2} = -4\frac{y^3}{x^3}$

c show that $\frac{d^3y}{dx^3} = 24\frac{y^4}{x^4}$.

8 Given that $y = e^x \sin x$ show that $\frac{d^4y}{dx^4} = -4y$.

9 $y = \sqrt[3]{(x-1)^4}$

a Find $\frac{dy}{dx}$ and $\frac{d^2y}{dx^2}$.

b With the aid of a graphics calculator or spreadsheet sketch the graphs[1] of y, $\frac{dy}{dx}$ and $\frac{d^2y}{dx^2}$ for $-2 \le x \le 3$.

c Comment on the continuity of the curves over this interval.

[The fact that a function is continuous does not imply that its derivatives are.]

[1] For the spreadsheet, y has to be written as '= ((x − 1)^4)^(1/3))'.

10 Let $f(x) = \frac{e^x - e^{-x}}{2}$, $g(x) = \frac{e^x + e^{-x}}{2}$ and $h(x) = \frac{e^x - e^{-x}}{e^x + e^{-x}}$.

a i Find $f'(x)$, $f''(x)$ and $f'''(x)$.

ii Find an expression for $f^{(n)}(x)$.

b State the relation between $f'(x)$ and $g(x)$ and $f(x)$ and $g'(x)$.

c i Prove that $h'(x) = \frac{1}{(g(x))^2}$.

ii Prove that $h''(x) = -\frac{f(2x)}{(g(x))^4}$.

Review 4

1 Find the derivative of $3x^2 + x + 1$ from first principles.

2 Differentiate $\frac{5x^4 + 4x}{3x^2}$.

3 If $f(x) = \cos 2x$, find $f'\left(\frac{2\pi}{3}\right)$.

4 Differentiate $\cos x \sqrt[3]{x^2}$.

5 Find the derivative of $\frac{\sin x}{(2x - 5)^2}$.

6 Given $f(x) = \sec 4x$, find $f'(x)$.

7 Find $\frac{dy}{dx}$ when $y = \operatorname{cosec} x \cdot \cot x$.

8 If $y = \operatorname{cosec}^3 x$ show that $\frac{dy}{dx} + 3y \cot x = 0$.

9 If $y = x^2 \ln x$ show that $\frac{dy}{dx} = x \ln(ex^2)$.

10 Given that $y(x) = \frac{\sin x}{e^x}$

a find i $\frac{dy}{dx}$ ii $\frac{d^2y}{dx^2}$ iii $\frac{d^3y}{dx^3}$ iv $\frac{d^4y}{dx^4}$

b express $\frac{d^4y}{dx^4}$ as a function of y.

11 If $y = e^{x^2}$ show that $\frac{d^2y}{dx^2} - 2x\frac{dy}{dx} - 2y = 0$.

Summary 4

1 Definition: the **derivative** of $f(x)$ is $\lim_{h \to 0}\left(\frac{f(x+h) - f(x)}{h}\right)$.

Notation: if $y = f(x)$ its derivative is denoted by $\frac{dy}{dx}$, $\frac{df}{dx}$, $f'(x)$ or f'.

***n*th derivative:** if $y = f(x)$, its second derivative is $\frac{d}{dx}\left(\frac{dy}{dx}\right) = \frac{d^2y}{dx^2}$.

In general, the nth derivative is denoted by $\frac{d^ny}{dx^n}$ or $f^{(n)}(x)$.

2 Standard derivatives

$f(x)$	$f'(x)$
x^n	nx^{n-1}
$\sin x$	$\cos x$
$\cos x$	$-\sin x$
$\tan x$	$\sec^2 x$
$\sec x$	$\sec x \tan x$
$\operatorname{cosec} x$	$-\operatorname{cosec} x \cot x$
$\cot x$	$-\operatorname{cosec}^2 x$
e^x	e^x
$\ln x$	$\frac{1}{x}$

3 Rules

Sum/difference: $y = f(x) \pm g(x) \Rightarrow \frac{dy}{dx} = \frac{df}{dx} \pm \frac{dg}{dx}$

Chain rule: Given $y = f(g(x))$ and $g(x) = u \Rightarrow y = f(u)$,

then $\frac{dy}{dx} = \frac{dy}{du} \times \frac{du}{dx} = f'(g(x)) \cdot g'(x)$

Product rule:

$$y = f(x) \cdot g(x) \Rightarrow \frac{dy}{dx} = \frac{df}{dx} \cdot g(x) + f(x) \cdot \frac{dg}{dx} = f'(x)g(x) + f(x)g'(x)$$

Quotient rule:

$$y = \frac{f(x)}{g(x)} \quad \Rightarrow \frac{dy}{dx} = \frac{\frac{df}{dx} g(x) - f(x)\frac{dg}{dx}}{(g(x))^2} = \frac{f'(x)g(x) - f(x)g'(x)}{(g(x))^2}$$

5 The properties of functions

Historical Note

In 1637, René Descartes published a book which became known as *Discourse on Method*. Attached to the book are three appendices, one of which, *La Géométrie,* explains his new invention: coordinate geometry. The main aim of this appendix was to bridge the gap between the two branches of mathematics, algebra and geometry. In *La Géométrie* Descartes develops, for the first time, the concept of *the equation of a curve*.

5.1 Definitions

Reminders

A function, f, is defined as a rule which assigns each member of a set A uniquely to a member of a set B.

A function f assigns exactly one value y to each x.
We write $y = f(x)$ or $f: x \to y$ ('f maps x to y').

y is referred to as the **image** of x in f.

Set A is referred to as the **domain** of the function and the set B, as the **co-domain**.

The subset of B which is the set of all images of the function is called the **range** of the function.

It is possible for $f(a) = f(b)$ and yet $a \neq b$.

In this chapter certain sets are used often and are assigned specific symbols.
N, the set of natural numbers $\{1, 2, 3, 4, ...\}$
W, the set of whole numbers $\{0, 1, 2, 3, 4, ...\}$
Z, the set of integers $\{...-3, -2, -1, 0, 1, 2, 3, ...\}$
Q, the set of rational numbers
R, the set of real numbers

Often restrictions have to be placed on these sets to provide a suitable domain and range.

This example shows the function $f: x \to x^2$ linking each member of the set $\{-2, -1, 0, 1, 2\}$ to members of the set $\{0, 1, 2, 3, 4\}$

$f: x \to x^2$

A: −2, −1, 0, 1, 2
B: 0, 1, 2, 3, 4

Note that to meet the definition of a function, each element of A has an image, and only one image.

The domain is $\{-2, -1, 0, 1, 2\}$.

The co-domain is $\{0, 1, 2, 3, 4\}$.

The range is $\{0, 1, 4\}$

$f(-2) = f(2) = 4$ but $-2 \neq 2$

Example 1

Consider the function $f(x) = \sqrt{x}$.

What would be a suitable domain and range?

R would be an unsuitable domain since negative values of x have no image in R, but the set of positive real numbers and zero do form a suitable domain, $R^+ + \{0\}$.

The largest corresponding range would be $R^+ + \{0\}$.

Example 2

Consider the function $f(x) = \dfrac{1}{x - 1}$.

What would be a suitable domain and range?

Here the set of real numbers, except 1, provides a suitable domain, $R - \{1\}$.
The function can take all real values except 0, so the corresponding range is $R - \{0\}$.

Exercise 5.1

1 i Write the largest suitable domain for each of these functions.

ii State the corresponding range where possible.

a $f(x) = \sin x$ b $f(x) = \sqrt{x - 2}$ c $f(x) = x!$ (x factorial)

d $f(x) = \tan x$ e $f(x) = x^2$ f $f(x) = 1 + \sin x$

g $f(x) = \sqrt{x^2}$ h $f(x) = \dfrac{1}{\sin x}$

2 The diagram illustrates the relation

$x^2 + y^2 = 5^2$

a State what value(s) of y correspond to an x value of i 4 ii 8

b Describe why $x^2 + y^2 = 5^2$ does not define a function on R.

c Describe suitable restrictions which would allow you to work with this relationship as a function.

3 When a relationship is graphed, it is relatively easy to identify whether or not the relationship is a function on R. A relation is not a function on R if there exists a vertical line

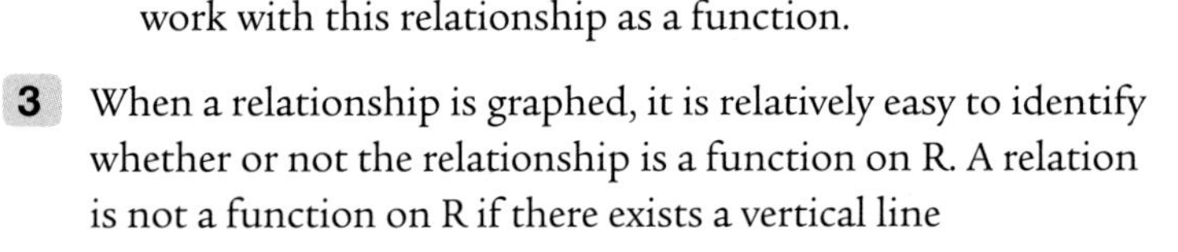

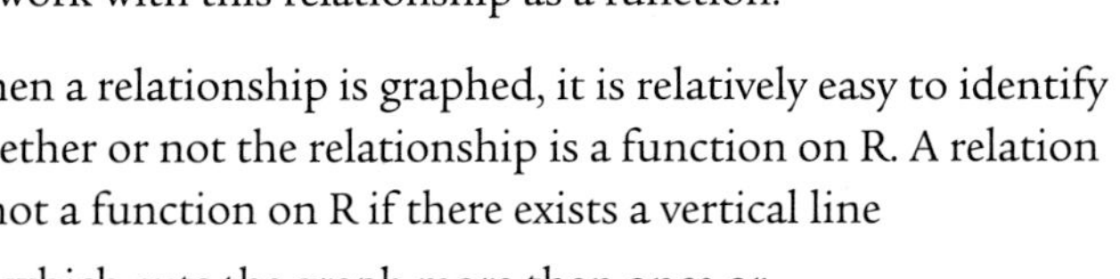

- which cuts the graph more than once or
- which does not cut the graph at all.

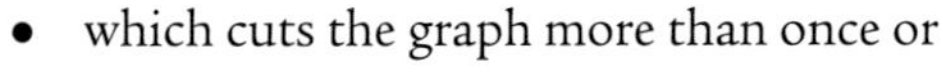

Suitable restrictions are also then easily identified.

Which of these graphs could represent a function on R?

a
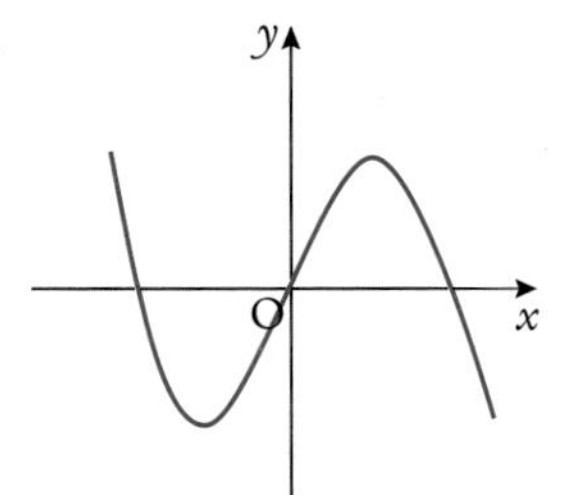

b
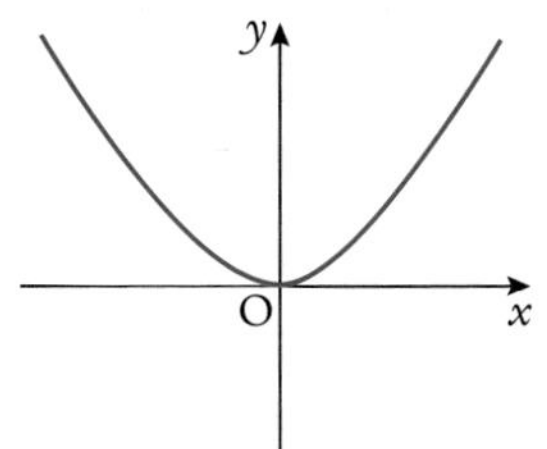

c
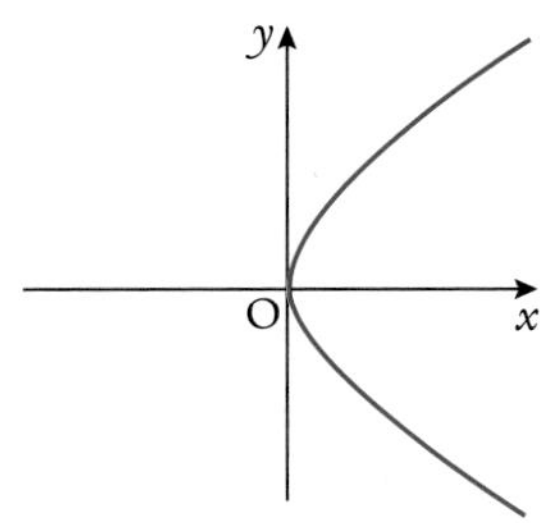

d
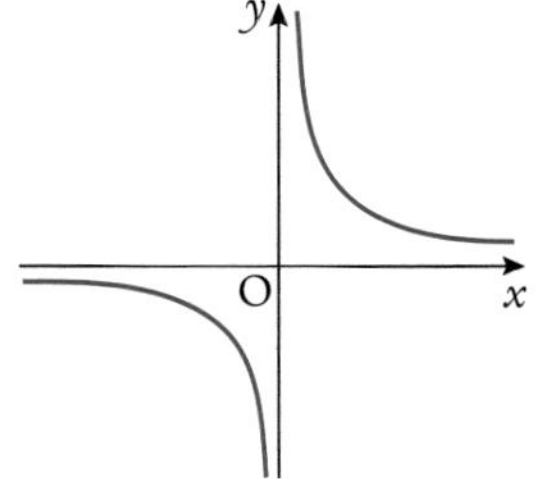

e
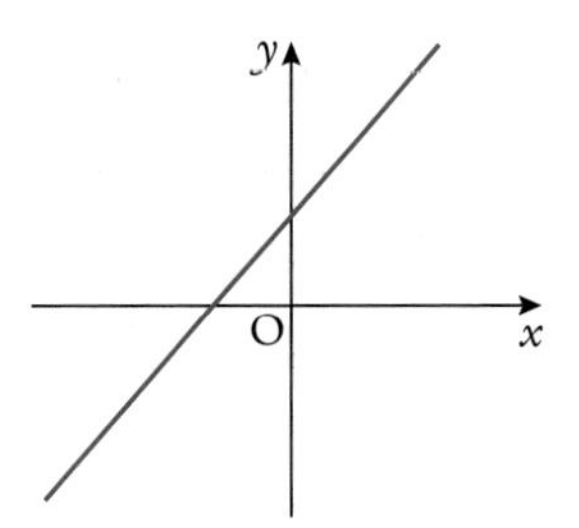

f
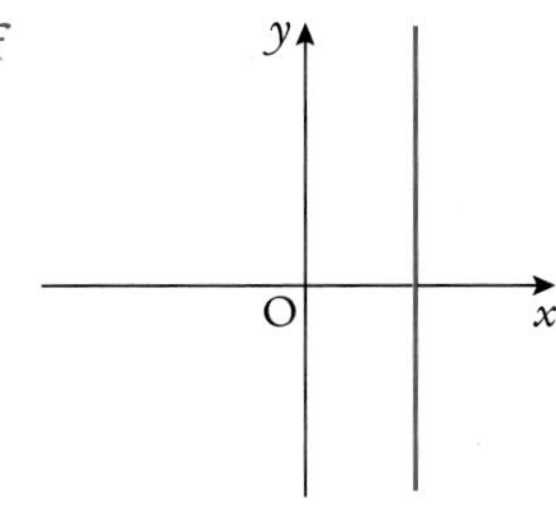

5.2 The modulus function, $y = |x|$

The modulus, or absolute value, of x is denoted by $|x|$ and is defined as

$$|x| = \begin{cases} x & \text{when } x \geq 0 \\ -x & \text{when } x < 0 \end{cases}$$

Examples are $|2| = 2$; $|-3| = 3$; $|2.97| = 2.97$; $|-5.87| = 5.87$; $|\sin 30°| = 0.5$; $|\sin 210°| = 0.5$

The properties of $|x|$ include

1. $|x| = \sqrt{x^2}$ $\qquad |-2| = \sqrt{(-2)^2} = \sqrt{4} = 2$
2. $|x + y| \leqslant |x| + |y|$ $\qquad |-3 + 2| \leqslant |-3| + |2| \ldots 1 \leqslant 3 + 2$
3. $|x \times y| = |x| \times |y|$ $\qquad |-3 \times 2| \leqslant |-3| \times |2|$
4. $|x| \leqslant a \Leftrightarrow -a \leqslant x \leqslant a$ $\qquad |5| \leq 8 \Leftrightarrow -8 \leq 5 \leq 8$
5. $|x| \geq a \Leftrightarrow -a \geq x$ or $x \geq a$ $\qquad |-2| \geq 1 \Leftrightarrow -1 \geq -2$ or $-2 \geq 1$

In this case $-1 \geq -2$ is true.

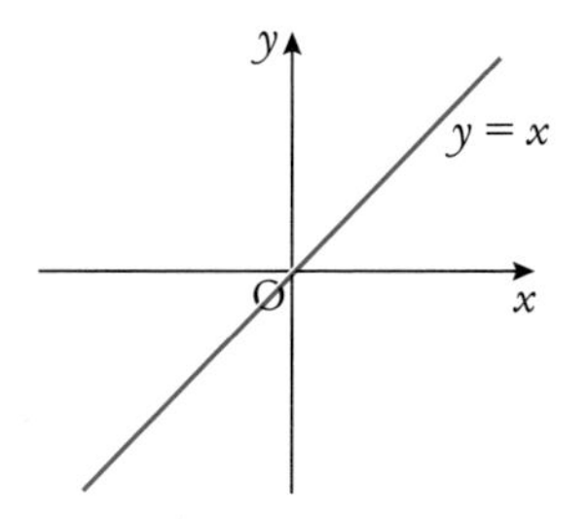

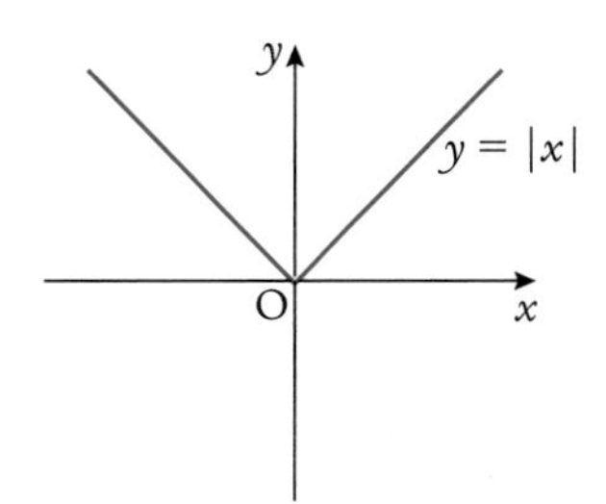

Spreadsheets make the function available using = ABS(x).
Here the spreadsheet has been asked to graph $y = |\sin x|$.

	A	B
1	X	ABS(SIN(x))
2	0	=ABS(SIN(A2))
3	=A2+PI()/12	=ABS(SIN(A3))
4	=A3+PI()/12	=ABS(SIN(A4))

Fill down to row 30.

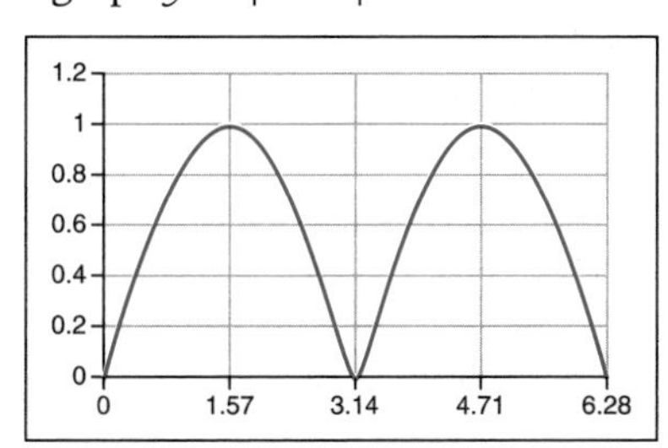

Note that to draw $y = |f(x)|$ we need only reflect the negative portions of the graph $y = f(x)$ in the x-axis.

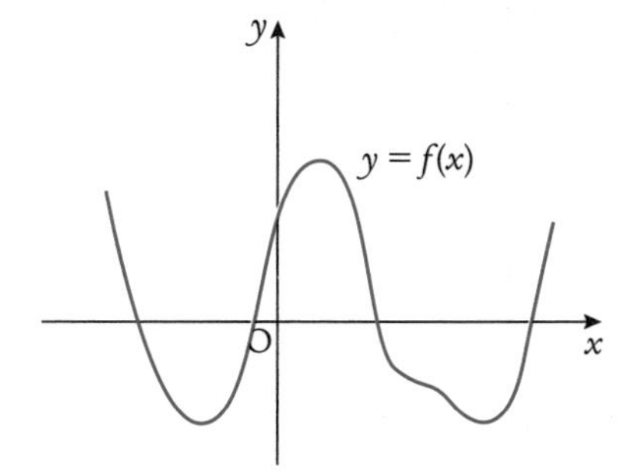

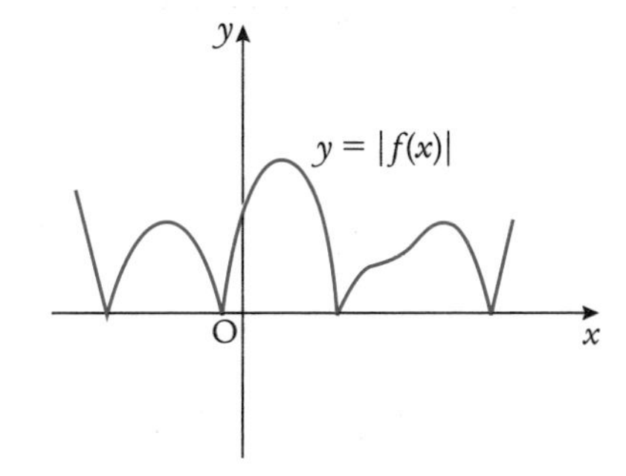

Exercise 5.2

For each of these functions sketch the graphs of $f(x)$ and $|f(x)|$.

1 $f(x) = x - 1$
2 $f(x) = 2x - 1$
3 $f(x) = \cos x°, 0 \leq x \leq 360$
4 $f(x) = x^2 - 1$
5 $f(x) = 1 - x^2$
6 $f(x) = x^2$
7 $f(x) = x^3$
8 $f(x) = \ln x, x > 0$
9 $f(x) = \tan x°, 0 \leq x \leq 360$

5.3 Inverse functions

A one-to-one correspondence is a special function where $a = b \Leftrightarrow f(a) = f(b)$.

In such a case the rule, f, which links each x in A to its image, $f(x)$, in B is reversible.

A rule then exists which links the image, $f(x)$, in B back to the corresponding x in A.

This rule is called the inverse of the function. It is denoted by f^{-1} and has the property that

$$y = f(x) \Leftrightarrow f^{-1}(y) = f^{-1}(f(x)) = x$$

For example $f(x) = 2x + 1$ has an inverse $f^{-1}(x) = \dfrac{x-1}{2}$.

Note that $f^{-1}(f(x)) = f^{-1}(2x + 1) = \dfrac{(2x+1) - 1}{2} = \dfrac{2x}{2} = x$.

If the point (x, y) lies on the graph $y = f(x)$ then (y, x) lies on the graph $y = f^{-1}(x)$.

The graph of the inverse function is the reflection of the graph of the function in the line $y = x$.

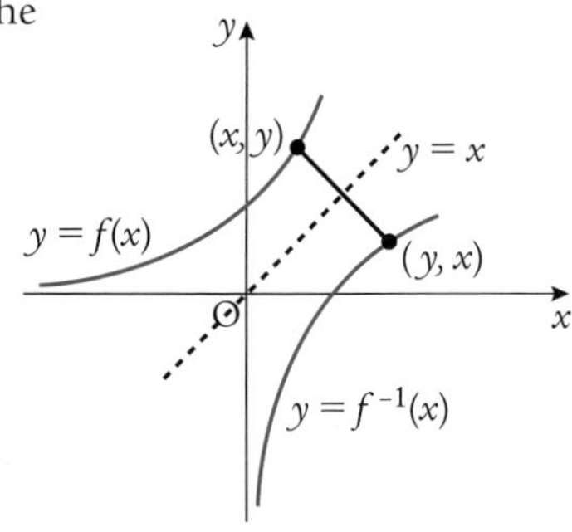

If the inverse exists then it can be found by interchanging x and y in the formula $y = f(x)$, that is, $x = f(y)$ and then making y the subject of the formula $y = f^{-1}(x)$.

Placing restrictions on the domain and range can often ensure that a function has an inverse.

Example 3

$f(x) = 4x^2 + 1$. Find $f^{-1}(x)$ and state a suitable domain and range for the function.

If the function can be represented by $y = 4x^2 + 1$ then its inverse, if it exists, can be represented by $x = 4y^2 + 1$

$$\Rightarrow y = \frac{\sqrt{x-1}}{2} \quad \text{Taking the positive root.}$$

$$\text{so } f^{-1}(x) = \frac{\sqrt{x-1}}{2}$$

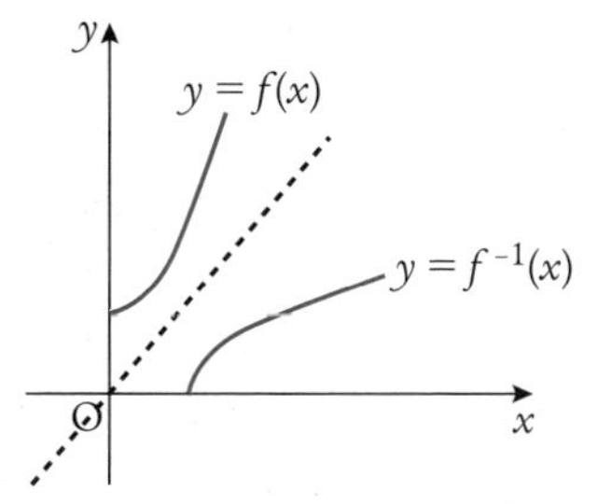

Note: $(x - 1) \geq 0$ if $f^{-1}(x)$ is real.

The largest suitable domain for this function is the set of numbers x such that $x \geq 1$ and x is real.
The corresponding range is, therefore, the set of numbers y such that $y \geq 0$ and y is real.

These sets of numbers can be written in a more compact fashion.
Domain $= \{x: x \geq 1, x \in R\}$ and range $= \{y: y \geq 0, y \in R\}$

The domain and range of the inverse function give us the range and domain respectively of the original function. For the function in Example 3, domain $= \{x: x \geq 0, x \in \mathrm{R}\}$ and range $= \{y: y \geq 1, y \in \mathrm{R}\}$

The diagram illustrates the situation.

Exercise 5.3

1 Each of these functions, $f(x)$, has an inverse.
Find a formula for the inverse function $f^{-1}(x)$.

a $f(x) = 3x + 4$ b $f(x) = 5x - 1$ c $f(x) = 3 - x$

d $f(x) = 4 - 2x$ e $f(x) = 8x^3$ f $f(x) = 1 - x^5$

g $f(x) = \dfrac{1}{x + 1}$ h $f(x) = \dfrac{x}{x - 1}$ i $f(x) = (x - 1)^{\frac{1}{3}}$

2 With suitable restrictions on the domain and range, each of these functions has an inverse. Find the inverse and state the largest suitable domain and range for the function.

a $f(x) = x^2$ b $f(x) = x^2 - 4$ c $f(x) = (x + 1)^2$

d $f(x) = (2x - 1)^2 - 1$ e $f(x) = x^2 + 6x - 1$ [Hint: complete the square.]

f $f(x) = \dfrac{1}{1 + x^2}$ g $f(x) = \sqrt{2x - 1}$

3 Each of these is the graph of a function.
Sketch the graph of its inverse.

a

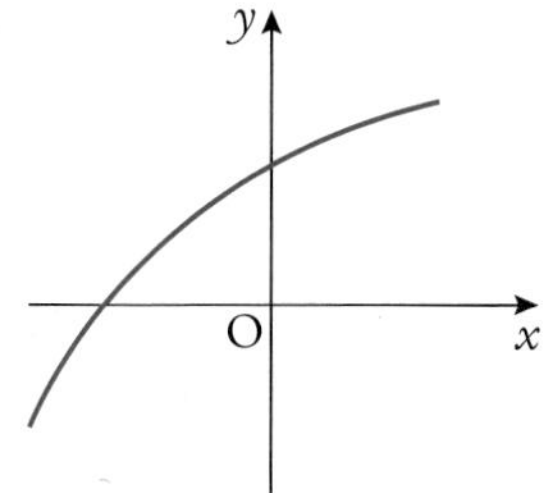

b

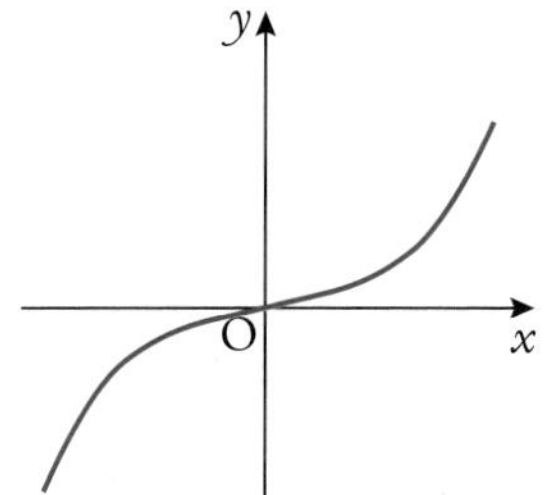

c

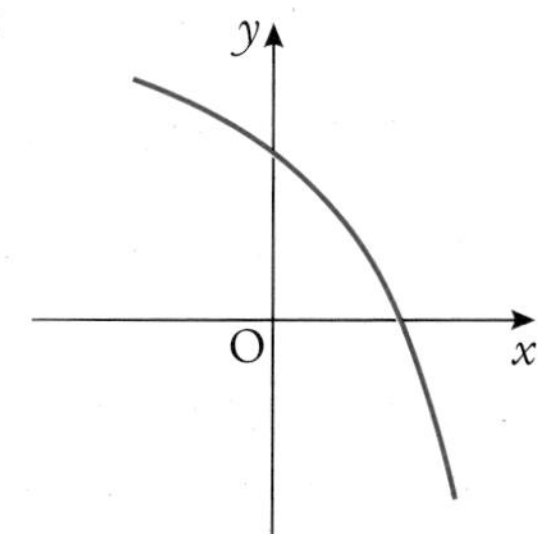

d

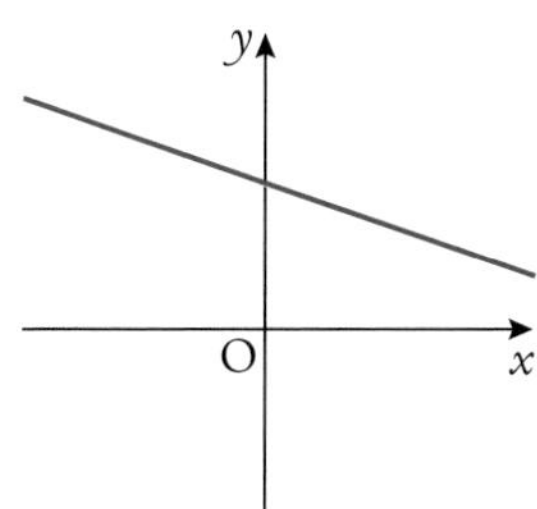

e

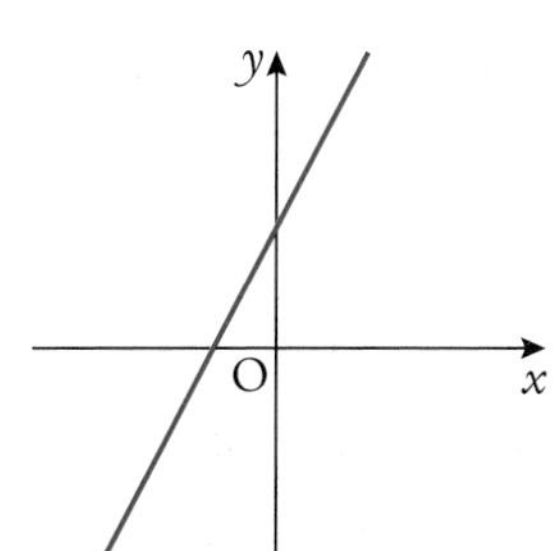

f

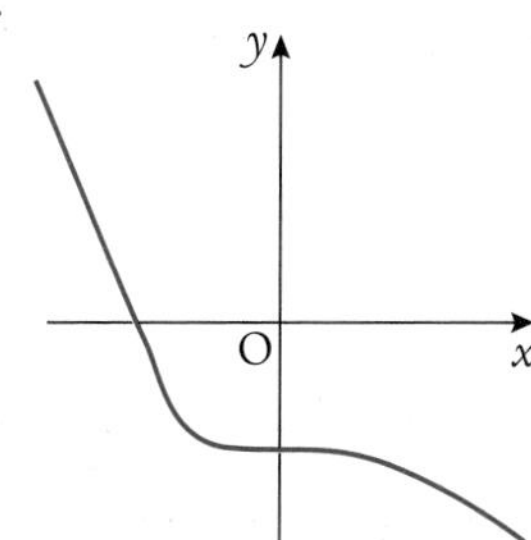

5.4 Inverse trigonometric functions

The sketches of Question 3 of Exercise 5.3 illustrate the fact that for a function to have an inverse it must be either increasing over its domain or decreasing over its domain.

If we wish to find restrictions so that a function has an inverse then we must look for a suitable domain where this is happening.

Example 4

For the function $f(x) = \sin x$

a draw a sketch of the function

b draw a sketch of the function reflected in the curve $y = x$

c identify the domain and range of the inverse function.

a

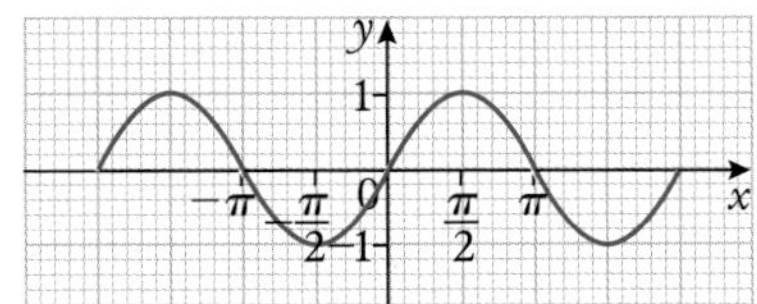

b

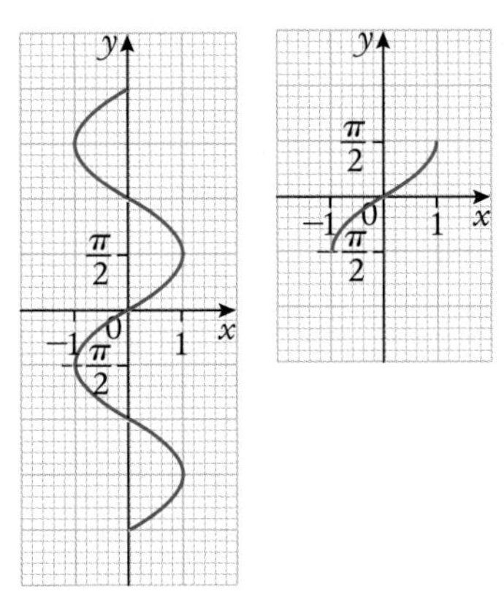

c To identify the curve of $f^{-1}(x) = \sin^{-1} x$, find the largest region over which the curve is always increasing (or always dezcreasing)

Domain $= \{x: -1 \leq x \leq 1; x \in R\}$; range $= \{y: -\frac{\pi}{2} \leq x \leq \frac{\pi}{2}; y \in R\}$

Exercise 5.4

1 a Make a sketch of $y = \cos x$.

b The inverse function $y = \cos^{-1} x$ has a domain of $-1 \leq x \leq 1$ and a range of $0 \leq y \leq \pi$.

Make a sketch of $y = \cos^{-1} x$ to illustrate this.

2 a Sketch $y = \tan x$.

b The inverse function $y = \tan^{-1} x$ has a domain of R and a range of $-\frac{\pi}{2} < y < \frac{\pi}{2}$.
Make a sketch of $y = \tan^{-1} x$.

3 With the aid of calculators, spreadsheets or otherwise, investigate the domain and range of

a $y = \sec x$ b $y = \sec^{-1} x$ c $y = \operatorname{cosec} x$

d $y = \operatorname{cosec}^{-1} x$ e $y = \cot x$ f $y = \cot^{-1} x$

[Hint: use =1/COS(**A1**) to calculate sec x.]

4 Each of these functions is defined so that an inverse exists.
For each:

i Make a sketch

ii Use it to help you sketch the inverse function

iii State a suitable domain and range for the given function.

a $f(x) = \sin 3x$ b $f(x) = 3 \sin x$ c $f(x) = 3 + \sin x$

d $f(x) = \cos 2x$ e $f(x) = 2 \cos x$ f $f(x) = 2 + \cos x$

g $f(x) = \sin x \cos x$ h $f(x) = \sin^2 x$ i $f(x) = \sin^2 x + \cos^2 x$

5 a Make a sketch of the function $f(x) = e^x$ marking on it a point to the left and to the right of the y-axis.

b State the domain and range of the function.

c i Sketch the inverse function

ii State its equation

iii Give the domain and range of the inverse.

6 For each of these functions

i Make a sketch

ii Use it to help you sketch the inverse function

iii State a suitable domain and range for the given function.

a $f(x) = e^{2x}$ b $f(x) = e^{-x}$ c $f(x) = e^x - 1$

d $f(x) = \ln 2x$ e $f(x) = \ln(x^2)$ f $f(x) = 3 + \ln x$

7 With the aid of a calculator or spreadsheet, or otherwise, explore the domain and range of

a $f(x) = e^x + e^{-x}$ b $f(x) = e^x - e^{-x}$ c $f(x) = \dfrac{10 \ln x}{x}$

[Hint: for a: = EXP(A1) + EXP(-A1); for c: = 10*LN(A1)/A1.]

5.5 Sketching polynomials

Reminders

When sketching the graph of a polynomial one should try to ascertain certain facts.

1 Where does the curve cut the y-axis? ... Where $x = 0$

2 Where does the curve cut the x-axis? ... Where $f(x) = 0$

3 Where are the stationary points? ... Where $f'(x) = 0$

4 How does $f(x)$ behave as x approaches $\pm\infty$?

Example 5

Given $f(x) = x^3 - x^2 - x + 1$, sketch the graph of $y = f(x)$.

1 $x = 0 \Rightarrow y = f(0) = 1$ so the curve cuts the y-axis at (0, 1).

2 $y = 0 \Rightarrow x^3 - x^2 - x + 1 = 0$

$\Rightarrow (x - 1)(x - 1)(x + 1) = 0$ Factorising

$\Rightarrow x = 1$ (twice) or $x = -1$

So the curve cuts the x-axis at (1, 0) and (−1, 0).

3 $f'(x) = 3x^2 - 2x - 1$

At stationary points, $f'(x) = 0$

$\Rightarrow 3x^2 - 2x - 1 = 0$

$\Rightarrow (3x + 1)(x - 1) = 0$

$\Rightarrow x = -\frac{1}{3}$ or $x = 1$

$f\left(-\frac{1}{3}\right) = \frac{32}{27}$; $f(1) = 0$

x	→	$-\frac{1}{3}$	→	1	→
$3x + 1$	−	0	+	+	+
$x - 1$	−	−	−	0	+
$f'(x)$	+	0	−	0	+
slope	/	—	\	—	/

A table of signs gives the nature of the stationary points.

A maximum turning point at $\left(-\frac{1}{3}, \frac{32}{27}\right)$; a minimum turning point at (1,0).

4 For very large positive values of x, $f(x)$ will be very large and positive.
The right-hand tail of the curve is in the first quadrant.
For very large negative values of x, $f(x)$ will be very large and negative.
The left-hand tail of the curve is in the third quadrant.
[You need only consider the x^3 term of $f(x)$ to see this.]

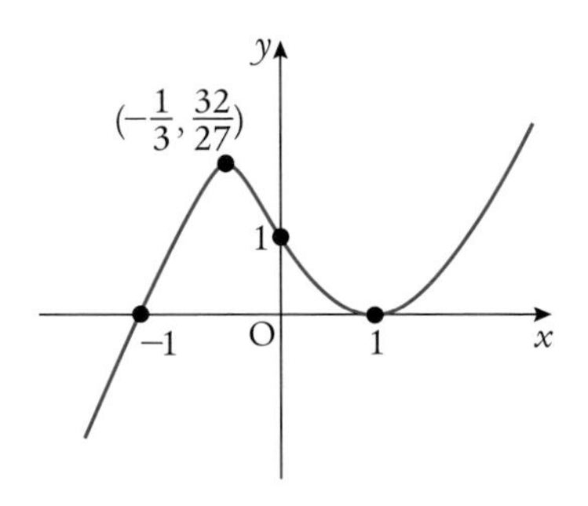

Exercise 5.5

1 Identify the stationary points of these functions and determine their natures.

a $f(x) = 2x^2 - 12x + 3$
b $f(x) = x^2 - 6x - 5$
c $f(x) = 2 - 6x + 3x^2$
d $f(x) = 2x^3 + 3x^2 - 12x + 1$
e $f(x) = 3 - 24x + 18x^2 - 4x^3$
f $f(x) = x^4 - 8x^2 + 16$

2 Make sketches of these polynomial functions.
Leave coordinates in surd form if necessary.

a $f(x) = x^4 - 4x^2$
b $f(x) = x^3 - 9x^2$
c $f(x) = x^3 - 12x - 16$
d $f(x) = (x - 9)(x - 1)(x - 6)$
e $f(x) = (x - 1)(x - 4)^2$

5.6 Extrema

Reminders

If a is in the domain of f:

1 Points where $f'(a) = 0$ or where $f'(a)$ does not exist are called **critical points**.

2 A function has a **local minimum** at a if $f(a) \leq f(x)$ for all x in some region centred at a.

3 A function has a **local maximum** at a if $f(a) \geq f(x)$ for all x in some region centred at a.

4 Local extreme values (minima or maxima) occur at critical points.
(Beware: not all critical points are local extrema – consider end-points.)

5 A function has an end-point minimum at a if $f(a) \leq f(x)$ for all x in a region close to a in the domain of f.

6 A function has an end-point maximum at a if $f(a) \geq f(x)$ for all x in a region close to a in the domain of f.

7 End-points are critical points.

8 A function has a global minimum at a if $f(a) \leq f(x)$ for all x in the domain of f.

9 A function has a global maximum at a if $f(a) \geq f(x)$ for all x in the domain of f.

Example 6

Sketch the function $f(x) = |3 + 2x - x^2|$ defined in the domain [0, 4), that is $0 \le x < 4$, and identify its extrema.

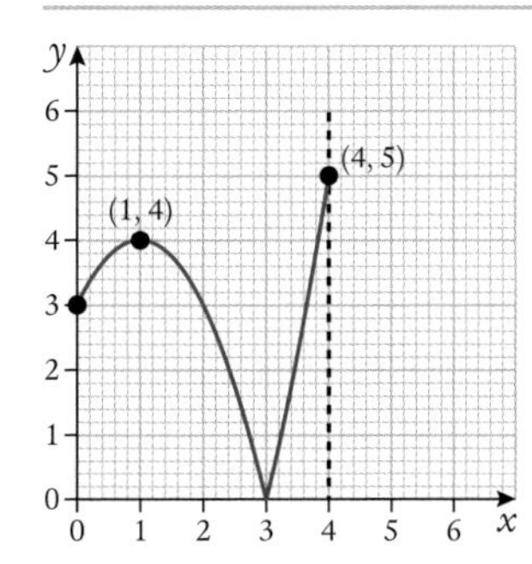

The critical points are (0, 3), (1, 4) and (3, 0).

(0, 3) is an end-point minimum since $f'(0)$ does not exist.

(1, 4) is a local maximum point since $f'(1) = 0$.

(3, 0) is a local minimum point since $f'(3)$ does not exist.

(4, 5) is not an end-point maximum since 4 is not in the domain.

The global minimum is (3, 0).

The function has no global maximum.

Exercise 5.6

1 Consider the nature of the end-points in these functions.

a $f(x) = x^2$ domain $[-1, 2]$ that is $-1 \leqslant x \leqslant 2$

b $f(x) = 4 - x^2$ domain $[-1, 1]$

c $f(x) = x^3 + x$ domain $[-3, 0]$

d $f(x) = 6 - x^3$ domain $(0, 2]$ that is $0 < x \leqslant 2$

e $f(x) = |2x|$ domain $[-2, 3)$ that is $-2 \leqslant x < 3$

2 Identify the critical points in these functions.

a $f(x) = x^2 + 2x + 1$ domain $[-2, 3]$

b $f(x) = \sqrt{x + 1}$ domain $[-1, 3]$

c $f(x) = \sqrt{x^2 + 9}$ domain $[-4, 6)$

d $f(x) = x^3 + x^2$ domain $(-2, 2]$

e $f(x) = x + \dfrac{1}{x}$ domain $(0, 3]$

3 **i** Find the critical points.

ii Identify end-points and local extrema.

iii Hence identify the global maxima and minima where they exist.

a $f(x) = x^2 - 4x - 5$ domain $[-2, 4]$

b $f(x) = |\cos x|$ domain $\left[\dfrac{\pi}{4}, \dfrac{2\pi}{3}\right]$

c $f(x) = |\ln x|$ domain $(0, e]$

d $f(x) = 8x^3 - 3x^4$ domain $[-1, 3]$

e $f(x) = \dfrac{x}{x^2 + 1}$ domain $[-2, 1)$

5.7 Concavity and points of inflexion

Concave ⟶) ⟵ Convex

An observer looking at this curve from the left would say it was concave; looking at it from the right he would say it was convex.

Examine this curve.

- In the region from A to B the gradient is increasing.
- Between B and C the gradient is decreasing.
- At B the gradient stopped increasing and began decreasing.

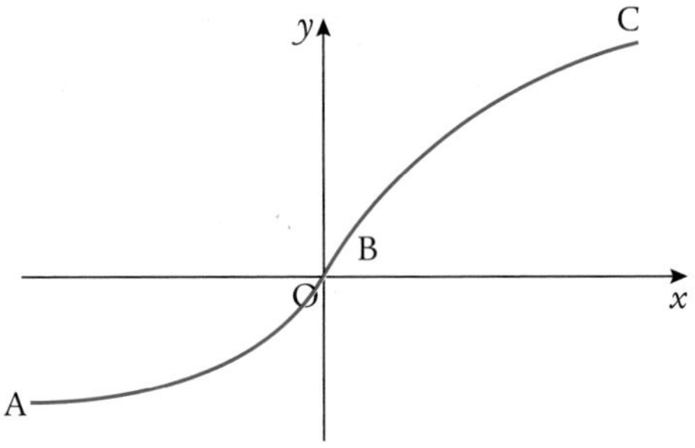

In mathematics we call a region in which the gradient is increasing **concave up** and one in which the gradient is decreasing **concave down**.

The derivative, $f'(x)$, measures the rate of change of the function $f(x)$ with respect to x (that is, it measures the gradient)
The second derivative, $f''(x)$, measures the rate of change of the gradient with respect to x.

When this is positive, that is $f''(x) > 0$, the curve is concave up.
When this is negative, that is $f''(x) < 0$, the curve is concave down.

These facts can be used instead of a table of signs to determine the nature of stationary points.

> If $f'(x) = 0$
> then $f''(x) > 0$ implies there is a minimum turning point at $x = a$
> $f''(x) < 0$ implies there is a maximum turning point at $x = a$

When $f''(x) = 0$ then the derived function is stationary.

A point where the concavity changes from being in one state to the other is called a **point of inflexion**.
One should look for points of inflexion where $f''(x) = 0$ or where $f''(x)$ does not exist.
A table of signs of $f''(x)$ will confirm any change of concavity.

Example 7

Do these functions have points of inflexion?

a $f(x) = x^4$

b $f(x) = x^5$

a $f(x) = x^4$

$\Rightarrow f'(x) = 4x^3$

$\Rightarrow f''(x) = 12x^2$

$\Rightarrow f''(0) = 0$

Is there a point of inflexion at $x = 0$?

x	→	0	→
$f''(x)$	+	0	+
concavity	up		up

No change... no point of inflexion.

b $f(x) = x^5$

$\Rightarrow f'(x) = 5x^4$

$\Rightarrow f''(x) = 20x^3$

$\Rightarrow f''(0) = 0$

Is there a point of inflexion at $x = 0$?

x	→	0	→
$f''(x)$	−	0	+
concavity	down		up

Change... there is a point of inflexion.

Exercise 5.7

1 Use the second derivative to prove the graph of

a $f(x) = x^2$ is always concave up b $f(x) = \ln x$ is always concave down.

2 Discuss the concavity of the graph of

a $f(x) = \sqrt{x}, x \geqslant 0$

b $f(x) = x + \frac{1}{x}$ in the interval $0 < x \leq 5$

c $f(x) = \tan x$ in the interval $-\frac{\pi}{2} < x < \frac{\pi}{2}$

d $f(x) = x^3 + 6$

e i $f(x) = \sec x$ in the interval $-\frac{\pi}{2} < x < \frac{\pi}{2}$

ii $f(x) = \sec x$ in the interval $\frac{\pi}{2} < x < \frac{3\pi}{2}$

3 a Identify the points of inflexion in the graph of $f(x) = \sin x$ in the interval $0 \leq x \leq 2\pi$.

b In each case say whether the gradient of the tangent at that point is positive or negative.

c Make a sketch of the curve over this interval and show these tangents.

4 Explore the concavity of $f(x) = \frac{1}{|x|}$ when a $x < 0$ b $x > 0$

5 Identify the points of inflexion of these curves.
In each case say whether the gradient of the tangent at that point is positive, negative or zero.

a $f(x) = x^3$

b $f(x) = x^4 - 6x^2$

c $f(x) = x^5 - 30x^3$

d $f(x) = \cot x$ in the interval $0 < x < \pi$

6 The zeros of a cubic function are x_1, x_2 and x_3.

If $(a, f(a))$ is the point of inflexion of the cubic function express a in terms of x_1, x_2 and x_3.

5.8 Odd and even functions

When sketching curves it can be useful to know of the existence of symmetries.

When $f(-x) = f(x)$ the curve is symmetrical about the y-axis. Such a function is known as an **even function**.

Example 8

Prove $f(x) = x^4 - 8x^2 + 3$ is an even function.

$$f(x) = x^4 - 8x^2 + 3$$

$$\Rightarrow f(-x) = (-x)^4 - 8(-x)^2 + 3$$

$$= x^4 - 8x^2 + 3$$

$$\Rightarrow f(-x) = f(x)$$

That is, $f(x)$ is an even function.

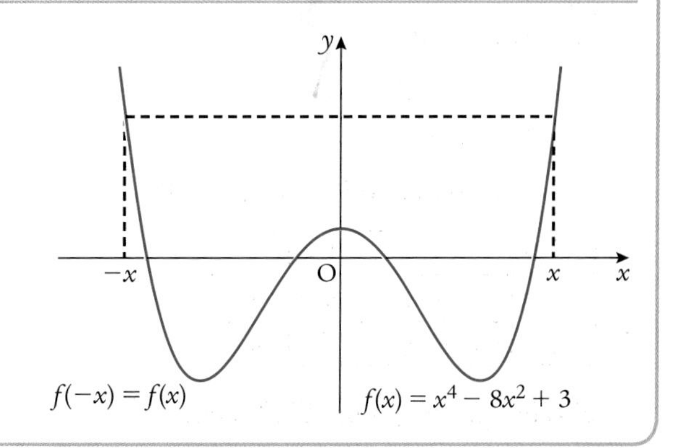

When $f(-x) = -f(x)$, the curve exhibits half-turn symmetry about the origin.
Such functions are termed **odd functions**.

Example 9

Prove $f(x) = x^3 - 2x$ is an odd function.

$$f(x) = x^3 - 2x$$
$$\Rightarrow \quad f(-x) = (-x)^3 - 2(-x)$$
$$= -x^3 + 2x$$
$$= -(x^3 - 2x)$$
$$\Rightarrow \quad f(-x) = -f(x)$$

That is, $f(x)$ is an odd function.

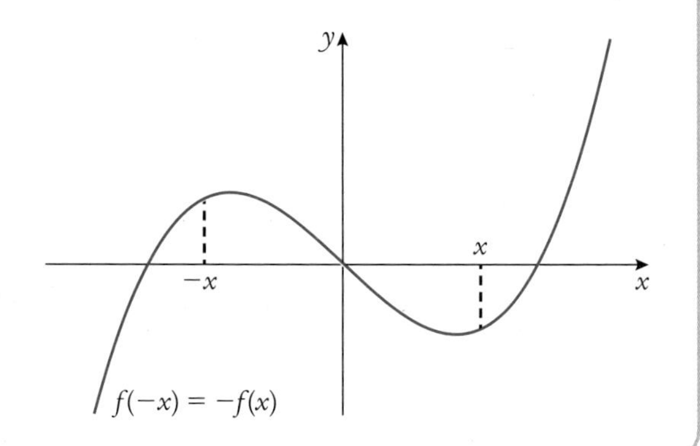

Exercise 5.8

1 a Prove that $2x^2 + 5$ is an even function. b Prove that $3x^5 + 7x^3 - 4x$ is an odd function.

2 For each of the functions below, say whether it is odd or even, and sketch enough of its graph to illustrate its symmetry.

a $f(x) = x^6$ b $f(x) = x^5$ c $f(x) = \sin x$

d $f(x) = \cos x$ e $f(x) = x^2 - 1$ f $f(x) = x + x^3$

3 Classify each of these functions as odd, even or neither.

a $f(x) = x$ b $f(x) = x^2 + x$ c $f(x) = \dfrac{x^2 + 1}{x^2}$

d $f(x) = x + \dfrac{1}{x}$ e $f(x) = 1 - \dfrac{1}{x}$ f $f(x) = \sin x \cos x$

g $f(x) = \sin x + \cos x$ h $f(x) = x^3 + x^2$ i $f(x) = e^{x^2}$

j $f(x) = e^x + e^{-x}$ k $f(x) = e^x - e^{-x}$ l $f(x) = \ln x$

5.9 Vertical asymptotes

$f(x)$ is a rational function if it can be expressed in the form $\dfrac{g(x)}{h(x)}$ where $g(x)$ and $h(x)$ are real polynomial functions of degree 1 or greater.

If $h(a) = 0$, and the denominator of the rational function is $h(x)$ then the rational function is not defined at a. Then as $x \to a$, $f(x) \to \pm\infty$ and the function is discontinuous at a.

A function is said to be **continuous** if $\lim_{x \to a} f(x) = f(a)$.

Example 10

How does $f(x) = \dfrac{1}{x - 1}$ behave in the neighbourhood of $x = 1$?

- As $x \to 1$, the denominator $x - 1 \to 0$ and $f(x) \to \infty$.
- As $x \to 1$ from the *left*, $x - 1 < 0$ and the numerator $1 > 0$, so $f(x) < 0$.
  To the left of the line $x = 1$, the curve $f(x) \to \infty^-$ (negative infinity).

- As $x \to 1$ from the *right*, $x - 1 > 0$ and the numerator $1 > 0$, so $f(x) > 0$. To the right of the line $x = 1$, the curve $f(x) \to \infty^+$ (positive infinity).

The line $x = 1$ is called a **vertical asymptote** of the function.
The function is said to approach the line $x = 1$ asymptotically.

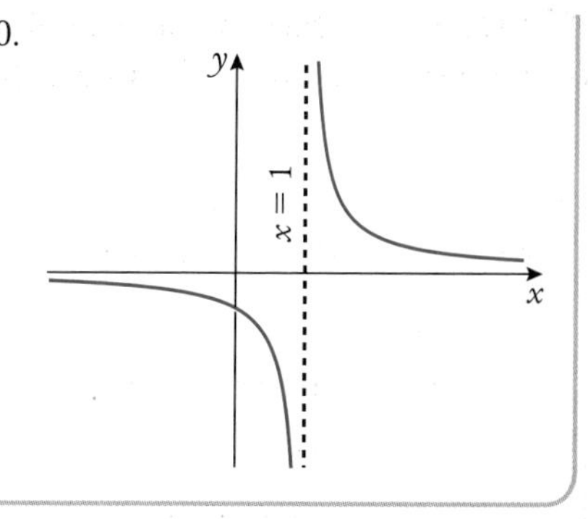

If $h(x)$ is the denominator of a rational function and $h(a) = 0$ then $x = a$ is a vertical asymptote of the rational function.

Exercise 5.9

1 For each function below,

i identify the vertical asymptotes

ii describe the behaviour of each function as it approaches its asymptotes from the left and from the right.

a $f(x) = \dfrac{x-1}{x+1}$ b $f(x) = \dfrac{1-x}{x+1}$ c $f(x) = \dfrac{3+x}{(x-1)(x+2)}$

d $f(x) = \dfrac{1}{x(2x+1)}$ e $f(x) = \dfrac{x-4}{(x-5)(x+1)}$ f $f(x) = \dfrac{x-1}{x^2-x-2}$

g $f(x) = \dfrac{x+3}{x^2-1}$ h $f(x) = \dfrac{1-x}{x^2-5x+6}$ i $f(x) = \dfrac{x+4}{x^3+1}$

2 Explore the behaviour of these functions near their asymptotes.

a $f(x) = \tan x$ b $f(x) = \sec x$ c $f(x) = x^{-1}$

d $f(x) = \dfrac{1}{|x|}$ e $f(x) = \dfrac{1}{\ln(x)}$ f $f(x) = \dfrac{1}{e^x - 1}$

3 Investigate the behaviour of $f(x) = \dfrac{x}{\sqrt{x^2}}$.

5.10 Horizontal and oblique asymptotes

If the function $f(x)$ can be expressed as $g(x) + \dfrac{m(x)}{n(x)}$, where $\dfrac{m(x)}{n(x)}$ is a proper rational function, then, as $x \to \infty$, $n(x) \to \infty$, $\dfrac{m(x)}{n(x)} \to 0$ and $f(x) \to g(x)$.

$f(x)$ is said to approach $g(x)$ asymptotically.

If $g(x)$ is a linear function, it is known as either a **horizontal** asymptote or an **oblique** asymptote depending on the gradient of the line $y = g(x)$.

The behaviour of the function as $x \to \infty^+$ and as $x \to \infty^-$ can be considered for each particular case.

Example 11

Find the asymptotes of $\dfrac{x+1}{x-1}$.

Vertical asymptote: Denominator is $x - 1$

$x - 1 = 0 \Rightarrow x = 1$ is a vertical asymptote.

Other asymptote: $y = \dfrac{x+1}{x-1} = 1 + \dfrac{2}{x-1}$ by polynomial division.

As $x \to \infty, y \to 1 + 0 \ldots y = 1$ is a horizontal asymptote.

As $x \to \infty^+, y \to 1 + 0^+$ so, to right, $f(x)$ approaches asymptote from above.

As $x \to \infty^-, y \to 1 + 0^-$ so, to left, $f(x)$ approaches asymptote from below.

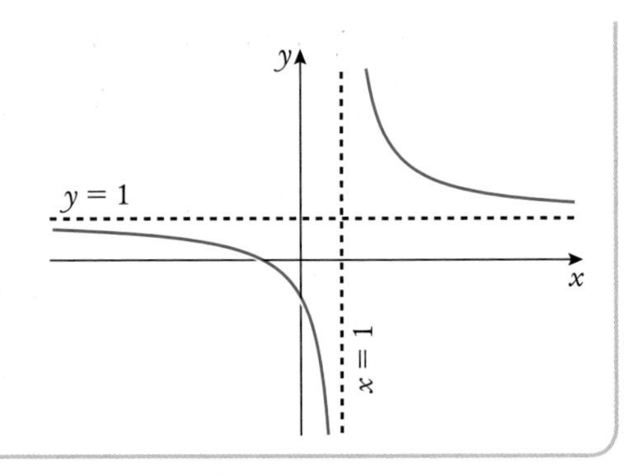

Example 12

Find the asymptotes of $f(x) = \dfrac{2x^2 + x - 3}{x + 1}$.

Vertical asymptote: Denominator is $x + 1$

$x + 1 = 0 \Rightarrow x = -1$ is a vertical asymptote.

Other asymptote: $f(x) = 2x - 1 - \dfrac{2}{x + 1}$ by polynomial division.

As $x \to \infty, y \to 2x - 1 - 0$ so $y = 2x - 1$ is an oblique asymptote.

As $x \to \infty^+, y \to 2x - 1 - 0^+$ so to right, $f(x)$ approaches asymptote from below.

As $x \to \infty^-, y \to 2x - 1 - 0^-$ so to left, $f(x)$ approaches asymptote from above.

Note: the curve cuts the y-axis when $x = 0$: $(0, -3)$; cuts x-axis when $y = 0$: $(1, 0)$ and $(-1.5, 0)$; and has no stationary points since $f'(x) \neq 0$ for any value of x.

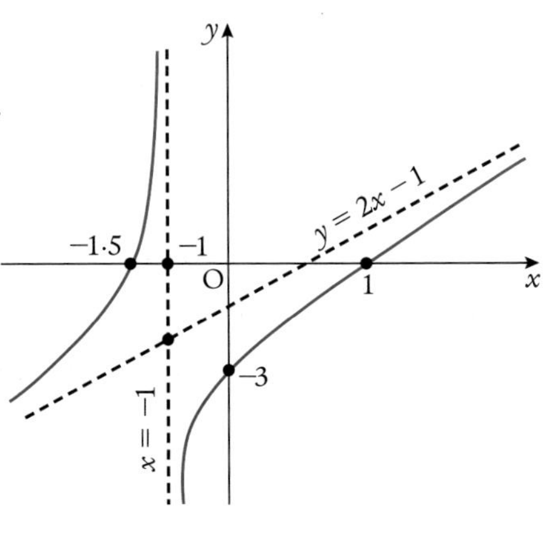

Exercise 5.10

1 For each function below

i give the equation of the vertical asymptotes

ii perform polynomial divisions as appropriate

iii state the non-vertical asymptotes

iv consider the behaviour of the function as it approaches these asymptotes.

a $f(x) = \dfrac{1}{x}$ **b** $f(x) = \dfrac{x + 1}{x}$ **c** $f(x) = \dfrac{x^2 + 2}{x}$

d $f(x) = \dfrac{x - 1}{x + 1}$ **e** $f(x) = \dfrac{1 - x}{x + 1}$ **f** $f(x) = \dfrac{x^2 + 1}{x + 1}$

g $f(x) = \dfrac{x^2 + 1}{x^2 - 1}$ **h** $f(x) = \dfrac{x}{x^2 + 1}$ **i** $f(x) = \dfrac{x - 1}{x^2 - x - 2}$

j $f(x) = \dfrac{x^2 + 3}{x - 1}$ **k** $f(x) = \dfrac{2x^2 + 2x - 3}{x + 2}$ **l** $f(x) = \dfrac{x^3 - 3x}{x^2 + 1}$

2 Given that $f(x) = g(x) + \dfrac{m(x)}{n(x)}$, where $\dfrac{m(x)}{n(x)}$ is a proper rational function, we know the non-vertical asyptote is $y = g(x)$.

The curve $y = f(x)$ cuts the curve $y = g(x)$ where $\dfrac{m(x)}{n(x)} = 0$.

Find where each of these cut their own asymptote.

a $f(x) = \frac{x^3 + 2x}{x^2 + 1}$ b $f(x) = \frac{2x^3 + x^2 + x + 1}{x^2}$

3 a Show that $\frac{x^3 - x^2 + 1}{x - 1}$ starts behaving like $y = x^2$ as $x \to \infty$.

b Comment on the behaviour of $\frac{x^3 - x^2 + 1}{x - 1}$ as $x \to \infty$.

5.11 Bringing it all together

When sketching curves, gather as much information as possible from the list below:

1 Intercepts

a Where does the curve cut the y-axis? $x = 0$

b Where does the curve cut the x-axis? $y = 0$

2 Extras

a Where is the function increasing? $f'(x) > 0$

b Where is the function decreasing? $f'(x) < 0$

3 Stationary points

a Where is the curve stationary? $f'(x) = 0$

b Where is the function concave up? [for minimum] $f''(x) > 0$

c Where is the function concave down? [for maximum] $f''(x) < 0$

d Are there horizontal points of inflexion? $f''(x) = 0$

4 Extras

Where are the non-horizontal points of inflexion? $f''(x) = 0$

5 Asymptotes

a Where are the vertical asymptotes? denominator $= 0$

b Where are the non-vertical asymptotes? $x \to \pm\infty$

A table of signs can be helpful to add detail.

Exercise 5.11

1 Sketch these graphs.

a $y = \frac{1}{x + 3}$ b $y = \frac{3}{2x + 8}$ c $y = \frac{x}{x + 2}$

d $y = \frac{x - 1}{x + 1}$ e $y = \frac{1 - x}{1 + x}$ f $y = \frac{x - 1}{x(x + 1)}$

g $y = \frac{x}{(x - 1)(x + 1)}$ h $y = \frac{x^2}{x + 1}$ i $y = x - \frac{1}{x}$

j $y = \frac{x^2}{1 - x}$ k $y = \frac{(2x + 3)(x - 6)}{(x + 1)(x - 2)}$ l $y = \frac{1}{(x - 2)(x - 4)}$

m $y = \frac{x^2 - x}{2x + 1}$ n $y = \frac{(x - 1)(x + 2)}{x - 2}$ o $y = \frac{x^2 - 3x - 10}{x - 2}$

2 Make use of the fact that the function is either odd or even to assist you in drawing its graph.

a $y = \frac{3}{x^2 - 3}$ b $y = \frac{x^2 - 9}{x}$ c $y = \frac{x^2 + 1}{x^2 - 1}$

3 a By examining the extrema of the function $f(x) = \frac{x}{x^2 + 1}$ prove that $-\frac{1}{2} \leq \frac{x}{x^2 + 1} \leq \frac{1}{2}$.

[Note that $x^2 + 1 > 0$ for all x.]

b i Is the function odd or even?

ii Sketch the graph $y = f(x)$.

4 a Prove that $2x^2 - x + 2 > 0$ for all x.

b Given that $f(x) = \frac{2x^2 + x + 2}{2x^2 - x + 2}$ and that $a \leq f(x) \leq b$ for all x, find the values of a and b.

c Sketch the graph of the function.

5 a Following similar logic to Questions **3** and **4**, a student studying the function $f(x) = \frac{3x^2 - 3}{6x - 10}$ came to the conclusion that $f(x) \geq 3$ *and* $f(x) \leq \frac{1}{3}$. What had he ignored?

b Make a sketch to illustrate the function.

6 a Show that the range of the function $f(x) = \frac{2x - 1}{2x^2 - 4x + 1}$ is R.

b Sketch the graph of the function.

Review 5

1 State the domain and range of the function $f(x) = x!$

2 A function is defined in the domain $(0, 2]$ as $f(x) = 2x^2 - 6x + 3$.

a Identify the critical points of the function.

b Find the local maxima and minima where they exist.

c What is the global maximum value of the function?

3 Describe the concavity of the function $f(x) = (x + 3)^3 + 1$ and identify the point of inflexion.

4 a Make a sketch of the function $f(x) = \sin^{-1} x$.

b State a suitable domain and range.

5 Draw sketches of the graphs of these rational functions.

a $\frac{x - 2}{x + 1}$ b $\frac{x + 3}{x^2 + x - 2}$ c $\frac{x^2}{x - 3}$

d $\frac{(x - 3)(x + 6)}{(x - 1)(x + 2)}$ e $\frac{x^2 + 2x - 3}{x + 1}$

Summary 5

1 A function, f, is a rule which links each member of a set A uniquely to a member of a set B.

2 Set A is referred to as the **domain** of the function and the set B, as the **co-domain**.
The subset of B which is the set of all images of the elements of the domain is called the **range** of the function.

3 If a is in the domain of f:

a Points where $f'(a) = 0$ or $f'(a)$ does not exist are called critical points.

b A function has a *local* minimum at a if $f(a) \le f(x)$ for all x in some region centred at a.

c A function has a *local* maximum at a if $f(a) \ge f(x)$ for all x in some region centred at a.

d Local extreme values (minima or maxima) occur at critical points.

e A function has an end-point minimum at a if $f(a) \le f(x)$ for all x in a region close to a in the domain of f.

f A function has an end-point maximum at a if $f(a) \ge f(x)$ for all x in a region close to a in the domain of f.

g End-points are critical points.

h A function has a *global* minimum at a if $f(a) \le f(x)$ for all x in the domain of f.

i A function has a *global* maximum at a if $f(a) \ge f(x)$ for all x in the domain of f.

4 a If $f''(a) > 0$ the curve is concave up at $x = a$.

b If $f''(a) < 0$ the curve is concave down at $x = a$.

c If $f'(a) = 0$ then

$$f''(a) > 0 \text{ implies there is a minimum turning point at } x = a$$
$$f''(a) < 0 \text{ implies there is a maximum turning point at } x = a.$$

5 When the domains of trigonometric functions are carefully defined, the inverse trigonometric functions can be defined.

$y = \sin^{-1} x$

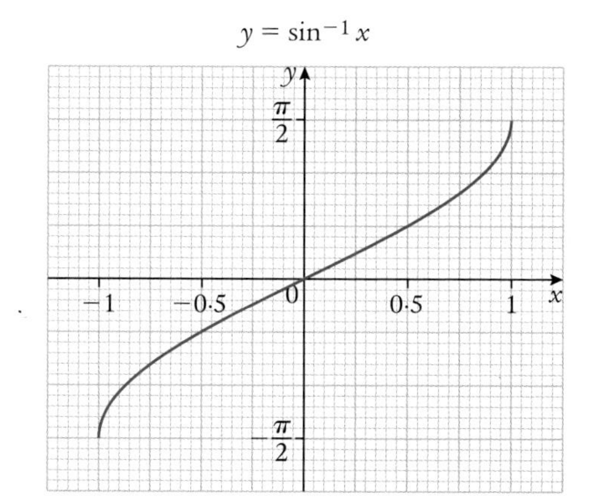

$f(x) = \sin^{-1}(x)$

Domain $[-1, 1]$

Range $\left[-\frac{\pi}{2}, \frac{\pi}{2}\right]$

$y = \cos^{-1} x$

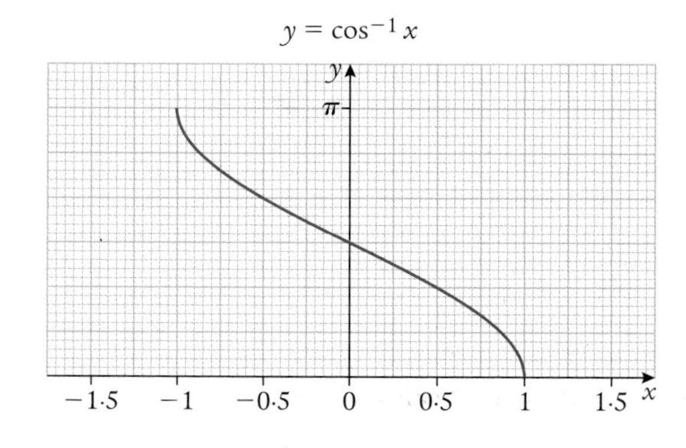

$f(x) = \cos^{-1}(x)$

Domain $[-1, 1]$

Range $[0, \pi]$

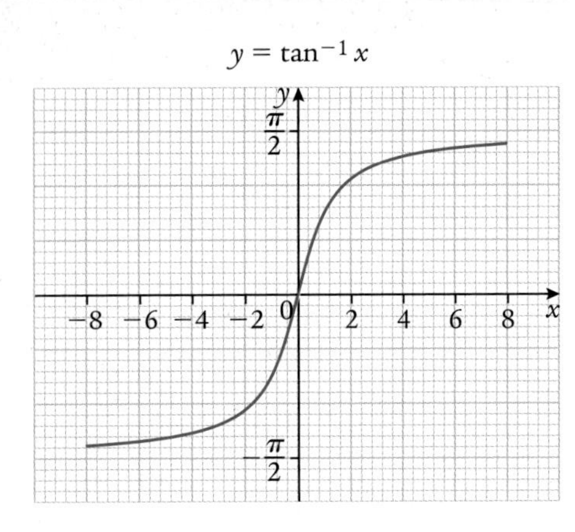

$f(x) = \tan^{-1}(x)$

Domain $(-\infty, \infty)$

Range $\left(-\frac{\pi}{2}, \frac{\pi}{2}\right)$

6 Symmetries

a A function is said to be **even** if it is symmetrical about the y-axis: $f(x) = f(-x)$.

b A function is said to be **odd** if it is symmetrical about the origin: $f(x) = -f(-x)$.

7 Asymptotes

A function which can be expressed in the form $f(x) = g(x) + \dfrac{m(x)}{n(x)}$

a has a vertical asymptote $x = a$ where $n(a) = 0$

b has a non-vertical asymptote $y = g(x)$, where $\dfrac{m(x)}{n(x)}$ is a proper rational function and the orders of m and n differ by no more than 2

c will cut its non-vertical asymptote when $m(x) = 0$.

6 Differential calculus 2

Historical Note

Leonhard Euler (1707–1783) was a Swiss mathematician though for most of his career he worked in St Petersburg in Russia. Much of the algebraic notation we use today is his invention, e, Σ, $f(x)$, etc.

Euler's first book *Introductio analysin infinitorum* was published in 1748. Part one of the book deals with algebraic analysis and in it Euler introduces the concept of a function as we know it and makes the distinction between explicit and implicit functions.

Part two of his book deals with coordinate geometry and in this section Euler introduces the idea of parametric equations.

6.1 Reminders

The chain rule

$\frac{dy}{dx} = \frac{dy}{du}\frac{du}{dx}$ or $\frac{d}{dx}f(g(x)) = f'(g(x)) \cdot g'(x)$

The inverse function

If f has an inverse then it is denoted by f^{-1}
and $f(f^{-1}(x)) = x = f^{-1}(f(x))$ for all x in the domain of f.

If $y = f(x)$ is the equation of a function
then $x = f(y)$ provides the equation of the inverse function.

The graph of the inverse function is the image of the graph of the function under reflection in the line $y = x$.

The inverse trigonometric functions

You are already familiar with the use of the inverse trigonometric functions:

1 The **inverse sine function**

In the domain $-\frac{\pi}{2} \leq x \leq \frac{\pi}{2}$, $y = \sin x \Leftrightarrow x = \sin^{-1} y$

2 The **inverse cosine function**

In the domain $0 \leq x \leq \pi$, $y = \cos x \Leftrightarrow x = \cos^{-1} y$

3 The **inverse tangent function**

In the domain $-\frac{\pi}{2} < x < \frac{\pi}{2}$, $y = \tan x \Leftrightarrow x = \tan^{-1} y$

Note that the domain of the trigonometric function is selected as the biggest domain near the origin where there is a one-to-one correspondence between x and y.

The graphs show the domains of the inverse functions.

The inverse sine

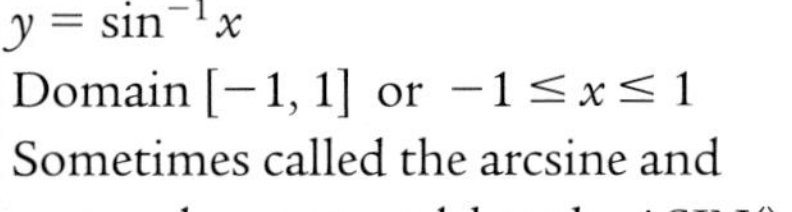

$y = \sin^{-1} x$

Domain $[-1, 1]$ or $-1 \leq x \leq 1$

Sometimes called the arcsine and accessed on a spreadsheet by ASIN().

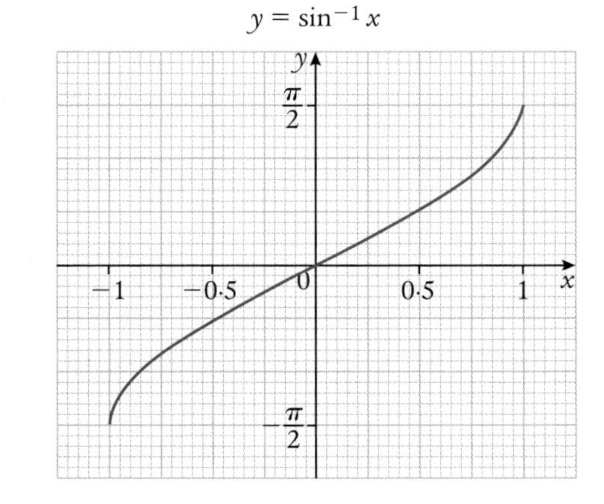

The inverse cosine

$y = \cos^{-1} x$

Domain $[-1, 1]$ or $-1 \leq x \leq 1$

Sometimes called the arccosine and

accessed on a spreadsheet by ACOS().

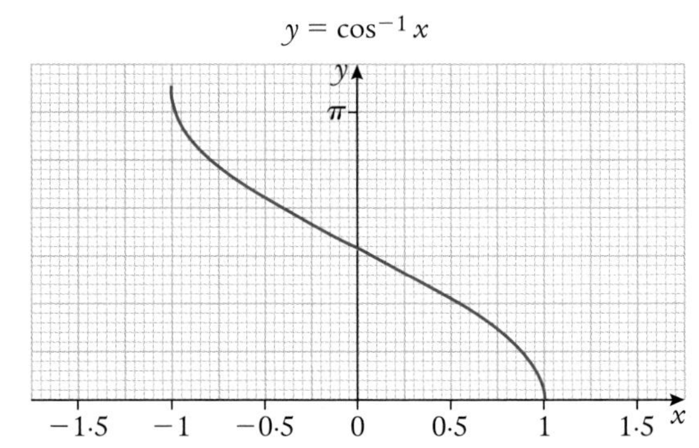

The inverse tangent

$y = \tan^{-1} x$

Domain $(-\infty, \infty)$ or $-\infty < x < \infty$

Sometimes called the arctangent and

accessed on a spreadsheet by ATAN().

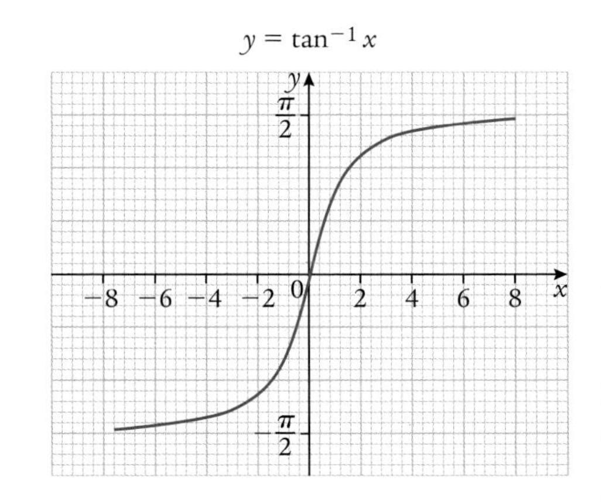

Derivatives of inverse functions

Consider the function f which has an inverse f^{-1}

$$\text{then } f(f^{-1}(x)) = x$$

Differentiating using the chain rule: $f'(f^{-1}(x)) \cdot \frac{d}{dx}(f^{-1}(x)) = 1$

$$\Rightarrow \frac{d}{dx}(f^{-1}(x)) = \frac{1}{f'(f^{-1}(x))}$$

Using Leibniz notation: $y = f^{-1}(x) \Rightarrow \frac{dy}{dx} = \frac{1}{\frac{dx}{dy}}$

This states that 'the rate of change of y with respect to x' is the reciprocal of 'the rate of change of x with respect to y'.

Alternatively, we can say 'the derivative of a function is the reciprocal of the derivative of its inverse'.

Example 1

Given $f(x) = x^3$ find $f'(x)$ and state the derivative of $f^{-1}(x)$.

$f'(x) = 3x^2$

$f^{-1}(x) = x^{\frac{1}{3}}$

$\Rightarrow \frac{d}{dx}(f^{-1}(x)) = \frac{1}{f'(f^{-1}(x))} = \frac{1}{3\left(x^{\frac{1}{3}}\right)^2} = \frac{1}{3x^{\frac{2}{3}}}$

This result can be more easily obtained by differentiating f^{-1} directly.
It is put forward here to illustrate a technique.

Example 2

Express $f(x) = x^2 + 2x + 3, x \geq 3$, in the form $p(x + q)^2 + r$.
Find $f'(x)$ and state the derivative of $f^{-1}(x)$.

Completing the square we get $f(x) = (x + 1)^2 + 2$.

Hence $f^{-1}(x) = \sqrt{x - 2} - 1$, taking the positive root since $x \geq 3$ is the domain of $f(x)$.

Also $f'(x) = 2x + 2$

$\Rightarrow \frac{d}{dx}(f^{-1}(x)) = \frac{1}{f'(f^{-1}(x))} = \frac{1}{2(\sqrt{x-2} - 1) + 2} = \frac{1}{2\sqrt{x-2}}$

Example 3

Given $y = \sin^{-1} x, -\frac{\pi}{2} \leq x \leq \frac{\pi}{2}$, find $\frac{dy}{dx}$.

$y = \sin^{-1} x \Leftrightarrow x = \sin y$

$\Rightarrow \frac{dx}{dy} = \cos y$

$\Rightarrow \frac{dy}{dx} = \frac{1}{\frac{dx}{dy}} = \frac{1}{\cos y}$

$\Rightarrow \frac{dy}{dx} = \frac{1}{\sqrt{1 - \sin^2 y}} = \frac{1}{\sqrt{1 - x^2}}$

$$\boxed{\frac{d}{dx}\sin^{-1} x = \frac{1}{\sqrt{1 - x^2}}}$$

Example 4

Given $y = \tan^{-1} x$, find $\frac{dy}{dx}$.

$y = \tan^{-1} x \Leftrightarrow x = \tan y$

$\Rightarrow \frac{dx}{dy} = \sec^2 y = \tan^2 y + 1 = x^2 + 1$

$\Rightarrow \frac{dy}{dx} = \frac{1}{\frac{dx}{dy}} = \frac{1}{x^2 + 1}$

$\sin^2 x + \cos^2 x = 1$

$\Rightarrow \tan^2 x + 1 = \sec^2 1$

$$\boxed{\frac{d}{dx}\tan^{-1} x = \frac{1}{x^2 + 1}}$$

Exercise 6.1

1 For each function $f(x)$, find the derivative of the inverse function $f^{-1}(x)$ using the technique illustrated in Example 1.

a $f(x) = x^5$ b $f(x) = x^{\frac{3}{4}}$ c $f(x) = 2x^{-2}, x > 0$

d $f(x) = x^2 + 1, x > 1$

2 In each case below

i Express $f(x)$ in the form $p(x + q)^2 + r$

ii Find $f^{-1}(x)$, taking the positive root

iii Find $f'(x)$ and state the derivative of $f^{-1}(x)$.

a $f(x) = x^2 + 4x + 5, x \geq 5$ b $f(x) = x^2 + 6x - 1, x \geq -1$

c $f(x) = 2x^2 - 2x + 1, x \geq 1$ d $f(x) = 3x^2 + 2x, x \geq 0$

3 a By considering $f(x) = e^x$, deduce that the derivative of $\ln x, x > 0$, is x^{-1}.

b If $g(x) = e^{2x+1}$ find the derivative of $\frac{1}{2}(\ln x - 1)$ by this technique.

4 Use the techniques shown in Example 3 to find the derivative of $\cos^{-1} x$.

5 Use the above technique to find $\frac{dy}{dx}$ for each of these expressions.

a $\tan^{-1}(x + 1)$

b $\sin^{-1}(3x + 1), -\frac{1}{3} \leq x \leq 0$

6 For each of these

i express y in the form $p(x + q)^2 + r$

ii make x the subject of the formula

iii find $\frac{dx}{dy}$

iv find $\frac{dy}{dx}$ and verify that $\frac{dy}{dx} = \frac{1}{\frac{dx}{dy}}$.

a $y = x^2 + 6x + 1, x \geq 1$ b $y = x^2 + 2x - 5, x \geq -5$

c $y = 3x^2 - 4x - 3, x \geq -3$ d $y = 2x^2 + 4x, x \geq 0$

7 When using spreadsheets or graphics calculators it is possible to get a good approximation for the graph of the derivative of a function:

if $f(x)$ is a function then $f'(x) \approx \frac{f(x + 0.0005) - f(x - 0.0005)}{0.001}$

a Compare the graph $y = \frac{\sin^{-1}(x + 0.0005) - \sin^{-1}(x - 0.0005)}{0.001}$ with $y = \frac{1}{\sqrt{1 - x^2}}$.

b Consider the derivatives of i $\cos^{-1}(x)$ ii $\tan^{-1}(x)$ iii $\ln x$ in a similar way.

[For spreadsheets: $\sin^{-1} x \equiv$ ASIN(X), $\cos^{-1} x \equiv$ ACOS(X), $\tan^{-1} x \equiv$ ATAN(X).]

6.2 Applying the chain rule to inverse trigonometric functions

$$\frac{d}{dx}\sin^{-1} x = \frac{1}{\sqrt{1 - x^2}}, \quad \frac{d}{dx}\cos^{-1} x = \frac{-1}{\sqrt{1 - x^2}}, \quad \frac{d}{dx}\tan^{-1} x = \frac{1}{1 + x^2}$$

Many examples using these three standard derivatives also involve the chain rule.

Example 5

Differentiate $\sin^{-1}\left(\frac{-1}{x}\right)$ where x does *not* lie in the region $-1 \le x \le 1$.

$$\frac{d}{dx}\sin^{-1}\left(\frac{-1}{x}\right) = \frac{1}{\sqrt{1-\left(\frac{-1}{x}\right)^2}}\frac{d}{dx}\left(\frac{-1}{x}\right) = \frac{\sqrt{x^2}}{\sqrt{x^2-1}}\cdot\frac{1}{x^2} = \frac{|x|}{\sqrt{x^2-1}}\cdot\frac{1}{x^2} = \frac{1}{|x|\sqrt{x^2-1}}$$

Example 6

Differentiate $\ln(1+\cos^{-1}x)$

$$\frac{d}{dx}\ln(1+\cos^{-1}x) = \frac{1}{1+\cos^{-1}x}\cdot\frac{d}{dx}(1+\cos^{-1}x) = \frac{1}{1+\cos^{-1}x}\cdot\frac{-1}{\sqrt{1-x^2}}$$

Exercise 6.2

1 Find the derivative of

a $\sin^{-1}x^2$ b $\tan^{-1}(x+2)$ c $\sin^{-1}\frac{1}{x}$ d $\tan^{-1}\frac{1}{\sqrt{x}}$

e $\cos^{-1}\frac{1}{x}$ f $\cos^{-1}ax$

2 Find the derived function in each case.

a $\sin^{-1}(e^x)$ b $\cos^{-1}(x+2)^2$ c $\sin^{-1}\sqrt{1-x^2}$

d $\sin^{-1}(\tan x)$ e $\sin^{-1}\left(\frac{x}{a}\right)$

3 Find $f'(x)$ for each of these expressions for $f(x)$.

a $\cos^{-1}e^{2x}$ b $\sin^{-1}\cos(x-1)$ c $\tan^{-1}(1+x)$

d $\cos^{-1}(\ln 3x)$ e $\sec^{-1}3x$

4 Differentiate

a $\ln(\tan^{-1}\sqrt{x})$ b $\ln\left(\sin^{-1}\frac{1}{\sqrt{x}}\right)$ c $\ln(\sin^{-1}e^x)$ d $e^{\sin^{-1}x}$

5 Calculate

a $f'(1)$ where $f(x) = e^{\tan^{-1}\frac{1}{x}}$ b $f'(0)$ where $f(x) = \ln(\cos^{-1}x)$

c $f'\left(\frac{3}{4}\right)$ where $f(x) = \sin(\tan^{-1}x)$ d $f'(\sqrt{3})$ where $f(x) = \cos\left(\tan^{-1}\frac{1}{x}\right)$

6 Find the gradient of the curve with equation

a $y = \ln(\sin^{-1}2x)$ where $x = \frac{1}{4}$ b $y = (x+\tan^{-1}x)^3$ where $x = 1$

c $y = \ln(\cos^{-1}(1-x))$ where $x = \frac{1}{2}$ d $y = e^{\tan^{-1}x^2}$ where $x = 1$

7 a For what values of x does $y = \ln\frac{2}{\tan^{-1}x}$ exist?

b Show that in this domain it is a decreasing function.

8 Show that $y = (\sin^{-1}3x)^4$ has a minimum turning point at the origin.

9 a For what range of values of x does the function given by $f(x) = (1+\cos^{-1}2x)^{\frac{1}{2}}$ exist?

b Show that this function is decreasing throughout its domain.

6.3 Applying the product and quotient rules to inverse trigonometric functions

Example 7

Differentiate $x^2 \cos^{-1} \sqrt{x}$.

$$\frac{d}{dx}(x^2 \cos^{-1} \sqrt{x}) = x^2 \frac{d}{dx}(\cos^{-1} \sqrt{x}) + \frac{d}{dx}(x^2) \cdot \cos^{-1}\sqrt{x} \qquad \text{(By the product rule)}$$

$$= x^2 \frac{-1}{\sqrt{1-x}} \cdot \frac{1}{2} x^{-\frac{1}{2}} + 2x \cos^{-1} \sqrt{x} \qquad \text{(By the chain rule)}$$

$$= 2x \cos^{-1} \sqrt{x} - \frac{x^{\frac{3}{2}}}{2\sqrt{1-x}}$$

Example 8

Find the derivative of $\tan^{-1}\left(\frac{1+\sin x}{1-\cos x}\right)$.

$$\tan^{-1}\left(\frac{1+\sin x}{1-\cos x}\right) = \frac{1}{1+\left(\frac{1+\sin x}{1-\cos x}\right)^2} \frac{d}{dx}\left(\frac{1+\sin x}{1-\cos x}\right) \qquad \text{(By the chain rule)}$$

$$= \frac{1}{1+\left(\frac{1+\sin x}{1-\cos x}\right)^2} \frac{(1-\cos x)\cos x - (1+\sin x)\sin x}{(1-\cos x)^2} \qquad \text{(By the quotient rule)}$$

$$= \frac{\cos x - \cos^2 x - \sin x - \sin^2 x}{(1-\cos x)^2 + (1+\sin x)^2}$$

$$= \frac{\cos x - \sin x - 1}{3 + 2\sin x - 2\cos x} \qquad \text{(Using } \sin^2 x + \cos^2 x = 1\text{)}$$

Exercise 6.3

1 Differentiate

a $x^2 \sin^{-1} x$ b $x \sin^{-1} x^2$ c $\sqrt{x} \cos^{-1} x$ d $\sqrt{x} \sin^{-1} \sqrt{x}$

2 Find the derivative of

a $(1 + x^2) \tan^{-1} x$ b $e^x \sin^{-1} x$ c $e^{2x} \cos^{-1}\left(\frac{x}{2}\right)$ d $\ln x \tan^{-1} x$

3 Find the derived function for each of these.

a $f(x) = \frac{\tan^{-1} x}{x}$ b $f(x) = \frac{\sin^{-1} x}{\sqrt{x}}$ c $f(x) = \frac{\cos^{-1} 2x}{x\sqrt{x}}$ d $f(x) = \frac{\tan^{-1}(x+1)}{x^2}$

4 Find $f'(x)$ for each of these.

a $f(x) = \frac{x}{\sin^{-1} x}$ b $f(x) = \frac{x^2}{\cos^{-1}(x-1)}$

c $f(x) = \frac{e^x}{\sin^{-1} 2x}$ d $f(x) = \frac{\ln x}{\tan^{-1} x}$

5 Calculate the gradient of the tangent to the curve with equation

a $y = \tan^{-1}\left(\frac{2x+3}{3x-2}\right)$ at $x = -\frac{1}{2}$ b $y = \sin^{-1}\left(\frac{1+2\cos x}{2+\cos x}\right)$ at $x = \frac{\pi}{6}$

6 Find the coordinates of the stationary point on the curve with equation

a $y = \tan^{-1}\left(\frac{e^x}{x}\right)$ b $y = \cos^{-1}\left(\frac{\ln x}{x}\right)$

7 Show that there are no turning points on the curve with equation $y = \sin^{-1}\left(\frac{1-x}{1+x}\right)$.

8 Express the derivative of $y = \tan^{-1}\left(\frac{2\sin x + \sin 2x}{2\cos x + \cos 2x}\right)$ in terms of $\cos x$.

9 a Show that $f(x) = \cos^{-1}\left(\frac{1-x^2}{1+x^2}\right)$ and $g(x) = 2\tan^{-1} x$ have the same derived function.

b This could be because $f(x) = g(x)$.
Prove, by trigonometry, that this is in fact true.

10 Find the right gradient of the curve $y = \sin^{-1}\left(\frac{x^3-1}{x^3+1}\right)$ at $x = 0$ and show that the gradient approaches this same value as $x \to \infty$.

11 Show that

a $y = (x-1)\cos^{-1}\left(\frac{x-1}{x}\right) \Rightarrow x(x-1)\sqrt{2x-1}\,\frac{dy}{dx} = yx\sqrt{2x-1} - (x-1)^2$

b $y = (x+1)\sin^{-1}\left(\frac{x}{x+1}\right) \Rightarrow (x+1)\sqrt{2x+1}\,\frac{dy}{dx} = y\sqrt{2x+1} + (x+1)$

c $y = x^2\tan^{-1}\left(\frac{x-1}{x+1}\right) \Rightarrow 2x\frac{dy}{dx} = \frac{2x^3}{x^2+1} + 4y$

d $y = e^x\cos^{-1}\left(\frac{x-1}{x+1}\right) \Rightarrow \sqrt{x}(x+1)\left(\frac{dy}{dx} - y\right) + e^x = 0$

e $y = 2x\sin^{-1}\left(\frac{\cos x}{x}\right) \Rightarrow x\frac{dy}{dx} - y = \frac{-2\,|x|\,(x\sin x + \cos x)}{\sqrt{x^2 - \cos^2 x}}$

f $y = x\tan^{-1}\left(\frac{e^x}{x}\right) \Rightarrow x\frac{dy}{dx} - y = \frac{x^2(x-1)e^x}{x^2 + e^{2x}}$

6.4 Implicit and explicit functions

The equations $3x + 4y = 24$ and $y = -\frac{3}{4}x + 6$ are different forms of the equation of a line.

In the latter form, y is expressed *explicitly* as a function of x.

In the form $3x + 4y = 24$, y is still a function of x, but this fact is expressed *implicitly*.

When the dependent variable, y, is expressed in terms of the independent variable, x (that is, it is the subject of the formula), the function is said to be **explicit**. When the dependent variable is not the subject of the formula, then the function is said to be **implicit**.

The equation of the circle in the form $x^2 + y^2 = 25$ is another example of an implicit function. When y is made the subject, $y = \pm\sqrt{25 - x^2}$ giving two explicit functions of x.

In such cases the implicit function is referred to as a **multiple-valued** function.

First derivatives of implicit functions

When a function is stated implicitly, it is often possible to find the derived function without having to find the explicit form first.

Example 9

Find the gradient of the tangent at A(3, −4) to the circle with equation $x^2 + y^2 = 25$.

Differentiating each term with respect to x,

$$2x + 2y\frac{dy}{dx} = 0$$

$$\Rightarrow \frac{dy}{dx} = -\frac{2x}{2y} = -\frac{x}{y}$$

So the gradient of the tangent at A(3, −4) $= -\frac{3}{-4} = \frac{3}{4}$.

Since y is a function of x, the chain rule must be applied to obtain the derivative of y^2.

$$\frac{d}{dx}y^2 = 2y\cdot\frac{dy}{dx}$$

Example 10

Find the gradient of the tangent at any point on the lemniscate (the figure-eight curve) with equation $x^4 = x^2 - y^2$.

Differentiating gives $4x^3 = 2x - 2y\dfrac{dy}{dx}$

$$\Rightarrow \frac{dy}{dx} = \frac{x(1 - 2x^2)}{y}$$

In this case the implicit equation can be rewritten in explicit form and the derivative found directly.

$$y = \pm\sqrt{x^2 - x^4} \quad \text{for} \quad -1 \le x \le +1$$

$$\Rightarrow \frac{dy}{dx} = \pm\frac{2x - 4x^3}{2\sqrt{x^2 - x^4}} = \frac{x(1-2x^2)}{y}$$

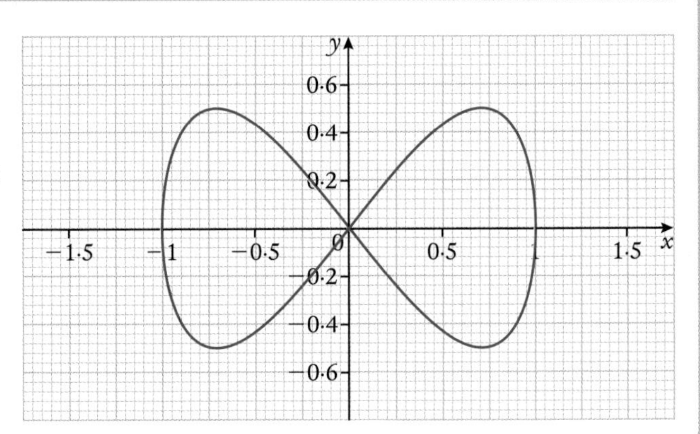

Example 11

For the curve with equation $x^3 - xy + y^2 = 1$, express $\dfrac{dy}{dx}$ in terms of x and y.

Note that the *product rule* is required when differentiating the term xy.

$$3x^2 - \left(1 \cdot y + x\frac{dy}{dx}\right) + 2y \cdot \frac{dy}{dx} = 0$$

$$\Rightarrow 3x^2 - y + (2y - x)\frac{dy}{dx} = 0$$

$$\Rightarrow \frac{dy}{dx} = \frac{y - 3x^2}{2y - x}$$

This original function can also be expressed explicitly by re-arranging the equation as $y^2 - xy + (x^3 - 1) = 0$ and applying the quadratic formula to give

$$y = \tfrac{1}{2}\left[x \pm \sqrt{4 + x^2 - 4x^3}\right]$$

A graphic calculator will exhibit two branches meeting where $4 + x^2 - 4x^3 = 0$, near the point (1.09, 0.54).

Example 12

If $(x + y)^3 = 3xy$, show that $\dfrac{dy}{dx} = \dfrac{y(y - 2x)}{x(2y - x)}$.

$$3(x + y)^2\left(1 + \frac{dy}{dx}\right) = 3y + 3x\frac{dy}{dx} \qquad \text{(Using the chain and product rules)}$$

$$\Rightarrow \frac{dy}{dx}\left((x + y)^2 - x\right) = y - (x + y)^2$$

$$\Rightarrow \frac{dy}{dx} = \frac{y - (x + y)^2}{(x + y)^2 - x}$$

We wish to make use of the original equation so multiply numerator and denominator by $(x + y)$ creating terms in $(x + y)^3$

$$\Rightarrow \frac{dy}{dx} = \frac{y(x + y) - (x + y)^3}{(x + y)^3 - x(x + y)} = \frac{y(x + y) - 3xy}{3xy - x(x + y)}$$

$$= \frac{y(y - 2x)}{x(2y - x)}$$

Exercise 6.4

1 Find $\frac{dy}{dx}$ for these implicit functions.

a $x^2 + 4xy + y^2 = 8$

b $x^2 = \ln y$

c $2x^2 + 2y^2 - 5x + 4y - 9 = 0$

d $x + 3 = e^y$

e $x^2 - xy + 3y^2 = 10$

f $x \tan y = e^x$

g $x^{\frac{2}{5}} + y^{\frac{2}{5}} = e^{\frac{2}{5}}$

h $\ln(x + y) = \tan^{-1} x$

i $5x^2 - 4xy + 3y^2 = 2$

j $\sin^{-1} x + \cos^{-1} y = 2x^3$

2 a i Given $x = \sin y$, find $\frac{dy}{dx}$ in terms of y.

ii Hence express $\frac{dy}{dx}$ in terms of x.

b Similarly deduce the derivative of

i $y = \cos^{-1} x$ ii $y = \tan^{-1} x$

3 Find an expression in terms of x and y for the gradient at the point (x, y) on the curve with equation $x^2 + y^2 = \frac{y}{x}$.

4 Prove that the curve $e^x + e^y - e = \frac{x}{y} + 1$ has a tangent at the point $(0, 1)$ which is parallel to the x-axis.

5 Find the equation of the tangent to the curve with equation $xy^4 + 3x^2y^2 = 28$ at the point $(1, 2)$.

6 Show that there is no point on the curve with equation $x + y = \ln(x - y)$ where the tangent is at $45°$ to the x-axis.

7 For the curve with equation $x \ln y = \cos x + \cos y$, show that the gradient at $x = 0$ is not defined.

8 Show that $x^2 = y^2 \ln y \Rightarrow \frac{dy}{dx} = \frac{2xy}{y^2 + 2x^2}$.

9 Find the equation of the tangent to the curve with equation $(x + 2y)^3 - 4x - 3y = 5$ at the point where it crosses the y-axis.

10 Find the gradient of the tangent at the point (e, e^2) on the curve given by $x \ln x + y \ln y = e(1 + 2e)$.

11 Show that $y = x - 1$ is the equation of the tangent at the point $\left(\frac{1}{2}, -\frac{1}{2}\right)$ to the curve with equation $\sin^{-1} x + \cos^{-1} y = \frac{5\pi}{6}$.

12 a Find the points of intersection of the parabola with equation $y^2 = 2x$ and the circle with equation $x^2 + y^2 = 8$.

b Use implicit differentiation to find the gradients of the tangents at the point of intersection in the first quadrant, and calculate the size of the angle between them.

13 Show that the point A(3, 2) lies on the circle with equation $(x - 6)^2 + (y - 5)^2 = 18$ and the parabola with equation $y^2 = 16 - 4x$ and that these curves share a common tangent at A.

14 a Find the coordinates of the four points of intersection of the ellipse with equation $\frac{x^2}{25} + \frac{y^2}{4} = 25$ and the hyperbola with equation $\frac{x^2}{16} - \frac{y^2}{9} = 21$.

b Show that these curves are **orthogonal**, that is, that at their points of intersection, their tangents are perpendicular.

15 Show that for $e^{x+y} = \ln(x - y)$, $\frac{dy}{dx}$ can be written as $\frac{1 - e^{a+x+y}}{1 + e^{a+x+y}}$ and state the appropriate expression for a.

16 Show that if $x + y = \frac{x}{y}$, then $\frac{dy}{dx}$ can be written as $\frac{y^3}{x^2(2 - y)}$.

6.5 Second derivatives of implicit functions

Higher-order derivatives can also be found implicitly.

Example 13

Find $\frac{dy}{dx}$ and $\frac{d^2y}{dx^2}$ in terms of x and y only for the function $y(x)$ defined implicitly by $x^2 + 2xy = 1$.

Differentiating $\quad 2x + 2y + 2x\frac{dy}{dx} = 0$

$$\Rightarrow \frac{dy}{dx} = -\frac{x+y}{x}$$

Now, using the quotient rule, $\frac{d^2y}{dx^2} = -\frac{x\left(1+\frac{dy}{dx}\right) - (x+y)\cdot 1}{x^2}$

Substituting for $\frac{dy}{dx}$ gives $= -\frac{x\left(1+\left(-\frac{x+y}{x}\right)\right) - (x+y)\cdot 1}{x^2} = \frac{x-x-y-x-y}{x^2}$

$$= -\frac{x+2y}{x^2}$$

Exercise 6.5

1 Find $\frac{dy}{dx}$ and $\frac{d^2y}{dx^2}$ in terms of x and y only, for each of these implicit functions.

a $x^2 + xy = 3$
b $x^3 + y^2 = 5$
c $\sqrt{x} + y^3 = 1$
d $xy = y^2 + 2$
e $(x+1)(y-1) = e^x$
f $xy^2 + 2 = y$
g $\ln(x+y) = x - y$
h $x^2 = y\ln y$
i $(x+y)^2 = e^y$
j $y = x(y + \sin x)$
k $y = \sin(x+y)$
l $x\sin^{-1}y = e^x$

2 Find the gradient of the tangent at the point A$(1, e)$ on the curve defined by $x\ln y + y\ln x = 1$ and determine whether the curve is concave up or concave down at A. (Note: if $f''(a) > 0$ then the curve is concave up at $x = a$.)

3 Find the gradient of the tangent at the point B $\left(\frac{\pi}{2}, \frac{\pi}{2}\right)$ on the curve defined by $x\cos y + y\cos x = 0$ and determine whether the curve is concave up or concave down at B.

4 Show that if $x^2 = e^y$ then $e^y\frac{d^2y}{dx^2} + 2x\frac{dy}{dx} = 2$.

5 If $y = xe^y$, show that $(1-y)\frac{d^2y}{dx^2} = (2-y)\left(\frac{dy}{dx}\right)^2$.

6 For the function defined implicitly by $x^3 - xy + y^2 = 1$ evaluate $\frac{dy}{dx}$ at $(1, 1)$ and $\frac{d^2y}{dx^2}$ at $(1, 0)$.

7 For the function $y(x)$ defined implicitly by $y\cos x = e^x$ evaluate $y'\left(\frac{\pi}{3}\right)$ and $y''\left(\frac{\pi}{3}\right)$.

8 Find two points on the curve with equation $x^2 - xy + y^2 = 3$ where the tangent is parallel to the x-axis and two points where the tangent is parallel to the y-axis.

9 Find two stationary points on the curve with equation $2x^2 - xy + 3y^2 = 46$, and by using the second derivative determine the nature of each.

6.6 Logarithmic differentiation

When a function is complicated by the occurrence of powers, roots, products and quotients of several factors it is useful to take logarithms before differentiating.

Example 14

Differentiate 2^{x+3}

Let $y = 2^{x+3}$

Take the log of both sides, $\ln y = \ln 2^{x+3}$

$$\Rightarrow \ln y = (x+3)\ln 2$$

Differentiating $\frac{1}{y}\frac{dy}{dx} = 1 \times \ln 2$

$$\Rightarrow \frac{dy}{dx} = y \ln 2$$

Substitute for y $\Rightarrow \frac{dy}{dx} = 2^{x+3}\ln 2$

Reminders

$\ln(x \times y) = \ln x + \ln y$

$\ln(x \div y) = \ln x - \ln y$

$\ln x^r = r \ln x$

Example 15

Find $\frac{dy}{dx}$ when $y = x^x$.

Take the log of both sides, $y = x^x \Rightarrow \ln y = x \ln x$.

Differentiating $\frac{1}{y}\frac{dy}{dx} = 1 \cdot \ln x + x \cdot \frac{1}{x} = \ln x + 1$

$$\Rightarrow \frac{dy}{dx} = y(\ln x + 1)$$

Substitute for y $\Rightarrow \frac{dy}{dx} = x^x(\ln x + 1)$

Example 16

Find $\frac{dy}{dx}$ when $y = \frac{(2x+1)^{\frac{1}{2}}(3x-1)^{\frac{2}{3}}}{(4x+3)^{\frac{3}{4}}}$.

Take the log of both sides: $\ln y = \frac{1}{2}\ln(2x+1) + \frac{2}{3}\ln(3x-1) - \frac{3}{4}\ln(4x+3)$

Differentiating: $\frac{1}{y}\frac{dy}{dx} = \frac{1 \cdot 2}{2(2x+1)} + \frac{2 \cdot 3}{3(3x-1)} - \frac{3 \cdot 4}{4(4x+3)}$

$$= \frac{1}{(2x+1)} + \frac{2}{(3x-1)} - \frac{3}{(4x+3)}$$

$$= \frac{(3x-1)(4x+3) + 2(2x+1)(4x+3) - 3(2x+1)(3x-1)}{(2x+1)(3x-1)(4x+3)}$$

$$\Rightarrow \frac{dy}{dx} = y\frac{16x^2 + 22x + 6}{(2x+1)(3x-1)(4x+3)}$$

$$= \frac{(2x+1)^{\frac{1}{2}}(3x-1)^{\frac{2}{3}}}{(4x+3)^{\frac{3}{4}}} \cdot \frac{16x^2 + 22x + 6}{(2x+1)(3x-1)(4x+3)}$$

$$= \frac{16x^2 + 22x + 6}{(2x+1)^{\frac{1}{2}}(3x-1)^{\frac{1}{3}}(4x+3)^{\frac{7}{4}}}$$

Exercise 6.6

1 Find the derivatives of these functions.

a $f(x) = 5^{2x}$ b $f(x) = (x+1)^{x-1}$ c $f(x) = e^{\sin^2 x}$

d $f(x) = 3^{e^x}$ e $f(x) = (\cos x)^x$

2 Find the derived function for each of these functions.

a $f(x) = x^{x^2}$ b $f(x) = \pi^{x^3}$ c $f(x) = \dfrac{e^x \sin x}{x}$

d $f(x) = xe^{-x}\cos x$ e $f(x) = (1 - x^3)^{\sin x}$

3 Show that for $y = e^{\cos 2x \cos^2 x}$, $\dfrac{dy}{dx} = -2\cos x \sin 3x \cdot e^{\cos 2x \cos^2 x}$.

4 Show that $y = e^{\cos^2 x} \Rightarrow \dfrac{d^2y}{dx^2} = (\sin^2 2x - 2\cos 2x)y$.

5 Show that the tangent to the curve with equation $y = (\sin x)^x$ at $x = \frac{\pi}{2}$ is parallel to the x-axis.

6 For the curve with equation $y = x^{\sin x}$ show that the tangent at $x = \frac{\pi}{2}$ is inclined at $\frac{\pi}{4}$ radians to the x-axis.

7 Find the equation of the tangent to the curve with equation $y = \dfrac{x(2x+1)^{\frac{3}{2}}}{(3x-4)^{\frac{2}{3}}}$ at the point where $x = 4$.

8 Find the gradient of the curve with equation $y = \dfrac{(x+3)^{\frac{1}{2}}}{x(x+2)^{\frac{1}{3}}}$ at the point where $x = 6$.

9 Find the value of x for which the graph of $y = \dfrac{x^{\frac{1}{2}}(3-x)^{\frac{1}{6}}}{(2x+1)^{\frac{2}{3}}}$ is stationary.

10 Differentiate a $\dfrac{(x+1)^{\frac{1}{2}}(x-1)^{\frac{1}{3}}}{(x+2)^{\frac{1}{4}}}$ b $\dfrac{(2x+3)^{\frac{5}{2}}}{x(x-1)^{\frac{2}{3}}}$

6.7 Parametric equations

Although we may have a function $y = f(x)$, it is sometimes more convenient to express the variables x and y as functions of a third variable, say, t.
$x = x(t)$ and $y = y(t)$ are called **parametric equations** and t is referred to as the parameter.

Each value of t will uniquely define a point $(x(t), y(t))$ on the curve $y = f(x)$.

For example, the equation of the line illustrated here is $3x + 4y = 24$.
The line can also be represented by the parametric equations

$x = 4(1 + t)$

$y = 3(1 - t)$

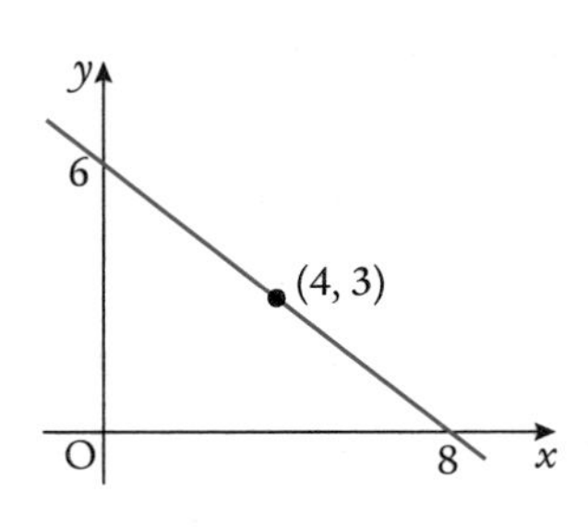

Note that $t = 1$ gives rise to the point $(8, 0)$ and $t = -1$ corresponds to the point $(0, 6)$.

It is also possible to eliminate the parameter from a pair of equations.
Given $x = x(t)$ and $y = y(t)$ we get, from the first equation, $t = x^{-1}(x)$.
Substituting in the second equation gives $y = y(x^{-1}(x))$.

This equation is referred to as the **constraint equation** of the function.

We can demonstrate this on the pair of parametric equations above.

$x = 4 + 4t$ and $y = 3 - 3t$

$\Rightarrow t = \dfrac{x - 4}{4}$ from the first equation

$\Rightarrow y = 3 - 3\left(\dfrac{x - 4}{4}\right)$ substituting into the second equation

$\Rightarrow 4y = 12 - 3x + 12$

$\Rightarrow 4y + 3x = 24$

Note that the parametric representation of a curve is not unique.

For any function $y = f(x)$, we can define a parameter u such that $x = k(u)$, and thus we can find a pair of equations $x = k(u)$ and $y = f(k(u))$.

For example, the pair

$x = 4(3 + u)$

$y = -3(1 - u)$

also represents the above line.

Parametric equations of the circle

Consider the pair of equations

$x = 4 + r\cos\theta$

$y = 3 + r\sin\theta$

where r is a constant.

To eliminate the parameter θ

$$r\cos\theta = x - 4 \Rightarrow r^2\cos^2\theta = (x-4)^2$$

$$r\sin\theta = y - 3 \Rightarrow r^2\sin^2\theta = (y-3)^2$$

$$\Rightarrow (x-4)^2 + (y-3)^2 = r^2\cos^2\theta + r^2\sin^2\theta$$

$$= r^2[\cos^2\theta + \sin^2\theta]$$

$$\Rightarrow (x-4)^2 + (y-3)^2 = r^2$$

which represents the circle centre (4, 3) radius r.

From the diagram it is clear that the parameter θ can be interpreted as the amount the radius rotates anti-clockwise from the x-direction.

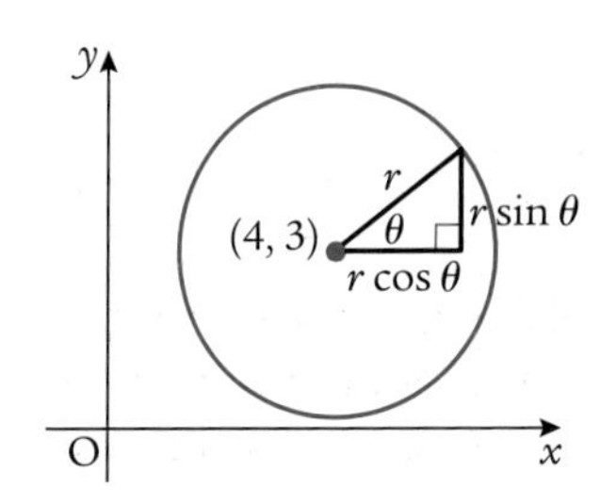

$(x-4)^2 + (y-3)^2 = r^2$ is the constraint equation of the circle and the parametric equations (also known as **freedom equations**) are

$x = 4 + r\cos\theta$

$y = 3 + r\sin\theta$

If we wish to draw a circle on a computer app, say, a spreadsheet, the parametric equations are more convenient.

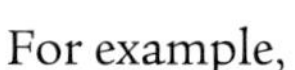

For example,

In cell D1 type: 6 [This is the radius of the circle]

In cell A1 type: 0

In cell A2 type: =A1+PI()/12 [Increase θ by $\frac{\pi}{12}$]

Fill down to A25. [Where $\theta = 2\pi$]

In cell B1 type: =4 + $D$1*COS(A1) [This is the x-coordinate]

Fill down to B25.

In cell C1 type: =3 + $D$1*SIN(A1) [This is the y-coordinate]

Fill down to C25.

Select B1 to C25 and insert a chart, using 'smooth lined scatter'.

This produces a circle with centre (4, 3) and radius 6.

Altering the contents of D1 will alter the size of the circle.

Make sure the grid is 'square' by adjusting the chart window.

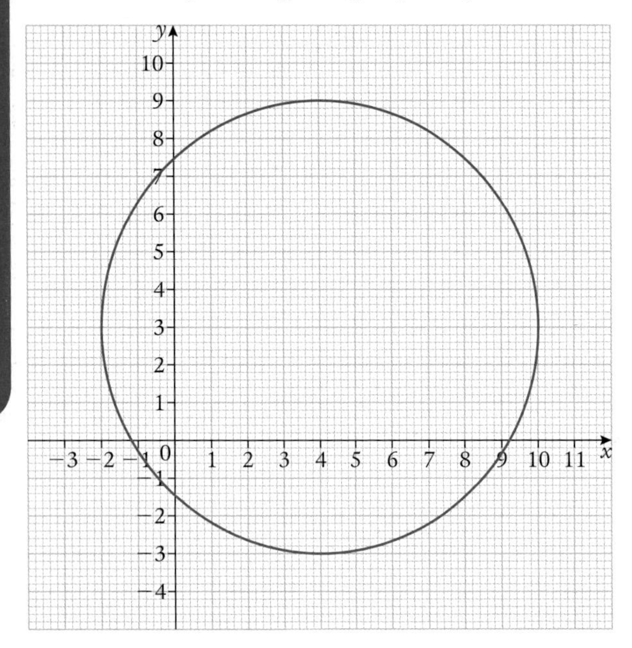

Example 17

a Find the constraint equation of the locus defined by the parametric equations $x = t + \frac{1}{t}$ and $y = t - \frac{1}{t}$.

b Find $\frac{dy}{dx}$.

c Sketch the curve.

---

a t can be eliminated by squaring both equations and subtracting them.

$x^2 = t^2 + 2 + t^{-2}$
$y^2 = t^2 - 2 + t^{-2}$
$\Rightarrow x^2 - y^2 = 4$

b Using implicit differentiation on the constraint equation

$2x - 2y\frac{dy}{dx} = 0 \Rightarrow \frac{dy}{dx} = \frac{x}{y}$

c Expressing the constraint equation explicitly we get $y = \pm\sqrt{x^2 - 4}$

$\Rightarrow x \leq -2$ or $x \geq 2$

We also know $t \neq 0$.

We can now sketch the curve using a spreadsheet.

- Use column A to run through the values of t from -4 to 4 in steps of 0.2.
- Use columns B and C to generate x-and y-values respectively.
- Delete x- and y-values where $t = 0$.
- Insert a chart depicting column B against C.

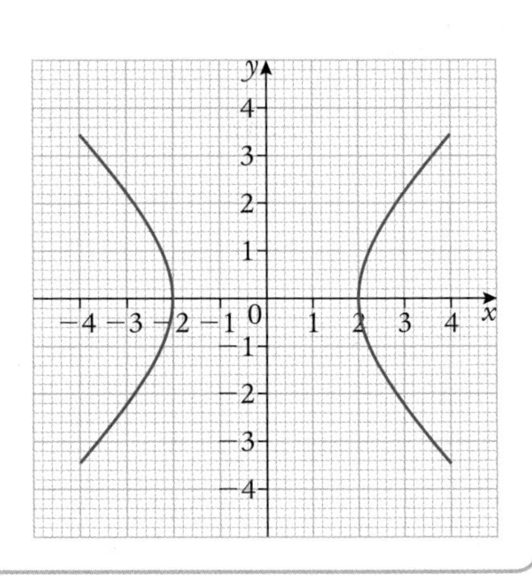

Exercise 6.7

1 For each of the pairs of parametric equations find the corresponding constraint equation.

Hint: when trigonometric ratios are involved, try squaring both sides of each equation.

a $x = 1 - t$, $y = 1 + 2t$ b $x = 3t$, $y = \frac{3}{t}$ c $x = 5p^2$, $y = 10p$

d $x = 4\cos\theta$, $y = 3\sin\theta$ e $x = 5\sec\theta$, $y = 12\tan\theta$ f $x = 3 + 2\sin\theta$, $y = 2 - 3\cos\theta$

g $x = \cos\theta + \sin\theta$, $y = \cos\theta - \sin\theta$ h $x = \frac{2 + 3t}{4}$, $y = \frac{3 - 4t}{5}$

2 Sketch the locus represented by each of the above pairs of equations.

3 Use a spreadsheet or graphics calculator to help you sketch these loci.

a $x = t^2$, $y = \frac{1}{t}$ b $x = e^t$, $y = e^{2t}$ c $x = t^2 + t$, $y = t^3$ d $x = 2\cos\theta + 3\sin\theta$, $y = 3\cos\theta - 2\sin\theta$

4 Some very aesthetic curves can be drawn using parametric equations. Explore these using a spreadsheet or graphics calculator.

a The Cardioid $x = 2\cos\theta + 2\cos^2\theta$, $y = 2\sin\theta + \sin 2\theta$

b The Loopless Limaçon $x = 4\cos\theta + 2\cos^2\theta$, $y = 4\sin\theta + \sin 2\theta$

c The Limaçon $x = 2\cos\theta + 4\cos^2\theta$, $y = 2\sin\theta + 2\sin 2\theta$

d The Archimedean Spiral $x = \theta\cos n\theta$, $y = \theta\sin n\theta$

where n determines the number of turns.

e The Lobiates $x = \cos\theta\cos n\theta$, $y = \sin\theta\cos n\theta$

where n determines the number of lobes.

6.8 First and second derivatives of parametric equations

When $x = x(t)$, $y = y(t)$ and $y = f(x)$ then $f'(x)$ and $f''(x)$ can be determined by making use of the chain rule.

$$f'(x) = \frac{dy}{dx} = \frac{dy}{dt} \times \frac{dt}{dx} = \frac{dy}{dt} \div \frac{dx}{dt}$$

$$f'(x) = \frac{y'(t)}{x'(t)}$$

$$f''(x) = \frac{d^2y}{dx^2} = \frac{d\left(\frac{dy}{dx}\right)}{dx} = \frac{d\left(\frac{dy}{dx}\right)}{dt} \times \frac{dt}{dx} = \frac{d\left(\frac{y'(t)}{x'(t)}\right)}{dt} \times \frac{1}{x'(t)}$$

Using the quotient rule,

$$f''(x) = \frac{x'(t)\cdot y''(t) - x''(t)\cdot y'(t)}{(x'(t))^2} \times \frac{1}{x'(t)}$$

$$f''(x) = \frac{x'(t)\cdot y''(t) - x''(t)\cdot y'(t)}{(x'(t))^3}$$

Example 18

Find $f'(x)$ and $f''(x)$ when $x = 4 + 4t$ and $y = 3 - 3t^2$.

$x = 4 + 4t \Rightarrow x'(t) = 4 \Rightarrow x''(t) = 0$

$y = 3 - 3t^2 \Rightarrow y'(t) = -6t \Rightarrow y''(t) = -6$

So $f'(x) = \dfrac{y'(t)}{x'(t)} = \dfrac{-6t}{4} = \dfrac{-3t}{2}$

and $f''(x) = \dfrac{x'(t) \cdot y''(t) - x''(t) \cdot y'(t)}{(x'(t))^3} = \dfrac{4 \cdot (-6) - 0 \cdot (-6t)}{(4)^3} = -\dfrac{3}{8}$

Example 19

Given the locus represented by the parametric equations

$x = 3 + 5 \cos \theta$

$y = 4 + 5 \sin \theta$

a find the point on the locus corresponding to a parameter value $\theta = \frac{\pi}{2}$

b find the gradient of the tangent at this point

c find the concavity at this point.

a $x\left(\frac{\pi}{2}\right) = 3 + 5 \cos \frac{\pi}{2} = 3$

$y\left(\frac{\pi}{2}\right) = 4 + 5 \sin \frac{\pi}{2} = 9$

The point on the locus is (3, 9).

b $x'(\theta) = -5 \sin \theta$; $y'(\theta) = 5 \cos \theta$

$\Rightarrow f'(x) = \dfrac{5 \cos \theta}{-5 \sin \theta} = -\cot \theta$

When $\theta = \frac{\pi}{2}, f'\left(x\left(\frac{\pi}{2}\right)\right) = -\cot \frac{\pi}{2} = 0.$

The tangent is horizontal.

c $x''(\theta) = -5 \cos \theta; y''(\theta) = -5 \sin \theta$

$\Rightarrow f''(x) = \dfrac{-5 \sin \theta (-5 \sin \theta) - (-5 \cos \theta)\, 5 \cos \theta}{(-5 \sin \theta)^3} = \dfrac{25(\sin^2 \theta + \cos^2 \theta)}{-125 \sin^3 \theta}$

$\Rightarrow f''(x) = \dfrac{-1}{5 \sin^3 \theta}$

$\Rightarrow f''\left(x\left(\frac{\pi}{2}\right)\right) = \dfrac{-1}{5 \sin^3 \frac{\pi}{2}} = -\frac{1}{5}$

$f''(x) < 0$, so the curve is concave down.

Exercise 6.8

1 Find $\dfrac{dy}{dx}$ and $\dfrac{d^2y}{dx^2}$ for the curve defined by each pair of parametric equations.

a $x = t$, $y = \dfrac{1}{t}$

b $x = t^2$, $y = \ln t$

c $x = t + \sin t$, $y = t - \cos t$

d $x = 3t^3 - t$, $y = 4t^2$

e $x = \theta - \sin \theta$, $y = 1 + \cos \theta$

2 A curve is defined by the equations $x = t^2 + \frac{2}{t}$ and $y = t^2 - \frac{2}{t}$.

a Find the coordinates of the turning point on the curve.

b Establish the nature of the turning point by considering the concavity of the curve.

3 a Find $\frac{dy}{dx}$ and $\frac{d^2y}{dx^2}$ for the curve defined by $x = t^2 - \frac{1}{t^2}$ and $y = t^2 + \frac{1}{t^2}$.

b Determine the coordinates of the turning point on the curve.

c Prove that the curve is always concave up.

4 For the curve defined by $x = \frac{2t}{1 - t^2}$, $y = \frac{1 + t^2}{1 - t^2}$ show that

a $\frac{dy}{dx} = \frac{x}{y}$ b $\frac{d^2y}{dx^2} = \frac{1}{y^3}$

5 A spiral is generated by the parametric equations $x = e^{\theta} \sin \theta, y = e^{\theta} \cos \theta$.

Find the coordinates and the nature of the turning points which occur when $0 \le \theta \le 2\pi$.

6 A curve is defined by $x = 2 \sin \theta + \cos 2\theta, y = 2 \cos \theta - \sin 2\theta, 0 \le \theta \le 2\pi$.

a Show that at the points where $\frac{dy}{dx} = 0$, $\left|\frac{d^2y}{dx^2}\right| = \frac{\sqrt{3}}{4}$.

b Find the points where the gradient is undefined.

7 A curve is defined by $x = (1 + t)^{\frac{1}{2}}, y = (1 - t)^{-\frac{1}{2}}$.

a Show that this graph has only one critical point and determine its nature.

b The curve has a vertical asymptote. Identify it by finding where the gradient is undefined.

8 $x = 1 + \sin^2 \theta$ and $y = 1 - \sec^2 \theta$ are the parametric representations of a curve.

Show that, at the point where $\tan \theta = 2$, the equation of the tangent is $25x + y = 41$.

9 An astroid is defined by $x = \sin^3 t - \cos^3 t, y = \sin^3 t + \cos^3 t$.

a Show that the equation of the tangent to the astroid at the point where $t = \tan^{-1} \frac{3}{4}$ is $5x + 35y = 24$.

b The curve cuts the axes where the gradient is zero or undefined.
Calculate the points of intersection of the curve with the axes.

10 a Find, in terms of θ, $\frac{dy}{dx}$ and $\frac{d^2y}{dx^2}$ for the curve defined by

$x = 1 + \sin \theta$

$y = \theta + \sin \theta \cos \theta$

b Show that the constraint equation of this curve is

$y = \sin^{-1}(x - 1) + (x - 1)\sqrt{2x - x^2}$.

c Find $\frac{dy}{dx}$ and $\frac{d^2y}{dx^2}$ by direct differentiation and verify that your results agree with your answers in part a.

11 a Identify the turning points on the curve defined by $x = \frac{3t}{1 + t^3}$, $y = \frac{3t^2}{1 + t^3}$.

b Show that there are no points of inflexion.

Review 6

1 Given that $f(x) = \frac{1}{2}(x^3 - 5)$, find

a $f'(x)$ and $f^{-1}(x)$

b the derivative of $f^{-1}(x)$, using the rule $\frac{df^{-1}(x)}{dx} = \frac{1}{f'(f^{-1}(x))}$.

2 Given that $y = (1 - x^2)^{\frac{1}{2}} + 4 \sin^{-1} x$ find $\frac{dy}{dx}$.

3 Differentiate $\sin^{-1} 5x$.

4 Find the gradient of the tangent to the curve $y = \ln \tan^{-1}(3x)$ where $x = \frac{1}{\sqrt{3}}$.

5 Differentiate $e^{\frac{x}{2}} \cos^{-1} 2x$.

6 Differentiate $\tan^{-1}\left(\frac{1 + \cos x}{\sin x}\right)$.

7 Given $\frac{1}{x} + \frac{1}{y} = \frac{1}{\pi}$, find $\frac{dy}{dx}$ and $\frac{d^2y}{dx^2}$.

8 Given $y = \frac{2^x}{x + 2}$, find the rate of change of y with respect to x, when $x = 2$.

9 Find the constraint equation of the curve defined parametrically by
$x = 2 + \frac{1}{t}, y = \frac{t^2 + 1}{t^2 - 1}$.

10 A curve is defined parametrically by $x = 2t - 3 - \frac{1}{t}, y = t - 1 - \frac{2}{t}$.

a i Find the equations of the tangents to the curve at the points where it crosses the x-axis.

ii Find the coordinates of the point of their intersection.

b Show that there are no points of inflexion on this curve.

Summary 6

1 Derivative of an inverse function

$$\frac{df^{-1}(x)}{dx} = \frac{1}{f'(f^{-1}(x))}$$

2 **Reciprocal derivative** $\frac{dx}{dy} = \frac{1}{\frac{dy}{dx}}$.

3 Derivatives of the inverse trigonometric functions

$$\frac{d\sin^{-1}x}{dx} = \frac{1}{\sqrt{1 - x^2}}; \frac{d\cos^{-1}x}{dx} = \frac{-1}{\sqrt{1 - x^2}}; \frac{d\tan^{-1}x}{dx} = \frac{1}{1 + x^2}$$

4 Implicit and explicit functions

a When the dependent variable, y, is expressed in terms of the independent variable, x (that is, it is the subject of the formula), the function is said to be **explicit**. When the dependent variable is not the subject of the formula, the function is said to be **implicit**.

b The chain rule is employed to differentiate terms which are functions of y.

$$\frac{d}{dx}g(y) = g'(y) \times \frac{dy}{dx}$$

5 Logarithmic differentiation

When a function is complicated by the occurrence of powers, roots, products and quotients of several factors it is useful to take logarithms before differentiating. For example

$$y = \frac{g(x)h(x)}{k(x)} \Rightarrow \ln y = \ln g(x) + \ln h(x) - \ln k(x)$$

and thus $\frac{1}{y}\frac{dy}{dx} = \frac{g'(x)}{g(x)} + \frac{h'(x)}{h(x)} - \frac{k'(x)}{k(x)}$

6 Parametric equations

a Given the function $y = f(x)$, it is sometimes more convenient to express the variables x and y as functions of a third variable, say, t.
Equations $x = x(t)$ and $y = y(t)$ are called **parametric equations** and t is referred to as the **parameter**.

b Each value of t will uniquely define a point $(x(t), y(t))$ on the curve $y = f(x)$.

c The equation $y = f(x)$ is often referred to as the **constraint equation** of the function.

7 Differentiating using parameters

$$f'(x) = \frac{y'(t)}{x'(t)}, f''(x) = \frac{x'(t)y''(t) - x''(t)y'(t)}{(x'(t))^3}$$

These results can be obtained by application of the chain rule.

7 Integral calculus

Historical note

While it is true that Sir Isaac Newton and Gottfried Leibniz are credited with inventing integral calculus, Archimedes, 287–212 BC, invented the main technique required to prove the fundamental theorem of calculus. His idea was to find the areas of curvilinear shapes by subdividing them into thin strips – so thin that they could be approximated by rectangles.

Using this technique, Archimedes succeeded in finding a formula for the area under a parabola.

7.1 Reminders

1 An **antiderivative** of a function $f(x)$ is a function $F(x)$ where $F'(x) = f(x)$.
For example, $f'(x^3) = 3x^2$ and so x^3 is an antiderivative of $3x^2$.
Of course, any function of the form $x^3 + c$, where c is a constant, is an antiderivative of $3x^2$.

The **indefinite** integral $\int f(x)\,dx = F(x) + c$ represents the family of antiderivatives of $f(x)$.

Example: $\int 3x^2\,dx = x^3 + c$

2 The **definite** integral of $f(x)$ between the limits of a and b can be defined as

$\int_a^b f(x)\,dx = F(b) - F(a)$ where $F'(x) = f(x)$

Example: $\int_1^2 3x^2\,dx = [x^3 + c]_1^2 = 2^3 + c - 1^3 - c = 7$

Note that the constant c need not be considered.

$$\int_1^2 3x^2\,dx = [x^3]_1^2 = 2^3 - 1^3 = 7$$

3 We can list standard integrals from our knowledge of standard derivatives.

a $\int ax^n\,dx = \frac{a}{n+1}x^{n+1} + c,\ n \neq -1$

b $\int \sin x\,dx = -\cos x + c$

c $\int \cos x\,dx = \sin x + c$

d $\int \sec^2 x\,dx = \tan x + c$

e $\int e^x\,dx = e^x + c$

f $\int \frac{1}{x}\,dx = \ln|x| + c$

[Note: this covers the case for $\int ax^n\,dx$ where $n = -1$: $\int ax^{-1}\,dx = \frac{1}{a}\ln|ax| + c$]

4 We can check an integration by differentiating the result.

$\frac{d}{dx}F(x) = f(x) \Rightarrow \int f(x)\,dx = F(x) + c$

Using the chain rule we know that $\frac{d}{dx}F(ax+b) = af(ax+b)$.

Thus $\int f(ax+b)\,dx = \frac{1}{a}F(ax+b) + c$

Example 1: $\int \cos(3x+1)\,dx = \frac{1}{3}\sin(3x+1) + c$

Example 2: $\int \frac{1}{5x-1}\,dx = \frac{1}{5}\ln(5x-1) + c$

5 Some basic rules.

a $\int af(x)\,dx = a\int f(x)\,dx$ where a is a constant

b $\int (f(x) + g(x))\,dx = \int f(x)\,dx + \int g(x)\,dx$

c $\int_a^c f(x)\,dx = \int_a^b f(x)\,dx + \int_b^c f(x)\,dx$

d $\int_a^b f(x)\,dx = -\int_b^a f(x)\,dx$

Example 1

Find the integral of $(4x+1)^2$ by two different methods and compare your answers.

Method 1 $\int (4x+1)^2\,dx = \frac{1}{3}(4x+1)^3 \cdot \frac{1}{4} + c_1 = \frac{1}{12}(4x+1)^3 + c_1$

Method 2 $\int (4x+1)^2\,dx = \int (16x^2 + 8x + 1)\,dx = \frac{16}{3}x^3 + 4x^2 + x + c_2$

Expanding the answer obtained by Method 1 we get $\frac{16}{3}x^3 + 4x^2 + x + \frac{1}{12} + c_1$.

Since we can choose $\frac{1}{12} + c_1 = c_2 =$ a constant, the answers are equivalent.

Exercise 7.1

1 Find each of these indefinite integrals.

a $\int (3x^5 + 4x^3)\,dx$

b $\int (2x^4 + \sin x)\,dx$

c $\int (3x+1)^2\,dx$

d $\int (x^2+1)^2\,dx$

e $\int \frac{2x^3+1}{x^2}\,dx$

f $\int \frac{x+1}{\sqrt{x}}\,dx$

g $\int \sec^2(2x+3)\,dx$

h $\int (4\sin 2x + 1)\,dx$

i $\int \cos(1-2x)\,dx$

2 Calculate these indefinite integrals.

a $\int (2x+5)^{-2}\,dx$

b $\int (4-3x)^{-2}\,dx$

c $\int (\sin(5x-1) - \cos(1-5x))\,dx$

d $\int (x^2+x+1)^2\,dx$

e $\int \frac{1-2x-x^2}{x}\,dx$

f $\int \sec^2(1-x)\,dx$

g $\int \sin(2-3x)\,dx$

h $\int (2\cos 2x + 3\sin(1-x))\,dx$

i $\int \left(2\cos(1-3x) + \frac{x^2}{3}\right)dx$

3 Find these indefinite integrals.

a $\int \frac{1}{2x}\,dx$ b $\int \frac{3}{2x+1}\,dx$ c $\int (4x+5)^{-1}\,dx$

d $\int e^{3x}\,dx$ e $\int 3e^{4x-1}\,dx$ f $\int 3e^{1-x}\,dx$

g $\int \frac{dx}{e^x}$ h $\int \left(\frac{1}{2x+1}+\frac{1}{3x-1}\right) dx$ i $\int \left(\frac{1}{e^{x+1}}+\frac{3}{3x-1}\right) dx$

j $\int \frac{x}{2x^2+3x}\,dx$ k $\int 4^x\,dx$ [Hint: $4^x = e^{x\ln 4}$] l $\int 4^{3x-1}\,dx$

[Hint: divide numerator and denominator by x.]

4 Evaluate these definite integrals.

a $\int_1^3 \frac{dx}{x+1}$ b $\int_0^{\frac{1}{2}} e^{2x-1}\,dx$ c $\int_0^1 \left(\frac{1}{2x+1}+\frac{1}{4x+1}\right) dx$

d $\int_0^{\frac{\pi}{3}} \sin x + \sec^2 x\,dx$ e $\int_1^e x + x^{-1}\,dx$ f $\int_1^{\frac{1}{3}} (3x-2)^{-1}\,dx$

5 Simplify the expression and then evaluate the definite integral.

a $\int_{-\frac{\pi}{4}}^{\frac{\pi}{4}} \frac{1+\cos^2 x}{\cos^2 x}\,dx$ b $\int_{-\frac{\pi}{4}}^{\frac{\pi}{4}} \frac{1+\sin^2 x}{\cos^2 x}\,dx$ c $\int_0^{\frac{\pi}{6}} \cos x \sec^3 x\,dx$

d $\int_2^6 \frac{x-2}{x^2-4}\,dx$ e $\int_0^3 \frac{x+2}{2x^2+7x+6}\,dx$ f $\int_0^{\pi} \frac{\sin 2x}{\sin x}\,dx$

Differentials

If $y = f(x)$ and if δy is the small change in y induced by a small change δx in x

then $\delta y \approx \lim_{\delta x \to 0} \frac{\delta y}{\delta x}\,\delta x$

That is, $\delta y \approx \frac{dy}{dx}\,\delta x$

The smaller δx becomes, the better the approximation for δy.

With this idea in mind, we *define* two quantities dy, the y-differential, and dx, the x-differential, by the equation

$$dy = \frac{dy}{dx}\,dx \text{ or } dy = f'(x)\,dx \text{ where } y = f(x).$$

Note that $\frac{dy}{dx}$ is the coefficient of dx and is often referred to as the **differential coefficient**.

For example if $y = x^2$ then we can write $dy = 2x\,dx$.

7.2 Integration by substitution

Suppose we have a function $f(x)$ with an antiderivative of $F(x)$.

That is, $\int f(x)\,dx = F(x) + c$ and $F'(x) = f(x)$.

Now suppose we have a function of the form $f(g(x)) \cdot g'(x)$ which we wish to integrate.

We wish to find $\int f(g(x)) \cdot g'(x)\,dx$.

Let $u = g(x)$: then, using differentials, we have $du = g'(x)\,dx$.

Our integral would become $\int f(u)\,du = F(u) + c = F(g(x)) + c$

We can check that this is indeed the integral we want by differentiating it using the chain rule:

$$\frac{d}{dx}(F(g(x)) + c) = F'(g(x)) \cdot g'(x)$$

$$= f(g(x)) \cdot g'(x) \text{ which is the original function.}$$

The technique is known as integration by **substitution** or by **change of variable**.

The technique depends on being able to identify $g(x)$.

Let us refer to $g(x)$ as the 'subject for change'.

Example 2

Find $\int 3x\,(2x^2 - 1)^4\,dx$.

We could use x^2, $2x^2$ or $2x^2 - 1$ as the subject for change – each would produce a useful '$x\,dx$'. However, selecting $2x^2 - 1$ will produce the greatest simplification.

Let $u = 2x^2 - 1$, then $du = 4x\,dx \Rightarrow x\,dx = \frac{1}{4}\,du$ and $\int 3x(2x^2 - 1)^4\,dx = \int \frac{3}{4}u^4\,du$

$\int \frac{3}{4}u^4\,du = \frac{3}{20}u^5 + c$

$\Rightarrow \int 3x(2x^2 - 1)^4\,dx = \frac{3}{20}(2x^2 - 1)^5 + c$

Example 3

Integrate $2x^3\sqrt{1 - x^4}$.

$I = \int 2x^3\sqrt{1 - x^4}\,dx$

Let $u = 1 - x^4$ then $du = -4x^3\,dx \Rightarrow x^3\,dx = -\frac{1}{4}\,du$

$I = \int -\frac{2}{4}u^{\frac{1}{2}}\,du = -\frac{2}{4}\cdot\frac{2}{3}u^{\frac{3}{2}} + c = -\frac{1}{3}u^{\frac{3}{2}} + c$

$= -\frac{1}{3}(1 - x^4)^{\frac{3}{2}} + c$

Example 4

Find $\int \cos x \sin^5 x\,dx$.

Let $u = \sin x$ then $du = \cos x\,dx$

So $\int \cos x \sin^5 x\,dx = \int u^5\,du = \frac{1}{6}u^6 + c$

$= \frac{1}{6}\sin^6 x + c$

Example 5

Find the integral of $\tan x$.

$I = \int \tan x\,dx = \int \frac{\sin x}{\cos x}\,dx$

Let $u = \cos x$ then $du = -\sin x\,dx$

$I = \int \frac{-du}{u} = -\ln u + c$

The integral of $\tan x$ is $-\ln(\cos x) + c$.

Exercise 7.2

1 Find these indefinite integrals.

a $\int 3x^2(x^3 + 3)^4 \, dx$ b $\int x(x^2 + 1)^5 \, dx$ c $\int (2x + 1)(x^2 + x + 1)^6 \, dx$

d $\int (x + 7)(x^2 + 14x)^{\frac{2}{3}} \, dx$ e $\int \frac{2x}{x^2 + 1} \, dx$ f $\int \frac{2}{\sqrt{x} + 1} \, dx$

g $\int 3x \sqrt[3]{x^2 + 1} \, dx$ h $\int \frac{1}{x} \ln x \, dx$ i $\int \frac{1}{x \ln x} \, dx$

j $\int \sin x \, e^{\cos x} \, dx$ k $\int (x + 2)e^{x^2 + 4x} \, dx$ l $\int \frac{\sin(\ln x)}{x} \, dx$

m $\int \sin x \cos^4 x \, dx$ n $\int \tan^3 x \sec^2 x \, dx$ o $\int \frac{\sec^2 x}{\sqrt{\tan x}} \, dx$

p $\int (3x + 1)\sqrt{3x^2 + 2x + 1} \, dx$ q $\int 3e^x(e^x + 1)^3 \, dx$ r $\int \frac{4e^{2x}}{3e^{2x} - 2} \, dx$

s $\int \cot x \, dx$ $\left[\text{Remember: } \cot x = \frac{\cos x}{\sin x}\right]$ t $\int \frac{2x + 5}{x^2 + 5x - 1} \, dx$

u $\int (x - 3)(x + 2)(2x - 1) \, dx$ [Hint: multiply $(x - 3)(x + 2)$ out.]

v $\int \frac{4x + 9}{(x + 4)(2x + 1)} \, dx$ w $\int \frac{e^x - e^{-x}}{e^x + e^{-x}} \, dx$ x $\int \frac{(\ln x)^2 + 2\ln x + 1}{x} \, dx$

2 a Find the derivative of $\ln(\cos x)$.

b Hence find $\int \tan x \ln(\cos x) \, dx$.

3 a Differentiate $\cot x$.

b Hence find $\int \operatorname{cosec}^2 x \cot^3 x \, dx$.

c Find $\int \frac{\operatorname{cosec}^2 x}{\cot^3 x} \, dx$.

4 a Show that $\frac{1}{1 + e^x} = \frac{e^{-x}}{1 + e^{-x}}$.

b Hence find i $\int \frac{1}{1 + e^x} \, dx$ ii $\int \frac{1}{1 - e^x} \, dx$

7.3 Further integration by substitution

In some situations the subject of the change is not obvious. Often a suitable subject will be suggested.

These trigonometric identities might help.

- $\sin^2 A + \cos^2 A = 1$
- $\sin 2A = 2 \sin A \cos A$
- $\cos 2A = \cos^2 A - \sin^2 A$
- $\cos 2A = 2\cos^2 A - 1$
- $\cos 2A = 1 - 2\sin^2 A$
- $\tan^2 A + 1 = \sec^2 A$

When the integral is of the form $\int \sqrt{a^2 - x^2} \, dx$, try $x = a \sin u$

That is, $u = \sin^{-1}\left(\frac{x}{a}\right)$

Example 6

Find $\int \sqrt{3 - x^2}\, dx$.

Let $x = \sqrt{3}\sin u$ then $dx = \sqrt{3}\cos u\, du$

$$I = \int \sqrt{3 - x^2}\, dx = \int \sqrt{3}\sqrt{3 - 3\sin^2 u} \cdot \cos u\, du = 3\int \sqrt{1 - \sin^2 u} \cdot \cos u\, du$$

$$= 3\int \cos u \cdot \cos u\, du = 3\int \cos^2 u\, du$$

$$= \frac{3}{2}\int (1 + \cos 2u)\, du = \frac{3}{2}\left(u + \frac{1}{2}\sin 2u\right) + c$$

To complete the problem we must express $\sin 2u$ in terms of $\sin u$ so we can substitute back: $\sin 2u = 2\sin u\cos u = 2\sin u\sqrt{1 - \sin^2 u}$.

So $I = \frac{3}{2}\left(u + \sin u\sqrt{1 - \sin^2 u}\right) + c$

Now, $x = \sqrt{3}\sin u \Rightarrow u = \sin^{-1}\left(\frac{x}{\sqrt{3}}\right)$ and $\sin u = \frac{x}{\sqrt{3}}$

$$\text{So } I = \frac{3}{2}\left(\sin^{-1}\left(\frac{x}{\sqrt{3}}\right) + \left(\frac{x}{\sqrt{3}}\right)\sqrt{1 - \left(\frac{x}{\sqrt{3}}\right)^2}\right) + c = \frac{3}{2}\left(\sin^{-1}\left(\frac{x}{\sqrt{3}}\right) + \left(\frac{x}{3}\right)\sqrt{3 - x^2}\right) + c$$

$$= \frac{1}{2}\left(3\sin^{-1}\left(\frac{x}{\sqrt{3}}\right) + x\sqrt{3 - x^2}\right) + c$$

When the integral is of the form $\int \frac{1}{a^2 + x^2}\, dx$, try $x = a\tan u$

That is, $u = \tan^{-1}\left(\frac{x}{a}\right)$

Example 7

Find $\int \frac{1}{3 + x^2}\, dx$.

Let $x = \sqrt{3}\tan u$ then $dx = \sqrt{3}\sec^2 u\, du$ and $u = \tan^{-1}\left(\frac{x}{\sqrt{3}}\right)$

$$I = \int \frac{1}{3 + x^2}\, dx = \int \frac{\sqrt{3}\sec^2 u}{3(1 + \tan^2 u)}\, du = \int \frac{\sqrt{3}\sec^2 u}{3\sec^2 u}\, du = \int \frac{1}{\sqrt{3}}\, du = \frac{u}{\sqrt{3}} + c$$

$$= \frac{1}{\sqrt{3}}\tan^{-1}\left(\frac{x}{\sqrt{3}}\right) + c$$

When the integral is of the form $\int kx\sqrt{a^2 + x^2}\, dx$, try $u^2 = a^2 + x^2$.

Example 8

Find $\int 2x\sqrt{3 + x^2}\, dx$.

Let $u^2 = 3 + x^2$ then $2u\, du = 2x\, dx \Rightarrow u\, du = x\, dx$

$$I = \int 2x\sqrt{3 + x^2}\, dx = \int 2u\sqrt{u^2}\, du = \int 2u^2\, du = \frac{2}{3}u^3 + c$$

$$= \frac{2}{3}(3 + x^2)^{\frac{3}{2}} + c$$

What to do when the integral is of the form $\int \sin^n x \cos^m x\, dx$, where one of n, m is odd:

let us say n is odd. Associate one factor of $\sin x$ with dx. Let the subject of change be $\cos x$. Make use of $\sin^2 x + \cos^2 x = 1$.

Example 9

Find $\int \sin^3 x \cos^2 x \, dx$.

$$I = \int \sin^3 x \cos^2 x \, dx = \int \sin^2 x \cos^2 x \sin x \, dx = \int (1 - \cos^2 x) \cos^2 x \sin x \, dx$$

Let $u = \cos x \Rightarrow du = -\sin x \, dx$

$$I = -\int (1 - u^2)u^2 \, du = \int u^4 - u^2 \, du = \tfrac{1}{5}u^5 - \tfrac{1}{3}u^3 + c$$

$$= \frac{1}{5}\cos^5 x - \frac{1}{3}\cos^3 x + c$$

Exercise 7.3

1 Use the method shown in Example **6** to find the integrals.

a $\int \sqrt{1 - x^2} \, dx$ b $\int \sqrt{9 - x^2} \, dx$ c $\int \sqrt{5 - x^2} \, dx$ d $\int \sqrt{1 - 2x^2} \, dx$

2 Use the substitution $x = a \sin u$, where a is an appropriate constant, and integrate these.

a $\dfrac{1}{\sqrt{1 - x^2}}$ b $\dfrac{1}{\sqrt{4 - x^2}}$ c $\dfrac{3}{\sqrt{25 - x^2}}$ d $\dfrac{1}{\sqrt{1 - 2x^2}}$

3 a Use the substitution $u = x^2$ to transform $\int \dfrac{2x}{\sqrt{1 - x^4}} \, dx$.

b Now use the substitution $u = \sin v$ to help you complete the integration.

4 Use the substitution $x = a \tan u$, where a is an appropriate constant, and integrate these.

a $\dfrac{1}{1 + x^2}$ b $\dfrac{1}{9 + x^2}$ c $\dfrac{3}{x^2 + 16}$ d $\dfrac{1}{1 + 4x^2}$

5 a Use the substitution $u = x^4$ to transform $\int \dfrac{x^3}{1 + x^8} \, dx$.

b Now use the substitution $u = \tan v$ to help you complete the integration.

c Find $\int \dfrac{\sin x}{1 + \cos^2 x} \, dx$ by using the substitution $u = \cos x$.

6 Use the method shown in Example **8** to find the integrals.

a $\int x\sqrt{1 - x^2} \, dx$ b $\int 2x\sqrt{4 - x^2} \, dx$ c $\int \dfrac{x}{2}\sqrt{16 - x^2} \, dx$ d $\int x\sqrt{1 - 3x^2} \, dx$

7 a Find $\int \sin x \cos^2 x \, dx$ by letting $u = \cos x$.

b Find $\int \sin^5 x \cos^2 x \, dx$ by letting $u = \cos x$.

c Find $\int \sin^3 x \cos^5 x \, dx$ by letting $u = \sin x$.

d Find $\int \sin x \cos x \, dx$ by letting $u = \sin x$.

e Find $\int \cos^3 x \, dx$ by letting $u = \sin x$.

f Find $\int \sin^5 x \, dx$ by letting $u = \cos x$.

8 a Given $u = 1 - \sqrt{x}$, show that $dx = 2(u - 1)\,du$.

b Hence find $\int \frac{2}{1 - \sqrt{x}}\,dx$.

c Similarly find $\int \frac{2}{1 + \sqrt{x}}\,dx$.

9 a Use the substitution $x = \tan u$ to transform $\int \frac{1}{x^2\sqrt{1 + x^2}}\,dx$.

b Now use the substitution $v = \sin u$ to complete the integration.

10 We wish to find $\int \operatorname{cosec} x\,dx$.

a Use $\operatorname{cosec} x = \frac{1}{\sin x}$ and $\sin 2A = 2\sin A\cos A$ to express the function in terms of $\sin\frac{x}{2}$ and $\cos\frac{x}{2}$.

b Multiply numerator and denominator by $\sec^2\frac{x}{2}$ to express the function in terms of $\sec\frac{x}{2}$ and $\tan\frac{x}{2}$.

c Use the substitution $u = \tan\frac{x}{2}$ to find $\int \operatorname{cosec} x\,dx$.

d Show that $\int \sec x\,dx = \ln|\sec x + \tan x| + c$ [Hint: differentiate]

11 Make use of the laws of logs and the substitution $u = \ln x$ to help with these integrals.

a $\int \frac{\ln(x^2)}{x}\,dx$ b $\int \frac{\ln\sqrt{x}}{x}\,dx$ c $\int \frac{\ln\sqrt{3x}}{2x}\,dx$ d $\int \frac{x^2 + \ln(x^2)}{x}\,dx$

7.4 Substitution and definite integrals

Assuming the function is continuous over the interval of integration, then exchanging the limits for x by the corresponding limits for u will save you having to substitute back after the integration process.

Example 10

Evaluate $\int_3^5 4x\sqrt{x^2 - 9}\,dx$.

Let $u = x^2 - 9$. Then $du = 2x\,dx$.

Limits: $\begin{cases} x = 3 \Rightarrow u = 3^2 - 9 = 0 \\ x = 5 \Rightarrow u = 5^2 - 9 = 16 \end{cases}$

$$I = \int_3^5 4x\sqrt{x^2 - 9}\,dx = \int_0^{16} 2\sqrt{u}\,du = \int_0^{16} 2u^{\frac{1}{2}}\,du = \left[\frac{4}{3}u^{\frac{3}{2}}\right]_0^{16}$$

$$= \tfrac{4}{3}(\sqrt{16})^3 - \tfrac{4}{3}(\sqrt{0})^3 = \tfrac{4}{3} \times 64 = \frac{256}{3} = 85\tfrac{1}{3}$$

Example 11

Evaluate $\int_0^{\frac{\pi}{2}} \cos x \sin^3 x\,dx$.

Let $u = \sin x$. Then $du = \cos x\,dx$.

Limits: $\begin{cases} x = 0 \Rightarrow u = \sin 0 = 0 \\ x = \frac{\pi}{2} \Rightarrow u = \sin\frac{\pi}{2} = 1 \end{cases}$

$$I = \int_0^{\frac{\pi}{2}} \cos x \sin^3 x\,dx = \int_0^1 u^3\,du = \left[\frac{u^4}{4}\right]_0^1$$

$$= \frac{1}{4} - \frac{0}{4} = \frac{1}{4}$$

Exercise 7.4

1 Evaluate these definite integrals using the substitution suggested.

a $\int_0^2 (x-2)(x^2-4x-5)^2\,dx$ [let $u = x^2 - 4x - 5$]

b $\int_{-1}^1 3x^2(1-x^3)^3\,dx$ [let $u = 1 - x^3$]

c $\int_0^1 x\sqrt{1-x^2}\,dx$ [let $u = 1 - x^2$]

d $\int_3^4 (2x+1)\sqrt{(x-3)(x+4)}\,dx$ [let $u = (x-3)(x+4)$]

e $\int_0^1 \frac{x+1}{x^2+2x+3}\,dx$ [let $u = x^2 + 2x + 3$]

f $\int_1^9 \frac{2\sqrt{x}+3}{\sqrt{x}}\,dx$ [let $u = 2\sqrt{x} + 3$]

g $\int_{\frac{\pi}{4}}^{\frac{\pi}{2}} \frac{\cos x}{\sin^3 x}\,dx$ [let $u = \sin x$]

h $\int_{\ln 2}^{\ln 5} e^x\sqrt{e^x-1}\,dx$ [let $u^2 = e^x - 1$]

i $\int_e^{e^2} \frac{dx}{x\ln x^3}$ [let $u = \ln x$]

j $\int_0^{\pi} \frac{\cos x - \sin x}{\cos x + \sin x}\,dx$ [let $u = \cos x + \sin x$]

k $\int_0^{\frac{\pi}{2}} \sin^2 x\cos^3 x\,dx$ [let $u = \sin x$]

l $\int_0^{\frac{\pi}{2}} \frac{\cos x}{1+\sin^2 x}\,dx$ [let $u = \sin x$ then let $u = \tan v$ *or* let $\sin x = \tan v$]

m $\int_0^{\frac{\pi}{3}} \sin^7 x\,dx$ [let $u = \cos x$]

n $\int_0^{\frac{\pi}{4}} \cos^5 x\,dx$ [let $u = \sin x$]

o $\int_0^{\frac{\pi}{4}} \sec^2 x\sqrt{3\tan x + 1}\,dx$ [let $u = \tan x$]

2 Find these integrals, evaluating where limits are given.
Suitable substitutions have been suggested.

a $\int_e^{e^3} \frac{(2+\ln x)^3}{x}\,dx$ [$u = 2 + \ln x$]

b $\int_0^{\frac{\pi^2}{16}} \frac{\sec^2\sqrt{x}}{\sqrt{x}}\,dx$ [$u^2 = x$]

c $\int \frac{x}{\sqrt{3+2x}}\,dx$ [$u^2 = 3 + 2x$]

d $\int \frac{3\,dx}{x(5\ln x + 4)^2}$ [$u = 5\ln x + 4$]

e $\int_4^9 \frac{2}{3+\sqrt{x}}\,dx$ [$u - 3 = \sqrt{x}$]

f $\int 2\sin x\,(2 - 3\cos x)^5\,dx$ [$u = 2 - 3\cos x$]

g $\int \frac{3}{\sqrt{9-x^2}}\,dx$ [$x = 3\sin u$]

h $\int_5^{10} \frac{x-5}{x-4}\,dx$ [$u = x - 4$]

i $\int \frac{e^{\frac{1}{x}}}{x^2}\,dx$ [$u = e^{\frac{1}{x}}$]

j $\int_0^{\sqrt{3}} \frac{x}{(4-x^2)^{\frac{3}{2}}}\,dx$ [$u^2 = 4 - x^2$]

7.5 Using standard substitutions

Some substitutions are so common that they can be treated as *standards* and, when their form is established, their integrals can be written without further ado.
Let $F(x)$ be the antiderivative of $f(x)$.

Form 1

$$\int f(ax+b)\,\mathrm{d}x = \frac{1}{a}F(ax+b)+c$$

Proof

Let $u = ax + b$. Thus $\mathrm{d}u = a\,\mathrm{d}x \Rightarrow \mathrm{d}x = \frac{\mathrm{d}u}{a}$.

The substitution gives $\int f(ax+b)\,\mathrm{d}x = \frac{1}{a}\int f(u)\,\mathrm{d}u = \frac{1}{a}F(u)+c$.

Substituting back: $\int f(ax+b)\,\mathrm{d}x = \frac{1}{a}F(ax+b)+c$ as required.

Example 12

Find $\int \sin(3x-1)\,\mathrm{d}x$

Comparing with the standard form, $\int \sin(3x-1)\,\mathrm{d}x = -\frac{1}{3}\cos(3x-1)+c$

Form 2

$$\int f'(x)f(x)\,\mathrm{d}x = \frac{1}{2}(f(x))^2+c$$

Proof

Let $u = f(x)$. Thus $\mathrm{d}u = f'(x)\,\mathrm{d}x$.

The substitution gives $\int f'(x)f(x)\,\mathrm{d}x = \int u\,\mathrm{d}u = \frac{1}{2}u^2+c$.

Substituting back: $\int f'(x)f(x)\,\mathrm{d}x = \frac{1}{2}(f(x))^2+c$ as required.

Example 13

Find $\int 3\sin(3x-1)\cos(3x-1)\,\mathrm{d}x$

Comparing with the standard form, $\int 3\sin(3x-1)\cos(3x-1)\,\mathrm{d}x = \frac{1}{2}\sin^2(3x-1)+c$

Form 3

$$\int \frac{f'(x)}{f(x)}\,\mathrm{d}x = \ln|f(x)|+c$$

Proof

Let $u = f(x)$. Thus $\mathrm{d}u = f'(x)\,\mathrm{d}x$.

The substitution gives $\int \frac{f'(x)}{f(x)}\,\mathrm{d}x = \int \frac{\mathrm{d}u}{u} = \ln|u|+c$.

Substituting back: $\int \frac{f'(x)}{f(x)}\,\mathrm{d}x = \ln|f(x)|+c$ as required.

Example 14

Find $\int \frac{x}{1+3x^2}\,dx$

Comparing with the standard form, $\int \frac{x}{1+3x^2}\,dx = \frac{1}{6}\int \frac{6x}{1+3x^2}\,dx = \frac{1}{6}\ln|1+3x^2| + c$

Exercise 7.5

1 State the integrals of each of these.

a $\int \sqrt[3]{3x-4}\,dx$ b $\int \sin(3-7x)\,dx$ c $\int \sec^2(2x-5)\,dx$ d $\int e^{1-6x}\,dx$

e $\int (8x+1)^{-1}\,dx$ f $\int (\sin(2x+1)+\cos(1-x))\,dx$ g $\int (e^{-x}+(3-x)^{-1})\,dx$

2 a Given that $\int \cot^2 x\,dx = -\cot x - x + c$, state $\int \cot^2(2x-1)\,dx$.

b Given that $\int \operatorname{cosec} x\,dx = \ln|\operatorname{cosec} x - \cot x| + c$, state $\int \operatorname{cosec}(4-3x)\,dx$.

3 State the integrals of each of these.

a $\int (2x+3)(x^2+3x+4)\,dx$ b $\int \sin x\cos x\,dx$ c $\int \frac{\ln x}{x}\,dx$

d $\int e^x(e^x+1)\,dx$ e $\int \tan x\sec^2 x\,dx$ f $\int (\cos x+\sin x)(\cos x-\sin x)\,dx$

g $\int (e^x+e^{-x})(e^x-e^{-x})\,dx$ h $\int (x^2+\tan x)(2x+\sec^2 x)\,dx$

4 It is given that $\sin 2x = 2\sin x\cos x$.

a Use Form 1 to find $\int \sin 2x\,dx$.

b Use Form 2 to find $\int 2\sin x\cos x\,dx$.

c Rationalise the apparent discrepancy.

5 Integrate

a $\frac{3x^2+4x-4}{x^3+2x^2-4x+1}$ b $\frac{2\cos 2x}{\sin 2x}$ c $\frac{3}{x+1}+\frac{2}{2x-1}$ d $\frac{1+e^x}{x+e^x}$

e $\frac{\sec^2 x}{\tan x}$ f $\frac{x^{-1}}{\ln x}$ g $\frac{3^x\ln 3}{3+3^x}$ h $\frac{x}{x^2-1}+\frac{x^2}{x^3-1}+\frac{x^3}{x^4-1}$

7.6 Using inverse trigonometric functions

We know from a previous chapter that $\frac{d}{dx}\sin^{-1}x = \frac{1}{\sqrt{1-x^2}}$.

From this we get $\int \frac{dx}{\sqrt{1-x^2}} = \sin^{-1}x + c$.

In general we have $\int \frac{dx}{\sqrt{a^2-x^2}} = \sin^{-1}\left(\frac{x}{a}\right) + c$.

Proof

$$\int \frac{dx}{\sqrt{a^2-x^2}} = \int \frac{dx}{a\sqrt{1-\left(\frac{x}{a}\right)^2}} = \frac{1}{a}\int \frac{dx}{\sqrt{1-\left(\frac{x}{a}\right)^2}} = \frac{1}{a}\cdot a\cdot\sin^{-1}\left(\frac{x}{a}\right) + c = \sin^{-1}\left(\frac{x}{a}\right) + c$$

Example 15

Find $\int \frac{dx}{\sqrt{5 - x^2}}$.

Comparing this with the 'standard', we see that $a = \sqrt{5}$, thus $\int \frac{dx}{\sqrt{5 - x^2}} = \sin^{-1}\left(\frac{x}{\sqrt{5}}\right) + c$.

Example 16

Find $\int \frac{dx}{\sqrt{5 - 2x^2}}$.

$$\int \frac{dx}{\sqrt{5 - 2x^2}} = \int \frac{dx}{\sqrt{2}\sqrt{\frac{5}{2} - x^2}} = \frac{1}{\sqrt{2}} \int \frac{dx}{\sqrt{\frac{5}{2} - x^2}}$$

Comparing this with the 'standard', we see that $a = \sqrt{\frac{5}{2}}$, thus $\int \frac{dx}{\sqrt{5 - 2x^2}} = \frac{1}{\sqrt{2}} \sin^{-1}\left(\sqrt{\frac{2}{5}}\right) x + c$.

Example 17

Find $\int \frac{dx}{\sqrt{5 - 2(3x + 2)^2}}$.

Using $\int f(x)\, dx = F(x) + c \Rightarrow \int f(ax + b)\, dx = \frac{1}{a} F(ax + b) + c$ [Form 1 above]

$$\int \frac{dx}{\sqrt{5 - 2(3x + 2)^2}} = \frac{1}{3\sqrt{2}} \sin^{-1}\left(\sqrt{\frac{2}{5}}(3x + 2)\right) + c$$

We also found that $\frac{d}{dx} \tan^{-1} x = \frac{1}{x^2 + 1}$.

From this we get $\int \frac{dx}{x^2 + 1} = \tan^{-1} x + c$.

In general we have $\int \frac{dx}{x^2 + a^2} = \frac{1}{a} \tan^{-1}\left(\frac{x}{a}\right) + c$.

Example 18

Find **a** $\int \frac{dx}{4 + x^2}$ **b** $\int \frac{dx}{4 + 2x^2}$ **c** $\int \frac{dx}{4 + (3x + 2)^2}$

a Comparing with the 'standard', we see $a = \sqrt{4} = 2$.

$$\int \frac{dx}{4 + x^2} = \frac{1}{2} \tan^{-1}\left(\frac{x}{2}\right) + c$$

b $\int \frac{dx}{4 + 2x^2} = \frac{1}{2} \int \frac{dx}{2 + x^2}$

Comparing with the 'standard', we see $a = \sqrt{2}$.

$$\frac{1}{2} \int \frac{dx}{2 + x^2} = \frac{1}{2\sqrt{2}} \tan^{-1}\left(\frac{x}{\sqrt{2}}\right) + c$$

c $\int \frac{dx}{4 + x^2} = \frac{1}{2} \tan^{-1}\left(\frac{x}{2}\right) + c \Rightarrow \int \frac{dx}{4 + (3x + 2)^2} = \frac{1}{3} \cdot \frac{1}{2} \tan^{-1}\left(\frac{3x + 2}{2}\right) + c = \frac{1}{6} \tan^{-1}\left(\frac{3x + 2}{2}\right) + c$

Example 19

Find $\int \frac{x+3}{4+x^2}\,dx$.

$$\int \frac{x+3}{4+x^2}\,dx = \int \frac{x}{4+x^2}\,dx + \int \frac{3}{4+x^2}\,dx = \frac{1}{2}\int \frac{2x}{4+x^2}\,dx + 3\int \frac{1}{4+x^2}\,dx$$

Note the adjustment to the first term to make the numerator the derivative of the denominator. The integral of each term is now apparent.

$$\frac{1}{2}\int \frac{2x}{4+x^2}\,dx + 3\int \frac{1}{4+x^2}\,dx = \frac{1}{2}\ln(4+x^2) + \frac{3}{2}\tan^{-1}\left(\frac{x}{2}\right) + c$$

Exercise 7.6

1 Find

a $\int \frac{dx}{\sqrt{16-x^2}}$ b $\int \frac{dx}{\sqrt{3-x^2}}$ c $\int \frac{dx}{\sqrt{32-2x^2}}$ d $\int \frac{dx}{\sqrt{5-3x^2}}$

2 Find

a $\int \frac{dx}{49+x^2}$ b $\int \frac{dx}{6+x^2}$ c $\int \frac{dx}{3x^2+75}$ d $\int \frac{dx}{5+2x^2}$

3 Evaluate

a $\int_0^3 \frac{dx}{\sqrt{36-x^2}}$ b $\int_0^1 \frac{dx}{\sqrt{3-x^2}}$ c $\int_{-1}^1 \frac{dx}{\sqrt{12-3x^2}}$ d $\int_0^1 \frac{dx}{\sqrt{3-2x^2}}$

4 Find correct to 3 dp where appropriate

a $\int_{-3}^3 \frac{dx}{81+x^2}$ b $\int_0^2 \frac{dx}{5+x^2}$ c $\int_5^{10} \frac{dx}{4x^2+100}$ d $\int_0^6 \frac{dx}{7+3x^2}$

5 Find

a $\int \frac{x-5}{25+x^2}\,dx$ b $\int \frac{7-x}{16+x^2}\,dx$ c $\int \frac{x-2}{x^2+2}\,dx$ d $\int \frac{3x-1}{x^2+49}\,dx$

6 a i Express x^2+2x+5 in the form $(x+a)^2+b$.

ii Find $\int \frac{dx}{x^2+4}$.

iii Hence find $\int \frac{dx}{x^2+2x+5}$

using $\int f(x)\,dx = F(x)+c \Rightarrow \int f(ax+b)\,dx = \frac{1}{a}F(ax+b)+c$.

b In a similar manner find

i $\int \frac{dx}{x^2+6x+25}$ ii $\int \frac{dx}{x^2+4x+13}$ iii $\int \frac{dx}{x^2+8x+18}$

7 Evaluate to 3 sf

a $\int_1^4 \frac{dx}{x^2+4x+13}$ b $\int_0^1 \frac{dx}{x^2+8x+52}$ c $\int_{-1}^1 \frac{dx}{x^2+4x+26}$

7.7 Integrating rational functions

We can make use of the skills attained when studying partial fractions to help us prepare functions for integration.

Example 20

Find $\int \frac{5x + 11}{(x + 1)(x + 3)} \, dx$. [Where the denominator has distinct linear factors.]

Using partial fractions,

$$\int \frac{5x + 11}{(x + 1)(x + 3)} \, dx = \int \frac{3}{x + 1} + \frac{2}{x + 3} \, dx$$

$$= 3 \ln|x + 1| + 2 \ln|x + 3| + c$$

Note: this answer can be simplified using the laws of logs and letting $c = \ln k$

$$= \ln|x + 1|^3 + \ln|x + 3|^2 + \ln k = \ln|k(x + 1)^3 (x + 3)^2|$$

$$\frac{5x + 11}{(x + 1)(x + 3)} = \frac{A}{x + 1} + \frac{B}{x + 3}$$

$$\Rightarrow 5x + 11 = A(x + 3) + B(x + 1)$$

$$x = -1 \Rightarrow 6 = 2A \Rightarrow A = 3$$

$$x = -3 \Rightarrow -4 = -2B \Rightarrow B = 2$$

Example 21

Find $\int \frac{x^2 - 4x + 13}{(x + 1)(x - 2)^2} \, dx$. [Where the denominator has a repeated linear factor.]

Using partial fractions,

$$\int \frac{x^2 - 4x + 13}{(x + 1)(x - 2)^2} \, dx = \int \frac{2}{x + 1} - \frac{1}{x - 2} + \frac{3}{(x - 2)^2} \, dx$$

$$= 2 \ln|x + 1| - \ln|x - 2| - \frac{3}{x - 2} + c$$

This answer can be simplified using the laws of logs.

$$= \ln|x + 1|^2 - \ln|x - 2| - \frac{3}{x - 2} + \ln k$$

$$= \ln\left|\frac{k(x + 1)^2}{x - 2}\right| - \frac{3}{x - 2}$$

$$\frac{x^2 - 4x + 13}{(x + 1)(x - 2)^2} = \frac{A}{(x + 1)} + \frac{B}{(x - 2)} + \frac{C}{(x - 2)^2}$$

$$\Rightarrow x^2 - 4x + 13 = A(x - 2)^2 + B(x + 1)(x - 2) + C(x + 1)$$

$$x = -1 \Rightarrow 18 = 9A \Rightarrow A = 2$$

$$x = 2 \Rightarrow 9 = 3C \Rightarrow C = 3$$

$$x = 0 \Rightarrow 13 = 4A - 2B + C = 8 - 2B + 3$$

$$\Rightarrow B = -1$$

Example 22

Find $\int \frac{2x^2 + 3x + 5}{(x - 1)(x^2 + 4)} \, dx$. [Where the denominator has an irreducible quadratic factor.]

Using partial fractions,

$$\int \frac{5x^2 - 2x + 7}{(x - 1)(x^2 + 4)} \, dx = \int \frac{2}{x - 1} + \frac{3x + 1}{x^2 + 4} \, dx$$

$$= \int \frac{2}{x - 1} \, dx + \frac{3}{2} \int \frac{2x}{x^2 + 4} \, dx + \int \frac{1}{x^2 + 4} \, dx$$

$$= 2 \ln|x - 1| + \frac{3}{2} \ln|x^2 + 4| + \frac{1}{2} \tan^{-1}\left(\frac{x}{2}\right) + c$$

$$\frac{5x^2 - 2x + 7}{(x - 1)(x^2 + 4)} = \frac{A}{x - 1} + \frac{Bx + C}{x^2 + 4}$$

$$\Rightarrow 5x^2 - 2x + 7 = A(x^2 + 4) + (Bx + C)(x - 1)$$

$$x = 1 \Rightarrow 10 = 5A \Rightarrow A = 2$$

$$x = 0 \Rightarrow 7 = 4A - C \Rightarrow 7 = 8 - C \Rightarrow C = 1$$

$$x = -1 \Rightarrow 14 = 5A + 2B - 2C \Rightarrow B = 3$$

Example 23

Find $\int \frac{3x^3 - 2x^2 - 4}{x^2 - x - 2}\,dx$. [When the numerator is of the same or greater order than the denominator.]

Perform a division.

This gives $\int \frac{3x^3 - 2x^2 - 4}{x^2 - x - 2}\,dx = \int 3x + 1 + \frac{7x - 2}{x^2 - x - 2}\,dx$

$= \int (3x + 1)\,dx + \int \frac{7x - 2}{(x + 1)(x - 2)}\,dx$

Using partial fractions,

$= \int (3x + 1)\,dx + \int \frac{3}{(x + 1)}\,dx + \int \frac{4}{(x - 2)}\,dx$

$= x + \frac{3}{2}x^2 + 3\ln|x + 1| + 4\ln|x - 2| + c$

$$
\begin{array}{r|l}
 & 3x + 1 \\
x^2 - x - 2 & 3x^3 - 2x^2 \quad - 4 \\
 & 3x^3 - 3x^2 - 6x \\
 & x^2 + 6x - 4 \\
 & x^2 - x - 2 \\
 & 7x - 2
\end{array}
$$

Exercise 7.7

1 Integrate each function by first resolving it into partial fractions.

a $\frac{3x + 7}{(x + 2)(x + 3)}$ b $\frac{3x + 9}{(x - 1)(x + 5)}$ c $\frac{2x - 7}{(x - 2)(x - 3)}$

d $\frac{13x + 3}{(3x + 1)(x - 1)}$ e $\frac{1}{(x - 1)(x + 2)}$ f $\frac{3}{(x - 5)(x + 1)}$

2 Integrate each function by first resolving it into partial fractions.
You will have to factorise the denominator first.

a $\frac{x - 1}{3x^2 - x}$ b $\frac{x + 5}{2x^2 + 3x + 1}$ c $\frac{5x - 2}{x^2 - 3x + 2}$ d $\frac{x + 9}{x^2 - 9}$

3 Integrate each function by first resolving it into partial fractions.

a $\frac{3x^2 - 1}{(x + 1)(x - 1)^2}$ b $\frac{2x^2 + 11x + 19}{(x - 1)(x + 3)^2}$ c $\frac{x^2 - 7x + 8}{x(x - 2)^2}$

d $\frac{1}{(x - 1)(x - 2)^2}$ e $\frac{x}{(x - 1)(x + 1)^2}$ f $\frac{x + 1}{2x(x + 3)^2}$

4 Integrate each function by first resolving it into partial fractions.

a $\frac{1}{x^3 + 2x^2 + x}$ b $\frac{x}{x^3 + 3x^2 - 4}$ c $\frac{3x + 1}{4x^3 - 4x^2 + x}$

5 Find

a $\int \frac{2x^2 + 1}{(x + 1)(x^2 + 2)}\,dx$ b $\int \frac{5x^2 + 3}{x(x^2 + 1)}\,dx$ c $\int \frac{3x^2 + 5}{(x - 1)(x^2 + 3)}\,dx$

d $\int \frac{1}{x(x^2 + 5)}\,dx$ e $\int \frac{x}{(x - 2)(x^2 + 3)}\,dx$

6 Perform a division, then integrate.

a $\int \frac{x^2 + 2x - 1}{x^2 - 1}\,dx$ b $\int \frac{6x^2 + 20x - 8}{2x^2 + 5x - 3}\,dx$ c $\int \frac{2x^3 + 3x^2 - 3x + 2}{2x^2 + x - 1}\,dx$

d $\int \frac{x^3 + 2x^2 - 4x + 3}{(x + 1)(x - 1)^2}\,dx$ e $\int \frac{x^4 + 5x^2 + 2x + 6}{x\,(x^2 + 2)}\,dx$ f $\int \frac{x^3 + 6x + 1}{x(x^2 + 5)}\,dx$

7 a Express $x^2 + 2x + 5$ in the form $(x + a)^2 + b$.

b Find $\int \frac{dx}{x^2 + 4}$. c Hence find $\int \frac{dx}{x^2 + 2x + 5}$.

d Hence find

i $\displaystyle\int \frac{x^2 + 3x + 4}{(x - 1)(x^2 + 2x + 5)}\,dx$ **ii** $\displaystyle\int \frac{x^2 + x + 4}{(x - 1)(x^2 + 2x + 5)}\,dx$

iii $\displaystyle\int \frac{2x^2 + x + 5}{(x - 1)(x^2 + 2x + 5)}\,dx$ [see the investigation that follows]

Investigation

How would you integrate a function of the form $f(x) = \dfrac{ax + b}{x^2 + cx + d}$ where $x^2 + cx + d$ is an irreducible quadratic?

1 Consider the function as being in the form $\dfrac{g(x)}{h(x)}$ where $g(x)$ is linear and $h(x)$ is quadratic. Rearrange $g(x)$ so that it looks like $Ah'(x) + B$ with $A, B \in \mathbb{R}$.

2 Split the fraction up: $\dfrac{g(x)}{h(x)} = \dfrac{Ah'(x) + B}{h(x)} = \dfrac{Ah'(x)}{h(x)} + \dfrac{B}{h(x)}$

3 The first term has an integral $\displaystyle\int \frac{Ah'(x)}{h(x)}\,dx = A\ln|h(x)| + c_1$

4 The denominator of the second term, $h(x)$, can be manipulated into the form $(x + a)^2 + b$. Then the integral of the second term is

$$\int \frac{B}{(x + a)^2 + b}\,dx = B \cdot \frac{1}{\sqrt{b}}\tan^{-1}\left(\frac{x + a}{\sqrt{b}}\right) + c_2$$

Example 24

Integrate the function $f(x) = \dfrac{g(x)}{h(x)} = \dfrac{x + 3}{x^2 + 4x + 13}$

Now, $h'(x) = 2x + 4$ so we can make $g(x) = \frac{1}{2}(2x + 4) + 1$.

$$f(x) = \frac{\frac{1}{2}(2x + 4) + 1}{x^2 + 4x + 13} = \frac{\frac{1}{2}(2x + 4)}{x^2 + 4x + 13} + \frac{1}{x^2 + 4x + 13} = \frac{\frac{1}{2}(2x + 4)}{x^2 + 4x + 13} + \frac{1}{(x + 2)^2 + 9}$$

$$\int f(x)\,dx = \int \frac{\frac{1}{2}(2x + 4)}{x^2 + 4x + 13}\,dx + \int \frac{1}{(x + 2)^2 + 9}\,dx$$

$$= \frac{1}{2}\ln|x^2 + 4x + 13| + \frac{1}{3}\tan^{-1}\left(\frac{x + 2}{3}\right) + c$$

8 Integrate these rational functions.

a $\dfrac{x}{x^2 + 6x + 25}$ **b** $\dfrac{3x + 4}{x^2 + 8x + 20}$ **c** $\dfrac{5x - 3}{x^2 + 10x + 26}$

d Now repeat Question 7d using a different method.

7.8 Integration by parts

Consider the three functions $f(x)$, $g(x)$ and $h(x)$ where $h(x)$ is the antiderivative of $g(x)$, that is $h(x) = \int g(x)\,dx$ and $h'(x) = g(x)$.

Use the product rule to differentiate $f(x)h(x)$:

$$\frac{d}{dx}(f(x)h(x)) = f'(x)\,h(x) + f(x)h'(x)$$

Integrate:

$$f(x)h(x) = \int f'(x)\,h(x)\,dx + \int f(x)h'(x)\,dx$$

Rearrange the terms:

$$\int f(x)h'(x)\,dx = f(x)h(x) - \int h(x)\,f'(x)\,dx$$

Substitute $h(x) = \int g(x)\,dx$ and $h'(x) = g(x)$:

$$\int f(x)g(x)\,dx = f(x)\int g(x)\,dx - \int\left[\int g(x)\,dx\right] f'(x)\,dx$$

Using this theorem we can transform the integral of a product of functions – and hope that we end up with a simpler integral. This is referred to as 'integration by parts'.

When selecting which function to call $f(x)$, we normally look for the one that becomes simpler when differentiated.

Having said that, we might not be able to integrate one of the functions – in which case we should not choose it to be $g(x)$.

Example 25

Integrate $x \cos x$.

Both the two functions, x and $\cos x$, can be integrated but x becomes simpler when differentiated.

So let $f(x) = x$ and $g(x) = \cos x$. This gives $f'(x) = 1$ and $\int g(x)\,dx = \sin x$.

So using $\int f(x)g(x)\,dx = f(x)\int g(x)\,dx - \int\left[\int g(x)dx\right] f'(x)\,dx$

$$\int x\cos x\,dx = x \cdot \sin x - \int \sin x \cdot 1\,dx = x\sin x - \int \sin x\,dx$$
$$= x\sin x + \cos x + c$$

Example 26

Find $\int e^x(2x + 1)\,dx$.

A quick check lets you see that both functions integrate but only $(2x + 1)$ simplifies when differentiated.

So $f(x) = 2x + 1 \Rightarrow f'(x) = 2$ and $\int g(x)\,dx = e^x$.

So $\int e^x(2x+1)\,dx = (2x+1)\cdot e^x - \int e^x \cdot 2\,dx = e^x(2x+1) - 2\int e^x\,dx$

$= e^x(2x+1) - 2e^x + c$

If desired, this can be simplified to give $= e^x(2x - 1) + c$.

Example 27

Find $\int x^3 \sin x\,dx$

$f(x) = x^3 \Rightarrow f'(x) = 3x^2$ and $\int g(x)\,dx = -\cos x$

$$\int x^3 \sin x\,dx = -x^3\cos x - \int -\cos x \cdot 3x^2\,dx = -x^3\cos x + 3\int x^2\cos x\,dx$$

We have simplified, but not solved, the problem.

Use the theorem again on the integral in the second term – this time using $f(x) = x^2$.

$$\int x^3\sin x\,dx = -x^3\cos x + 3\left[x^2\sin x - \int \sin x \cdot 2x\,dx\right] = -x^3\cos x + 3x^2\sin x - 6\int x\sin x\,dx$$

Applying the theorem a third time gives

$$\int x^3\sin x\,dx = -x^3\cos x + 3x^2\sin x - 6\left[-x\cos x - \int -\cos x \cdot 1\,dx\right]$$
$$= -x^3\cos x + 3x^2\sin x + 6x\cos x - 6\int \cos x\,dx$$

The remaining integral part is a 'standard', giving us

$$\int x^3\sin x\,dx = -x^3\cos x + 3x^2\sin x + 6x\cos x - 6\sin x + c$$

Exercise 7.8

1 Integrate each function using integration by parts.

a $x \sin x$ b xe^x c $x \ln x$ [Hint: let $f(x) = \ln x$]

d $3x \sec^2 x$ e $x\sqrt{x+1}$ f $(3x+2)\cos x$

g $(4-x)e^{2x}$ h $(2x+1)\ln x$ i xe^{-x}

j $x^{-5}\ln x$ k $\sqrt{x}\ln x$ l $\sin x \ln(\cos x)$

2 Find these integrals, using integration by parts.

a $\int (2x+1)\sec^2 2x \, dx$ b $\int (3x^2+2x-2)\ln(x+1)\, dx$ c $\int (3x^2-1)\ln(x-1)\, dx$

d $\int (1-4x)\sin(2x-3)\, dx$ e $\int (9x+1)e^{3x-1}\, dx$ f $\int \sqrt{x+1}\ln(x+1)\, dx$

g $\int (2x+1)e^{4-x}\, dx$ h $\int \sec^2 x \ln(\tan x)\, dx$

3 The trigonometric identities $\cos 2x = 1 - 2\sin^2 x = 2\cos^2 x - 1$ can be used to make certain integrals accessible.

a Express i $\sin^2 x$ ii $\cos^2 x$ in terms of $\cos 2x$.

b Find these integrals, using integration by parts.

i $\int x \sin^2 x \, dx$ ii $\int x \cos^2 x \, dx$

c i What do you get when you sum your answers to part b?

ii Could this have been deduced without performing the integrations?

4 Integrate by parts

a $x\tan^{-1} x$ [Hint: x^2 can be written as $(x^2+1)-1$]

b $x\sin^{-1} x$ [Hint: x^2 can be written as $1-(1-x^2)$]

c $x\cos^{-1} x$ [Hint: $\frac{d}{dx}\cos^{-1} x = \frac{-1}{\sqrt{1-x^2}}$]

5 Integrate by parts [you must apply the theorem more than once in each case]

a $x^2 \sin x$ b $x^3 \cos x$ c $x^3 e^x$ d $(x+1)^2 e^x$ e $x(\ln x)^2$

f $x(1-\ln x)^2$ g $(1-x)^2 e^{-x}$ h $\frac{x^2}{\sqrt{x+1}}$ i $\frac{x^3}{(x-1)^4}$ j $(x+1)^2\sqrt{x-1}$

6 Evaluate these definite integrals. [Use integration by parts.]

a $\int_0^{\pi} x \sin x \, dx$ b $\int_0^{e} xe^{3x}\, dx$ c $\int_0^{1} (2x+1)^2 e^{-x}\, dx$

d $\int_0^{\frac{\pi}{2}} x^2 \sin 2x \, dx$ e $\int_1^{5} x^3\sqrt{x-1}\, dx$ f $\int_0^{1} (x+1)(\ln(x+1))^2\, dx$

7.9 Special cases

If you are asked for $\int h(x)\, dx$ and you only know $h'(x)$, it can be useful to consider a factor of 1 as $f(x)$ in the context of integration by parts.

Example 28

Find $\int \ln x \, dx$.

We cannot immediately integrate $\ln x$, but we know its derivative.

$\int \ln x \, dx$ can be rewritten as $\int 1 \cdot \ln x \, dx$

Now let $f(x) = \ln x \Rightarrow f'(x) = \frac{1}{x}$ and $g(x) = 1 \Rightarrow \int g(x)\,dx = x$

So $\int \ln x\,dx = \ln x \cdot x - \int x \cdot \frac{1}{x}\,dx = x\ln x - \int 1\,dx = x\ln x - x + c$

Sometimes the desired integral reappears in your working.

Example 29

Find $\int \sin x \cos 3x\,dx$.

Neither function becomes simpler when differentiated and both can be integrated so either can be used as $f(x)$. However, choosing $\cos 3x$ will avoid fractions.

$$\int \sin x \cos 3x\,dx = \cos 3x \cdot -\cos x - \int -\cos x \cdot -3\sin 3x\,dx$$

$$= -\cos 3x \cos x - 3\int \cos x \sin 3x\,dx$$

Now you have chosen to connect $f(x)$ with the multiple-angle function, do not change your mind.

$$= -\cos 3x \cos x - 3\left[\sin x \sin 3x - \int \sin x \cdot 3\cos 3x\,dx\right]$$

$$\int \sin x \cos 3x\,dx = -\cos 3x \cos x - 3\sin x \sin 3x + 9\int \sin x \cos 3x\,dx$$

Note that the original integral has appeared on the right-hand side of the equation. Rearrange the equation to bring both terms containing the integral together.

$$-8\int \sin x \cos 3x\,dx = -\cos 3x \cos x - 3\sin x \sin 3x + c$$

$$\Rightarrow \int \sin x \cos 3x\,dx = \tfrac{1}{8}(\cos 3x \cos x + 3\sin x \sin 3x) + c$$

Sometimes introducing a factor of 1 *and* a reappearance of the original integral occurs.

Example 30

Find $\int \sqrt{1-x^2}\,dx$.

$$\int \sqrt{1-x^2}\,dx = \int 1\cdot(1-x^2)^{\frac{1}{2}}\,dx = x\cdot(1-x^2)^{\frac{1}{2}} - \int x\cdot\tfrac{1}{2}(1-x^2)^{-\frac{1}{2}}\cdot -2x\,dx$$

$$= x\cdot(1-x^2)^{\frac{1}{2}} + \int \frac{x^2}{\sqrt{1-x^2}}\,dx$$

$$= x\cdot(1-x^2)^{\frac{1}{2}} - \int \frac{(1-x^2)-1}{\sqrt{1-x^2}}\,dx = x\cdot(1-x^2)^{\frac{1}{2}} - \int \frac{(1-x^2)}{\sqrt{1-x^2}}\,dx + \int \frac{1}{\sqrt{1-x^2}}\,dx$$

$$\Rightarrow \int \sqrt{1-x^2}\,dx = x(1-x^2)^{\frac{1}{2}} - \int \sqrt{(1-x^2)}\,dx + \int \frac{1}{\sqrt{1-x^2}}\,dx$$

The integral has reappeared on the right-hand side.

$$\Rightarrow 2\int \sqrt{1-x^2}\,dx = x(1-x^2)^{\frac{1}{2}} + \int \frac{1}{\sqrt{1-x^2}}\,dx$$

$$\Rightarrow \int \sqrt{1-x^2}\,dx = \tfrac{1}{2}x(1-x^2)^{\frac{1}{2}} + \tfrac{1}{2}\sin^{-1}x + c$$

Exercise 7.9

1 Use integration by parts to find

a $\int \ln 3x \, dx$ b $\int \ln ax \, dx$ where a is a constant

c $\int \log_{10} x \, dx$ d $\int \sin^{-1} x \, dx$ e $\int \tan^{-1} x \, dx$

f $\int \ln (1 + x^2) \, dx$ g $\int (\ln x)^2 \, dx$ h $\int \ln (1 - x^2) dx$ [Hint: partial fractions]

2 Find the integral. [Note: look out for a reappearance of the original function.]

a $\int e^x \sin x \, dx$ b $\int e^{2x} \sin x \, dx$ c $\int e^x \sin 3x \, dx$ d $\int e^{2x} \sin 3x \, dx$

e $\int \sin 2x \cos x \, dx$ f $\int \cos x \cos 4x \, dx$ g $\int \sin x \sin 6x \, dx$ h $\int \sin 2x \cos 3x \, dx$

i $\int e^{-x} \sin x \, dx$ j $\dfrac{\cos 2x}{e^x}$ k $\dfrac{\sin 3x}{e^{2x}}$

3 Two functions, p and q, are defined such that $p'(x) = q(x)$ and $q'(x) = p(x)$.

a Find $\int p(x) \, q(x) \, dx$.

b Verify that $p(x) = \dfrac{e^x + e^{-x}}{2}$ and $q(x) = \dfrac{e^x - e^{-x}}{2}$ fit the definition.

c Verify your answer to part **a**.

4 a Show, by differentiation, that $\int \dfrac{dx}{\sqrt{x^2 - 1}} = \ln \left| x + \sqrt{x^2 - 1} \right|$. b Hence find $\int \sqrt{x^2 - 1} \, dx$.

7.10 Applications of integration

Integration has numerous applications.

Through its use in solving differential equations (see Chapter **8**), it can be used to model many situations, including rectilinear motion (see Chapter **11**). It can also be used to calculate areas, volumes and curve lengths and other geometric quantities, some of which we can examine here.

Application 1: Area between the curve of $y = f(x)$ and the x-axis

We examined this situation in the Higher course.

The shaded area between the curve $y = f(x)$ and the x-axis, A, is a function of x, the ordinate passing through P.

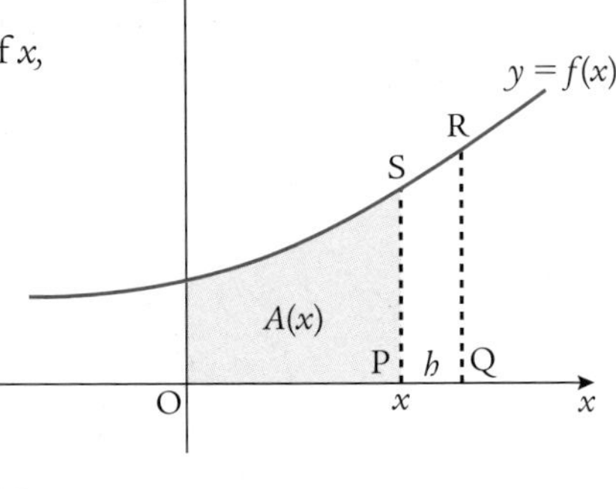

The area bound by the curve, the x-axis, PS and QR is $A(x + h) - A(x)$.

It can be approximated by a trapezium, the vertices having coordinates P$(x, 0)$, Q$(x + h, 0)$, R$(x + h, f(x + h))$, S$(x, f(x))$

The area of the trapezium can be computed as $\frac{h}{2}(f(x + h) + f(x))$

so $A(x + h) - A(x) \approx \frac{h}{2}(f(x + h) + f(x))$, tending to equality as h tends to zero.

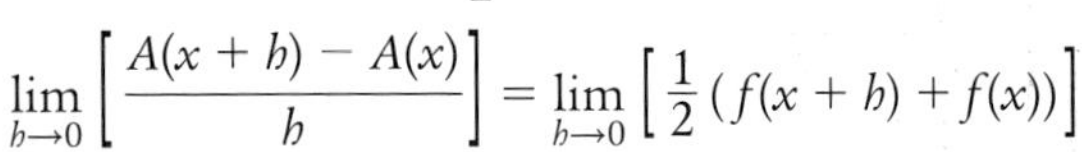

$$\lim_{h \to 0} \left[\frac{A(x + h) - A(x)}{h} \right] = \lim_{h \to 0} \left[\frac{1}{2}(f(x + h) + f(x)) \right]$$

Taking the limit we get $A'(x) = \frac{1}{2}[f(x) + f(x)] = f(x)$.

Integrating gives $A(x) = \int_0^x f(x) \, dx$.

The area, A, trapped between $x = a$ and $x = b$

$$A = A(b) - A(a) = \int_a^b f(x) \, dx$$

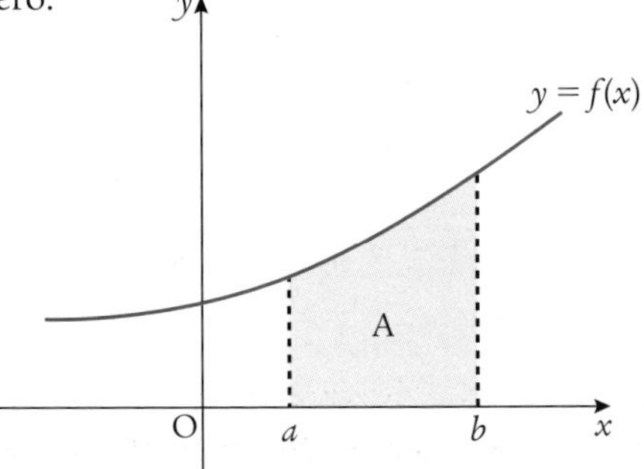

Application 2: Area between the curve of $y = f(x)$ and the y-axis

Using a similar argument we can use integration to calculate the area trapped between the curve and the y-axis.

The shaded area, B, trapped between $y = f(a)$ and $y = f(b)$ can be computed using

$$B = \int_{f(a)}^{f(b)} f^{-1}(y)\,dy$$

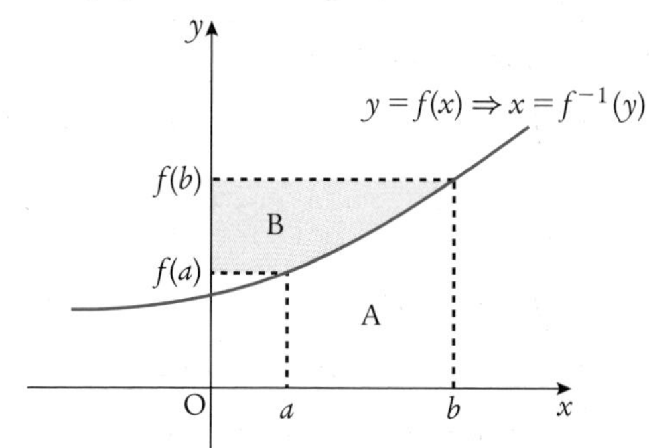

Integrals as the limit of a sum

An alternative way of looking at application 1 leads us to a more useful definition of the integral.

Consider the area under $y = f(x)$ between $x = a$ and $x = b$.

We split the interval $a \le x \le b$ into strips of width Δx (pronounced 'delta x' – it is equivalent to h in the arguments above). We can approximate the area under the curve as the sum of the areas of all the rectangles of width Δx and height $f(x)$.

The smaller we make Δx, the greater the number of strips and the better the approximation.

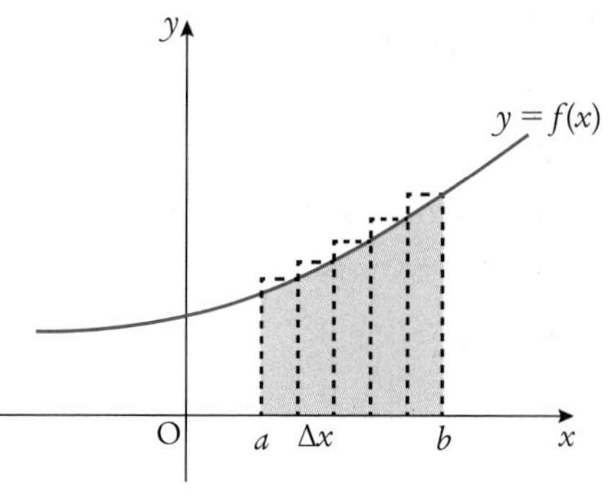

So the area under the curve is given by $\lim\limits_{\Delta x \to 0}\left(\sum\limits_{x=a}^{b} f(x)\Delta x\right)$. From above, we know this to be $\int_a^b f(x)\,dx$.

We can define the integral as the limit of a sum as Δx *tends to zero*.

$$\int_a^b f(x)\,dx = \lim_{\Delta x \to 0}\left(\sum_{x=a}^{b} f(x)\Delta x\right)$$

So if we can approximate a quantity by a sum of small elements, we should be able to find an integral that we can use to calculate the quantity accurately.

Application 3: Volume (revolved around the x-axis)

Consider that the function $y = f(x)$ is revolved around the x-axis between $x = a$ and $x = b$. A solid will be defined. Can we calculate its volume?

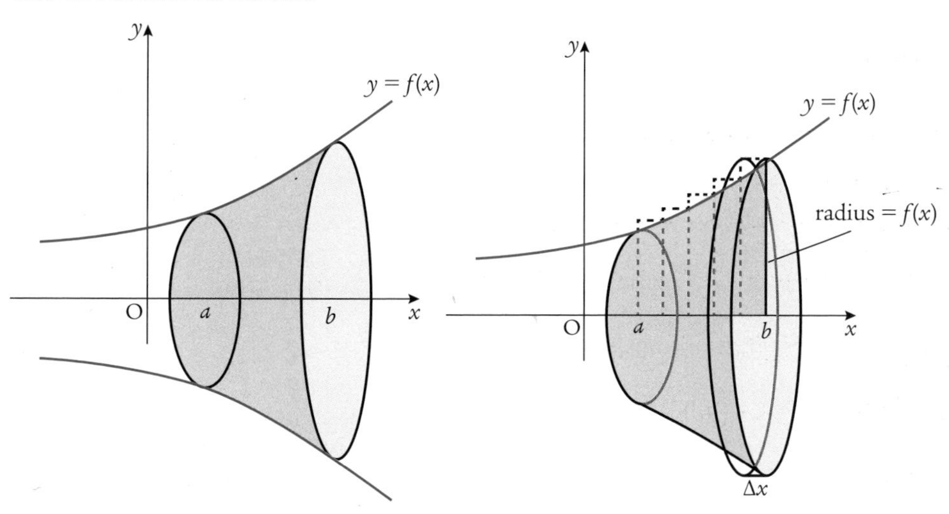

If we consider the area under $y = f(x)$ as a series of rectangles as before, then, as we revolve $f(x)$, each rectangle will trace out a cylinder. Using the formula for the volume of a cylinder, $V = \pi r^2 h$, we get the volume of one element, $V = \pi(f(x))^2\,\Delta x$.

Summing all the elements between $x = a$ and $x = b$ gives $\sum_{x=a}^{b} \pi(f(x))^2\,\Delta x$.

Now, taking the limit as Δx tends to zero: $V = \lim_{\Delta x \to 0} \sum_{x=a}^{b} \pi(f(x))^2\,\Delta x = \int_a^b \pi(f(x))^2\,dx$

This is often quoted as $V = \int_a^b \pi y^2\,dx$

– you must express y as a function of x before integrating.

Application 4: Volume (revolved around the y-axis)

By a similar argument, the volume of the solid generated by revolving $y = f(x)$ about the y-axis can be calculated using the formula $V = \int_{f(a)}^{f(b)} \pi(f^{-1}(y))^2\,dy$.

This is often quoted as $V = \int_{f(a)}^{f(b)} \pi x^2\,dy$

– you must express x as a function of y before integrating.

Exercise 7.10

1 The chart shows $y = \dfrac{1}{4\sqrt{4 - x^2}}$ in the interval $-\frac{\pi}{2} \le x \le \frac{\pi}{2}$.

Calculate the area trapped between the curve and the x-axis in this interval.

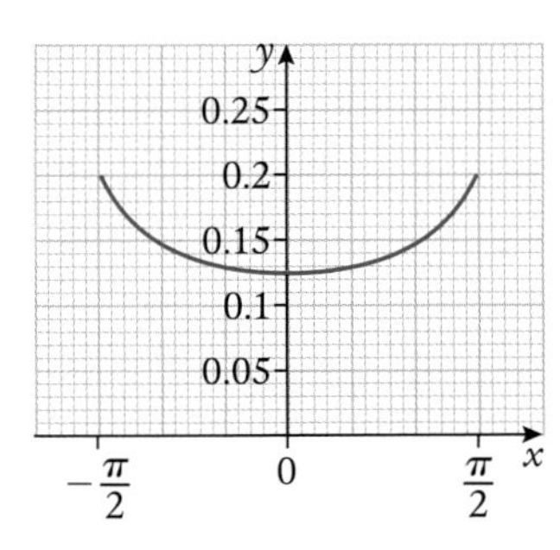

2 The graph shows $y = \dfrac{4\pi}{4x + 3\pi}$ and $y = \tan x$ in the interval $0 \le x \le \frac{\pi}{3}$.

a Show that the point of intersection of the two curves is $\left(\frac{\pi}{4}, 1\right)$.

b Find the area trapped between the two curves in this interval.

Reminder: this means you need to evaluate

$$\int_0^{\frac{\pi}{4}} \left(\frac{4\pi}{4x + 3\pi} - \tan x\right) dx + \int_{\frac{\pi}{4}}^{\frac{\pi}{3}} \left(\tan x - \frac{4\pi}{4x + 3\pi}\right) dx$$

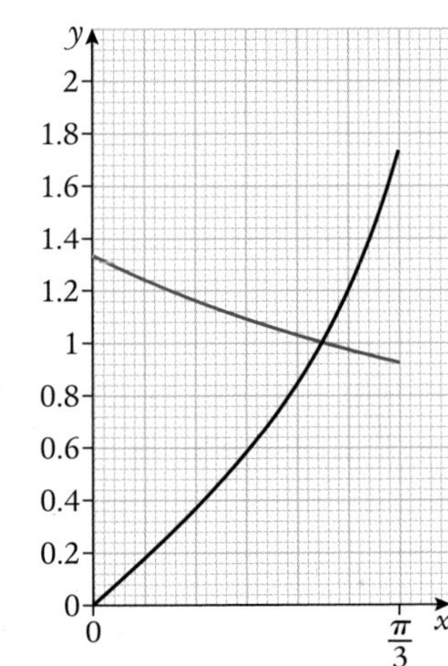

3 The graph shows $y = \cos x \sin^3 x$, $0 \le x \le \pi$.

Calculate the area trapped between the curve and the x-axis over this interval.

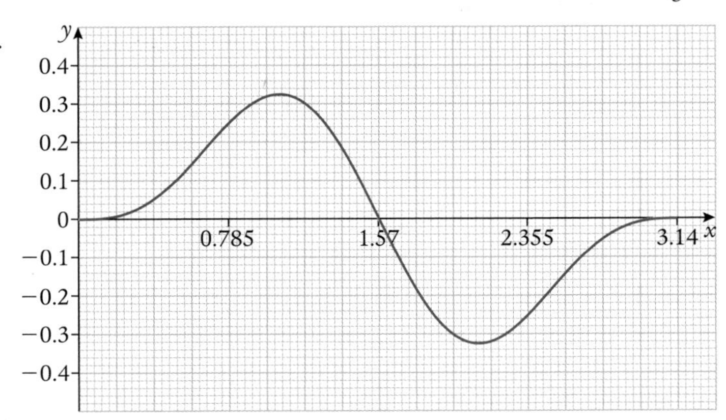

4 This is a sketch of $y = \cos x\, e^{\sin x}$, $0 \le x \le 2\pi$.

a Verify that it cuts the x-axis at $\frac{\pi}{2}$ and $\frac{3\pi}{2}$.

b Calculate the area trapped between the curve and the x-axis in this interval.

[Hint: make the substitution $u = \sin x$.]

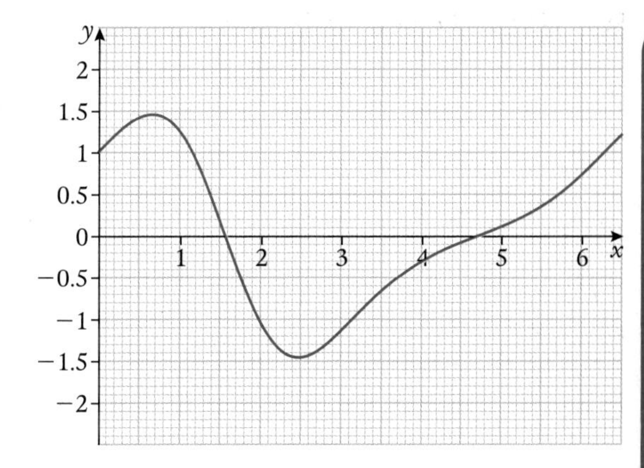

5 a Find where the curves $y = \dfrac{2x - 5}{(x - 4)(x - 1)}$ and $y = \dfrac{1}{(4 - x)}$ intersect in the interval $1.5 \le x \le 2.5$.

b Calculate the area trapped between the two curves in this interval.

6 The sketch shows $y = x^2 + 1$ close to the origin.

a State the y-values corresponding to $x = 2$ and $x = 3$.

b Express x in terms of y, considering the positive root only.

c Calculate the shaded area.

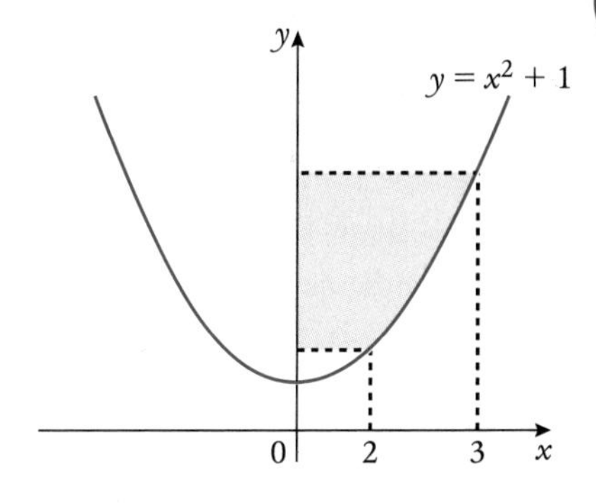

7 Calculate the area trapped between the function $y = \dfrac{\sqrt{x} + 1}{2}$ and the y-axis in the interval $1 \le x \le 9$.

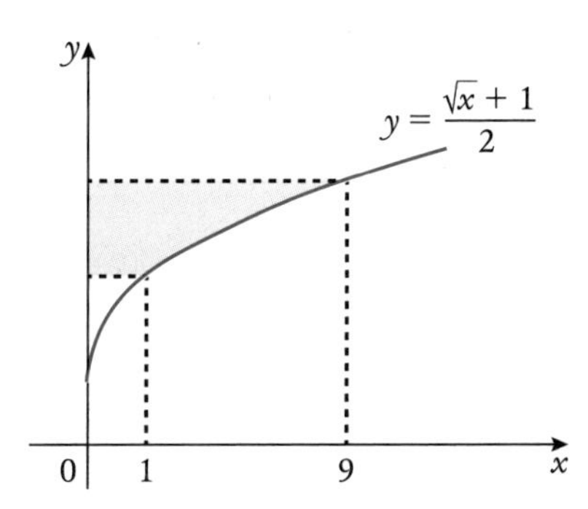

8 a State where $y = e^x$ crosses the y-axis.

b Sketch the curve in the interval $-1 \le x \le 1$.

c Calculate the area trapped between the y-axis and the curve $y = e^x$.

9 The sketch shows $y = \ln x$ and $y = x - 2$ close to the origin.

Calculate the shaded area trapped between $y = \ln x$, $y = x - 2$, $y = 1$ and $y = 0.5$.

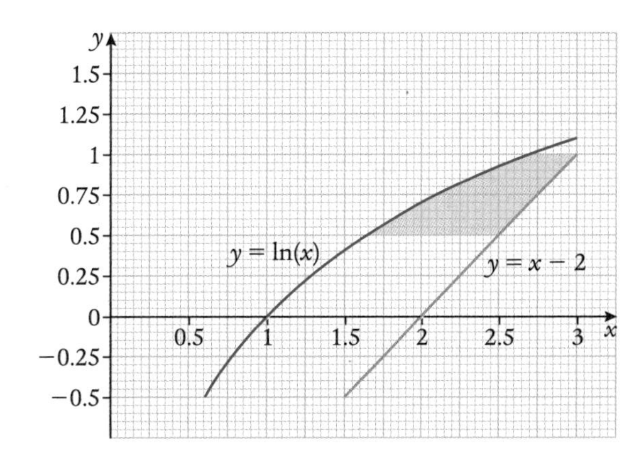

10 The graph of $y = e^x \sin x$, $0 \le x \le \frac{4\pi}{3}$, is drawn.

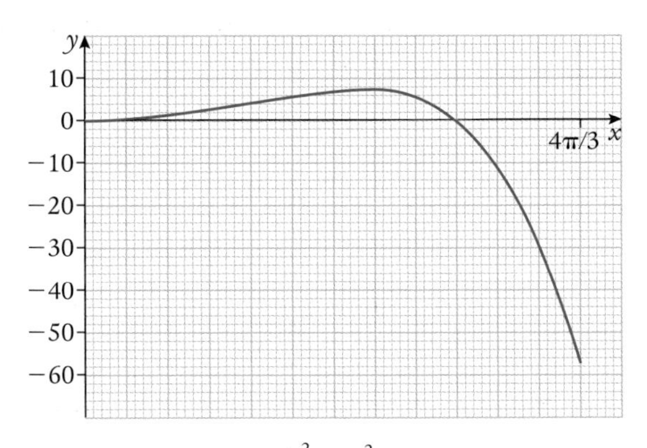

a Calculate the area trapped between the curve and the x-axis in this interval.

b Calculate, to 2 significant figures, the fraction of the area that is above the x-axis.

11 The equation of an ellipse, centre the origin, and major axis lying on the x-axis, is $\frac{x^2}{a^2} + \frac{y^2}{b^2} = 1$ (see diagram for explanation of a and b).

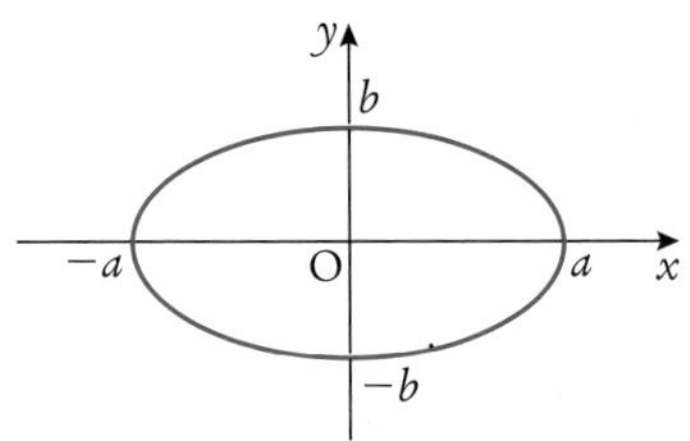

If the shape is rotated about the x-axis, the solid generated is called a *prolate* spheroid. Each cross-section perpendicular to the x-axis is a circle.
In theory, a rugby ball takes this shape.

a Find a formula for the volume of the prolate spheroid using $V = \int_{-a}^{a} \pi y^2 \, dx$.

b If, instead, the shape is rotated about the y-axis, the shape generated is called an *oblate* spheroid. Your geography teacher will tell you the Earth is an oblate spheroid.

Find a formula for the volume of the oblate spheroid using $V = \int_{-b}^{b} \pi x^2 \, dy$.

c Use integration to find a formula in terms of a and b for the area of the ellipse. Comment on the case where $a = b$.

12 **a** When a line with equation $y = mx$ is rotated about the x-axis in the interval $0 \le x \le h$, a cone is generated. When $x = h$, $y = r$. $\left[\text{That is, } m = \frac{r}{h}.\right]$

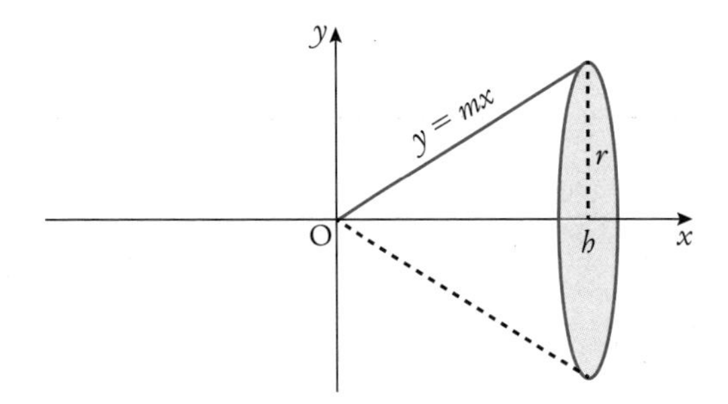

Use integration to find a formula in r and h for the volume of a cone.

b When the line is rotated about the x-axis in the interval $h_1 \le x \le h_2$, a truncated cone is generated. Use integration to find its volume.

c When the line $y = r$, where r is a constant, is rotated about the x-axis in the interval $0 \le x \le h$, a cylinder of height h and radius r is generated.
Use integration to find a formula for its volume.

d $x^2 + y^2 = r^2$ is the equation of a circle. $y = \sqrt{r^2 - x^2}$ is the equation of the semicircle shown.

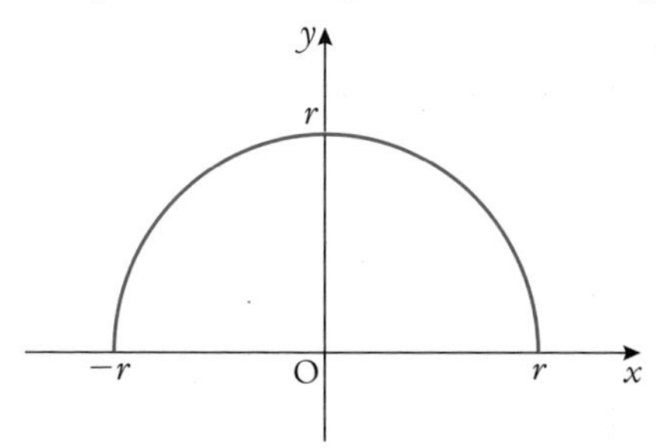

i If this is rotated about the x-axis, a sphere is generated. Use integration to find a formula for its volume.

ii When the portion of this semicircle in the interval $r - h \leq x \leq r$ is rotated about the x-axis, the cap of a sphere is generated. Its height is h.

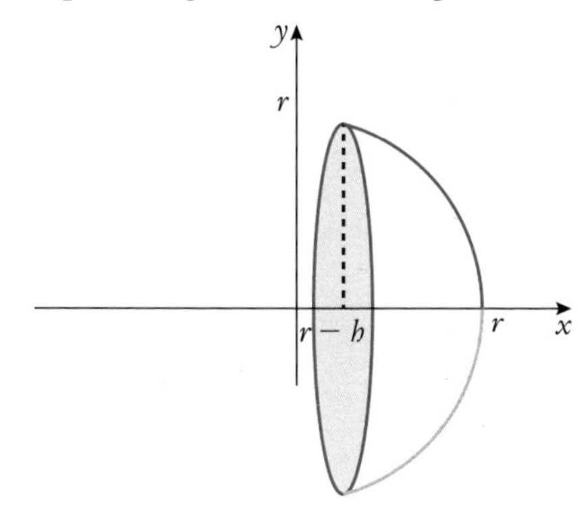

Use integration to find a formula for its volume.

iii What is the radius of the base of the cap?

13 a Draw a sketch of the curve $y = x^2 + 2x - 3$ in the interval $0 \leq x \leq 2$.

b Express the equation in the form $y = (x + a)^2 + b$.

c Hence find an expression for x^2 in terms of y.

d The curve is rotated around the y-axis. What is the volume of the shape generated?

14 The curve $y = \sin(x^2)$ is rotated about the y-axis in the interval $0 \leq x \leq \sqrt{\frac{\pi}{2}}$.

Find the volume of the solid generated.

Review 7

1 Find

a $\int \cos(3x + 1)\,dx$ b $\int \sqrt[3]{2 - 5x}\,dx$ c $\int \sec^2(2x + 3)\,dx$

d $\int 3e^{4-x}\,dx$ e $\int \frac{3}{(2x+1)^3}\,dx$ f $\int \frac{2}{5x - 2}\,dx$

g $\int 3^x\,dx$ h $\int 3^{2x+5}\,dx$ i $\int \sin^2 x\,dx$

2 Use the substitutions suggested to integrate these.

a $\int (2x + 1)\sqrt{x^2 + x + 1}\,dx$, using $u = x^2 + x + 1$

b $\int (x + 1)(x^2 + 2x - 5)^6\,dx$, using $u = x^2 + 2x - 5$

c $\int \frac{3-x}{\sqrt{1+6x-x^2}}\,dx$, using $u = 1 + 6x - x^2$

d $\int \sin^2 x \cos x\,dx$, using $u = \sin x$

e $\int \sin^3 x \cos^2 x\,dx$, using $u = \cos x$

f $\int \frac{1}{x^2+9}\,dx$, using $x = 3\tan u$

g $\int \frac{1}{\sqrt{3-x^2}}\,dx$, using $x = \sqrt{3}\sin u$

h $\int x^2\sqrt{3-x^3}\,dx$, using $u^2 = 3 - x^3$

3 Evaluate each of these using the suggested substitution.

a $\int_0^2 3x^2 e^{x^3}\,dx$, using $u = x^3$

b $\int_0^{\frac{\pi}{2}} \sin x\sqrt{\cos x}\,dx$, using $u = \cos x$

4 State the integrals of these.

a $\frac{\sin x}{\cos x}$ b $\frac{2x+5}{x^2+5x-3}$ c $\frac{1}{x\ln x}$ d $\frac{\sec^2 x}{\tan x}$ e $\frac{1-\sec^2 x}{x-\tan x}$ f $\frac{e^{-x}}{1-e^{-x}}$

5 State the integrals of

a $\frac{1}{x^2+1}$ b $\frac{1}{\sqrt{1-x^2}}$ c $\frac{1}{x^2+81}$ d $\frac{1}{\sqrt{121-x^2}}$ e $\frac{1}{\sqrt{7-x^2}}$

6 Integrate with the aid of partial fractions.

a $\frac{3x+1}{(x-1)(x+3)}$ b $\frac{x^2+5x-5}{(x-1)^2(x+2)}$ c $\frac{3x^2+3x+8}{(x+1)(x^2+3)}$ d $\frac{x^4}{(x-1)(x-2)}$

7 Find

a $\int (3x+4)\sin x\,dx$ b $\int x^2 e^{2x+1}\,dx$ c $\int e^{3x}\cos(2x+1)\,dx$ d $\int \tan^{-1} 2x\,dx$

8 Calculate the area trapped between $y = \frac{1}{(x-1)(x-3)}$, the x-axis, $x = 1.5$ and $x = 2.5$.

9 Calculate the area trapped between $y = \tan x$ and the y-axis in the interval $0 \le x \le \frac{\pi}{4}$.

10 A parabola cuts the x-axis at $x = 1$ and $x = 5$. Its vertex is at $(3, 4)$.
When it is rotated about the x-axis in the interval $1 \le x \le 5$, it generates a solid.
Calculate the volume of this solid.

Summary 7

1 An **antiderivative** of a function $f(x)$ is a function $F(x)$ where $F'(x) = f(x)$.

2 The **definite integral:** $\int_a^b f(x)\,dx = F(b) - F(a)$ where $F'(x) = f(x)$.

3 Standard integrals

a $\int ax^n\,dx = \frac{a}{n+1}x^{n+1} + c,\ n \neq -1$

b $\int ax^{-1}\,dx = \int \frac{a}{x}\,dx = a\ln x + c$

c $\int \sin x\,dx = -\cos x + c$

d $\int \cos x\,dx = \sin x + c$

e $\int \sec^2 x\,dx = \tan x + c$

f $\int e^x \, dx = e^x + c$

g $\int \ln x \, dx = x \ln x - x + c$

h $\int \frac{dx}{\sqrt{a^2 - x^2}} = \sin^{-1}\left(\frac{x}{a}\right) + c$

i $\int \frac{dx}{a^2 + x^2} = \frac{1}{a}\tan^{-1}\left(\frac{x}{a}\right) + c$

This list can be expanded by making use of the theorem that

if $\int f(x) \, dx = F(x) + c$ then $\int f(ax + b) \, dx = \frac{1}{a} F(ax + b) + c$

4 Special forms

a $\int \frac{f'(x)}{f(x)} \, dx = \ln |f(x)| + c$

b $\int f'(x) f(x) \, dx = \frac{1}{2}[f(x)]^2 + c$

5 Integration by substitution

a If $y = f'(x)$ then the differentials dx and dy are defined by $dy = f'(x) \, dx$ or in Leibniz notation $dy = \frac{dy}{dx} dx$.

b If we have an integral of the form $\int g(f(x)) \cdot f'(x) \, dx$ then by letting $u = f(x)$ we get $du = f'(x) \, dx$ and the integral becomes $\int g(u) \, du$.

c When the technique is used on a definite integral, the values of x which are the limits must be exchanged for the corresponding values of u.

6 Integration by parts

a When we wish to integrate the product of two functions $f(x)$ and $g(x)$ we can make use of the theorem

$$\int f(x) \, g(x) \, dx = f(x) \int g(x) \, dx - \int \left[\int g(x) \, dx \right] \cdot f'(x) \, dx$$

b In general we would try to select $f(x)$ as being the function which simplifies when differentiated.

c Sometimes we select $f(x)$ as being the function that is not readily integrated.

d Sometimes we introduce a factor of 1 to be $g(x)$ for example in the case of $\ln x$.

7 a We can interpret the definite integral as being the limit of a sum

for example $\int_a^b f(x) \, dx = \lim_{\Delta x \to 0} \left(\sum_{x=a}^{b} f(x)\Delta x \right)$

b This opens the way to many applications. In this chapter we examined:

Application 1: area between the curve of $y = f(x)$ and the x-axis.

$$A = \int_a^b f(x) \, dx$$

Application 2: area between the curve of $y = f(x)$ and the y-axis.

$$B = \int_{f(a)}^{f(b)} f^{-1}(y) \, dy$$

Application 3: volume (revolved around the x-axis)

$$V = \int_a^b \pi \, (f(x))^2 \, dx$$

Application 4: volume (revolved around the y-axis)

$$V = \int_{f(a)}^{f(b)} \pi \, (f^{-1}(y))^2 \, dy$$

8 Differential equations

Historical note

A differential equation is one which relates a function to some of its derivatives.

The solution to such an equation is the set of functions that satisfy it.

Like many branches of mathematics, the methods for solving differential equations have been developed as the need arose from physical situations. Using these methods, Daniel Bernoulli was able to develop his theories on fluid flow – Bernoulli's Principle is used constantly in the designing and development of aircraft, ships, bridges and other structures where air or water pressure plays a vital part.

8.1 First-order differential equations

First-order differential equations are equations where $\frac{dy}{dx}$ is the highest derivative present.

Order and degree

The **order** of a differential equation is the order of the highest derivative.

The **degree** of a differential equation is the degree of the highest power of the highest differential.

For example

$\frac{dy}{dx} = x + 4$	1st order	1st degree
$x^2\frac{dy}{dx} + 2y = 1$	1st order	1st degree
$\left(\frac{dy}{dx}\right)^2 + x + y = 0$	1st order	2nd degree
$\frac{d^2y}{dx^2} + 2\frac{dy}{dx} - x = 1$	2nd order	1st degree

Equations with separable variables

Where the variables are separable, the equations take the general form $f(y)\frac{dy}{dx} = g(x)$.

Using differentials we get $f(y)\frac{dy}{dx}\,dx = g(x)\,dx \Rightarrow f(y)\,dy = g(x)\,dx$.

Integrating should lead to a general solution.

$$\int f(y)\,dy = \int g(x)\,dx$$
$$\Rightarrow F(y) = G(x) + c$$

where $F(y)$ and $G(x)$ are the antiderivatives of $f(y)$ and $g(x)$ respectively and c is the constant of integration.

This leads to a family of functions – a different function for each value of the constant of integration.

If a particular pair of values (x, y) is known then the corresponding value of c can be found and a particular solution identified.

The particular pair of values (x, y) are referred to as the **initial conditions.**

Example 1

Find the general solution to the differential equation $\dfrac{dy}{dx} = \dfrac{1}{2x - 1}$.

$\dfrac{dy}{dx} = \dfrac{1}{2x-1} \Rightarrow \dfrac{dy}{dx}\,dx = \dfrac{1}{2x-1}\,dx$ [Using differentials]

$\Rightarrow dy = \dfrac{dx}{2x-1}$ [The variables are now separated]

$\Rightarrow \int dy = \int \dfrac{dx}{2x-1}$ [Integrating both sides]

$\Rightarrow y = \frac{1}{2}\ln|2x-1| + c$ [An explicit solution]

$= \frac{1}{2}\ln|2x-1| + \ln A$ [c is a constant: call it $\ln A$]

$= \ln|A\sqrt{2x-1}|$ [A tidier solution]

Example 2

a Find the general solution to the equation $\dfrac{dy}{dx} = 1 - y$.

b Find the particular solution corresponding to the initial condition that when $x = 1, y = 2$.

a $\dfrac{dy}{dx} = 1 - y \Rightarrow \dfrac{dy}{1-y} = dx$ [The variables are now separated]

$\Rightarrow \int \dfrac{dy}{1-y} = \int dx$ [Integrating both sides]

$\Rightarrow -\ln|1-y| = x + c$ [An implicit solution]

$\Rightarrow \ln|1-y| = -x - c$

$\Rightarrow 1 - y = e^{-x-c} = e^{-x}.e^{-c} = Ae^{-x}$ [Not essential – but tidier]

$\Rightarrow y = 1 - Ae^{-x}$ [An explicit solution]

b $x = 1\, y = 2 \Rightarrow 2 = 1 - Ae^{-1}$ [Using the initial conditions ...]

$\Rightarrow Ae^{-1} = -1 \Rightarrow A = e$ [... to find A]

$\Rightarrow y = 1 - ee^{-x} = 1 - e^{1-x}$ [The particular solution]

Example 3

a Find the general solution of the differential equation $\dfrac{dy}{dx} = 2xy$.

b Find the particular solution given the initial condition that when $x = 1, y = 4$.

a $\dfrac{dy}{dx} = 2xy \Rightarrow \dfrac{1}{y}\,dy = 2x\,dx$ [The variables are now separated]

$\Rightarrow \int \dfrac{dy}{y} = \int 2x\,dx$ [Integrating both sides]

$\Rightarrow \ln y = x^2 + c$ [An implicit solution]

$\Rightarrow y = e^{x^2+c}$ [An explicit solution]

$= e^{x^2}e^{c}$ [e^c is a constant: call it A]

$= Ae^{x^2}$ [A tidier solution]

The graph charts some of the infinite set of solutions.

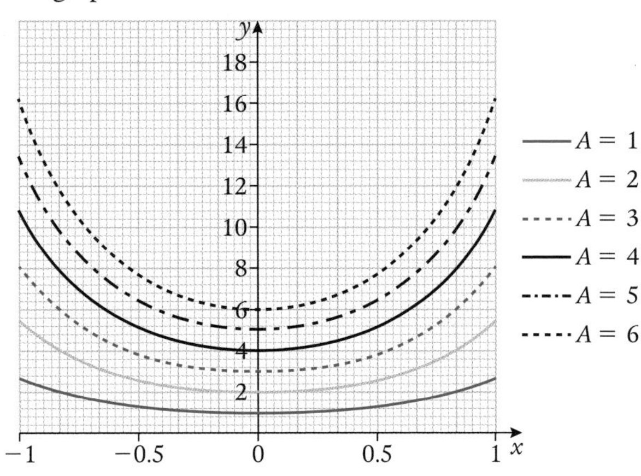

b $x = 1, y = 4 \Rightarrow 4 = Ae^{1^2}$

$\Rightarrow A = \dfrac{4}{e}$

So the particular solution corresponding to the given initial conditions is $y = \dfrac{4}{e}e^{x^2} = 4e^{x^2-1}$.

Exercise 8.1

1 Find the general solution of each of these differential equations stating the solution explicitly, where possible.

a $\dfrac{dy}{dx} - 3x = 0$

b $x\dfrac{dy}{dx} - 1 = 0$

c $2x\dfrac{dy}{dx} - (x - 1) = 0$

d $(1 + x^2)\dfrac{dy}{dx} = 1$

e $\dfrac{dy}{dx} - xe^x = 0$

f $\sec x\dfrac{dy}{dx} - \sin^2 x = 0$

g $\dfrac{dy}{dx} - y = 0$

h $\sin y\dfrac{dy}{dx} - \cos y = 0$

i $\dfrac{dy}{dx} - \sqrt{1 - y^2} = 0$

j $\dfrac{dy}{dx} = (y + 1)(y - 2)$

k $\dfrac{dy}{dx} - \dfrac{1}{e^y \cos y} = 0$

l $\dfrac{dy}{dx} = \dfrac{1}{\ln y}$

m $3y\dfrac{dy}{dx} - 2x^2 = 0$

n $\dfrac{dy}{dx} = \dfrac{\sin x}{\cos y}$

o $5x\dfrac{dy}{dx} = \sqrt{1 - y^2}$

p $\dfrac{dy}{dx} = e^x \cos^2 y$

q $\dfrac{dy}{dx} = e^{x+y}$

r $\dfrac{dy}{dx} = xy(y - 1)$

2 Find the particular solution to each of these differential equations.

a $x\dfrac{dy}{dx} = 1$ given that $y = 4$ when $x = 1$

b $(9 + x^2)\dfrac{dy}{dx} = 1$ given that $y = 1$ when $x = \dfrac{3\pi}{4}$

c $\dfrac{dy}{dx} = xe^x$ given that $y = e$ when $x = 1$

d $2y\dfrac{dy}{dx} = y^2 + 1$ given that $y = 0$ when $x = 1$

e $(1 + e^y)\dfrac{dy}{dx} = e^y$ given that $y = 0$ when $x = 1$

f $\dfrac{dy}{dx} = \dfrac{\sec y}{y}$ given that $y = \frac{\pi}{2}$ when $x = \frac{\pi}{4}$

g $2x\dfrac{dy}{dx} = 3y + 1$ given that $y = 5$ when $x = 2$

h $\sin^2 y \cos^2 x\dfrac{dy}{dx} = 1$ given that $y = \frac{\pi}{12}$ when $x = \frac{\pi}{4}$

i $x^2\dfrac{dy}{dx} - y^2 = 0$ given that $y = 1$ when $x = 2$

j $\dfrac{dy}{dx} = e^{x+y} \sin x$ given that $y = \ln 2$ when $x = 0$

k $\frac{dy}{dx} = \frac{y-1}{(x-2)(x+1)}$ given that $y = 5$ when $x = -\frac{10}{7}$

l $\frac{x}{y}\frac{dy}{dx} = \ln y$ given that $y = e$ when $x = 2$

[Hint: use the substitution $u = \ln y$.]

m $e^x \frac{dy}{dx} = x\sqrt{y}$ given that $y = 4$ when $x = 0$

n $e^{\sqrt{y}} \frac{dy}{dx} = \ln x$ given that $y = 0$ when $x = 1$

3 **Investigation**

A function in x and y is said to be homogeneous if, on replacing x by ax and y by ay, for all values of a, the function has the same value.

For example $\frac{xy}{x^2 + y^2}$ is homogeneous because

$$\frac{ax \cdot ay}{a^2x^2 + a^2y^2} = \frac{a^2xy}{a^2x^2 + a^2y^2} = \frac{xy}{x^2 + y^2}$$

a State which of these are homogeneous functions.

i $\frac{xy}{x+y}$ ii $\frac{x-y}{x+y}$ iii $\frac{x}{x+y}$ iv $\frac{xy + x^2}{xy + y^2}$

b Examine this differential equation and verify that you cannot separate the variables: $\frac{dy}{dx} = \frac{x}{x+y}$.

If $y = f(x)$, we can define a function $v = \frac{f(x)}{x}$ so that $y = xv$.

By the product rule, $\frac{dy}{dx} = \frac{d(xv)}{dx} = x\frac{dv}{dx} + 1 \cdot v = x\frac{dv}{dx} + v$.

Perform this substitution in the equation.

$$\frac{dy}{dx} = \frac{x}{x+y} \Rightarrow x\frac{dv}{dx} + v = \frac{x}{x + xv}$$

Because the function is homogeneous, we lose x on the right-hand side – and now the variables are separable.

$$x\frac{dv}{dx} = \frac{1}{1+v} - v = -\frac{v}{1+v}$$

$$\Rightarrow \left(\frac{1+v}{v}\right) dv = -\frac{1}{x} dx \Rightarrow \int\left(\frac{1+v}{v}\right) dv = -\int\frac{1}{x} dx$$

$$\Rightarrow \ln|v| + v = -\ln|x| + c$$

If desired, this can be tidied up using the laws of logs, and v can be replaced by $\frac{y}{x}$ to get an implicit solution.

c Perform this substitution and then separate the variables in these differential equations.

i $\frac{dy}{dx} = \frac{x+y}{x-y}$ ii $\frac{dy}{dx} = \frac{xy}{x^2 - y^2}$ iii $\frac{dy}{dx} = \frac{y}{x+y}$

8.2 Modelling using differential equations

Example 4

Newton's Law of Cooling states that the rate at which an object cools is proportional to the *difference* between its temperature and that of its surroundings.

Let T be the temperature difference at time t.

Initially the temperature is T_0 (that is, $T = T_0$ at $t = 0$). Note that T_0 is a constant.

Express T in terms of t.

Rate of cooling is proportional to temperature difference: $\frac{dT}{dt} \propto T$

$\Rightarrow \frac{dT}{dt} = kT$ [Where k is the constant of proportionality]

$\Rightarrow \frac{1}{T} dt = k\, dt \Rightarrow \int\frac{1}{T} dt = \int k\, dt$ [Separating variables and integrating]

Unit 1: Methods

$\Rightarrow \ln T = kt + c$ [Where c is the constant of integration]

$\Rightarrow T = e^{kt+c} = e^{kt}\,e^{c} = Ae^{kt}$ [Where $A = e^{c}$: we have a general solution]

The initial conditions are given: at $t = 0$, $T = T_0$.

Hence $T_0 = Ae^0 \Rightarrow A = T_0$.

Hence the particular solution gives the relation between T and t, namely $\Rightarrow T = T_0e^{kt}$.

Example 5

It was suggested that the rate at which a rumour spread around a school was proportional to the number of students who had *not* heard the rumour. There were 1000 students in the school. N is the number of students who had heard the rumour on day t and N_0 was the number who knew it initially [$t = 0$].

a Express N explicitly in terms of t.

b If $N_0 = 10$ and $N_1 = 100$ what is the value of N_{10} to the nearest whole number?

a $\dfrac{dN}{dt} \propto 1000 - N$

$\dfrac{dN}{dt} = k(1000 - N)$ where k is the constant of proportionality.

$\Rightarrow \dfrac{dN}{1000 - N} = k\,dt \Rightarrow \displaystyle\int \frac{dN}{1000 - N} = \int k\,dt$

$\Rightarrow -\ln|1000 - N| = kt + c$

At $t = 0$, $N = N_0$.

$\Rightarrow -\ln|1000 - N_0| = c$

$\Rightarrow -\ln|1000 - N| = kt - \ln|1000 - N_0|$

$\Rightarrow \ln|1000 - N_0| - \ln|1000 - N| = kt \Rightarrow \ln\left|\dfrac{1000 - N_0}{1000 - N}\right| = kt$

$\Rightarrow \dfrac{1000 - N_0}{1000 - N} = e^{kt} \Rightarrow 1000 - N = \dfrac{1000 - N_0}{e^{kt}}$

$\Rightarrow N = \dfrac{1000e^{kt} - 1000 + N_0}{e^{kt}}$

b Given that $N_0 = 10$ and $N_1 = 100$, we have

$\Rightarrow 100 = \dfrac{1000e^{k} - 1000 + 10}{e^{k}}$

$\Rightarrow 1000e^{k} - 100e^{k} = 1000 - 10$

$\Rightarrow e^{k} = \dfrac{990}{900} = 1.1$

So the model becomes $N = \dfrac{1000 \cdot 1.1^{t} - 990}{1.1^{t}}$

When $t = 10$, $\Rightarrow N = \dfrac{1000 \cdot 1.1^{10} - 990}{1.1^{10}} = 618$ to the nearest whole number.

Example 6

A boy is trying to collect 500 football stickers for an album. It is believed that the size of his collection, y stickers, x days after he started collecting can be modelled by $\dfrac{dy}{dx} = ky(500 - y)$.[1]

a Express y explicitly as a function of x given that when $x = 1$, $y = 10$ and $k = 0.00012$

b The boy can send away for the last 50 stickers. After how many days' collecting does the model predict this will happen?

[1] This comes from the conjecture that the rate of change of his collection in stickers per day is proportional both to the number of stickers collected so far [y] and the number of stickers still to collect [$500 - y$].

Even though the question gives a numerical value for k it is better to use the variable and substitute for it at the end.

a $\frac{dy}{dx} = ky(500 - y) \Rightarrow \frac{dy}{y(500 - y)} = k\,dx$ [Variables separated]

$\Rightarrow \int \frac{dy}{y(500 - y)} = \int k\,dx$

$\Rightarrow \frac{1}{500} \int \frac{1}{y} + \frac{1}{500 - y}\,dy = \int k\,dx$ [Using partial fractions]

$\Rightarrow \frac{1}{500} (\ln|y| - \ln|500 - y|) = kx + c$ [An implicit solution]

$\Rightarrow \ln\left|\frac{y}{500 - y}\right| = 500kx + 500c$

$\Rightarrow \frac{y}{500 - y} = e^{500kx + 500c} = Ae^{500kx}$ [Letting $e^{500c} = A$]

$\Rightarrow y = 500Ae^{500kx} - yAe^{500kx}$

$\Rightarrow y(1 + Ae^{500kx}) = 500Ae^{500kx}$

$\Rightarrow y = \frac{500Ae^{500kx}}{1 + Ae^{500kx}}$ [An explicit general solution]

$= \frac{500Ae^{0.06x}}{1 + Ae^{0.06x}}$ [Using $k = 0.00012$]

b On day 1 the boy had ten stickers: $x = 1, y = 10$.
[Hint: we are best off substituting in the first line where A appeared:

$\frac{y}{500 - y} = Ae^{0.06x} \Rightarrow \frac{10}{500 - 10} = Ae^{0.06} \Rightarrow A = \frac{e^{-0.06}}{49}$]

Substituting in the general solution:

$$\Rightarrow y = \frac{500\frac{e^{0.06}}{49}e^{0.06x}}{1 + \frac{e^{-0.06}}{49}e^{0.06x}} = \frac{\frac{500}{49}e^{0.06x-0.06}}{1 + \frac{500}{49}e^{0.06x-0.06}} = \frac{500\,e^{0.06(x-1)}}{49 + 500\,e^{0.06(x-1)}}$$

He can send away for the last 50 when he has $y = 450$ stickers.

Using the implicit form: $\frac{y}{500 - y} = Ae^{0.06x} \Rightarrow \frac{450}{500 - 450} = \frac{e^{-0.06}}{49}e^{0.06x}$

$\Rightarrow 9 \times 49 = e^{0.06(x-1)} \Rightarrow \ln 441 = 0.06(x - 1)$

$\Rightarrow x = \frac{\ln 441}{0.06} + 1 = 102$ to 3 sf

He can send for the last stickers after 102 days.

Exercise 8.2

1 Write a mathematical model in the form of a differential equation for each of these statements.

a The rate of change of displacement (s) with time (t) is directly proportional to the displacement.

b The rate of change of displacement (s) with time (t) is inversely proportional to the time.

c A sphere of volume V and radius r is expanding such that the rate of increase in its volume is directly proportional to the size of its equator.

d The rate of change of the number of books bought, B, with respect to cost, is inversely proportional to the cost of a book, £C.

2 As you climb a mountain by the sea, your view to the horizon improves. The rate at which the distance to the horizon, D km, changes with respect to the height climbed, h m, can be obtained from the model $\frac{dD}{dh} = \frac{k}{\sqrt{h}}$ where k is a constant. At sea level ($h = 0$) the distance to the horizon is 8 km.

a Express D in terms of h and constants.

b After climbing 100 m above sea level the distance to the horizon is 55 km.

Find a formula which relates D to h.

c How far can you see to the horizon when you have climbed 850 m?

3 Over the course of an illness, a patient's temperature is measured and averaged, T °F, daily.

Its change can be modelled by $\frac{dT}{dt} = -\frac{2}{5}t + \frac{3}{2}$ where t is the time measured in days.

a When $t = 0$ at the onset of the illness, the patient's temperature was normal: 98.4 °F.

Express T in terms of t explicitly.

b How many days elapse before the patient's temperature returns to normal?

4 A new TV series has a prospective target audience in mind. As the weeks go by after the launch of the series the percentage of the target audience watching the programme, V%, is expected to grow according to the model $\frac{dV}{dt} = ke^{-0.3t}$ where t is measured in weeks and k is a constant.

a Express V in terms of t and the constants k and c where c is the constant of integration.

b Initially none of the audience are watching (when $t = 0, V = 0$).

Express c in terms of k.

c After five weeks 77.7% of the target audience are watching.

Express V in terms of t.

d After 10 weeks 90% of the target audience are watching.

Is the model holding up? Comment.

5 When the rate of growth (or decay) of a quantity is proportional to the magnitude of the quantity, then the growth is said to be *unrestricted*.

A rumour spreads through a population in such a way that the rate at which the number of people who have heard the rumour, n, grows is proportional to the number of people who have heard the rumour. That is, $\frac{dn}{dt} = kn$ where k is a constant of proportion.

Express n explicitly in terms of t given that when $t = 0, n = 3$ (three people started the rumour) and that when $t = 2, n = 60$.

6 The rate at which the value of a car, £V, depreciates at any given time is proportional to the value of the car at that time.

a Write a differential equation involving V and t, where V is the value of the car after t years.

b Initially, when $t = 0$, the car is valued at £20 000. After two years the car has lost £2500.

Find the particular solution to the differential equation to express V in terms of t.

c i When will the car be worth only £10 000?

ii What will the car be worth after 10 years?

7 A learner driver has to learn 400 facts for her test. The rate at which the number of facts she can recall grows is proportional to the number of facts still to memorise.

She applies herself regularly to the task on a daily basis. Her learning can be modelled using a second type of growth model, $\frac{\mathrm{d}F}{\mathrm{d}t} = k(400 - F)$ where F is the number of facts memorised and t is the time measured in days since she started the task. Initially she knew no facts. After five days she could memorise 250 facts.

a Express F explicitly in terms of t.

b When she can remember 80% of the facts she can claim to have mastery of the topic.

For how many days will she have to study to claim mastery?

8 In a third model, the *restricted* growth model, the quantity again has a limit to which it can grow. The rate of increase of the quantity at a particular time is jointly proportional to the quantity present at that time and the quantity needed to reach the limit.

In a small island there are 2000 inhabitants. An islander returns from his holidays and brings a flu virus with him. It spreads among the population according to the model $\frac{\mathrm{d}P}{\mathrm{d}t} = kP(2000 - P)$ where P is the number with the virus after t days and k is the constant of proportion.

a With the aid of partial fractions show that $\frac{1}{2000}\ln\left(\frac{P}{2000 - P}\right) = kt + c$ where k and c are constants.

b Assuming that $P = 1$ when $t = 0$, find the value of c to 1 significant figure.

c If 20 people have contracted the virus after five days

i express t in terms of P

ii express P in terms of t.

d Help will have to be flown in if more than 50% of the inhabitants contract the virus.

Estimate the number of days before this happens.

9 Mildew hits a crop of corn in a field. Its spread can be modelled by $\frac{\mathrm{d}P}{\mathrm{d}t} = kP(100 - P)$ where P is the percentage of the field affected in day t. When $t = 0$, $P = 1$. When $t = 5$, $P = 60$.

a Express P in terms of t.

b Estimate the time it will take for 80% to be affected.

10 The number of radioactive atoms in a substance falls as time progresses.

The rate of decay, $\frac{\mathrm{d}n}{\mathrm{d}t}$, of the number of radioactive atoms is proportional to n, the number of atoms present at time t seconds.

In one particular sample there are initially 200 radioactive atoms present.

After 10 000 s there remain 199 radioactive atoms.

The *half-life* of a substance is defined as the time it takes for the number of radioactive atoms to halve.

Determine the half-life of the substance.

11 The supergrowth model for world population is given by the equation $\frac{\mathrm{d}P}{\mathrm{d}t} = 0.015P^{1.2}$ where P is the population of the world in millions and t is the time in years with $t = 0$ representing 2015.

Given that the population in 2015 was 7200 million find the model's prediction for the world population in the year 2025.

12 Consider a particular object falling through the air. Its velocity increases due to the force of gravity. If the object is x metres above the Earth at time t seconds and falling with velocity v ms^{-1}, Newton's laws of motion give us

$\frac{dv}{dt} = -g$ where g is the gravitational constant (≈ 9.8 ms^{-2}).

At the start $t = t_0$, $v = v_0$ and $x = x_0$.

a Determine an equation for v in terms of t.

b By definition, the velocity $v = \frac{dx}{dt}$. Express x explicitly in terms of t.

13 You borrow £50 000 for a mortgage. The interest rate is 6%.

a In a 'simple-interest bank' they calculate the interest due each month so that the amount owed after one year is given by $V = \left(1 + \frac{0.06}{12}\right)^{12} V_0$ where V_0 is the initial amount borrowed.

Calculate how much is owed at the end of one year on a mortgage loan of £50 000.

b In a more realistic bank they calculate the interest *continuously* . The amount owed after one year, V, is modelled by the differential equation $\frac{dV}{dt} = 0.06V$.

Calculate the *extra* interest charged at the end of one year if the interest is calculated continuously.

14 The rate at which petrol leaks from the bottom of a tank is proportional to the square root of the depth of the petrol above the bottom of the tank.

Thus we can model the situation by $\frac{dV}{dt} = -k\sqrt{V}$ where V is volume of petrol in the tank at time t hours and k is a *positive* constant.

Consider a cuboid tank with a base of area 5 m^2 and height 20 m, initially full. The tank is losing petrol at the rate of 2 m^3 per hour when it is one-quarter full.

a Determine a formula modelling the volume of petrol, V, in the tank at time t.

b How long will it take for the tank to empty?

8.3 First-order linear differential equations

A first-order linear differential equation can be expressed in the form

$$\frac{dy}{dx} + P(x)y = Q(x) \qquad (1)$$

To solve this, we first consider the derivative of the product $I(x)y$

$$\frac{d}{dx}(I(x)y) = I(x)\frac{dy}{dx} + I'(x)y$$

From this we see

$$\int\left(I(x)\frac{dy}{dx} + I'(x)y\right) dx = I(x)y + c. \qquad (2)$$

If we can make the left-hand side of (1) look like $I(x)\frac{dy}{dx} + I'(x)y$ then we can simply write its integral.

Multiply throughout (1) by $I(x)$

$$I(x)\frac{dy}{dx} + I(x)P(x)y = I(x)Q(x) \qquad (3)$$

Equating the coefficients of y in (2) and (3) we get $I(x)P(x) = I'(x)$

Separating the variables $P(x) = \frac{I'(x)}{I(x)} \Rightarrow \int P(x)\, dx = \int \frac{I'(x)}{I(x)}\, dx$

$$\Rightarrow \int P(x)\, dx = \ln |I(x)|$$

$$\Rightarrow I(x) = e^{\int P(x)\, dx}$$

This is known as the **integrating factor**.

If we multiply a linear differential equation by its integrating factor then the *integral* of the left-hand side is $ye^{\int P(x)\,dx}$ and we are left looking for the integral of $e^{\int P(x)\,dx}Q(x)$ We do not need to worry about a constant of integration when finding the integrating factor, as any function fitting this form will do the job. We can let $c = 0$.

Example 7

Solve the differential equation $x\frac{dy}{dx} + 2y = x^2$.

Step 1: make the coefficient of $\frac{dy}{dx}$ unity, in this case by dividing throughout by x, giving $\frac{dy}{dx} + \frac{2}{x}y = x$. This is now in the standard form of a linear differential equation. This allows us to identify $P(x)$, the coefficient of y.

Step 2: calculate the integrating factor.

$$P(x) = \frac{2}{x} \Rightarrow \int P(x)\,dx = \int \frac{2}{x}\,dx = 2\ln|x|$$

$$\Rightarrow e^{\int P(x)\,dx} = e^{2\ln|x|} = e^{\ln x^2} = x^2$$

Step 3: multiply the differential equation, $\frac{dy}{dx} + \frac{2}{x}y = x$, by the integrating factor.

$$x^2\frac{dy}{dx} + x^2\frac{2}{x}y = x^2x$$

$$\Rightarrow x^2\frac{dy}{dx} + 2xy = x^3$$

Step 4: integrate both sides – remembering that the integral of the left-hand side is 'engineered' to be $ye^{\int P(x)\,dx} = x^2y$.

$$\Rightarrow \int\left(x^2\frac{dy}{dx} + 2xy\right)dx = \int x^3\,dx$$

$$\Rightarrow x^2y = \int x^3\,dx$$

$$\Rightarrow x^2y = \frac{x^4}{4} + c$$

$$\Rightarrow y = \frac{x^2}{4} + \frac{c}{x^2}$$

Note that the solution is made of two parts:

- a **particular solution**, in this case $y = \frac{x^2}{4}$. It satisfies the original equation.
- a **complementary function**, in this case $y = \frac{c}{x^2}$, containing an arbitrary constant.

It satisfies the differential equation, $\frac{dy}{dx} + P(x)y = 0$.

Example 8

Solve the differential equation $\frac{dy}{dx} - 2xy = 3x$.

The coefficient of $\frac{dy}{dx}$ is 1 and the coefficient of y is $P(x) = -2x$.

So $\int P(x)\,dx = \int -2x\,dx = -x^2$.

The integrating factor is $e^{\int P(x)\,dx} = e^{-x^2}$.

Multiply throughout the equation: $e^{-x^2}\frac{dy}{dx} - 2e^{-x^2}xy = 3xe^{-x^2}$.

Integrate: $\int\left(e^{-x^2}\frac{dy}{dx} - 2e^{-x^2}xy\right)dx = \int 3xe^{-x^2}\,dx$

$$\Rightarrow e^{-x^2}y = \int 3xe^{-x^2}\,dx$$

Integrate the right-hand side by substitution.

Let $u = -x^2 \Rightarrow du = -2x\,dx \Rightarrow x\,dx = -\frac{1}{2}\,du$

$\Rightarrow \int 3xe^{-x^2}\,dx = \int -\frac{3}{2}e^u\,du = -\frac{3}{2}e^u + c = -\frac{3}{2}e^{-x^2} + c$

Solution to equation is $e^{-x^2}y = -\frac{3}{2}e^{-x^2} + c$

$$\Rightarrow y = -\frac{3e^{-x^2}}{2e^{-x^2}} + \frac{c}{e^{-x^2}}$$

$$= -\frac{3}{2} + ce^{x^2}$$

A particular solution is $y = -\frac{3}{2}$; the complementary function is $y = ce^{x^2}$.

Example 9

Solve the differential equation $\cos x\frac{dy}{dx} + 2y\sin x = 1$.

Make coefficient of $\frac{dy}{dx}$ unity: $\frac{dy}{dx} + 2y\tan x = \sec x$.

$P(x) = 2\tan x \Rightarrow \int P(x)\,dx = 2\ln|\cos x| = \ln(\cos^2 x)$. Note: $|A^2| = A^2$.

$e^{\int P(x)\,dx} = e^{\ln(\cos^2 x)} = \cos^2 x$

Multiply throughout: $\cos^2 x\frac{dy}{dx} + y\cos^2 x\tan x = \cos^2 x\sec x$

$\cos^2 x\frac{dy}{dx} + y\cos^2 x\tan x = \cos x$

Integrating: $y\cos^2 x = \int \cos x\,dx = \sin x + c$

Divide throughout by the coefficient of y: $y = \frac{\sin x}{\cos^2 x} + \frac{c}{\cos^2 x}$.

A particular solution is $y = \frac{\sin x}{\cos^2 x}$; the complementary function is $y = \frac{c}{\cos^2 x}$.

Exercise 8.3

1 Solve each of these first-order linear differential equations.

a $\frac{dy}{dx} + y = e^x$

b $\frac{dy}{dx} + 3y = e^{-x}$

c $\frac{dy}{dx} + 4y = \sin x$

d $\frac{dy}{dx} + \frac{y}{x} = e^x$

e $\frac{dy}{dx} + \frac{3y}{x} = x^3$

f $\frac{dy}{dx} + \frac{2y}{x} = e^x$

g $\frac{dy}{dx} + \frac{y}{x-1} = x + 1$

h $\frac{dy}{dx} + \frac{2xy}{x^2+1} = \cos x$

i $\frac{dy}{dx} + y\cot x = \cos x$

j $\frac{dy}{dx} + 2xy = x$

k $\frac{dy}{dx} + y\sin x = 3\sin x$

l $\frac{dy}{dx} + 3yx^2 = e^{-x^3}$

m $\frac{dy}{dx} + 3yx^2 = e^x(3x^2 + 1)$

n $\frac{dy}{dx} + y\ln x = e^x x^{1-x}\cos x$

o $\frac{dy}{dx} + ye^x = e^x$

p $\frac{dy}{dx} - \frac{y}{x+2} = \frac{6}{x+1}$

q $\frac{dy}{dx} - \frac{2y}{2x-1} = \frac{1}{x-1}$

r $\frac{dy}{dx} - \frac{y}{x} = \frac{x}{x^2+1}$

s $\frac{dy}{dx} - \frac{y}{x} = \frac{x}{\sqrt{4-x^2}}$

2 Find general solutions for these differential equations.

a $3\dfrac{dy}{dx} + y = 6e^x$

b $x\dfrac{dy}{dx} + y = \cos x$

c $(x^2 + x)\dfrac{dy}{dx} + (4x + 2)y = x - 1$

d $\dfrac{1}{2}\dfrac{dy}{dx} + (x + 1)y = x + 1$

e $e^x\dfrac{dy}{dx} + y = 1$

f $\cos x\dfrac{dy}{dx} + 3y\sin x = 2$

g $x\dfrac{dy}{dx} - y = x^2\cos x$

h $(x+1)\dfrac{dy}{dx} - y = \dfrac{1}{x-1}$

i $(x+1)\dfrac{dy}{dx} - y = \dfrac{1}{x^2+2}$

3 Find the particular solution to each equation with the given initial conditions.

a $\dfrac{dy}{dx} + \dfrac{y}{2} = e^x$; when $x = 0, y = e$

b $\dfrac{dy}{dx} + \dfrac{y}{x} = \sin x$; when $x = \pi, y = 2$

c $\dfrac{dy}{dx} + \dfrac{2xy}{x^2+1} = \sin x$; when $x = 0, y = 5$

d $\dfrac{dy}{dx} - \dfrac{y}{x-3} = \dfrac{4}{x+1}$; when $x = 4, y = \ln 5$

e $\dfrac{dy}{dx} - y\ln x = x^x\sin x$; when $x = \pi, y = \pi^\pi$

f $\dfrac{dy}{dx} - y\tan x = (x+1)\sin 2x$; when $x = 0, y = 1$

4 Express each in the standard form for a first-order linear differential equation and then solve.

a $\dfrac{dy}{dx} = \dfrac{x\sqrt{x}\ln x - y}{x}$

b $\dfrac{dy}{dx} = \dfrac{x^2\sin^3 x + y\cos x}{\sin x}$

5 a Solve the differential equation $y = x\dfrac{dy}{dx} + k$ where k is a constant.

b When $x = 1, y = 3$ and when $x = 3$, $y = 7$. Use these initial conditions to find k and c, the constant of integration.

c Comment on your result.

6 a Solve the differential equation $\dfrac{dy}{dx} = ay + b$, where a and b are constants.

b A sky diver falls, accelerating under gravity.

He is also decelerating because of air resistance which is directly proportional to his velocity, V ms^{-1}.

The situation can be modelled by $\dfrac{dV}{dt} = 10 - kV$ where t seconds is the time that has elapsed in the 'dive'. k is a positive constant.

i Solve the equation to express V in terms of t given that at $t = 0$, $V = 0$. $[V(0) = 0]$

ii Terminal velocity is the limit V approaches as t increases.

Find this terminal velocity.

7 Take another look at the growth model where the rate of growth is proportional to the room for growth. Suppose there is a limit L to the population. Let N be the population at time t.
The model is $\dfrac{dN}{dt} = k(L - N)$ where k is the constant of proportion $(k > 0)$.

a Rewrite the equation in the standard form of a linear differential equation.

b Solve it using an integrating factor.

c Verify that as t tends to infinity, N tends to L.

d In a particular scenario, the population is recorded as a percentage of the actual limit. So $L = 100$. Time is measured in days.

i If $N(0) = 4$ and $N(10) = 50$, find the constants in the model.

ii What percentage of the limit is reached by 35 days?

8.4 Second-order linear differential equations

Differential equations of the form $a\dfrac{d^2y}{dx^2} + b\dfrac{dy}{dx} + cy = Q(x)$ where a, b and c are constants are called second-order linear differential equations.

When $Q(x) = 0$ then the equations are referred to as **homogeneous**, and when $Q(x) \neq 0$ then the equations are **non-homogeneous**.

Homogeneous equations

$$a\frac{d^2y}{dx^2} + b\frac{dy}{dx} + cy = 0$$

Where the integration involved in solving a first-order equation generated a single arbitrary constant, the implicit need to perform two integrations here will generate two arbitrary constants.

So the solution to such an equation must include two arbitrary constants to be completely general.

Theorem 1

If $y = f(x)$ and $y = g(x)$ are two solutions to the equation then so is $y = f(x) + g(x)$.

Proof

$y = f(x)$ is a solution $\Rightarrow a\dfrac{d^2f}{dx^2} + b\dfrac{df}{dx} + cf = 0$

$y = g(x)$ is a solution $\Rightarrow a\dfrac{d^2g}{dx^2} + b\dfrac{dg}{dx} + cg = 0$

Adding gives

$$a\frac{d^2f}{dx^2} + a\frac{d^2g}{dx^2} + b\frac{df}{dx} + b\frac{dg}{dx} + cf + cg = 0 = a\left(\frac{d^2f}{dx^2} + \frac{d^2g}{dx^2}\right) + b\left(\frac{df}{dx} + \frac{dg}{dx}\right) + c(f + g)$$

The additive law of differentiation gives

$$a\frac{d^2(f+g)}{dx^2} + b\frac{d(f+g)}{dx} + c\,(f + g) = 0$$

... and so $y = f(x) + g(x)$ is a solution to the differential equation.

A trial solution and the auxiliary equation

The solution to the equation $b\dfrac{dy}{dx} + cy = 0$ takes the form $y = Ae^{mx}$.

So it is reasonable to consider it as a possible solution for $a\dfrac{d^2y}{dx^2} + b\dfrac{dy}{dx} + cy = 0$.

$y = Ae^{mx} \Rightarrow \dfrac{dy}{dx} = Ame^{mx} \Rightarrow \dfrac{d^2y}{dx^2} = Am^2e^{mx}$

If $y = Ae^{mx}$ is a solution it will satisfy the equation $a\dfrac{d^2y}{dx^2} + b\dfrac{dy}{dx} + cy = 0$.

Substituting in the equation gives

$aAm^2e^{mx} + bAme^{mx} + cAe^{mx} = 0$

$\Rightarrow am^2 + bm + c = 0,\ Ae^{mx} \neq 0$

Solving this quadratic will provide two values $m = m_1$ and $m = m_2$ which will then give us two solutions, $y = Ae^{m_1x}$ and $y = Be^{m_2x}$.

Two different coefficients, A and B, are used to distinguish two arbitrary constants.

Now by the theorem above this gives a solution $y = Ae^{m_1x} + Be^{m_2x}$.

The two arbitrary constants ensure that all solutions are covered.

The equation $am^2 + bm + c = 0$ is called the **auxiliary equation**.

The type of solution we get for the differential equation depends on the nature of the roots of this equation.

There are three cases to consider.

Case 1: When the roots are real and distinct [$b^2 - 4ac > 0$]

Example 10

Find the general solution of $\frac{d^2y}{dx^2} - 7\frac{dy}{dx} + 10y = 0$.

The auxiliary equation is $m^2 - 7m + 10 = 0$

$\Rightarrow (m - 2)(m - 5) = 0$

$\Rightarrow m = 2$ or $m = 5$

Thus the general solution to $\frac{d^2y}{dx^2} - 7\frac{dy}{dx} + 10y = 0$ is $y = Ae^{2x} + Be^{5x}$.

Particular solutions

To find values for the two arbitrary constants we must be given initial conditions which will allow us to set up a system of equations to solve for A and B.

This may be, for example, two points (x, y) or a point and the gradient at that point.

Example 11

Find the particular solution of $2\frac{d^2y}{dx^2} - 5\frac{dy}{dx} - 3y = 0$ given that when $x = 0, y = 3$ and $\frac{dy}{dx} = 2$.

The auxiliary equation is $2m^2 - 5m - 3 = 0$

$\Rightarrow (2m + 1)(m - 3) = 0$

$\Rightarrow m = -\frac{1}{2}$ or $m = 3$

Thus the general solution to $2\frac{d^2y}{dx^2} - 5\frac{dy}{dx} - 3y = 0$ is $y = Ae^{-\frac{1}{2}x} + Be^{3x}$.

$y = Ae^{-\frac{1}{2}x} + Be^{3x} \Rightarrow \frac{dy}{dx} = -\frac{1}{2}Ae^{-\frac{1}{2}x} + 3Be^{3x}$

Initial condition 1: $y = 3$ when $x = 0 \quad \Rightarrow 3 = A + B \quad (1)$

Initial condition 2: $\frac{dy}{dx} = 2$ when $x = 0 \Rightarrow 2 = -\frac{1}{2}A + 3B \quad (2)$

$(2) \times 2 \quad 4 = -A + 6B \quad (3)$

$(3) + (1) \quad 7 = 0 + 7B \quad \Rightarrow B = 1$

Substitute in (1) $\quad 3 = A + 1 \quad \Rightarrow A = 2$

Thus the particular solution we want is $y = 2e^{-\frac{1}{2}x} + e^{3x}$.

Exercise 8.4

1 Find the general solution in each case.

a $\frac{d^2y}{dx^2} + \frac{dy}{dx} - 6y = 0$ b $\frac{d^2y}{dx^2} - 6\frac{dy}{dx} + 5y = 0$ c $2\frac{d^2y}{dx^2} + \frac{dy}{dx} - 6y = 0$

d $6\frac{d^2y}{dx^2} + \frac{dy}{dx} - y = 0$ e $3\frac{d^2y}{dx^2} - 19\frac{dy}{dx} + 6y = 0$ f $8\frac{d^2y}{dx^2} + 10\frac{dy}{dx} - 3y = 0$

g $4\frac{d^2y}{dx^2} + 8\frac{dy}{dx} + 3y = 0$ h $3\frac{d^2y}{dx^2} + 13\frac{dy}{dx} + 4y = 0$ i $6\frac{d^2y}{dx^2} + 11\frac{dy}{dx} - 10y = 0$

j $5\frac{d^2y}{dx^2} + 6\frac{dy}{dx} + y = 0$

2 Find the particular solution in each case given the initial conditions.

a $\frac{d^2y}{dx^2} - 5\frac{dy}{dx} + 6y = 0$ when $x = 0, y = 4$ and $\frac{dy}{dx} = 10$

b $2\frac{d^2y}{dx^2} - \frac{dy}{dx} - y = 0$ when $x = 0, y = 1$ and $\frac{dy}{dx} = -2$

c $\frac{d^2y}{dx^2} - 6\frac{dy}{dx} + 8y = 0$ when $x = 0, y = 5$ and $\frac{dy}{dx} = 16$

d $9\frac{d^2y}{dx^2} + 9\frac{dy}{dx} + 2y = 0$ when $x = 0, y = 4$ and $\frac{dy}{dx} = -2$

e $\frac{d^2y}{dx^2} - 4\frac{dy}{dx} = 0$ when $x = 0, y = 3$ and when $x = \frac{1}{4}, y = 1 + 2e$

8.5 Case 2: When the roots are real and coincident [$b^2 - 4ac = 0$]

If the roots are coincident and both equal to m then the above strategy would produce a solution of $y = Ae^{mx} + Be^{mx} = (A + B)e^{mx}$. However, $A + B$ is the equivalent of a single constant and we need *two* arbitrary constants for a general solution to these equations.

Luckily another theorem helps.

Theorem 2

If $y = Ae^{mx}$ is a solution then so is $y = Axe^{mx}$.

Proof

As before, $y = Ae^{mx}$ is a solution

$\Rightarrow aAm^2e^{mx} + bAme^{mx} + cAe^{mx} = 0 = Ae^{mx}(am^2 + bm + c) \Rightarrow am^2 + bm + c = 0$

We also know that this has coincident roots, namely $m = -\frac{b}{2a} \Rightarrow 2am + b = 0$

$y = Axe^{mx} \Rightarrow \frac{dy}{dx} = Axme^{mx} + Ae^{mx} \Rightarrow \frac{d^2y}{dx^2} = Axm^2e^{mx} + Ame^{mx} + Ame^{mx}$

Substituting in $a\frac{d^2y}{dx^2} + b\frac{dy}{dx} + cy = 0$ we get

$a(Axm^2e^{mx} + Ame^{mx} + Ame^{mx}) + b(Axme^{mx} + Ae^{mx}) + cAxe^{mx}$

$= aAxm^2e^{mx} + aAme^{mx} + aAme^{mx} + bAxme^{mx} + bAe^{mx} + cAxe^{mx}$

$= aAxm^2e^{mx} + bAxme^{mx} + cAxe^{mx} + aAme^{mx} + aAme^{mx} + bAe^{mx}$

$= Axe^{mx}(am^2 + bm + c) + Ae^{mx}(2am + b)$

$= Axe^{mx}(0) + Ae^{mx}(0) = 0$

giving that $y = Axe^{mx}$ is a solution as required.

So, if the auxiliary equation has coincident roots, m, then we can generate two solutions $y = Ae^{mx}$ and $y = Bxe^{mx}$ and hence a general solution $y = Ae^{mx} + Bxe^{mx}$.

Example 12

Find the particular solution to the equation $4\frac{d^2y}{dx^2} - 4\frac{dy}{dx} + 1 = 0$ given that when $x = 0, y = 3$ and $\frac{dy}{dx} = 1$.

The auxiliary equation is $4m^2 - 4m + 1 = 0$

$$\Rightarrow (2m - 1)(2m - 1) = 0$$

$$\Rightarrow m = \frac{1}{2} \text{ twice}$$

Thus the general solution to $4\frac{d^2y}{dx^2} - 4\frac{dy}{dx} + 1 = 0$ is $y = Ae^{\frac{1}{2}x} + Bxe^{\frac{1}{2}x}$.

$y = Ae^{\frac{1}{2}x} + Bxe^{\frac{1}{2}x} \Rightarrow \frac{dy}{dx} = \frac{1}{2}Ae^{\frac{1}{2}x} + \frac{1}{2}Bxe^{\frac{1}{2}x} + Be^{\frac{1}{2}x}$

Initial condition 1: $y = 3$ when $x = 0 \Rightarrow 3 = A + B$ (1)

Initial condition 2: $\frac{dy}{dx} = 1$ when $x = 0 \Rightarrow 1 = \frac{1}{2}A + B$ (2)

$$(1) - (2) \quad 2 = \frac{1}{2}A \Rightarrow A = 4$$

$$\text{Substitute in (1)} \quad 3 = 4 + B \Rightarrow B = -1$$

Thus the particular solution we want is $y = 4e^{\frac{1}{2}x} + xe^{\frac{1}{2}x}$.

Exercise 8.5

1 Find the general solution in each case.

a $\frac{d^2y}{dx^2} - 4\frac{dy}{dx} + 4y = 0$

b $\frac{d^2y}{dx^2} + 8\frac{dy}{dx} + 16y = 0$

c $4\frac{d^2y}{dx^2} + 4\frac{dy}{dx} + y = 0$

d $4\frac{d^2y}{dx^2} + 12\frac{dy}{dx} + 9y = 0$

e $9\frac{d^2y}{dx^2} - 6\frac{dy}{dx} + y = 0$

f $16\frac{d^2y}{dx^2} + 40\frac{dy}{dx} + 25y = 0$

g $\frac{d^2y}{dx^2} - 10\frac{dy}{dx} + 25y = 0$

h $\frac{d^2y}{dx^2} = 0$

i $a\frac{d^2y}{dx^2} - 6a\frac{dy}{dx} + 9ay = 0$ where a is a constant

2 Find the particular solution in each case given the initial conditions.

a $\frac{d^2y}{dx^2} + 12\frac{dy}{dx} + 36y = 0$ when $x = 0, y = 1$ and when $x = 1, y = 3e^{-6}$

b $\frac{d^2y}{dx^2} - 8\frac{dy}{dx} + 16y = 0$ when $x = 0, y = 2$ and $\frac{dy}{dx} = 11$

c $9\frac{d^2y}{dx^2} - 12\frac{dy}{dx} + 4y = 0$ when $x = 0, y = 2$ and $\frac{dy}{dx} = \frac{7}{3}$

d $25\frac{d^2y}{dx^2} - 10\frac{dy}{dx} + y = 0$ when $x = 0, y = -1$ and when $x = 5, y = 14e$

8.6 Case 3: When the roots are non-real [$b^2 - 4ac < 0$]

This part requires some knowledge that will not fully be explored until Chapter 12.
However, to keep this case with the others, a light introduction should suffice.

When we try to solve a quadratic equation where the discriminant is less than zero, we get a result of the form $x = a \pm \sqrt{-b}$ where b is a positive number.
In the past you have dismissed this case by saying that *there are no real roots*.

However, if we define a number, i, such that $i^2 = -1 \Leftrightarrow \sqrt{-1} = i$ then we can have things like $\sqrt{-4} = \sqrt{4 \times -1} = \sqrt{4} \times \sqrt{-1} = 2i$.

Similarly $\sqrt{-9} = 3i$, $\sqrt{-5} = i\sqrt{5}$.

For example: consider the solutions of the equation $x^2 - 6x + 13 = 0$.

Using the quadratic formula, $x = \frac{6 \pm \sqrt{36 - 52}}{2} = \frac{6 \pm \sqrt{-16}}{2} = \frac{6 \pm 4i}{2} = 3 \pm 2i$.

These two solutions are not real numbers. They are referred to as **complex** numbers.
In fact, pairs of the form $p \pm iq$ where p and q are real are called **complex conjugates.**

Back to solving differential equations.

> If the solutions of the auxiliary equation are a pair of complex conjugates $m_1 = p + iq$ and $m_2 = p - iq$ it can be shown that the general solution to the second-order differential equation is $y = e^{px}(A \cos qx + B \sin qx)$ where A and B are the arbitrary constants.

The proof depends on material which is beyond the scope of this course, but you *will* be expected to work with the result.

Example 13

Find the general solution to the equation $\frac{d^2y}{dx^2} - 4\frac{dy}{dx} + 29 = 0$.

The auxiliary equation is $m^2 - 4m + 29 = 0$

$\Rightarrow m = \frac{4 \pm \sqrt{16 - 116}}{2} = \frac{4 \pm \sqrt{-100}}{2} = \frac{4 \pm 10i}{2} = 2 \pm 5i$

Thus the general solution is $y = e^{2x}(A \cos 5x + B \sin 5x)$.

Exercise 8.6

1 Find the general solution in each case.

a $\frac{d^2y}{dx^2} - 4\frac{dy}{dx} + 5y = 0$ b $\frac{d^2y}{dx^2} - 2\frac{dy}{dx} + 5y = 0$ c $\frac{d^2y}{dx^2} + 2\frac{dy}{dx} + 10y = 0$

d $\frac{d^2y}{dx^2} + 6\frac{dy}{dx} + 13y = 0$ e $4\frac{d^2y}{dx^2} - 4\frac{dy}{dx} + 5y = 0$ f $4\frac{d^2y}{dx^2} + 4\frac{dy}{dx} + 101y = 0$

2 Find the particular solution in each case given the initial conditions.

a $\frac{d^2y}{dx^2} - 6\frac{dy}{dx} + 10y = 0$ when $x = 0, y = 2$ and $\frac{dy}{dx} = 9$

b $\frac{d^2y}{dx^2} - 4\frac{dy}{dx} + 8y = 0$ when $x = 0, y = 1$ and $\frac{dy}{dx} = 6$

c $\frac{d^2y}{dx^2} - 10\frac{dy}{dx} + 26y = 0$ when $x = 0, y = 3$ and $\frac{dy}{dx} = 16$

d $9\frac{d^2y}{dx^2} - 6\frac{dy}{dx} + 82y = 0$ when $x = 0, y = 3$ and $\frac{dy}{dx} = 16$

8.7 Bringing it together

Examine the auxiliary equation

Case 1 Two distinct roots, m_1 and m_2.
$y = Ae^{m_1x} + Be^{m_2x}$

Case 2 Two coincident roots, m.
$y = Ae^{mx} + Bxe^{mx}$

Case 3 Two complex roots, $p \pm qi$.
$y = e^{px}(A \cos qx + B \sin qx)$

Exercise 8.7

1 Find the general solution in each case.

a $\frac{d^2y}{dx^2} - 3\frac{dy}{dx} - 10y = 0$

b $4\frac{d^2y}{dx^2} - 4\frac{dy}{dx} + y = 0$

c $\frac{d^2y}{dx^2} - 2\frac{dy}{dx} + 10y = 0$

d $\frac{d^2y}{dx^2} - 6\frac{dy}{dx} + 9y = 0$

e $\frac{d^2y}{dx^2} - y = 0$

f $\frac{d^2y}{dx^2} - 4\frac{dy}{dx} + 13y = 0$

g $4\frac{d^2y}{dx^2} - 12\frac{dy}{dx} + 9y = 0$

h $4\frac{d^2y}{dx^2} - 12\frac{dy}{dx} + 5y = 0$

i $2\frac{d^2y}{dx^2} - \frac{dy}{dx} - 3y = 0$

j $8\frac{d^2y}{dx^2} + 10\frac{dy}{dx} + 3y = 0$

8.8 Non-homogeneous equations

Non-homogeneous equations take the form $a\frac{d^2y}{dx^2} + b\frac{dy}{dx} + cy = Q(x)$

Suppose $g(x)$ is a particular solution $\quad a\frac{d^2g}{dx^2} + b\frac{dg}{dx} + cg = Q(x)$

Suppose $g(x) + k(x)$ is another solution

$$a\frac{d^2(g+k)}{dx^2} + b\frac{d(g+k)}{dx} + c(g+k) = Q(x)$$

$$\Rightarrow a\frac{d^2g}{dx^2} + a\frac{d^2k}{dx^2} + b\frac{dg}{dx} + b\frac{dk}{dx} + cg + ck = Q(x)$$

$$\Rightarrow a\frac{d^2k}{dx^2} + b\frac{dk}{dx} + ck + a\frac{d^2g}{dx^2} + b\frac{dg}{dx} + cg = Q(x)$$

$$\Rightarrow a\frac{d^2k}{dx^2} + b\frac{dk}{dx} + ck + Q(x) = Q(x)$$

$$\Rightarrow a\frac{d^2k}{dx^2} + b\frac{dk}{dx} + ck = 0$$

This is a second-order homogeneous equation, for which we now know how to get the general solution, with its two arbitrary functions, for $k(x)$.

- $g(x)$ is referred to as the **particular integral** (PI).
- $k(x)$ is called the **complementary function** (CF).

Their sum, $g(x) + k(x)$, forms the general solution to the non-homogeneous equation

$$a\frac{d^2y}{dx^2} + b\frac{dy}{dx} + cy = Q(x)$$

Example 14

Find the general solution to the equation $\frac{d^2y}{dx^2} - 7\frac{dy}{dx} + 10y = 20x - 4$.

First find the CF The auxiliary equation is $m^2 - 7m + 10 = 0$.

$m^2 - 7m + 10 = 0 \Rightarrow (m-2)(m-5) = 0 \Rightarrow m = 2 \text{ or } x = 5$

So the complementary function is $y = Ae^{2x} + Be^{5x}$.

Finding the PI The choice of $g(x)$ will be explored in greater detail in the next section. However, we generally start by guessing that $y = g(x)$ will take the same general shape as $Q(x)$. In this question a linear function, so try $y = ax + b$.

$$y = ax + b \Rightarrow \frac{dy}{dx} = a \Rightarrow \frac{d^2y}{dx^2} = 0$$

Substitute these details into the equation:

$0 - 7a + 10(ax + b) = 20x - 4$

$\Rightarrow 10ax + (10b - 7a) = 20x - 4$

Equating coefficients: $\Rightarrow 10a = 20$ and $10b - 7a = -4$

$\Rightarrow a = 2$ and $b = 1$

So the particular integral is $y = 2x + 1$.

The general solution is $y = Ae^{2x} + Be^{5x} + 2x + 1$.

Example 15

Find the general solution to the equation $\frac{d^2y}{dx^2} - 2\frac{dy}{dx} + 5y = 30 \sin x$.

First find the CF: The auxiliary equation is $m^2 - 2m + 5 = 0$.

$$m = \frac{2 \pm \sqrt{4 - 20}}{2} = 1 \pm 2i$$

So the complementary function is $y = e^x(A \cos 2x + B \sin 2x)$.

Finding the PI: $Q(x) = 3 \sin x$. For $g(x)$ try $y = a \sin x + b \cos x$

$$\Rightarrow \frac{dy}{dx} = a \cos x - b \sin x \text{ and } \Rightarrow \frac{d^2y}{dx^2} = -a \sin x - b \cos x$$

Substituting into the original equation:

$(-a \sin x - b \cos x) - 2(a \cos x - b \sin x) + 5(a \sin x + b \cos x) = 30 \sin x$

$\Rightarrow (4a + 2b) \sin x - (2a - 4b) \cos x = 30 \sin x$

Equating coefficients: $4a + 2b = 30$ and $2a - 4b = 0$

Solving the system of equations gives $a = 6$ and $b = 3$.

The particular integral is $y = 6 \sin x + 3 \cos x$.

The general solution is $y = e^x(A \cos 2x + B \sin 2x) + 6 \sin x + 3 \cos x$.

Exercise 8.8

1 Find the *particular integral* in each case using the hint given.

a $\frac{d^2y}{dx^2} + 5\frac{dy}{dx} + 2y = 4x + 6$ Try the form $y = ax + b$.

b $\frac{d^2y}{dx^2} + 3\frac{dy}{dx} + 2y = x^2$ Try the form $y = ax^2 + bx + c$.

c $2\frac{d^2y}{dx^2} - \frac{dy}{dx} + 3y = 2 \cos x$ Try the form $y = a \cos x + b \sin x$.

d $3\frac{d^2y}{dx^2} - 5\frac{dy}{dx} - 2y = 20e^{3x}$ Try the form $y = ae^{3x}$.

2 Find the *general solution* to each equation.
The form of the particular integral is given.

a $\frac{d^2y}{dx^2} + 3\frac{dy}{dx} + 3y = 21e^x$ Try the form $y = ae^x$.

b $\frac{d^2y}{dx^2} + 6\frac{dy}{dx} + 9y = 18x + 3$ Try the form $y = ax + b$.

c $\frac{d^2y}{dx^2} - 2\frac{dy}{dx} + 10y = 11(\cos x - \sin x)$ Try the form $y = a\cos x + b\sin x$.

d $\frac{d^2y}{dx^2} + 7\frac{dy}{dx} + 12y = 12x^2 + 2x + 7$ Try the form $y = ax^2 + bx + c$.

8.9 Identifying the form of the particular integral

Consider the non-homogeneous equation $a\frac{d^2y}{dx^2} + b\frac{dy}{dx} + cy = Q(x)$.
The particular integral will make the LHS of this equation equal to $Q(x)$.

- So our initial choice for the PI is to choose the same form as $Q(x)$.

Each term of the complementary function makes the LHS equal to 0.
If we let the PI take the same form as one of these terms, we will make $Q(x) = 0$.
But we know $Q(x) \neq 0$ by the definition of the non-homogeneous equation.

- So if we cannot use the same form as $Q(x)$, try the same form as $xQ(x)$.
- If, for the same reason, we cannot use the same form as $xQ(x)$, we should try the same form as $x^2Q(x)$.

Examples of particular integrals

With CF $y = Ae^{3x} + Be^{2x}$

- if $Q(x) = 2x$ for PI try $y = ax + b$, the general linear function
- if $Q(x) = 2e^{4x}$ for PI try $y = ae^{4x}$, an exponential function of the same power
- if $Q(x) = 2e^{3x}$ for PI try $y = axe^{3x}$, we cannot simply use $y = ae^{3x}$ as it is in the CF
- if $Q(x) = 3\cos x$ for PI try $y = a\cos x + b\sin x$, the general wave function
- if $Q(x) = x^2 + 2$ for PI try $y = ax^2 + bx + c$, the general quadratic function

With CF $y = A + Be^{2x}$

- if $Q(x) = 2x + 1$ for PI try $y = x(ax + b)$, since A is a linear function $y \neq ax+b$

With CF $y = Ae^{2x} + Bxe^{2x}$

- if $Q(x) = 3e^{2x}$ for PI try ax^2e^{2x}, since choices ae^{2x} and axe^{2x} are both in the CF

With CF $y = A\sin 3x + B\cos 3x$

- if $Q(x) = 3\sin 3x$ for PI try $x(a\sin 3x + b\cos 3x)$

Example 16

Find the general solution to the equation $\frac{d^2y}{dx^2} - 4\frac{dy}{dx} + 3y = 6e^x$.

Auxiliary equation is $m^2 - 4m + 3 = 0 \Rightarrow (m-1)(m-3) = 0 \Rightarrow m = 1$ or $m = 3$.
The complementary function is $y = Ae^x + Be^{3x}$.
$Q(x) = 6e^x$ so we might consider $y = ae^x$ as the PI,
but this form is present in the CF. So try $y = axe^x$.
$y = axe^x \Rightarrow \frac{dy}{dx} = axe^x + ae^x \Rightarrow \frac{d^2y}{dx^2} = axe^x + ae^x + ae^x$

Substitute in equation: $axe^x + 2ae^x - 4(axe^x + ae^x) + 3axe^x = 6e^x$

$\Rightarrow -2ae^x = 6e^x \Rightarrow a = -3$, so the PI is $y = -3xe^x$.

The general solution is $y = Ae^x + Be^{3x} - 3xe^x$.

Example 17

Find the particular solution to the equation $\frac{d^2y}{dx^2} + y = 2x + 1$ given that when $x = 0, y = 3$ and $\frac{dy}{dx} = 5$.

Auxiliary equation: $m^2 + 1 = 0 \Rightarrow m = \pm\sqrt{-1} = \pm i$ giving $p = 0$ and $q = 1$

Complementary function: $y = e^{0x}(A \sin 1 \cdot x + B \cos 1 \cdot x) = A \sin x + B \cos x$

$Q(x) = 2x + 1$, so for PI try: $y = ax + b$ [Check there is no conflict with the CF]

$y = ax + b \Rightarrow \frac{dy}{dx} = a \Rightarrow \frac{d^2y}{dx^2} = 0$

Substitute in equation: $0 + ax + b = 2x + 1$

Equating coefficients: $a = 2$ and $b = 1$, so PI is $y = 2x + 1$

General solution: $y = A \sin x + B \cos x + 2x + 1$

$\Rightarrow \frac{dy}{dx} = A \cos x - B \sin x + 2$

When $x = 0, y = 3$: $3 = A \sin 0 + B \cos 0 + 2 \cdot 0 + 1 \Rightarrow B + 1 = 3 \Rightarrow B = 2$

When $x = 0, \frac{dy}{dx} = 5$: $5 = A \cos 0 - B \sin 0 + 2 = A + 2 \Rightarrow A = 3$

The particular solution is: $y = 3 \sin x + 2 \cos x + 2x + 1$

Exercise 8.9

1 Find the general solution to each of these.

a $\frac{d^2y}{dx^2} + 2\frac{dy}{dx} - 3y = 3x + 1$

b $\frac{d^2y}{dx^2} - 3\frac{dy}{dx} + 2y = x^2 + 2x + 1$

c $2\frac{d^2y}{dx^2} + 3\frac{dy}{dx} - 2y = e^{\frac{x}{2}}$

d $2\frac{d^2y}{dx^2} + 7\frac{dy}{dx} + 3y = 50 \sin x$

e $\frac{d^2y}{dx^2} + 6\frac{dy}{dx} + 9y = 50e^{2x}$

f $\frac{d^2y}{dx^2} - 10\frac{dy}{dx} + 25y = 4e^{5x}$

g $4\frac{d^2y}{dx^2} - 4\frac{dy}{dx} + y = 5x - 3$

h $\frac{d^2y}{dx^2} - 6\frac{dy}{dx} + 10y = 6e^{4x}$

i $\frac{d^2y}{dx^2} - 4\frac{dy}{dx} + 8y = 1$

j $\frac{d^2y}{dx^2} + 4y = 8 \sin 2x$

2 Find the particular solution to each of these differential equations.

a $\frac{d^2y}{dx^2} - 5\frac{dy}{dx} + 6y = 12x + 8$, when $x = 0, y = 2$ and $\frac{dy}{dx} = 6$

b $\frac{d^2y}{dx^2} - 3\frac{dy}{dx} + 2y = e^x$, when $x = 0, y = 3 - e$ and $x = 1, y = e$

c $2\frac{d^2y}{dx^2} - 3\frac{dy}{dx} + y = x^2$, when $x = 0, y = 9$ and $\frac{dy}{dx} = 5$

d $\frac{d^2y}{dx^2} - 2\frac{dy}{dx} + y = 6e^x$, when $x = 0, y = -1$ and when $x = 1, y = 4e$

e $\frac{d^2y}{dx^2} + 4y = 6 \cos x$, when $x = 0, y = 3$ and when $x = \frac{\pi}{4}, y = 2 + \sqrt{2}$

3 A particle is moving along the x-axis. Its motion can be modelled by a differential equation of the form $\frac{d^2x}{dt^2} + m\frac{dx}{dt} + nx = 0$.

Initially ($t = 0$), $x = 10$ and the velocity is zero $\left(\frac{dx}{dt} = 0\right)$.

Consider three situations:

a $m = 4, n = 3$ b $m = 4, n = 4$ c $m = 4, n = 5$

Find formulae for the displacement and velocity in each situation and describe the motion that takes place.

Review 8

1 Find the general solution to the differential equation $\frac{dy}{dx} = y \sin x$.

2 Find the particular solution to the equation $\frac{dy}{dx} = 1 + y^2$ given that when $x = 0, y = 1$.

3 Find the general solution to $(x - 1)\frac{dy}{dx} + y = \cos x\sqrt{\sin x}$.

4 Find the particular solution to the equation $\frac{dy}{dx} + y = \cos x$ given that when $x = 0, y = \frac{3}{2}$.

5 Find the general solution to each of these.

a $2\frac{d^2y}{dx^2} + 5\frac{dy}{dx} + 2y = 0$ b $4\frac{d^2y}{dx^2} - 12\frac{dy}{dx} + 9y = 0$

c $\frac{d^2y}{dx^2} - 4\frac{dy}{dx} + 13y = 0$

6 Find the particular solution to $\frac{d^2y}{dx^2} - \frac{dy}{dx} - 6y = 0$ given that when $x = 0, y = 8$ and $\frac{dy}{dx} = 1$.

7 Find the general solution to each of these.

a $2\frac{d^2y}{dx^2} + 5\frac{dy}{dx} + 2y = 4x + 8$ b $4\frac{d^2y}{dx^2} - 12\frac{dy}{dx} + 9y = 3e^x$

c $\frac{d^2y}{dx^2} - 4\frac{dy}{dx} + 13y = 13x^2 + 5x + 11$

8 Find a particular solution in each case.

a $\frac{d^2y}{dx^2} - \frac{dy}{dx} - 6y = 3x + 2$ given that when $x = 0, y = 6$ and $\frac{dy}{dx} = 2$

b $\frac{d^2y}{dx^2} - 2\frac{dy}{dx} + y = 10e^x$ given that when $x = 0, y = -2$ and when $x = 1, y = 0$

c $\frac{d^2y}{dx^2} + 2\frac{dy}{dx} + 5y = 1$ given that when $x = 0, y = 5.2$ and $\frac{dy}{dx} = -2$

Summary 8

1 **First-order** differential equations.

a Variables separable: general form $f(y)\frac{dy}{dx} = g(x)$.

Express in the form $f(y)\,dy = g(x)\,dx$ and integrate to get the solution $\int f(y)\,dy = \int g(x)\,dx + C$

b **Linear** differential equations: general form $\frac{dy}{dx} + P(x)y = Q(x)$.

- Find the **integrating factor** (IF) $= e^{\int P(x)\,dx}$.
- Multiply throughout by the IF to make the equation

  $\frac{d}{dx}\left(ye^{\int P(x)\,dx}\right) = e^{\int P(x)\,dx}Q(x)$

  to get solution $ye^{\int P(x)\,dx} = \int\left(e^{\int P(x)\,dx}Q(x)\right)dx + C$

2 Second-order differential equations.

- General form $a\frac{d^2y}{dx^2} + b\frac{dy}{dx} + cy = Q(x)$.
- **Auxiliary equation** for this differential equation: $am^2 + bm + c = 0$.

a **Homogeneous equations**: general form $a\frac{d^2y}{dx^2} + b\frac{dy}{dx} + cy = 0$.

Referring to the roots of the auxiliary equation we find there are three cases to consider when looking for general solutions.

i Roots are distinct: m_1 and m_2. Solution $y = Ae^{m_1x} + Be^{m_2x}$.

ii Roots are coincident: m. Solution $y = Ae^{mx} + Bxe^{mx}$.

iii Roots are complex: $p \pm qi$. Solution $y = e^{px}(A \sin qx + B \cos qx)$.

b **Non-homogeneous equations:**

- General form $a\frac{d^2y}{dx^2} + b\frac{dy}{dx} + cy = Q(x)$; $Q(x) \neq 0$.
- The general solution to the corresponding homogeneous equation is called the **complementary function** (CF).
- A particular solution to the non-homogeneous equation is called a **particular integral** (PI).
- The general solution to the non-homogeneous equation:

  $y = \text{CF} + \text{PI}$

- When looking for the PI:

  i Try the general form of the functions to which $Q(x)$ belongs.

  ii If this is already part of the CF then try the form of $xQ(x)$.

  iii If *this* is already part of the CF then try the form of $x^2Q(x)$.

3 A **particular solution** to any differential equation is obtained when we find the values of the arbitrary constants which correspond to some **initial conditions**. Generally the initial conditions can be

a a value of x and the corresponding y-value

b a value of x and the corresponding value of $\frac{dy}{dx}$.

i For a first-order differential equation one set of initial conditions is required to find the one arbitrary constant.

ii For a second-order differential equation two sets of initial conditions are required to find the two arbitrary constants.

9 Arithmetic and geometric progression

Historical note

Sequences and series have been studied in mathematics for as far back as written records go. Geometric progressions have been deciphered on Babylonian tablets (2000 BC). Problems involving arithmetic and geometric sequences appear on the Ahmes Papyrus (1650 BC).

Euclid (c 300 BC) wrote 13 books referred to collectively as his *Elements*. In Book VIII he derives a formula for the sum of a geometric progression.

9.1 Sequences and arithmetic sequences

Reminders

- A **sequence** is an ordered list of numbers where each term is obtained according to a fixed rule.
- A **series**, or **progression**, is a sum, the terms of which form a sequence.
- The nth term of a sequence is often denoted by u_n, so that, for example, u_1 is the first term.
- A sequence can be defined by a recurrence relation where u_{n+1} is expressed as a function of earlier terms.
- A **first-order recurrence relation** is where u_{n+1} is expressed as a function of u_n.
- A **linear** first-order recurrence relation is where $u_{n+1} = ru_n + d$ where r and d are constants.
- A sequence can be defined by a formula for u_n given in the form $u_n = f(n)$.
- Knowing the first few terms of a sequence is *not* enough to identify the sequence. For example, given the start 1, 2, 3, ..., the following generate the start, but each produces a different fourth term.

  $u_n = \frac{1}{2}(6 - 9n + 6n^2 - n^3)$ gives $u_4 = 1$

  $u_n = \frac{1}{3}(6 - 8n + 6n^2 - n^3)$ gives $u_4 = 2$

  $u_n = \frac{1}{6}(6 - 5n + 6n^2 - n^3)$ gives $u_4 = 3$

  $u_n = n$ gives $u_4 = 4$

  $u_n = \frac{1}{6}(n^3 - 6n^2 + 17n - 6)$ gives $u_4 = 5$

  $u_n = \frac{1}{3}(19n^3 - 114n^2 + 212n - 114)$ gives $u_4 = 42$
- Knowing the first few terms of a sequence *and* knowing that it is generated by a first-order linear recurrence relation is enough to allow us to uniquely identify the next term.
  Knowing u_1, u_2, u_3, and that the relation is of the form $u_{n+1} = ru_n + d$
  we can form a system of equations and solve for r and d.
- If, for some value of n in the relation $u_{n+1} = ru_n + d$, you obtain $u_{n+1} = u_n = k$ then k is referred to as a **fixed point**.
  The fixed point is called **stable** if, for any other u_n, the terms of the sequence move towards, or converge on, the value k. When $|r| < 1$, the fixed point is stable.
  The fixed point is called **unstable** if, for any other u_n, the terms of the sequence move away, or diverge from, the value k. When $|r| > 1$, the fixed point is unstable.

Arithmetic sequences

If a sequence is generated so that, for all n,

$$u_{n+2} - u_{n+1} = u_{n+1} - u_n = d$$

then the sequence is known as an **arithmetic sequence**.

The constant, d, is referred to as the **common difference**.

$u_{n+1} - u_n = d \Rightarrow u_{n+1} = u_n + d$, a linear first-order recurrence relation with $r = 1$ and $d \neq 0$.

Traditionally u_1 is represented by the letter a, so $u_1 = a$.

The *n*th term

$$u_n = a + (n - 1)d$$

Proof

Given the recurrence relation $u_{n+1} = u_n + d$, $u_1 = a$,
the first few terms are $u_1 = a$, $u_2 = a + d$, $u_3 = a + 2d$, $u_4 = a + 3d$, ...
The pattern of terms suggests that $u_n = a + (n - 1)d$.

When $n = 1$ $\quad u_1 = a + (1 - 1)d = a$. $\qquad$ The statement is true for $n = 1$.

Suppose that the statement is true for $n = k$.
Then $u_k = a + (k - 1)d$. $\qquad$ (1)
Consider $n = k + 1$

$u_{k+1} = u_k + d$ $\qquad$ (By definition)
$= a + (k - 1)d + d$ $\qquad$ (Using (1))
$= a + (k - 1 + 1)d = a + ((k + 1) - 1)d$

Hence the statement is true for $n = k + 1$.
Being true for $n = k$ implies it is true for $n = k + 1$.
Since it is true when $n = 1$, then by induction, it is true $\forall\, n \in N$.

Example 1

Find **a** the nth term **b** the 10th term of the arithmetic sequence 6, 11, 16, ...

a By inspection $a = 6$; $d = 11 - 6 = 5$.
Hence $u_n = a + (n - 1)d \Rightarrow u_n = 6 + (n - 1) \cdot 5$
$= 1 + 5n$

b $u_{10} = 1 + 5 \cdot 10 = 51$

Example 2

Find the arithmetic sequence for which $u_3 = 9$ and $u_7 = 17$.

$u_3 = 9 \Rightarrow a + (n - 1)d = a + (3 - 1)d = a + 2d \Rightarrow 9 = a + 2d$ $\qquad$ (1)

$u_7 = 17 \Rightarrow a + (n - 1)d = a + (7 - 1)d = a + 6d \Rightarrow 17 = a + 6d$ $\qquad$ (2)

Subtract (2) − (1) $8 = 4d \Rightarrow d = 2$

Substitute in (1) $9 = a + 4 \Rightarrow a = 5$

So the sequence starts 5, 7, 9, 11 and has an nth term, $u_n = 5 + (n - 1) \cdot 2 = 2n + 3$.

Example 3

Given the arithmetic sequence 2, 8, 14, 20, ..., for what value of n is $u_n = 62$?

$a = 2, d = 8 - 2 = 6$ $\Rightarrow u_n = 2 + (n - 1) \cdot 6 = 6n - 4$

Given $u_n = 62$ $\Rightarrow 6n - 4 = 62$

$\Rightarrow n = 11$

Exercise 9.1

1 Identify a and d in each of these arithmetic sequences.

a 5, 8, 11, ... b 3, 4, 5, ... c 0, −3, −6, ...

d −1, 4, 9, ... e −3, −7, −11, ... f 0, 7, 14, ...

g 3, 2.8, 2.6, ... h $\frac{1}{15}, \frac{1}{5}, \frac{1}{3}, \ldots$ i $\frac{1}{4}, \frac{1}{7}, \frac{1}{28}, \ldots$

2 Find the nth term for each of these arithmetic sequences.

a 2, 3, 4, ... b 16, 12, 8, ... c 5, 3, 1, ...

d −8, −5, −2, ... e 14, 10, 6, ... f −4, −9, −14, ...

g −0.5, −1.1, −1.7, ... h $\frac{3}{20}, \frac{1}{5}, \frac{1}{4}, \ldots$ i $\frac{1}{36}, -\frac{1}{9}, -\frac{1}{4}, \ldots$

3 a Find the value of n when $a = 2, d = 3$ and $u_n = 14$.

b Which term in the sequence 12, 7, 2, ... is −18?

c If, in an arithmetic sequence $u_1 = -2$ and $u_2 = -6$, which term has the value −46?

4 a Find the value of d when $a = 7$ and $u_{26} = 107$.

b An arithmetic sequence starts with 10. Its 50th term is −382.
What is the common difference?

c Find terms u_2 to u_5 of the arithmetic sequence when the first term is 3 and the 15th term is −4.

5 a For a particular sequence, $u_{51} = 98$. If $d = 2$, find a.

b In an arithmetic sequence the 13th term is 65 and the common difference is 4. Find the first term.

c A man starts with a pile of pebbles. He repeatedly removes three pebbles.
What was the original size of the pile if the 18th term of the sequence he creates is 9?
[Treat the original pile as the first term.]

6 a Identify the arithmetic sequence in each case by listing the first four terms.

i $u_6 = 22$ and $u_8 = 30$ ii $u_5 = -3$ and $u_{11} = -15$ iii $u_{11} = 10$ and $u_{21} = 12$

b The 16th term of an arithmetic sequence is −38. The 25th term is −65.

i Identify the sequence.

ii What is the largest number smaller than −300 that is a term in the sequence?

7 An arithmetic sequence is defined by $u_n = 3n + 9$.

a Find analytically the value of x such that $3u_x = u_{4x}$.

b If a sequence is defined by $u_n = mn + c$, where m and c are integer constants, show that if $3u_x = u_{4x}$ then m is a factor of $2c$.

8 a Show that ln 5, ln 10, ln 20 could be the first three terms of an arithmetic sequence and state the value of d, the common difference.

b Find u_n, expressing your answer in the form $u_n = \ln(A)$.

c For what *value* of x does u_x first exceed 50?

9 A concert hall has its seat arranged so that the number of seats in each row forms an arithmetic sequence. Starting at the front, the rows are labeled Row A, B, C etc. Row G has 56 seats. Row P has 110 seats.

a How many seats are in the front row?

b Which is the first row with more than 70 seats?

c How many more seats are in row H than row B?

d Each row is 30 cm higher than the row in front.
Height is measured as 'height above the stage'.
Row G is 240 cm above the stage.

i How high is row n above the stage?

ii How high is the front row above the stage?

10 In an athletics stadium the seats surround the field, rising in terraces.
The number of seats in the rows form an arithmetic sequence.
There are 880 seats in row 6 and 1200 seats in row 26.

a How many seats are in i the front row ii the 10th row?

b A neighbouring stadium has 500 seats in the front row and 800 seats in row 10. Show that the number of seats in the rows does not form an arithmetic sequence.

11 A kitchen roll comprises a long unbroken length of paper tissue wrapped round a central tube of diameter 1 cm. The paper is 0.3 mm thick.

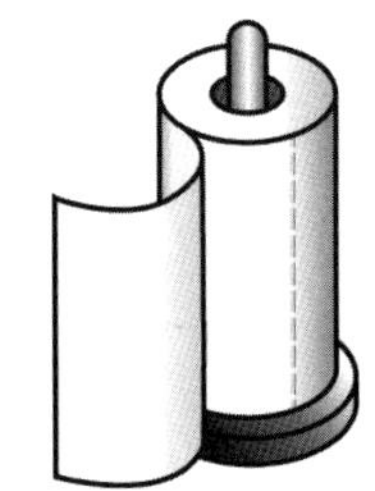

a Show that the diameters of the roll after each complete turn form an arithmetic sequence, and state the values of a and d.

b Show that the circumferences of each complete turn also form an arithmetic sequence.

c What is the circumference of the 14th turn?

Historical note

According to Gauss, when he was 10 years old, it was the habit of the teacher, Mr Büttner, to give the class a very long problem to solve to keep them busy. One day they were asked for the sum of the first 100 whole numbers. This might be expected to occupy a 10-year old boy for about an hour. Gauss, however, totalled the sequence in seconds using this strategy.

Consider the sum	$S = 1 + 2 + 3 + \dots + 98 + 99 + 100$
Reverse the sum	$S = 100 + 99 + 98 + \dots + 3 + 2 + 1$
Add the two sums	$2S = 101 + 101 + 101 + \dots + 101 + 101 + 101$
A simple multiplication	$2S = 10\,100$
Halve the answer	$S = 5050$

9.2 The sum to *n* terms of an arithmetic sequence

An arithmetic series, or arithmetic progression (AP), is a sum whose terms form an arithmetic sequence. Its value, to n terms, denoted by S_n, can be found using:

$$S_n = \frac{1}{2}n(2a + (n - 1)d)$$

Proof

You can use Gauss' strategy to prove this directly.

$S_n = a + (a + d) + (a + 2d) + (a + 3d) + ... + (a + (n - 2)d) + (a + (n - 1)d)$

Reversing the order

$$S_n = (a + (n - 1)d) + (a + (n - 2)d) + ... + (a + 3d) + (a + 2d) + (a + d) + a$$

Adding

$$2S_n = (2a + (n - 1)d) + (2a + (n - 1)d) + ... + (2a + (n - 1)d) + (2a + (n - 1)d)$$
$$= n(2a + (n - 1)d)$$
$$\Rightarrow S_n = \frac{1}{2}n(2a + (n - 1)d)$$

Example 4

Find the sum of the first 10 terms of the arithmetic sequence which starts 2, 8, 14, ...

$a = 2, d = 8 - 2 = 6, n = 10$

Substituting in $S_n = \frac{1}{2}n(2a + (n - 1)d)$ gives

$S_n = \frac{1}{2} \cdot 10 \cdot (2 \cdot 2 + (10 - 1) \cdot 6) = 5(4 + 54) = 290$

Example 5

When does the sum of the arithmetic sequence which starts 1, 7, 13, 19, ..., first exceed 100?

$a = 1, d = 7 - 1 = 6$

Substituting in $S_n = \frac{1}{2}n(2a + (n - 1)d)$ gives

$S_n = \frac{1}{2}n(2 + (n - 1)6) = 3n^2 - 2n$

$S_n > 100 \Rightarrow 3n^2 - 2n > 100 \Rightarrow 3n^2 - 2n - 100 > 0$

Solving $3n^2 - 2n - 100 = 0$ gives $n = 6.1$ or $n = -5.4$ (to 1dp)
Given that $n \in \mathbb{N}$, and from a quick sketch, you see that
$n = 7$ gives the first term greater than 100.

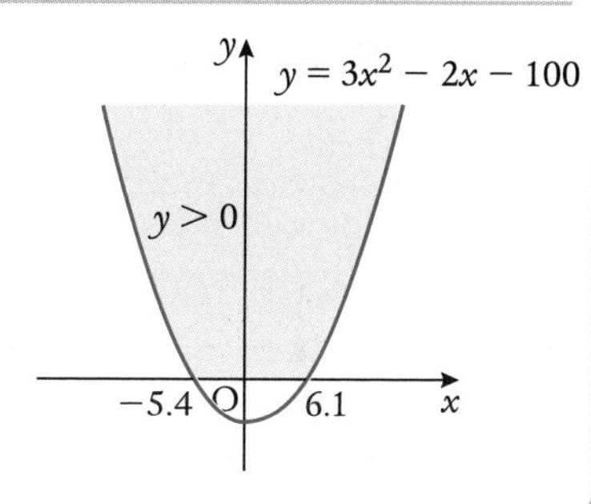

Example 6

The sum of the first five terms of an arithmetic sequence is 85; the sum of the first 10 terms is 295. What is the sum of the first 20 terms?

$S_5 = 85 \Rightarrow \frac{5}{2}(2a + 4d) = 85 \quad \Rightarrow 2a + 4d = 34 \quad (1)$

$S_{10} = 295 \Rightarrow \frac{10}{2}(2a + 9d) = 295 \Rightarrow 2a + 9d = 59 \quad (2)$

Subtracting (2) − (1) $5d = 25 \Rightarrow d = 5$

Substitute in (1) $\quad 2a + 4 \cdot 5 = 34 \Rightarrow a + 10 = 17 \Rightarrow a = 7$

So $S_{20} = \frac{20}{2}(2a + 19d) = 20 \cdot 7 + 190 \cdot 5 = 140 + 950 = 1090$

Exercise 9.2

1 a Calculate the sum to 10 terms of the arithmetic series which starts 2 + 8 + 14 + ...

b Find S_{16} for an arithmetic series when $u_1 = 7, u_2 = 28$ and $u_3 = 49$.

c Find the required sum when each of these is an AP.

i $4 + 9 + 14 + \ldots : S_{20}$

ii $6 + 20 + 34 + \ldots : S_{50}$

iii $(-1) + (-8) + (-15) + \ldots : S_{15}$

iv $-9 - 7 - 5 - \ldots : S_{10}$

2 The first two terms of an arithmetic sequence are 14 and 25 in that order.

a Find the sum of the first 15 terms and the first 16 terms.

b Hence calculate the 16th term.

c Repeat this process for if the first two terms are 25 and 14 in that order.

3 Find these sums, given that each is an arithmetic series.

a $7 + 8 + 9 + \ldots + 40$

b $17 + 24 + 31 + \ldots + 360$

c $-16 + (-18) + \ldots + (-54)$

d $5 - 3 - 11 - \ldots - 83$

e $0.3 + 0.7 + 1.1 + \ldots + 2.3$

f $\frac{1}{12} + \frac{1}{6} + \frac{1}{4} + \frac{1}{3} + \ldots + 5$

4 a The sum of the first 80 terms of an arithmetic series is 25 680.
The common difference is 8. What is the first term?

b The sum of the first 41 terms of an arithmetic series is 0.
The common difference is 7. What is the first term?

5 a The first term of an arithmetic progression is 5 and the last term is 50.
The sum of the terms is 440. How many terms are in the progression?

b The first term of an AP is a, the last term is L. Consider Gauss' strategy and form a relationship between a, L, n and S_n.

c The first term of a particular AP is a natural number, and the last term is 10 times bigger. The sum of the terms is 363. Assuming that the AP has more than one term, there are seven APs which fit the description. Find them.

6 a An arithmetic series starts with 8, has 20 terms and totals 2440.
Calculate the common difference.

b The first 60 terms of an arithmetic progression sum to 891.
If the first term is 0.1, what is the common difference?

7 a The first three terms of an arithmetic sequence total 30. The next three total 69. What is the sum of the three after that?

b The sum of the first four terms of an arithmetic sequence is -2.
The next three total 51. What is the 16th term?

8 An historical problem (16th century).
100 eggs are placed in a straight line, one step apart.
A basket is situated one step from the start of the line.
A person walks away from the basket, picks up the first egg and returns it to the basket. He then walks to the second egg, picks it up and returns it to the basket. He continues in this fashion until all the eggs are in the basket.
How many steps did he take?

9 The first three terms of an arithmetic sequence are x, $x + 7$ and bx, where $b, x \in \mathbb{N}$.

a Express x in terms of b.

b Identify all the sequences which fit the description.

c Calculate the sum to 10 terms in each case.

10 a An arithmetic sequence is such that $u_1 = x$ and $u_7 = x^3$.
Prove that if $x \in \mathbb{N}, x > 1$, then $d \in \mathbb{N}$.

b An arithmetic sequence is such that $u_1 = x$ and $S_4 = 4x^3$.
Prove that if $x \in \mathbb{N}, x > 1$, then d is divisible by 4.

11 A roll of sticky tape is wound round a spindle of radius 5 cm.
The tape is 0.05 cm thick.

a Taking each complete winding as approximately circular, and keeping π in your answer, find the circumference of each of the first five windings.

b If there are 200 windings on the roll calculate the total length of tape on the roll.

12 Puzzle. Two horses, A and B, are moving apart. A fly continually flits between them as they part. It flew 1 m from A to B. It then had to fly 3 m to get back to A (so it is $1 - 3$ m from where it started). It then flew 5 m to reach B, then 7 back to A, $(1 - 3 + 5 - 7)$.

a Express $1 - 3 + 5 - 7 + 9 - \ldots + (4n - 3) - (4n - 1)$ in terms of n.
[Hint: treat it as two APs.]

b Find, in terms of n, $4 - 7 + 10 - 13 + \ldots + 3n + 1 - ((3n + 1) + 1)$. [Be careful]

c Find the sum of $1 + 8 + 4 + 7 + 7 + 6 + 10 + \ldots$ for $2n$ terms.

13 An arithmetic sequence starts $a_1, a_2, a_3, a_4, a_5, a_6, \ldots$
Show that the terms $(a_1 + a_2 + a_3), (a_4 + a_5 + a_6), (a_7 + a_8 + a_9), \ldots$ also form an arithmetic sequence.

9.3 Geometric sequences

If a sequence is generated so that, for all $x \in \mathbb{N}$,

$$u_{n+2} \div u_{n+1} = u_{n+1} \div u_n = r$$

then the sequence is known as a **geometric sequence**. The constant r is referred to as the **common ratio**.
$u_{n+1} \div u_n = r \Rightarrow u_{n+1} = ru_n$ which is a first-order linear recurrence relation $(d = 0, r \neq 0, 1)$
Again u_1 is traditionally represented by the letter a. $[u_1 = a]$

The *n*th term of a geometric sequence

$$u_n = ar^{n-1}$$

Proof

This can be proved by induction.
By definition, $u_1 = a, u_2 = ar, u_3 = ar^2, u_4 = ar^3, \ldots$ the pattern suggests $u_n = ar^{n-1}$.

Consider $n = 1$, we know $u_1 = a$, by definition.
The formula gives $u_1 = ar^{1-1} = ar^0 = a$. So the statement is true for $n = 1$.

Suppose that the statement is true for $n = k$. Thus, we assume $u_k = ar^{k-1}$
Consider when $n = k + 1$, $u_{k+1} = u_k r$ by definition.

So $u_{k+1} = u_k r = (ar^{k-1})r = ar^{k-1+1} = ar^{(k+1)-1}$.

That is, $u_{k+1} = ar^{(k+1)-1}$.
If the statement is true for $n = k$ then it is true for $n = k + 1$.
Since it is true for $n = 1$ then it is true for all $n \in \mathbb{N}, n \geq 1$.

Example 7

Find a the nth term, b the 10th term of the geometric sequence 4, 8, 16, ...

a By inspection $a = 4$ and $r = 8 \div 4 = 2$

$u_n = ar^{n-1} \Rightarrow u_n = 4 \times 2^{n-1}$

b $u_{10} = 4 \times 2^{10-1} = 4 \times 2^9 = 2048$

Example 8

Find the geometric sequence whose third term is 48 and whose eighth term is 49 152.

$u_3 = ar^2 = 48$ (1)

$u_8 = ar^7 = 49\,152$ (2)

Dividing (2) ÷ (1) $\frac{u_8}{u_3} = \frac{49\,152}{48} = \frac{ar^7}{ar^2} \Rightarrow r^5 = 1024$

$\Rightarrow r = \sqrt[5]{1024} = 4$

Substitute in (1) $a \times 4^2 = 48 \Rightarrow a = 48 \div 16 = 3$.

So the sequence starts 3, 12, 48, 192, ... and $u_n = 3 \times 4^{n-1}$.

Example 9

Given the geometric sequence 6, 12, 24, 48, ... find the value of n for which $u_n = 49\,152$.

By inspection $a = 6$ and $r = 12 \div 6 = 2$.

The term we require has $u_n = 6 \times 2^{n-1} = 49\,152$

$\Rightarrow 2^{n-1} = 49\,152 \div 6 = 8192$

$\Rightarrow \ln 2^{n-1} = \ln 8192$

$\Rightarrow (n - 1) \ln 2 = \ln 8192$

$\Rightarrow n - 1 = \frac{\ln 8192}{\ln 2} = 13$

$\Rightarrow n = 14$

Exercise 9.3

1 For each of these geometric sequences i identify a and r ii find an expression for the nth term.

a 1, 4, 16, 64, ...

b 3, −12, 48, −192

c 1536, 768, 384, 192, ...

d 3645, −1215, 405, −135, ...

e 1, 0.1, 0.01, 0.001, ...

f $\frac{1}{2}, \frac{3}{8}, \frac{9}{32}, \frac{27}{128}, \ldots$

g 0.12, 0.048, 0.0192, 0.00768, ...

h 18.4, 20.24, 22.264, 24.4904, ...

2 a The first term of a geometric sequence is 3. The common ratio is 6. Calculate the sixth term.

b In a geometric sequence, $u_1 = 0.5$, $u_2 = 0.3$. What is term 5?

c In a geometric sequence, $u_2 = 12$, $u_3 = 24$. Calculate u_{10}.

3 The fourth term of a geometric sequence is 500. The eighth term is 312 500.

a Find an expression for the nth term.

b What is the difference between the seventh and eighth terms?

c Show that the terms generated by calculating the difference between adjacent terms in this sequence also form a geometric sequence. Give the first term and the common ratio.

4 a The first two terms of a geometric sequence are 342 and 1710 in that order. Which term has the value 1 068 750?

b If $u_1 = 1710$, $u_2 = 342$, what is the first term in the sequence that has a value of less than 1?

c Two geometric sequences are defined by their first and second terms.

Sequence 1: $u_1 = p, u_2 = q$ Sequence 2: $v_1 = q, v_2 = p$

Express the ratio of $\frac{u_n}{v_n}$ in terms of r, the common ratio of the first sequence.

5 a The first term of a geometric sequence is 3. The 10th term is 1536.
Calculate the common ratio.

b The common ratio of a geometric sequence is 0.7 and the 23rd term is 0.4
Calculate the first term correct to the nearest whole number.

6 a Show that the first three terms of an arithmetic sequence cannot also be the first three terms in a geometric progression. Use proof by contradiction.

b The terms $a, a + d, a + xd$ form the start of a geometric sequence.

i Express x in terms of a and d.

ii Express the common ratio in terms of x.

c $a, ar, a + 2d$ are the first three terms of a geometric sequence.

Given that $r > 0$, express r in terms of a and d.

7 If a, m, b are three consecutive terms in a geometric sequence then m is referred to as the geometric mean of a and b.

a Express m in terms of a and b.

b Find the geometric mean of

i 3 and 75 ii 2 and 32 iii $\frac{1}{2}$ and $\frac{2}{25}$ iv 0.1 and 0.064

c 2464, a, b, c, 154 start a geometric sequence. Calculate a, b and c.

8 A gearing system works best when the number of teeth on the gear train form a geometric sequence. The terms, of course, must be rounded to the nearest whole number.

a Calculate the unknown number of teeth in each of these three-wheel gear systems.

i 8 teeth, x teeth, 18 teeth ii 14 teeth, 21 teeth, y teeth

iii z teeth, 14 teeth, 49 teeth

b A certain type of gear has four wheels in the train. Again, working to the nearest whole number, calculate the unknown terms in each of the trains.

i $16, x, y, 54$ ii $20, 30, p, q$ iii $25, 30, a, b$

9 The population of a particularly endangered species increases annually by 4%.
Initially there are 4000 breeding pairs.

a Calculate the number of breeding pairs after

i one year ii two years iii three years.

b Show that successive populations form a geometric sequence and state the common ratio.

c The species will be taken off the danger list when its population exceeds 6000.
After how many years will this happen?

10 A investment increases at a rate of r% per year.
The initial size of the investment is £P.
The size of the investment at the end of year n is £A_n.

a Find an expression for A_1.

b Find an expression for A_2 in terms of P and r.

c The successive amounts in the bank form a geometric sequence.
Find an expression for the common ratio in terms of r.

d Hence or otherwise find an expression for A_n.

11 In an experiment, a ball of radius 1 cm, made of 'super rubber', is dropped from a height.
On its first bounce it reached the height of 8 m. On its second it reached the height of 6.4 m.

a Successive bounces form a geometric sequence.
Calculate the height reached on the seventh bounce (to 1 dp).

b The ball effectively stops when the bounce is less than the radius of the ball (1 cm). After how many bounces will this happen?

12 A piece of news is spread by word of mouth through a village.
The spread can be modelled by $P_t = P_0 e^{at}$ where P_0 is the number of people who know the news to begin with.
P_t is the number of people who know the news after t days.

a i Show that the number of people who have the news on day 1, 2, 3, ... forms a geometric sequence.

ii State the common ratio.

b If $P_0 = 3$ and $P_1 = 8$, how many people will have heard the news by the end of day 6?

c The village has a population of 7500. After how many days will all people have heard the news?

9.4 The sum to *n* terms of a geometric series

A geometric series, or geometric progression (GP), is a sum whose terms form a geometric sequence.
Its value to n terms is given by this formula.

$$S_n = \frac{a(1 - r^n)}{1 - r}$$

Proof

A direct proof.

The sum is $S_n = a + ar + ar^2 + ar^3 + ... + ar^{n-2} + ar^{n-1}$ (1)

Multiply throughout by r $rS_n = ar + ar^2 + ar^3 + ar^4 + ... + ar^{n-1} + ar^n$ (2)

Subtract (1) − (2) $S_n - rS_n = a - ar^n$

$$\Rightarrow S_n(1 - r) = a(1 - r^n)$$

$$\Rightarrow S_n = \frac{a(1 - r^n)}{(1 - r)}, r \neq 1$$

Example 10

Find the sum to eight terms of the geometric sequence whose first term is 5 and whose common ratio is 1.2.

$$a = 5, r = 1.2, n = 8 \Rightarrow S_n = \frac{5(1 - 1.2^8)}{(1 - 1.2)} = 82.50 \text{ (4 sf)}$$

Example 11

A geometric sequence begins 4, 6, 9, ...
What is the smallest value of n for which $S_n > 200$?

$a = 4, r = 6 \div 4 = 1.5 \Rightarrow S_n = \dfrac{4(1 - 1.5^n)}{(1 - 1.5)}$

$\dfrac{4(1 - 1.5^n)}{(1 - 1.5)} > 200 \Rightarrow (1 - 1.5^n) < \dfrac{200 \times 0.5}{4}$

$\Rightarrow (1 - 1.5^n) < -25 \Rightarrow 1.5^n > 26$

$\Rightarrow \ln(1.5^n) > \ln 26 \Rightarrow n > \dfrac{\ln 26}{\ln 1.5} \Rightarrow n > 8.035$ (4 sf)

So the smallest value of n for which the sum exceeds 200 is $n = 9$.

Example 12

The first four terms of a geometric series sum to 45. The first eight sum to 765.
Find any series that fits the description.

$S_4 = \dfrac{a(1 - r^4)}{(1 - r)} = 45$ and $S_8 = \dfrac{a(1 - r^8)}{(1 - r)} = 765$

Dividing, we get $\dfrac{765}{45} = \dfrac{(1 - r^8)}{(1 - r^4)} = 17$

$\Rightarrow r^8 - 17r^4 + 16 = 0$

$\Rightarrow (r^4 - 1)(r^4 - 16) = 0$

$\Rightarrow (r - 1)(r + 1)(r^2 + 1)(r - 2)(r + 2)(r^2 + 4) = 0$

$\Rightarrow r = \pm 1$ or $r = \pm 2$

Since $r \neq 1$ and $r = -1$ makes sum 0 then $r = -2, 2$.
Substitution provides corresponding values for a
$a = -9$ when $r = -2$; $a = 3$ when $r = 2$

So two series fit the description.
Series 1: $-9 + 18 - 36 + 72 - 144 + ...$
Series 2: $3 + 6 + 123 + 48 + ...$

Exercise 9.4

1 Find the sum of each geometric sequence to the required number of terms.

a 3, 6, 12, ... to eight terms

b 5, 20, 80, ... to seven terms

c 4, −12, 36, ... to 10 terms

d 3, 12, 48, ... to six terms

e 2, −4, 8, ... to 12 terms

f −3, 6, −12, ... to 10 terms

2 Evaluate each geometric series to the number of specified terms.

a $\frac{1}{2} + \frac{1}{4} + \frac{1}{8} + ...$ to eight terms

b $1 - \frac{1}{2} + \frac{1}{4} - \frac{1}{8} + ...$ to nine terms

c $\frac{1}{4} + \frac{1}{16} + \frac{1}{64} + ...$ to 10 terms

d $1 - \frac{1}{3} + \frac{1}{9} - \frac{1}{27} + ...$ to 12 terms

e $16 + 8 + 4 + ...$ to nine terms

f $0.55 + 1.1 + 2.2 + ...$ to 10 terms

3 a How many terms of the series $8 + 24 + 72 + ...$ must be added to get a sum of 26 240?

b At which term does the sum $1.5 + 6 + 24 + ...$ exceed one million?

4 A geometric series has a common ratio of 3. Its sum to eight terms is 39 360.

a Calculate the first term. b Calculate the sum to six terms.

5 a The sum of the third and fourth terms of a geometric series is 240.
The sum of the seventh and eighth terms is 61 440.
Identify the two possible series which fit this description.

b Show that the sum to 10 terms is the same for both series.

c Comment on the sums to nine terms.

6 a The sum of the first three terms of a GP is 744. The sum of the next three is 93 000. Find the series.

b Find the sum of the seventh, eighth and ninth terms.

7 a, $a - 12$, $a + 12$ are the first three terms of a geometric sequence.

a What is the value of a? b Calculate the sum of the first 10 terms.

8 Edouard Lucas, a 19th century French mathematician, studied sequences which are now called after him. A Lucas sequence is one where $u_{n+1} = u_n + u_{n-1}$, that is, each term is the sum of the previous two terms in the sequence. The Fibonacci sequence is a special case of a Lucas sequence.

a Letting $u_1 = 1$ and $u_2 = x$, find a Lucas sequence which is also a geometric sequence.

b Let ϕ represent the common ratio of this sequence.

i Find an expression for S_n in terms of ϕ.

ii Verify for $n = 6$, $n = 7$ and $n = 8$ that S_n can also be expressed as $\phi^{n+1} - \phi$.

c It is said that any Lucas sequence behaves more and more like a geometric sequence as the size of n increases. Investigate this claim.

9 When making a guitar, the spacings between the frets on the neck are mathematically fixed.
Each spacing is $\frac{17}{18}$ of the previous spacing.

a If the first spacing (between the nut and the first fret) is 4 cm, calculate the distance between the sixth and ninth frets.

b If the 12th fret is placed half way between the nut and the bridge, what is the distance between the nut and the bridge?

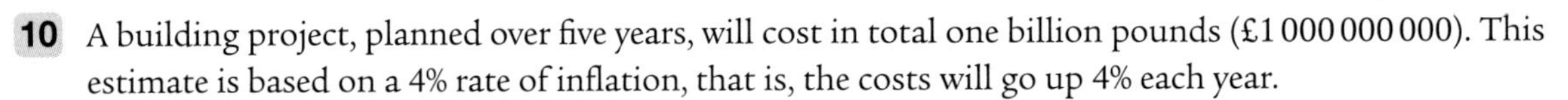

10 A building project, planned over five years, will cost in total one billion pounds (£1 000 000 000). This estimate is based on a 4% rate of inflation, that is, the costs will go up 4% each year.

a Calculate, to 3 significant figures, the estimated costs for *each* of the five years.

b If, instead, the actual rate of inflation is 6%, calculate the extra cost of the five-year project. [Assume that the first year cost is the same.]

11 A pendulum is slowly coming to rest. With each swing, the arc is reduced by 3%. Each swing takes the same time, 1.5 s. The first sweep is a 20° arc.

a How many degrees has the pendulum swept through in six swings?

b How long will it take before a total exceeding 180° has been swept through? Only count complete swings.

12 A certain type of tree used for hedging is planted when it is 1 m tall. It grows so that its annual *increase* in height in any year is $\frac{9}{10}$ of the increase in height in the previous year. In its first year it grew by 1 m.

a What is the height of the plant after

i one year ii two years iii five years iv 16 years?

b Compare the heights after five years and after 16 years.

c By comparing the height at year 50 with that of year 100, make a conjecture about the height of the tree in the long term.

13 On a tour of a Highland distillery the guides like to talk of the angels' share. When whisky is distilled it is stored in large wooden casks for eight years to mature. Each year, because of evaporation, a certain amount is lost. These successive amounts remaining form a geometric sequence whose sum after eight years represents 10% of the volume of the cask when originally laid down. This loss is what is referred to as the angels' share.

a If V_0 represents the original volume, find an expression for V_n, the volume at the end of year n when $n = 1, 2, 3$ and 4 (work to 3 sf).

b A deluxe whisky is laid down for 12 years. What is the angels' share in this case?

9.5 Infinite series, partial sums and sum to infinity

An **infinite series** is a series which has an infinite number of terms.
When we have an infinite series then S_n is defined as the sum of the first n terms of that series.
Such a sum is referred to as a **partial sum** of that series.

If the partial sum S_n tends towards a limit as n tends to infinity, then the limit is called the sum to infinity of the series.

Arithmetic series

Consider the sum to n terms of an arithmetic series.

$$S_n = \frac{n}{2}(2a + (n-1)d) = \frac{n}{2}((2a-d) + nd) = \frac{n^2}{2}\left(\frac{(2a-d)}{n} + d\right)$$

As $n \to \infty$, $\frac{2a+d}{n} \to 0$ giving $S_n \approx \frac{n^2 d}{2}$ when n is very large.

As $n \to \infty$, then $S_n \to \pm\infty$ depending on the value of d.

The sum to infinity of an arithmetic series is undefined.

Geometric series

Consider the sum to n terms of a geometric series.

$$S_n = \frac{a(1-r^n)}{1-r}, r \neq 1$$

- Case 1: $|r| > 1, n \to \infty \Rightarrow r^n \to \infty \Rightarrow S_n \to \infty$

  The sum to infinity of a geometric series is undefined when $|r| > 1$.

- Case 2: $|r| < 1, n \to \infty \Rightarrow r^n \to 0 \Rightarrow S_n \to \frac{a}{1-r}$

  The sum to infinity of a geometric series $S_\infty = \frac{a}{1-r}$ when $|r| < 1$.

Example 13

Find the sum to infinity of the geometric series 36 + 12 + 4 + ..., if it exists.

$a = 36; r = \frac{12}{36} = \frac{1}{3} \Rightarrow |r| < 1 \Leftrightarrow S_\infty$ exists.

$$S_\infty = \frac{a}{1-r} = \frac{36}{1-\frac{1}{3}} = 54$$

Example 14

Express the recurring decimal 0.151515... as a vulgar fraction.

0.151515... = 0.15 + 0.0015 + 0.000015 + ...

So $a = 0.15; r = \frac{0.0015}{0.15} = 0.01 \Rightarrow |r| < 1 \Leftrightarrow S_\infty$ exists.

$$S_\infty = \frac{0.15}{1-0.01} = \frac{15}{99} = \frac{5}{33}$$

Example 15

Given that 18 and 6 are two adjacent terms of an infinite geometric progression with a sum to infinity of 90, find the first term.

Since a sum to infinity exists $\Rightarrow |r| < 1 \Rightarrow r = \frac{6}{18} = \frac{1}{3}$

$S_\infty = \frac{a}{1-r} \Rightarrow \frac{a}{1-\frac{1}{3}} = 90 \Rightarrow a = 90 \times \frac{2}{3} = 60$

The first term is 60.

Example 16

What conditions must be met before the series $1 + 3x + 9x^2 + \ldots$ has a sum to infinity?

Note that $\frac{u_2}{u_1} = \frac{u_3}{u_2} = \frac{3x}{1} = 3x$ and so the series is geometric.

This will have a sum to infinity if $|r| < 1 \Rightarrow |3x| < 1 \Rightarrow -1 < 3x < 1$

$\Rightarrow -\frac{1}{3} < x < \frac{1}{3}$

Exercise 9.5

1 Find the sum to infinity of these infinite geometric progressions.

a $2 + 1 + 0.5 + \ldots$ b $100 + 20 + 4 + \ldots$ c $8 + 2 + 0.5 + \ldots$

d $9 - 3 + 1 - \ldots$ e $500 - 100 + 20 - \ldots$ f $147 + 21 + 3 + \ldots$

2 Identify which of these geometric series tend to a limit and find the limit.

a $7 + 1 + \frac{1}{7} + \ldots$ b $1 + 1.5 + 2.25 + \ldots$ c $18 + 9 + 4.5 + \ldots$

d $0.5 - 0.25 + 0.125 - \ldots$ e $\frac{2}{5} + \frac{4}{25} + \frac{8}{125} + \ldots$ f $\frac{1}{36} + \frac{1}{18} + \frac{1}{9} + \ldots$

3 a A geometric series has a sum to infinity of 50.
The common ratio is 0.6.
What is the first term of the series?

b The first term of an infinite geometric series is 50.
The third term is 2.
Show that a sum to infinity exists and find it.

4 a Express each of these recurring decimals as an infinite geometric series, and hence as a vulgar fraction in its simplest form.

i 0.282828... ii 0.345345... iii 0.041414...

b By considering a sum to infinity, show that 0.99999... is mathematically equivalent to 1.

c i By considering 0.0454545... as $\frac{1}{10} \times 0.454545\ldots$ express it as a vulgar fraction.

ii By considering 0.9454545... as $\frac{9}{10} + 0.0454545\ldots$ express it as a vulgar fraction.

d Express each of these recurring decimals as a vulgar fraction in its simplest form.

i 0.022222... ii 0.722222... iii 0.754444...

5 Given that numbers 75 and 18.75 are adjacent terms of an infinite geometric series with a sum to infinity of 6400, find

a the first term

b the partial sum S_5.

6 A ball is thrown to the ground. It bounces to a height of 4 m. The characteristics of the rubber are such that, thereafter, the ball rebounds to 0.8 of its previous height at each bounce.
Let u_n represent the distance travelled, from ground to ground, in the nth bounce ($u_1 = 8$ m – up 4 m and down 4 m).

a Write the first three terms of the geometric series generated.

b Work out the total distance travelled after

i five bounces ii 10 bounces (correct to 2 dp).

c What is the limit of this distance as n tends to infinity?

7 Identify for what range of values of x these series have a sum to infinity.

a $3 + 3x + 3x^2 + ...$

b $16 + 8x + 4x^2 + ...$

c $\frac{1}{x} + 4 + 16x + ..., x \neq 0$

d $5 + 20\sqrt{x} + 80x + ...$

e $2 + \frac{6}{x} + \frac{18}{x^2} + ...$

f $32x^{10} + 8x^8 + 2x^6 + ...$

g $27x - 9x^2 + 3x^3 - ...$

h $x + \frac{1}{3}x(x-2) + \frac{1}{9}x(x-2)^2 + ...$

i $81 + 27(x+5) + 9(x+5)^2 + ...$

j $2x + \frac{4x}{x-1} + \frac{8x}{(x-1)^2} + ...$

8 In the fifth century BC, a Greek philosopher, Zeno of Elea, posed a series of paradoxes which puzzled his contemporaries. The most famous of these is the story of Achilles and the tortoise.

Achilles can move 100 times faster than the tortoise. The tortoise is given 1000 m head start. Zeno argued that Achilles could not overtake the tortoise: when Achilles reaches the starting position, T_0, of the tortoise, the tortoise will have moved to T_1, 10 m away.

When Achilles reaches T_1, the tortoise will have moved to T_2, 0.1 m away.

When Achilles reaches T_2, the tortoise will have moved to T_3, 0.001 m away.

The tortoise will always have moved on!

a i What is the sum to infinity of the series $1000 + 10 + 0.1 + 0.001 + ...$?

ii Interpret your answer in the context of the story.

b Assume that Achilles runs at a steady 10 m/s.

i The times taken at each stage of the run form a series.
Write the start of the series.

ii Calculate the sum to infinity of this series.

iii Does this help to resolve the paradox?

c Read up on Zeno's other paradoxes.

9 An analogous situation to the above is the problem of finding when the minute hand and hour hand of a clock are coincident.

a Consider three o'clock as the starting position.

i How much faster is the minute hand than the hour hand?

ii How long does it take for the minute hand to reach the starting position of the hour hand (that is, the 3 on the dial)?

iii How far has the hour hand moved on?

iv By considering the sum to infinity, what is the first time after three o'clock that the hands of a clock are coincident?

b What is the first time after six o'clock that the hands of a clock are coincident?

10 **An unresolved puzzle**

A lamp is switched on. One minute later it is switched off. Half a minute later it is switched on. A quarter of a minute later it is switched off, and so on.

Is the lamp on or off after 2 min?

Review 9

1 An arithmetic sequence starts 5, 14, 23, ...

a Find an expression for the nth term of the sequence.

b What is the number that is closest to 300 in the sequence?

2 The seventh term in an arithmetic sequence is -50 and the 12th term is -90.

a Identify the sequence.

b For what value of n is $u_n = -250$?

3 An arithmetic sequence has a common difference of 9 and the 91st term equals 800. What is the first term?

4 Find the sum of the first 21 terms of the arithmetic sequence which starts 30, 37, 44.

5 The sum of the first 24 terms of an arithmetic sequence is 858.
The sum to 25 terms is 900. Identify the sequence.

6 How many terms must be added before the sum of the arithmetic sequence 7, 8.2, 9.4, ... exceeds 1000?

7 a Find an expression for the nth term of the geometric sequence which starts 12, 24, 48, ...

b Which term in this sequence is closest to 3000?

8 The first term of a geometric sequence is 7. The sixth term is 1701.
Find the common ratio.

9 The common ratio of a geometric sequence is 0.4 and the seventh term is 0.8192. Find the first term.

10 Find the sum to 10 terms of the geometric sequence

a 1.5, 4.5, 13.5, ...   b $1\frac{2}{3}, \frac{5}{9}, \frac{5}{27}, \ldots$

11 The first two terms of a geometric series add up to 10.5 and the next two add up to 42. Find the sum of the first eight terms.

12 a When will the sum of the series $50 + 30 + 18 + \ldots$ first exceed 124?

b State why you know the sum to infinity of this series exists, and find it.

13 Find the sum to infinity of the series whose first two terms are 17 and 13.6.

14 Express these recurring decimals as vulgar fractions.

a 0.545454...   b 0.3181818181...

15 For what range of values of x does this series have a sum to infinity?

$2x + 4x(x + 3) + 8x(x + 3)^2 + \ldots$

Summary 9

1 a A **sequence** is an ordered list of numbers where each term is obtained according to a fixed rule.

b A **series**, or **progression**, is a sum, the terms of which form a sequence.

c The nth term of a sequence is denoted by u_n.

d A sequence can be defined by a recurrence relation where u_{n+1} is given as a function of lower/earlier terms.

e A first-order recurrence relation is where u_{n+1} is given as a function of u_n.

f A sequence can be defined by a formula for u_n given in the form of a function $u_n = f(n)$.

2 **a** When $r = 1$ and $d \neq 0$, that is, $u_{n+1} = u_n + d$, then the sequence is called **arithmetic**.

b For an arithmetic sequence $u_{n+1} - u_n = u_{n+2} - u_{n+1} = d$ and u_1 is denoted by a.

c The nth term of an arithmetic sequence is given by $u_n = a + (n - 1)d$.

d The sum to n terms of an arithmetic sequence is given by

$S_n = \frac{n}{2}(2a + (n - 1)d) = \frac{n}{2}(a + L)$ where L is the last term.

3 **a** When $r \neq 0, 1$ and $d = 0$, that is, $u_{n+1} = ru_n$, then the sequence is called **geometric**.

b For a geometric sequence $u_{n+1} \div u_n = u_{n+2} \div u_{n+1} = r$ and $u_1 = a$.

c The nth term of a geometric sequence is given by $u_n = ar^{n-1}$.

d The sum to n terms of a geometric sequence is given by $S_n = \dfrac{a(1 - r^n)}{1 - r}$.

e The sum to n terms of an infinite series is often referred to as a **partial sum**.

f When $|r| < 1$ then $r^n \to 0$ as $n \to \infty$ and the sum to infinity, which is the limit to which the partial sums tend, is denoted by S_∞ and $S_\infty = \dfrac{a}{1 - r}$.

10 Sigma notation and power series

Historical note

Leonhard Euler was born in 1707 in Switzerland though he spent most of his working life in St Petersburg and Berlin.

His list of accomplishments in mathematics is huge. He was the first to consider sine and cosine as functions, he brought together the Leibniz and Newton calculus methods and he is personally responsible for much of the notation we use today.

- e for the base of natural logs
- i for $\sqrt{-1}$
- π for the ratio of circumference to diameter
- $f(x)$ for a function
- $\sum$ (sigma) to represent summation

It is this last piece of notation that we wish to consider here.

10.1 Sigma notation

You may have already used this notation in Chapter **3**. It was employed as a 'shorthand' when summing terms of a series.

Definition: $\sum_{r=a}^{b} f(r) = f(a) + f(a+1) + f(a+2) + \ldots + f(b-1) + f(b)$

Explanation

- We have the rth term of the series, $f(r)$.
- We have a starting value, $r = a$.
- We have an end value, $r = b$.
- We evaluate $f(r)$ for all the integer values of r between a and b, inclusive.
- We sum the series generated.

Some results

1 $\sum_{r=a}^{b} kf(r) = kf(a) + kf(a+1) + kf(a+2) + \ldots + kf(b-1) + kf(b)$

$\Rightarrow \sum_{r=a}^{b} kf(r) = k(f(a) + f(a+1) + f(a+2) + \ldots + f(b-1) + f(b))$

$\Rightarrow \sum_{r=a}^{b} kf(r) = k\sum_{r=a}^{b} f(r)$

2 When $f(r) = 1, f(1) = 1, f(2) = 1, f(3) = 1$, etc.

So $\sum_{r=1}^{n} 1 = 1 + 1 + 1 + ... + 1 + 1$ for n terms

$$\Rightarrow \boxed{\sum_{r=1}^{n} 1 = n}$$

3 $\sum_{r=1}^{b} f(r) = f(1) + f(2) + ... + f(a-1) + f(a) + f(a+1) + ... + f(b-1) + f(b)$

$$\Rightarrow \sum_{r=1}^{b} f(r) = [f(1) + f(2) + ... + f(a-1)] + [f(a) + f(a+1) + ... + f(b-1) + f(b)]$$

$$\Rightarrow \sum_{r=1}^{b} f(r) = \sum_{r=1}^{a-1} f(r) + \sum_{r=a}^{b} f(r)$$

or more usefully, $\sum_{r=a}^{b} f(r) = \sum_{r=1}^{b} f(r) - \sum_{r=1}^{a-1} f(r)$

4 When $f(r) = r, f(1) = 1, f(2) = 2, f(3) = 3$, etc.

So $\sum_{r=1}^{n} r = 1 + 2 + 3 + ... + (n-1) + n$

... an arithmetic progression with $a = 1$ and $d = 1$

$$\Rightarrow \boxed{\sum_{r=1}^{n} r = \tfrac{1}{2}n(n+1)}$$

5
$$\begin{aligned}\sum_{r=1}^{n} [f(r) + g(r)] &= f(1) + g(1) + f(2) + g(2) + ... + f(n-1) + g(n-1) + f(n) + g(n) \\ &= f(1) + f(2) + ... + f(n-1) + f(n) + g(1) + g(2) + ... + g(n-1) + g(n) \\ &= [f(1) + f(2) + ... + f(n-1) + f(n)] + [g(1) + g(2) + ... + g(n-1) + g(n)]\end{aligned}$$

$$\Rightarrow \sum_{r=1}^{n} [f(r) + g(r)] = \sum_{r=1}^{n} f(r) + \sum_{r=1}^{n} g(r)$$

6
$$\begin{aligned}\sum_{r=1}^{n} f(r+1) - \sum_{r=1}^{n} f(r) &= [f(2) + f(3) + ... + f(n) + f(n+1)] \\ &\quad - [f(1) + f(2) + ... + f(n)]\end{aligned}$$

$$\Rightarrow \sum_{r=1}^{n} f(r+1) - \sum_{r=1}^{n} f(r) = f(n+1) - f(1)$$

7 $\sum_{r=1}^{n} ar + b$

$\sum_{r=1}^{n} ar + b = \sum_{r=1}^{n} ar + \sum_{r=1}^{n} b$ By result **5**

$= a\sum_{r=1}^{n} r + b\sum_{r=1}^{n} 1$ By result **1**

$= \tfrac{1}{2}an(n+1) + bn$ By results **2** and **4**

Example 1

A series has an nth term $u_n = 3n - 5$.

a Express the sum to n terms as a function of n.

b Evaluate $\sum_{r=6}^{15} (3r - 5)$.

a $\sum_{r=1}^{n} (3r - 5) = 3\sum_{r=1}^{n} r - 5\sum_{r=1}^{n} 1$

$= \frac{3}{2}n(n + 1) - 5n = \frac{3}{2}n^2 + \left(\frac{3}{2} - 5\right)n = \frac{n}{2}(3n - 7)$

b $\sum_{r=6}^{15} (3r - 5) = \sum_{r=1}^{15} (3r - 5) - \sum_{r=1}^{5} (3r - 5)$

$= \frac{15}{2}(3 \cdot 15 - 7) - \frac{5}{2}(3 \cdot 5 - 7) = \frac{15}{2}(38) - \frac{5}{2}(8)$

$= 265$

Example 2

Express the series $2 + 5 + 8 + \ldots + 29$ in sigma notation.

The series is an arithmetic progression with $a = 2$ and $d = 3$,
so $u_n = 2 + (n - 1) \cdot 3 = 3n - 1$
The last term is 29, so $3n - 1 = 29 \Rightarrow n = 10$

Hence the series can be expressed as $\sum_{r=1}^{10} (3r - 1)$.

Example 3

a Express $\sum_{r=1}^{n} \left(\sqrt{r+1} - \sqrt{r}\right)$ as a function of n.[1]

b Hence evaluate $\sum_{r=4}^{15} \left(\sqrt{r+1} - \sqrt{r}\right)$.

a $\sum_{r=1}^{n} \left(\sqrt{r+1} - \sqrt{r}\right) = \sqrt{n+1} - \sqrt{1} = \sqrt{n+1} - 1$ Using result **6**

b $\sum_{r=4}^{15} \left(\sqrt{r+1} - \sqrt{r}\right) = \sum_{r=1}^{15} \left(\sqrt{r+1} - \sqrt{r}\right) - \sum_{r=1}^{3} \left(\sqrt{r+1} - \sqrt{r}\right)$

$= \left[\sqrt{15+1} - 1\right] - \left[\sqrt{3+1} - 1\right] = \sqrt{16} - 1 - \sqrt{4} + 1$

$= 2$

Exercise 10.1

1 Evaluate

a $\sum_{r=1}^{4} 3r$ b $\sum_{r=1}^{20} 7$ c $\sum_{r=1}^{6} 2r^2$ d $\sum_{r=1}^{10} (4r + 1)$ e $\sum_{r=1}^{5} (r^2 + r + 1)$

[1] By this we mean a function of n without the use of sigma notation or ellipsis (...).

2 Evaluate these summations. (Check your limits.)

a $\sum_{r=0}^{5} 7r$ b $\sum_{r=4}^{5} 3r^2$ c $\sum_{r=2}^{6} (1-2r)$ d $\sum_{r=0}^{4} \sqrt{r}$ e $\sum_{r=2}^{6} \frac{1}{r}$

3 Expand to show the first three terms and the last two.

a $\sum_{r=1}^{n} 5r$ b $\sum_{r=1}^{n} (1+r)$ c $\sum_{r=0}^{n} (2r-3)$ d $\sum_{r=0}^{n} (5-2r)$ e $\sum_{r=1}^{2n} (r^2-1)$

4 Express as a function of n

a $\sum_{r=1}^{n} 2r$ b $\sum_{r=1}^{n} -1$ c $\sum_{r=1}^{n} (6r-1)$ d $\sum_{r=1}^{n} (4-3r)$ e $\sum_{r=1}^{2n} (r-8)$

5 Express each in sigma notation. For example, $1 + 3 + 5 + \ldots + 15 = \sum_{r=1}^{8} 2r - 1$.

a $3 + 7 + 11 + \ldots + 79$

b $7 + 12 + 17 + \ldots + 252$

c $6 + 12 + 18 + \ldots 60$

d $\sqrt{2} + \sqrt{3} + 2 + \sqrt{5} + \ldots + 100$

e $1 + \frac{1}{3} + \frac{1}{5} + \frac{1}{7} + \ldots + \frac{1}{15}$

f $10 + 7 + 4 + \ldots + (-23)$

6 a Expand each of these, listing the first five terms.

i $\sum_{r=1}^{n} (-1)^r$ ii $\sum_{r=1}^{n} (-1)^{r-1}$ iii $\sum_{r=1}^{n} (-1)^r\, 2r$ iv $\sum_{r=1}^{n} (-1)^{r-1}\, 3r$

b Expand i $\sum_{r=1}^{n} (-1)^{r-1}(3r-4)$ ii $\sum_{r=1}^{n} (-1)^{r-1}(rx^r)$ iii $\sum_{r=0}^{n} (-1)^{r-1}\, r!\, x^r$

c Express each arithmetic series in sigma notation, going to the nth term.

i $3 - 8 + 13 - \ldots$ ii $7 - 9 + 11 - \ldots$ iii $-4 + 6 - 8 + \ldots$

d Express each geometric series in sigma notation, going to the nth term.

i $1 + x + x^2 + x^3 + \ldots$ ii $1 - x + x^2 - x^3 + \ldots$ iii $1 - 3x + 9x^2 - 27x^3 + \ldots$

7 What problem(s) might you encounter when trying to evaluate these summations.

a $\sum_{r=1}^{10} \frac{1}{r-6}$ b $\sum_{r=1}^{10} \frac{1}{\sqrt{5-r}}$

8 Find the value of the unknown in each case.

a $\sum_{r=1}^{n} (2r+3) = 117$ b $\sum_{r=1}^{n} (4-5r) = -148$

9 Use the fact that $\sum_{r=1}^{n} f(r+1) - \sum_{r=1}^{n} f(r) = f(n+1) - f(1)$ to help you express each sum without the aid of sigma notation explicitly as a function of n.

a $\sum_{r=1}^{n} ((r+1)^2 - r^2)$ Hint: $\sum_{r=1}^{n} ((r+1)^2 - r^2) = \sum_{r=1}^{n} (r+1)^2 - \sum_{r=1}^{n} r^2$

b $\sum_{r=1}^{n} \sqrt{r+1} - \sqrt{r}$ c $\sum_{r=1}^{n} \sin(r+1) - \sin r$

d $\sum_{r=1}^{n} \left(\frac{1}{r+1} - \frac{1}{r}\right)$ e $\sum_{r=2}^{n} \left(\frac{1}{r} - \frac{1}{r-1}\right)$ f $\sum_{r=2}^{n} \left(\frac{1}{r-1} - \frac{1}{r}\right)$

10 a Express $\sum_{r=1}^{n} f(r) - \sum_{r=1}^{n} f(r-1)$ without sigma notation.

b Express $\sum_{r=1}^{n} f(r-1) - \sum_{r=1}^{n} f(r)$ without sigma notation.

c Express $\sum_{r=1}^{n} f(r+2) - \sum_{r=1}^{n} f(r)$ without sigma notation.

11 a Express $\ln\left(1+\frac{1}{n}\right)$ in the form $\ln\left(\frac{a}{b}\right)$.

b Hence express it in the form $\ln a - \ln b$.

c Express $\sum_{r=1}^{n} \ln\left(1+\frac{1}{r}\right)$ as a function of n without sigma notation.

d Evaluate $\sum_{r=1}^{9} \log_{10}\left(1+\frac{1}{r}\right)$.

e Find the value of $\log_{10}\left(2 \times 1\frac{1}{2} \times 1\frac{1}{3} \times 1\frac{1}{4} \times 1\frac{1}{5} \times ... \times 1\frac{1}{99}\right)$.

12 Consider the series $\frac{1}{2}+\frac{1}{6}+\frac{1}{12}+\frac{1}{20}+ ...$

a Verify that it can be expressed as $\frac{1}{1 \cdot 2}+\frac{1}{2 \cdot 3}+\frac{1}{3 \cdot 4}+\frac{1}{4 \cdot 5}+ ...$

b Both the first factors and the second factors form arithmetic sequences.
Assuming this pattern continues, find an expression for the nth term of the series in the form $\frac{1}{f(n)g(n)}$.

c Use partial fractions to express this in the form $\frac{A}{f(n)}+\frac{B}{g(n)}$.

d Hence express the sum to n terms of the series in terms of n.

e Repeat this with the series

i $\frac{1}{20}+\frac{1}{30}+\frac{1}{42}+\frac{1}{56}+ ...$ ii $\frac{1}{90}+\frac{1}{72}+\frac{1}{56}+\frac{1}{42}+ ...$ iii $\frac{1}{3}+\frac{1}{15}+\frac{1}{35}+\frac{1}{63}+ ...$

10.2 Sigma notation – further results

Let us consider another proof of the result $\sum_{r=1}^{n} r = \frac{n}{2}(n+1)$. The steps will prove useful when we wish to extend our knowledge.

Proof

Step 1. We wish to find $\sum_{r=1}^{n} r$ when all we know is $\sum_{r=1}^{n} 1$, and result **6** above.

Consider the identity: $(r+1)^2 = r^2 + 2r + 1$

Step 2. Summing both sides, $\sum_{r=1}^{n} (r+1)^2 = \sum_{r=1}^{n} (r^2+2r+1) = \sum_{r=1}^{n} r^2 + 2\sum_{r=1}^{n} r + \sum_{r=1}^{n} 1$

Step 3. Rearrange: $\sum_{r=1}^{n} (r+1)^2 - \sum_{r=1}^{n} r^2 = 2\sum_{r=1}^{n} r + \sum_{r=1}^{n} 1$

Step 4. Use what we know regarding $\sum_{r=1}^{n} 1 = n$, and result **6**.

$$(n+1)^2 - 1 = 2\sum_{r=1}^{n} r + n$$

Step 5. Make what we want the subject of the formula: $\sum_{r=1}^{n} r = \frac{1}{2}[(n+1)^2 - 1 - n]$

Step 6. Tidy up. $\sum_{r=1}^{n} r = \frac{1}{2}(n^2+n) = \frac{n}{2}(n+1)$

Example 4

Find $\sum_{r=1}^{n} r^2$

We use the steps in the above direct proof: we know $\sum_{r=1}^{n} 1$, $\sum_{r=1}^{n} r$, and result **6** above.

Step 1. Consider the identity: $(r+1)^3 = r^3 + 3r^2 + 3r + 1$

Step 2. Sum both sides: $\sum_{r=1}^{n} (r+1)^3 = \sum_{r=1}^{n} r^3 + 3\sum_{r=1}^{n} r^2 + 3\sum_{r=1}^{n} r + \sum_{r=1}^{n} 1$

Step 3. Rearrange: $\sum_{r=1}^{n} (r+1)^3 - \sum_{r=1}^{n} r^3 = 3\sum_{r=1}^{n} r^2 + 3\sum_{r=1}^{n} r + \sum_{r=1}^{n} 1$

Step 4. Use what we know: $(n+1)^3 - 1 = 3\sum_{r=1}^{n} r^2 + \frac{3n}{2}(n+1) + n$

Step 5. Make $\sum_{r=1}^{n} r^2$ the subject: $\sum_{r=1}^{n} r^2 = \frac{1}{3}\left[(n+1)^3 - \frac{3n}{2}(n+1) - n - 1\right]$

Step 6. Tidy up:

$$\sum_{r=1}^{n} r^2 = \frac{1}{6}[2n^3 + 6n^2 + 6n + 2 - 3n^2 - 3n - 2n - 2]$$
$$= \frac{1}{6}[2n^3 + 3n^2 + n]$$
$$= \frac{n}{6}(n+1)(2n+1)$$

Sums of integer powers

$\sum_{r=1}^{n} 1 = n$ | $\sum_{r=1}^{n} r = \frac{n}{2}(n+1)$ | $\sum_{r=1}^{n} r^2 = \frac{n}{6}(n+1)(2n+1)$

Proof by induction

The above results can also be proved by induction – useful, but only if you *know* the result to begin with.

Example 5

Prove $\sum_{r=1}^{n} r^2 = \frac{n}{6}(n+1)(2n+1)$ by induction.

When $n = 1$, we know $1^2 = 1$. $\sum_{r=1}^{1} r^2 = \frac{1}{6}(1+1)(2 \cdot 1 + 1) = \frac{1}{6} \times 2 \times 3 = 1$

So the statement is true for $n = 1$.

Assume that the statement is true for some $n = k$.

$$\sum_{r=1}^{k} r^2 = \frac{k}{6}(k+1)(2k+1) \qquad (1)$$

Consider when $n = k + 1$:

$$\sum_{r=1}^{k+1} r^2 = \sum_{r=1}^{k} r^2 + (k+1)^2 \qquad \text{By definition}$$

$$\Rightarrow \sum_{r=1}^{k+1} r^2 = \frac{k}{6}(k+1)(2k+1) + (k+1)^2 \qquad \text{Using (1)}$$

$$\Rightarrow \sum_{r=1}^{k+1} r^2 = \frac{k+1}{6}[k(2k+1) + 6(k+1)] = \frac{k+1}{6}(2k^2 + 7k + 6)$$

$$\Rightarrow \sum_{r=1}^{k+1} r^2 = \frac{k+1}{6}(k+2)(2k+3)$$

$$\Rightarrow \sum_{r=1}^{k+1} r^2 = \frac{[k+1]}{6}([k+1]+1)(2[k+1]+1)$$

Thus the statement is true for $n = k + 1$.

So, statement true for $n = k$ implies that the statement is true for $n = k + 1$, and, since it is true for $n = 1$, then by induction, it is true for all $n \geq 1, n \in \mathbb{N}$.

Example 6

Prove by induction that $\frac{1}{1 \times 2} + \frac{1}{2 \times 3} + \frac{1}{3 \times 4} + \ldots + \frac{1}{n \times (n+1)} = \frac{n}{n+1}$

When $n = 1$, we know $\frac{1}{1 \times 2} = \frac{1}{2}$ and $\sum_{r=1}^{1} \frac{1}{r(r+1)} = \frac{1}{1+1} = \frac{1}{2}$

So the statement is true for $n = 1$.

Assume that the statement is true for some $n = k$.

$$\sum_{r=1}^{k} \frac{1}{r(r+1)} = \frac{k}{k+1} \qquad (1)$$

Consider when $n = k + 1$:

$$\sum_{r=1}^{k+1} \frac{1}{r(r+1)} = \sum_{r=1}^{k} \frac{1}{r(r+1)} + \frac{1}{(k+1)(k+1+1)} \qquad \text{By definition}$$

$$= \frac{k}{k+1} + \frac{1}{(k+1)(k+1+1)} \qquad \text{Using (1)}$$

$$= \frac{k(k+2)+1}{(k+1)(k+2)} = \frac{k^2+2k+1}{(k+1)(k+2)} = \frac{(k+1)^2}{(k+1)(k+2)}$$

$$= \frac{(k+1)}{(k+2)} = \frac{([k+1])}{([k+1]+1)}$$

Thus the statement is true for $n = k + 1$.

So, statement true for $n = k$ implies that the statement is true for $n = k + 1$, and, since it is true for $n = 1$, then by induction, it is true for all $n \geq 1, n \in \mathbb{N}$.

Exercise 10.2

1 Express each of these as a function of n without the use of the sigma notation.

a $\sum_{r=1}^{n} 3r^2$ b $\sum_{r=1}^{n} (2r^2 + 3)$ c $\sum_{r=1}^{n} (r^2 + 3r - 1)$

d $\sum_{r=1}^{n} (5r^2 - 3r - 2)$ e $\sum_{r=1}^{n} (4 - 2r - 3r^2)$ f $\sum_{r=1}^{n} (r-2)(r+1)$

2 Evaluate

a $\sum_{r=1}^{7} 2r^2$ b $\sum_{r=1}^{10} (r^2 + 5)$ c $\sum_{r=1}^{20} (r^2 - 4r)$

d $\sum_{r=1}^{100} (2 - 3r - r^2)$ e $\sum_{r=1}^{12} (r+4)(r-3)$ f $\sum_{r=1}^{9} (2r-1)(r-1)$

3 a Use the direct method given for $\sum_{r=1}^{n} r$ and $\sum_{r=1}^{n} r^2$ to prove that $\sum_{r=1}^{n} r^3 = \left[\frac{n}{2}(n+1)\right]^2$

[A pleasing result: $\sum_{r=1}^{n} r^3 = \left[\sum_{r=1}^{n} r\right]^2$ for example $1^3 + 2^3 + 3^3 + 4^3 + 5^3 = (1 + 2 + 3 + 4 + 5)^2$]

b Prove the result again using proof by induction.

4 Express each of these as a function of n without the use of the sigma notation.

a $\sum_{r=1}^{n} 4r^3$ b $\sum_{r=1}^{n} (r^3 + 3r)$ c $\sum_{r=1}^{n} (2r^3 + 4r - 3)$

d $\sum_{r=1}^{n} (r^3 + r^2 + r + 1)$ e $\sum_{r=1}^{n} r^2(r - 1)$ f $\sum_{r=1}^{n} (r - 3)(r - 1)^2$

5 Evaluate

a $\sum_{r=1}^{5} 5r^3$ b $\sum_{r=1}^{10} (r^3 + r)$ c $\sum_{r=1}^{8} (r^3 - 2r - 1)$

d $\sum_{r=1}^{50} r(r + 1)(r + 2)$ e $\sum_{r=1}^{12} (r + 4)(r - 3)$ f $\sum_{r=1}^{25} r(r - 1)(r + 1)$

6 By first considering the nth term, find the sum to n terms of these series. (All factors have been arranged to emphasise the sequences they follow.)

a $2 \cdot 4 + 3 \cdot 5 + 4 \cdot 6 + 5 \cdot 7 + \ldots$ where $a \cdot b$ means $a \times b$

b $1 \cdot 2 + 4 \cdot 3 + 7 \cdot 4 + 10 \cdot 5 + \ldots$

c $1 \cdot 3 + 3 \cdot 5 + 5 \cdot 7 + 7 \cdot 9 + \ldots$

d $1 \cdot 3 + 5 \cdot 7 + 9 \cdot 11 + \ldots$

e $1 \cdot 1 + 2 \cdot 4 + 3 \cdot 9 + 4 \cdot 16 + \ldots$

f $1 \cdot 4 + 2 \cdot 9 + 3 \cdot 16 + 4 \cdot 25 + \ldots$

g $2 \cdot 3 + 3 \cdot 8 + 4 \cdot 15 + 5 \cdot 24 + \ldots$

h $0 + 3 + 8 + 15 + 24 + \ldots$

i $-1 + 2 + 7 + 14 + 23 + \ldots$

j $1 \cdot 2 \cdot 3 + 2 \cdot 3 \cdot 4 + 3 \cdot 4 \cdot 5 + \ldots$

k $2 \cdot 3 \cdot 4 + 3 \cdot 4 \cdot 5 + 4 \cdot 5 \cdot 6 + \ldots$

7 Evaluate

a $1^3 + 3^3 + 5^3 + 7^3 + \ldots + 21^3$

b $8^3 + 9^3 + 10^3 + 11^3 + \ldots + 20^3$

c $1^2 + 2^3 + 3^2 + 4^3 + 5^2 + 6^3 + \ldots + 49^2 + 50^3$

8 Prove by induction that

a $\sum_{r=1}^{n} 3^r = \frac{3}{2}(3^n - 1)$

b $\sum_{r=1}^{n} 2n - 1 = n^2$

c $1^2 + 3^2 + 5^2 + \ldots + (2n - 1)^2 = \frac{4}{3}n(n - 1)(n + 1) + n$

d $2^3 + 4^3 + 6^3 + \ldots + (2n)^3 = 2n^2(n + 1)^2$

e $\frac{1}{1 \cdot 3} + \frac{1}{3 \cdot 5} + \frac{1}{5 \cdot 7} + \ldots \frac{1}{(2n - 1) \cdot (2n + 1)} = \frac{n}{2n + 1}$

10.3 Power series

An infinite series of the form $a_0 + a_1x + a_2x^2 + a_3x^3 + ... + a_rx^r + ...$ is referred to as a power series, where $a_0, a_1, a_2, a_3, ... a_r ...$ are constants, some of which may be zero.

An important consideration of the power series is the question of its behaviour as r tends to infinity.

We have seen when studying geometric series that as long as $r \neq 1$ then the series either

- tends to a **limit** as n tends to infinity (when $-1 < r < 1$) ... **convergent**
- tends to infinity as n tends to infinity (when $r < -1$ or $r > 1$) ... **divergent**.

Though really beyond the scope of the course, a similar test has been devised to study the behaviour of the power series as n tends to infinity.

For the series we will be examining in this course, we only require a part of the test.

Given that the series is $\sum_{r=0}^{\infty} a_rx^r = a_0 + a_1x + a_2x^2 + a_3x^3 + ... + a_rx^r + ...$,

if $\lim_{n\to\infty}\left|\frac{u_{n+1}}{u_n}\right| < 1$, which means $\lim_{n\to\infty}\left|\frac{a_{n+1}x}{a_n}\right| < 1$, then the series converges.

In certain cases, when the coefficients $a_0, a_1, a_2, a_3, ... a_r ...$ are functions of n, the sum to infinity can be determined.

Example 7

Find the sum to infinity of the series $S = 1 + 3x + 5x^2 + 7x^3 + ... + (2n - 1)x^n + ...$ and state the values of x for which the sum is valid.

Note: the constant coefficients form a **linear recurrence relation**, $u_{n+1} = u_n + 2; u_1 = 1$.
This generally points to a familiar strategy.

$$S = 1 + 3x + 5x^2 + 7x^3 + ... + (2n - 1)x^{n-1} + ... \quad (1)$$

Multiply throughout by x $\quad xS = 1x + 3x^2 + 5x^3 + 7x^4 + ... + (2n - 1)x^n ... \quad (2)$

Subtract (1) − (2) $\quad S(1 - x) = 1 + 2x + 2x^2 + 2x^3 + 2x^4 + ... + 2x^{n-1} + ...$

Consider the partial sum

$$S_n(1 - x) = 1 + 2x + 2x^2 + 2x^3 + 2x^4 + ... + 2x^{n-1}$$
$$= (2 + 2x + 2x^2 + 2x^3 + 2x^4 + ... + 2x^{n-1}) - 1$$

We can find the sum to n terms of the geometric series

$$\Rightarrow S_n(1 - x) = \frac{2(1 - x^n)}{1 - x} - 1 = \frac{2(1 - x^n) - 1 + x}{1 - x}$$

$$\Rightarrow S_n = \frac{2(1 - x^n) - 1 + x}{(1 - x)^2}$$

Now, as long as $|x| < 1$, as $n \to \infty$, $x^n \to 0$

$$\Rightarrow S_\infty = \frac{2(1 - 0) - 1 + x}{(1 - x)^2} = \frac{1 + x}{(1 - x)^2}$$

Summarising, $S_\infty = \frac{1 + x}{(1 - x)^2}$ when $-1 < x < 1$.

Example 8

Find the sum to infinity of the series $S = 1 + 3x + 7x^2 + 15x^3 + ... + (2n - 1)\,x^n + ...$ and state the values of x for which the sum is valid.

Note: the constant coefficients form a **linear recurrence relation**, $u_{n+1} = 2u_n + 1; u_1 = 1$.

$$S = 1 + 3x + 7x^2 + 15x^3 + ... \quad (1)$$

Multiply throughout by x $\quad Sx = x + 3x^2 + 7x^3 + 15x^4 + ... \quad (2)$

Subtract (1) − (2) $\quad S(1 - x) = 1 + 2x + 4x^2 + 8x^3 + 16x^4 + ...$

We now have a geometric series: $a = 1, r = 2x$.

A sum to infinity exists when $|r| < 1 \Rightarrow |2x| < 1$

$$S_\infty(1 - x) = \frac{a}{1 - r} = \frac{1}{1 - 2x}$$

$$\Rightarrow S_\infty = \frac{1}{(1 - 2x)(1 - x)} \text{ for } |2x| < 1 \Rightarrow -\tfrac{1}{2} < x < \tfrac{1}{2}$$

Exercise 10.3

1 For each of these power series,

i find the sum to infinity

ii identify the values of x for which the sum to infinity is valid.

a $S = 2 + 6x + 10x^2 + 14x^3 + ... + (4n - 2)x^n + ...$

b $S = 3 + 8x + 13x^2 + 18x^3 + ... + (5n - 2)x^n + ...$

c $S = 12 + 10x + 8x^2 + 6x^3 + ... + (14 - 2n)x^n + ...$

d $S = 17 + 12x + 7x^2 + 2x^3 + ... + (22 - 5n)x^n + ...$

e $S = 2 + 6x + 18x^2 + 54x^3 + ...$

f $S = 96 + 48x + 24x^2 + 12x^3 + ...$

g $S = 1 + 4x + 13x^2 + 40x^3 + ...$

h $S = 3 + 5x + 9x^2 + 17x^3 + ...$

i $S = 2 + 10x + 42x^2 + 170x^3 + ...$

j $S = 4 + 16x + 76x^2 + 376x^3 + ...$

2 Find the sum to infinity of each power series, identifying the conditions for such a sum to exist.

a $S = a + (a + d)x + (a + 2d)x^2 + (a + 3d)x^3 + ... + (a + (n - 1)d)x^n + ...$

b $S = a + arx + ar^2x^2 + ar^3x^3 + ...$

c $S = a + (ba + c)x + (b^2a + bc + c)x^2 + (b^3a + b^2c + bc + c)x^3 + ...$

10.4 Maclaurin expansion

Historical note

Colin Maclaurin (1698–1746) did much work on power series following on from the work of the English mathematician Brook Taylor.

He showed that many power series, under the right circumstances, converge. He also showed that, within the valid domain of values of x, a series is a function of x.

The exponential function

$$e^x = \sum_{r=0}^{\infty} \frac{x^r}{r!} = 1 + \frac{x}{1!} + \frac{x^2}{2!} + \frac{x^3}{3!} + ...$$

Proof

Let $f(x) = e^x = a_0 + a_1x^1 + a_2x^2 + a_3x^3 + ...$

Step 1. We know that $f(0) = e^0 = a_0 + a_1 \cdot 0 + a_2 \cdot 0 + ... \Rightarrow a_0 = 1$

Step 2. Differentiate: $f'(x) = e^x = a_1 + 2a_2x + 3a_3x^2 + 4a_4x^3 + ...$

We know that $f'(0) = e^0 = 1 \Rightarrow a_1 = 1$

Step 3. Differentiate: $f''(x) = e^x = 2a_2 + 3 \cdot 2a_3x + 4 \cdot 3a_4x^2 + 5 \cdot 4a_5x^3 + \ldots$

We know that $f''(0) = e^0 = 1 \Rightarrow 2a_2 = 1 \Rightarrow a_2 = \frac{1}{2}$

Step 4. Differentiate: $f'''(x) = e^x = 3 \cdot 2a_3 + 4 \cdot 3 \cdot 2a_4x + 5 \cdot 4 \cdot 3a_5x^2 + 6 \cdot 5 \cdot 4a_6x^3 + \ldots$

We know that $f'''(0) = e^0 = 1 \Rightarrow 3 \cdot 2a_3 = 1 \Rightarrow a_3 = \frac{1}{3 \cdot 2}$

Step 5. Differentiate: $f^{(4)}(x) = e^x = 4 \cdot 3 \cdot 2a_4 + 5 \cdot 4 \cdot 3 \cdot 2a_5x + 6 \cdot 5 \cdot 4 \cdot 3a_6x^2 + \ldots$

We know that $f^{(4)}(0) = e^0 = 1 \Rightarrow 4 \cdot 3 \cdot 2a_4 = 1 \Rightarrow a_4 = \frac{1}{4 \cdot 3 \cdot 2}$

Step 6. Differentiate: $f^{(5)}(x) = e^x = 5 \cdot 4 \cdot 3 \cdot 2a_5 + 6 \cdot 5 \cdot 4 \cdot 3 \cdot 2a_6x + 7 \cdot 6 \cdot 5 \cdot 4 \cdot 3a_7x^2 + \ldots$

We know that $f^{(5)}(0) = e^0 = 1 \Rightarrow 5 \cdot 4 \cdot 3 \cdot 2a_5 = 1 \Rightarrow a_5 = \frac{1}{5 \cdot 4 \cdot 3 \cdot 2}$

Repeating this yields $f(x) = e^x = a_0 + a_1x^1 + a_2x^2 + a_3x^3 + \ldots$

$$\Rightarrow e^x = 1 + x^1 + \frac{x^2}{2} + \frac{x^3}{3 \cdot 2} + \frac{x^4}{4 \cdot 3 \cdot 2} + \frac{x^5}{5 \cdot 4 \cdot 3 \cdot 2} + \ldots$$

$$= \frac{1}{0!} + \frac{x^1}{1!} + \frac{x^2}{2!} + \frac{x^3}{3!} + \frac{x^4}{4!} + \frac{x^5}{5!} + \ldots$$

This can be condensed as $e^x = \sum_{r=0}^{\infty} \frac{x^r}{r!}$

Note that $\left|\frac{u_{n+1}}{u_n}\right| = \frac{x^{n+1}}{(n+1)!} \cdot \frac{n!}{x^n} = \frac{x}{n+1}$ and as $n \to \infty \Rightarrow \frac{x}{n+1} \to 0 \Rightarrow \forall x \in R, \left|\frac{u_{n+1}}{u_n}\right| < 1$

So the power series converges for all values of x.

So the expansion $e^x = \frac{1}{0!} + \frac{x^1}{1!} + \frac{x^2}{2!} + \frac{x^3}{3!} + \frac{x^4}{4!} + \frac{x^5}{5!} + \ldots$ is valid for all $x \in R$.

This is often referred to as Maclaurin's expansion for e^x.

Exercise 10.4

1 The expansion $e^x = \frac{1}{0!} + \frac{x^1}{1!} + \frac{x^2}{2!} + \frac{x^3}{3!} + \frac{x^4}{4!} + \frac{x^5}{5!} + \ldots$ has to be taken to infinity for it to be exactly true. However, you get a good approximation by summing the first few terms.

a $e^2 = 7.38$ to 3 significant figures.
How many terms of the expansion would have to be used to get the same accuracy?

b Explore this situation for

i $e^{3.4} = 30.0$ to 3 sf. **ii** $e^4 = 54.6$ to 3 sf.

c A spreadsheet can be used the investigate the usefulness of the series.

	A	B	C	D	E	F	G	H	I	J	K	L
1	x	e^x	terms: 1	2	3	4	5	6	7	8	9	10
2	−2	0.1353	−1	1	−0.333	0.333	0.067	0.156	0.13	0.137	0.135	0.135
3	−1	0.3679	0	0.5	0.333	0.375	0.367	0.368	0.368	0.368	0.368	0.368
4	0	1	1	1	1	1	1	1	1	1	1	1
5	1	2.7183	2	2.5	2.667	2.708	2.717	2.718	2.718	2.718	2.718	2.718
6	2	7.3891	3	5	6.333	7	7.267	7.356	7.381	7.387	7.389	7.389
7	2.1	8.1662	3.1	5.305	6.849	7.659	7.999	8.118	8.154	8.163	8.166	8.166
8	2.2	9.025	3.2	5.62	7.395	8.371	8.8	8.958	9.007	9.021	9.024	9.025

Column A has been used for x-values; column B for e^x-values.
The values in Column A can be entered 'manually' to allow better control of the investigation.
The other columns give the sum to 1, 2, 3, 4, ... terms of the expansion.
In D1 type 2; in E1 type = D1 + 1; fill right to column L.

In B2 type = EXP(A2)
In C2 type = 1+A2 ^ (1/FACT(1)) ... actually the sum of the first two terms
In D2 type = C2+$A2 ^ (D$1/FACT(D$1)) ... fill right to column L
Fill B2 to L2 down as far as you wish.

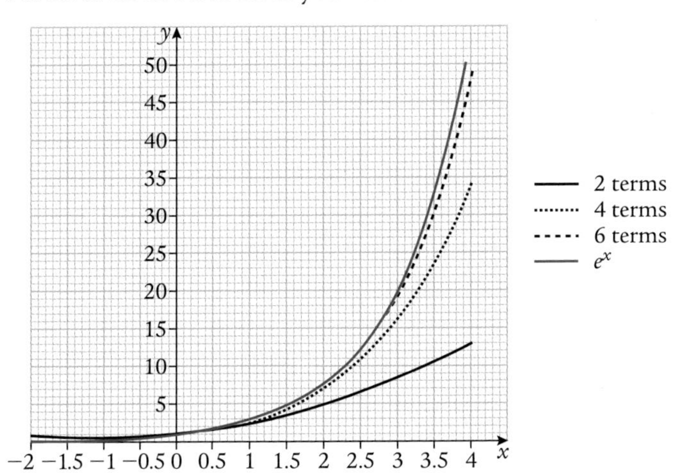

The chart shows how the graphs tend to $y = e^x$ as the number of terms used increases.

2 Given that $\sin x$ can be expressed as $\sin x = a_0 + a_1x + a_2x^2 + a_3x^3 + \dots$

a find the value of a_0 using the fact that $\sin 0 = 0$

b **i** differentiate both sides of the equation

ii find the value of a_1 using the fact that $\cos 0 = 1$

c **i** differentiate both sides again

ii find a_2 by letting $x = 0$.

d Repeat this process to find the next three terms in Maclaurin's expansion for $\sin x$.

e By considering the value of $\left|\frac{u_{n+1}}{u_n}\right|$ as n tends to infinity, show that the expansion is valid for all x.

3 **a** Given that $\cos x$ can be expressed as $\cos x = a_0 + a_1x + a_2x^2 + a_3x^3 + \dots$, find the first five non-zero terms of Maclaurin's expansion for $\cos x$.

b By differentiating Maclaurin's expansion for $\sin x$, verify the expansion for $\cos x$.

10.5 Maclaurin series for *f*(*x*)

$$f(x) = \sum_{r=0}^{\infty} \frac{f^{(r)}(0)x^r}{r!} = f(0) + \frac{f'(0)x}{1!} + \frac{f''(0)x^2}{2!} + \frac{f'''(0)x^3}{3!} + \dots$$

Proof

Consider the same technique of differentiation used on the general function $f(x)$.

Let $f(x) = a_0 + a_1x + a_2x^2 + a_3x^3 + \dots$

Step 1. $f(x) = a_0 + a_1x + a_2x^2 + a_3x^3 + a_4x^4 + \dots$ Letting $x = 0$ we get $a_0 = f(0)$

Step 2. $f'(x) = a_1 + 2a_2x + 3a_3x^2 + 4a_4x^3 + \dots$ Letting $x = 0$ we get $a_1 = f'(0)$

Step 3. $f''(x) = 2a_2 + 3 \cdot 2a_3x + 4 \cdot 3a_4x^2 + \dots$ Letting $x = 0$ we get $a_2 = \frac{f''(0)}{2}$

Step 4. $f'''(x) = 3 \cdot 2a_3 + 4 \cdot 3 \cdot 2a_4x + 5 \cdot 4 \cdot 3a_5x^2 \dots$ Letting $x = 0$ we get $a_3 = \frac{f'''(0)}{3 \cdot 2}$

Step 5. $f^{(4)}(x) = 4 \cdot 3 \cdot 2a_4 + 5 \cdot 4 \cdot 3 \cdot 2a_5x + 6 \cdot 5 \cdot 4 \cdot 3 \cdot a_5x^2 + \dots$ Let $x = 0$ to get $a_4 = \frac{f^{(4)}(0)}{4 \cdot 3 \cdot 2}$

In general the nth coefficient will be $a_n = \frac{f^{(n)}(0)}{n!}$ where we are defining
$f^{(0)}(x) = f(x); f^{(1)}(x) = f'(x); f^{(2)}(x) = f''(x); f^{(3)}(x) = f'''(x)$.

This can be proved by induction.

This leads to the conclusion that a function $f(x)$ is associated with a power series by Maclaurin's theorem:

$$f(x) = \frac{f(0)}{0!}x^0 + \frac{f'(0)}{1!}x^1 + \frac{f''(0)}{2!}x^2 + \frac{f'''(0)}{3!}x^3 + \frac{f^{(4)}(0)}{4!}x^4 + \dots$$

Using sigma notation $f(x) = \sum_{r=0}^{\infty} \frac{f^{(r)}(0)}{r!}x^r$.

The region for which the expansion is valid can be ascertained by considering

$$\lim_{n\to\infty}\left|\frac{u_{n+1}}{u_n}\right| = \lim_{n\to\infty}\left|\frac{f^{(n+1)}(0)x^{n+1}}{(n+1)!} \times \frac{n!}{f^{(n)}(0)x^n}\right| = \lim_{n\to\infty}\left|\frac{f^{(n+1)}(0)}{f^{(n)}(0)} \times \frac{x}{n+1}\right|$$

The expansion is valid when $\lim_{n\to\infty}\left|\frac{f^{(n+1)}(0)}{f^{(n)}(0)} \times \frac{x}{n+1}\right| < 1$.

Example 9

Find the first six terms of Maclaurin's expansion for $\sqrt{1+x}$.

$f(x) = (1+x)^{\frac{1}{2}}$ $\Rightarrow f(0) = (1+0)^{\frac{1}{2}} = 1$

$f'(x) = \frac{1}{2}(1+x)^{-\frac{1}{2}}$ $\Rightarrow f'(0) = \frac{1}{2}(1+0)^{-\frac{1}{2}} = \frac{1}{2}$

$f''(x) = -\frac{1}{2}\cdot\frac{1}{2}(1+x)^{-\frac{3}{2}}$ $\Rightarrow f''(0) = -\frac{1}{2}\cdot\frac{1}{2}(1+0)^{-\frac{3}{2}} = -\frac{1}{2}\cdot\frac{1}{2} = -\frac{1}{4}$

$f'''(x) = \frac{1}{2}\cdot\frac{1}{2}\cdot\frac{3}{2}(1+x)^{-\frac{5}{2}}$ $\Rightarrow f'''(0) = \frac{1}{2}\cdot\frac{1}{2}\cdot\frac{3}{2}(1+0)^{-\frac{5}{2}} = \frac{1}{2}\cdot\frac{1}{2}\cdot\frac{3}{2} = \frac{3}{8}$

$f^{(4)}(x) = -\frac{1}{2}\cdot\frac{1}{2}\cdot\frac{3}{2}\cdot\frac{5}{2}(1+x)^{-\frac{7}{2}}$ $\Rightarrow f^{(4)}(0) = -\frac{1}{2}\cdot\frac{1}{2}\cdot\frac{3}{2}\cdot\frac{5}{2}(1+0)^{-\frac{7}{2}} = -\frac{1}{2}\cdot\frac{1}{2}\cdot\frac{3}{2}\cdot\frac{5}{2} = -\frac{15}{16}$

$f^{(5)}(x) = \frac{1}{2}\cdot\frac{1}{2}\cdot\frac{3}{2}\cdot\frac{5}{2}\cdot\frac{7}{2}(1+x)^{-\frac{9}{2}}$ $\Rightarrow f^{(5)}(0) = \frac{1}{2}\cdot\frac{1}{2}\cdot\frac{3}{2}\cdot\frac{5}{2}\cdot\frac{7}{2}(1+0)^{-\frac{9}{2}} = \frac{1}{2}\cdot\frac{1}{2}\cdot\frac{3}{2}\cdot\frac{5}{2}\cdot\frac{7}{2} = \frac{105}{32}$

$f^{(6)}(x) = -\frac{1}{2}\cdot\frac{1}{2}\cdot\frac{3}{2}\cdot\frac{5}{2}\cdot\frac{7}{2}\cdot\frac{9}{2}(1+x)^{-\frac{11}{2}}$ $\Rightarrow f^{(6)}(0) = -\frac{1}{2}\cdot\frac{1}{2}\cdot\frac{3}{2}\cdot\frac{5}{2}\cdot\frac{7}{2}\cdot\frac{9}{2}(1+0)^{-\frac{11}{2}} = -\frac{1}{2}\cdot\frac{1}{2}\cdot\frac{3}{2}\cdot\frac{5}{2}\cdot\frac{7}{2}\cdot\frac{9}{2} = \frac{945}{64}$

So the first six terms of Maclaurin's series for $\sqrt{1+x}$ are

$$1 + \frac{1}{2\cdot 1!}x - \frac{1}{4\cdot 2!}x^2 + \frac{3}{8\cdot 3!}x^3 - \frac{15}{16\cdot 4!}x^4 + \frac{105}{32\cdot 5!}x^5 = 1 + \frac{1}{2}x - \frac{1}{8}x^2 + \frac{1}{16}x^3 - \frac{5}{128}x^4 + \frac{7}{256}x^5$$

The following notes apply to the expansion of $\sqrt{1+x}$.

1 $f^{(n)}(0) = (-1)^{n+1}\frac{1\cdot 3\cdot 5 \dots (2n-3)}{2^n}; n \geq 2$

2 $\sqrt{1+x} = 1 + \frac{1}{2}x - \frac{1}{8}x^2 + \frac{1}{16}x^3 - \frac{5}{128}x^4 + \frac{7}{256}x^5 - \dots = 1 + \sum_{r=1}^{\infty}(-1)^{r+1}\frac{f^{(r)}(0)}{r!}x^r$

The adjustments made to the sigma notation are to account for the signs of the first two terms being + but thereafter alternating between + and −.

3 $\lim_{n\to\infty}\left|\frac{u_{n+1}}{u_n}\right| = \lim_{n\to\infty}\left|\frac{(-1)^{n+2}\,1\cdot 3\cdot 5\dots(2n-3)(2n-1)}{2^{n+1}} \times \frac{(-1)^{n+1}\cdot 2^n}{1\cdot 3\cdot 5\dots(2n-3)} \times \frac{x}{n+1}\right|$

$$= \lim_{n\to\infty}\left|-\frac{(2n-1)}{2n+2}x\right| = \lim_{n\to\infty}\left|-\frac{\left(2-\frac{1}{n}\right)}{2+\frac{2}{n}}x\right| = |-x| = |x|$$

So the series is convergent for $|x| < 1$.

Generalizations

It can be proved that, within the region of validity,

- An expansion for $f'(x)$ can be found by differentiating the expansion for $f(x)$.
- An expansion for $\int f(x)\,dx$ can be found by integrating the expansion for $f(x)$.

Exercise 10.5

1 Use the Maclaurin series to find a series for

a $f(x) = \frac{1}{1+x}$ b $f(x) = \sqrt{1-x}$ c $f(x) = \frac{1}{(1+x)^3}$

d $f(x) = x + \cos x$ e $f(x) = \sec x$ f $f(x) = \ln(\cos x)$

2 $\ln x$ is not defined for $x = 0$. However $\ln(1 + x)$ is.

a Find an expansion for **i** $\ln(1 + x)$ **ii** $\ln(1 - x)$

b Differentiate to find an expansion for $\frac{1}{1+x}$.
Compare this with your answer to **1 a**.

3 Find the first four non-zero terms in the expansion of

a $e^x \sin x$ b $\tan x$ c $x \sin x$ d $f(x) = \frac{x}{1+x}$

4 a Use the Maclaurin series to find a power series for $(1 + x)^n$.
This expansion is often referred to as the **binomial series**.

b By rewriting $(a + b)^n$ as $a^n\left(1 + \frac{b}{a}\right)^n$ find a power series for it.

c Hence write a series for

i $(1 + x^2)^{-1}$ **ii** $(1 - x^2)^{-1}$ **iii** $\frac{1}{\sqrt{1 - x^2}} = (1 - x^2)^{-\frac{1}{2}}$

d By integrating your result in **c i**, find an expansion for $\tan^{-1} x$.
[Use the fact that $\tan^{-1} 0 = 0$ to evaluate the constant of integration.]

e By integrating your result in **c iii**, find an expansion for $\sin^{-1} x$.
[Use the fact that $\sin^{-1} 0 = 0$ to evaluate the constant of integration.]

f Find an expansion for $\cos^{-1} x$.

5 **A slight diversion**
If you have enough knowledge of complex numbers to have tackled differential equations then you know enough to tackle this question.

It refers to the notion that $\sqrt{-1} = i$ and that a number of the form $z = a + bi$ is called complex. Both a and b are real numbers but a is called the real part and b is called the imaginary part of z.

We know $e^x = \frac{1}{0!} + \frac{x^1}{1!} + \frac{x^2}{2!} + \frac{x^3}{3!} + \frac{x^4}{4!} + \frac{x^5}{5!} + \ldots$ is true *for all x*.

a Write an expansion for **i** e^{-x} **ii** e^{3x} **iii** **ii** e^{ax}

b Now write an expansion for e^{ix} keeping in mind that $i^2 = -1$.

c Separate the real from the imaginary terms to create two series.

d Examine the series to determine a connection between $\sin x$, $\cos x$ and e^x.

Note: you may have already used the result in the chapter on differential equations, that is,

$e^{i\theta} = \cos\theta + i\sin\theta$

10.6 Approximating using Maclaurin's series

For practical purposes, when we wish to evaluate a function using its equivalent power series, we only evaluate a partial sum.
The number of terms taken for a partial sum will depend on the accuracy required.

We can judge the number of terms in part by using these facts:

- All the series examined are convergent (in some region of validity).
  In practice you will only be asked to use series which satisfy this condition.
- Within this region each term is less than the term before it (a necessary condition for convergence).
- When the series is an alternating series, the actual value of the function will lie between two consecutive partial sums.

Example 10

Find sin (0.5) correct to 4 decimal places.

$\sin x = \frac{x}{1!} - \frac{x^3}{3!} + \frac{x^5}{5!} - \frac{x^7}{7!} + \frac{x^9}{9!} - \ldots$ thus $\sin 0.5 = \frac{0.5}{1!} - \frac{0.5^3}{3!} + \frac{0.5^5}{5!} - \frac{0.5^7}{7!} + \frac{0.5^9}{9!} - \ldots$

The sine series is an alternating series.
We need only evaluate partial sums looking for repetition to 5 decimal places.
We are looking for the nth term to be zero (correct to 5 dp).

A calculator check tells us that $|u_7| = \frac{0.5^7}{7!} = 0.000001\ldots = 0$ (to 5 dp).

All subsequent $|u_n| = 0$ to 5 dp.

So, $\sin 0.5 \approx \frac{0.5}{1!} - \frac{0.5^3}{3!} + \frac{0.5^5}{5!} = 0.5 - 0.02083 + 0.00026$
$= 0.4794$ (to 4 dp)

Note: a spreadsheet can be used to explore the goodness of fit of the partial sum with the function.
Here $\sin x$ is being compared with $\frac{x}{1!} - \frac{x^3}{3!} + \frac{x^5}{5!} - \frac{x^7}{7!}$.
The fit is good over the domain $0 \le x \le \pi$.

	A	B	C
1	x	Maclaurin 4 terms	sin x
2	0	0	0
3	0.2	0.1986693	0.19866933
4	0.4	0.3894183	0.38941834
5	0.6	0.5646424	0.56464247
6	0.8	0.7173557	0.71735609

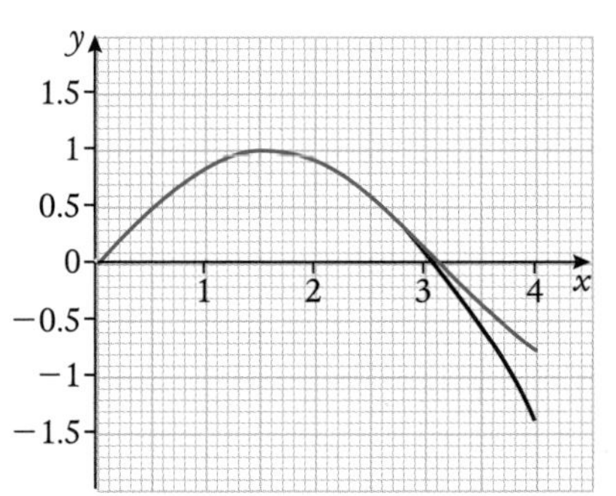

Example 11

Find $e^{0.5}$ correct to 3 decimal places.

$e^x = \frac{1}{0!} + \frac{x^1}{1!} + \frac{x^2}{2!} + \frac{x^3}{3!} + \frac{x^4}{4!} + \frac{x^5}{5!} + \ldots$

$\Rightarrow e^{0.5} = \frac{1}{0!} + \frac{0.5^1}{1!} + \frac{0.5^2}{2!} + \frac{0.5^3}{3!} + \frac{0.5^4}{4!} + \frac{0.5^5}{5!} + \frac{0.5^7}{7!} + \ldots$

A quick check shows $\frac{0.5^5}{5!} = 0.00026\ldots = 0$ (to 3 dp)

$\Rightarrow e^{0.5} = \frac{1}{0!} + \frac{0.5^1}{1!} + \frac{0.5^2}{2!} + \frac{0.5^3}{3!} + \frac{0.5^4}{4!} + \frac{0.5^5}{5!} = 1.649$ (to 3 dp)

Note: consider the ratio $\frac{u_{n+1}}{u_n} = \frac{0.5^{n+1}}{(n+1)!} \times \frac{n!}{0.5^n} = \frac{0.5}{n+1}$.

We can see that when n exceeds 4, then each term is less than one-tenth of the term before it.

So $\frac{0.5^7}{7!} < 0.000026$... In fact it is 0.000 001...

Exercise 10.6

1 For each of these expressions

i use Maclaurin's series to four terms to estimate the value of the expansion

ii use the corresponding function button on your calculator to help you state the degree of accuracy obtained.

a $\sin 0.9$ b $\cos 1.5$ c $e^{2.4}$ d e

e $1.5^{\frac{1}{3}}$ [Hint: expand $(1+x)^3$ and set $x = 0.5$.]

f 1.5^{-3} g 0.5^{-2} h $\ln(1 \cdot 5)$

2 a Calculate the value of sin 0.7 correct to 4 decimal places.

b How many terms of the power series must be evaluated to give cos 1·8 correct to 4 decimal places?

c Estimate the value of $1.5^{1.5}$ correct to 3 decimal places.

3 a Write out the power series to six terms, for

i $\ln(1+x)$ ii $\ln(1-x)$

b Hence, using the laws of logarithms, deduce a series to six terms for $\ln\left(\frac{1+x}{1-x}\right)$.

c The calculator gives $\ln(1.5) = 0.405\,465\,108$ to 9 decimal places.

i Letting $x = 0.5$, evaluate the six-term power series for $\ln(1+x)$.

ii Letting $x = 0.2$, evaluate the six-term power series for $\ln\left(\frac{1+x}{1-x}\right)$.

d Which of the above methods would appear to be more useful?

e When estimating the value of $\ln(1.8)$ using the series for $\ln\left(\frac{1+x}{1-x}\right)$ we want $\frac{1+x}{1-x} = 1.8$.

i Solve this equation for x. ii Estimate the value of $\ln(1.8)$.

10.7 Composite functions

Example 12

Express, as power series in x, a e^{ax} b e^{ax+b}

We know that $e^k = \frac{1}{0!} + \frac{k^1}{1!} + \frac{k^2}{2!} + \frac{k^3}{3!} + \frac{k^4}{4!} + \frac{k^5}{5!} + \ldots$ for all k.

a Setting $k = ax$, $e^{ax} = \frac{1}{0!} + \frac{(ax)^1}{1!} + \frac{(ax)^2}{2!} + \frac{(ax)^3}{3!} + \frac{(ax)^4}{4!} + \frac{(ax)^5}{5!} + \ldots = \sum_{r=0}^{\infty} a^r \frac{x^r}{r!}$

... a power series in x.

b Setting $k = ax + b$,

$$e^{ax+b} = \frac{1}{0!} + \frac{(ax+b)^1}{1!} + \frac{(ax+b)^2}{2!} + \frac{(ax+b)^3}{3!} + \frac{(ax+b)^4}{4!} + \frac{(ax+b)^5}{5!} + \ldots$$

... which is *not* a power series in x.

We should rewrite $e^{ax+b} = e^{ax}e^{b}$, then

$$e^{ax}e^{b} = e^{b}\left(\frac{1}{0!} + \frac{(ax)^1}{1!} + \frac{(ax)^2}{2!} + \frac{(ax)^3}{3!} + \frac{(ax)^4}{4!} + \frac{(ax)^5}{5!} + ...\right) = e^{b}\sum_{r=0}^{\infty} a^r\frac{x^r}{r!}$$

... a power series in x.

Example 13

Express $\sin\left(3x + \frac{\pi}{3}\right)$ as a power series in x.

We make use of the expansions $\sin k = k - \frac{k^3}{3!} + \frac{k^5}{5!} - \frac{k^7}{7!} + ...$ and $\cos k = 1 - \frac{k^2}{2!} + \frac{k^4}{4!} - \frac{k^6}{6!} + ...$

[Again, merely setting k as $\left(3x + \frac{\pi}{3}\right)$ will not yield a power series in x.]

So, expanding gives $\sin\left(3x + \frac{\pi}{3}\right) = \sin 3x \cos\frac{\pi}{3} + \cos 3x \sin\frac{\pi}{3} = \frac{1}{2}\sin 3x + \frac{\sqrt{3}}{2}\cos 3x$

$$\sin\left(3x + \frac{\pi}{3}\right) = \frac{1}{2}\left(3x - \frac{(3x)^3}{3!} + \frac{(3x)^5}{5!} - ...\right) + \frac{\sqrt{3}}{2}\left(1 - \frac{(3x)^2}{2!} + \frac{(3x)^4}{4!} - ...\right)$$

$$= \frac{1}{2}\left(\sqrt{3} + 3x - \frac{\sqrt{3}(3x)^2}{2!} - \frac{(3x)^3}{3!} + \frac{\sqrt{3}(3x)^4}{4!} + \frac{(3x)^5}{5!} - \frac{\sqrt{3}(3x)^6}{6!} - \frac{(3x)^7}{7!} + ...\right)$$

$$= \frac{1}{2}\left(\sqrt{3} + 3x - \frac{\sqrt{3}\cdot 3^2}{2!}x^2 - \frac{3^3}{3!}x^3 + \frac{\sqrt{3}\cdot 3^4}{4!}x^4 + \frac{3^5}{5!}x^5 - \frac{\sqrt{3}\cdot 3^6}{6!}x^6 - ...\right)$$

which is a power series in x.

Note: this can be tidied using sigma notation in a variety of ways.

$$= \frac{1}{2}\left(\left(\frac{\sqrt{3}(3x)^0}{0!} + \frac{(3x)^1}{1!}\right) - \left(\frac{\sqrt{3}(3x)^2}{2!} + \frac{(3x)^3}{3!}\right) + \frac{\sqrt{3}(3x)^4}{4!} + \frac{(3x)^5}{5!} - \left(\frac{\sqrt{3}(3x)^6}{6!} + \frac{(3x)^7}{7!}\right) + ...\right)$$

$$= \frac{1}{2}\sum_{r=0}^{\infty}(-1)^r\left(\frac{\sqrt{3}(3x)^{2r}}{(2r)!} + \frac{(3x)^{2r+1}}{(2r+1)!}\right)$$

Exercise 10.7

1 Given $e^x = \frac{1}{0!} + \frac{x^1}{1!} + \frac{x^2}{2!} + \frac{x^3}{3!} + \frac{x^4}{4!} + \frac{x^5}{5!} + ...$, devise power series in x for

a e^{4x} **b** e^{-x} **c** $e^{\frac{x}{2}}$ **d** e^{3x+1} **e** e^{1-2x} **f** e^{x^2}

2 Given $\sin x = \frac{x^1}{1!} - \frac{x^3}{3!} + \frac{x^5}{5!} - \frac{x^7}{7!} + ...$, devise power series in x for

a $\sin 3x$ **b** $\sin(-2x)$ **c** $\sin\left(\frac{x}{2}\right)$ **d** $\sin x^2$

3 Given $\cos x = \frac{x^0}{0!} - \frac{x^2}{2!} + \frac{x^4}{4!} - \frac{x^6}{6!} + ...$, devise power series in x for

a $\cos 4x$ **b** $\cos(-3x)$ **c** $\cos\left(\frac{x}{4}\right)$ **d** $\cos x^2$

4 Make use of trigonometric identities to find power series in x for

a $\sin\left(x + \frac{\pi}{2}\right)$ **b** $\sin\left(2x + \frac{\pi}{6}\right)$ **c** $\sin(\pi - 3x)$

d $\cos\left(2x + \frac{\pi}{2}\right)$ **e** $\cos\left(3x + \frac{\pi}{4}\right)$ **f** $\cos\left(\frac{\pi}{3} - x\right)$

5 **a** By using the identity $\cos 2x = 2\cos^2 x - 1$, find a series expansion for $\cos^2 x$.

b Similarly, find a series expansion for $\sin^2 x$.

6 Given that $\tan x = x + \frac{1}{3}x^3 + \frac{2}{15}x^5 + \frac{17}{315}x^7 + \frac{62}{2835}x^9 + ...$, find power series for

a $\tan 3x$ **b** $\tan(-x)$ **c** $\tan\left(\frac{x}{2}\right)$

7 Given that $\tan^{-1} x = x - \frac{1}{3}x^3 + \frac{1}{5}x^5 - \frac{1}{7}x^7 + \frac{1}{9}x^9 + \ldots$,

a find power series for

i $\tan^{-1} 3x$ ii $\tan^{-1}(-x)$ iii $\tan^{-1}\left(\frac{x}{2}\right)$

b Given that $\tan^{-1} 1 = \frac{\pi}{4}$, use the expansion above to estimate the value of π.

8 a By expressing $\ln(3 + x)$ as $\ln 3\left(1 + \frac{x}{3}\right) = \ln 3 + \ln\left(1 + \frac{x}{3}\right)$ find a power series expansion for $\ln(3 + x)$. State the region of validity for x.

b Find power series for each of these expressions.

i $\ln(4 + x)$ ii $\ln(2 + 3x)$ iii $\ln(1 + x^2)$

9 a Given $e^x = 1 + x + \frac{x^2}{2!} + \frac{x^3}{3!} + \frac{x^4}{4!} + \frac{x^5}{5!} + \ldots$ and $\sin x = x - \frac{x^3}{3!} + \frac{x^5}{5!} - \frac{x^7}{7!} + \ldots$ consider the product $e^x \sin x = \left(1 + x + \frac{x^2}{2!} + \frac{x^3}{3!} + \frac{x^4}{4!} + \frac{x^5}{5!} + \ldots\right)\left(x - \frac{x^3}{3!} + \frac{x^5}{5!} - \frac{x^7}{7!} + \ldots\right)$ and find the first five terms of the power series of $e^x \sin x$.

b Similarly find the first five terms of the power series for

i $e^x \cos x$ ii $e^x \ln(1 + x)$

Review 10

1 List the terms in each series and evaluate the sum.

a $\sum_{r=1}^{6} (r^2 + 1)$ b $\sum_{r=1}^{5} \frac{1}{r+1}$ c $\sum_{r=2}^{5} \left(r + \frac{1}{r}\right)$ d $\sum_{r=0}^{4} (r + 1)(r + 2)$

2 Express each sum using sigma notation.

a $4 + 7 + 10 + 13 + 16 + 19 + 22$

b $3 + 9 + 15 + 21 + 27 + \ldots + 117$

c $2 + 6 + 12 + 20 + \ldots + n(n + 1) + \ldots + 9900$

d $1 + \frac{1}{3} + \frac{1}{5} + \frac{1}{7} + \frac{1}{9} + \ldots + \frac{1}{99}$

e $\frac{1}{6} + \frac{1}{12} + \frac{1}{20} + \frac{1}{30} + \frac{1}{42} + \ldots + \frac{1}{930}$

3 The triangular numbers are generated by the recurrence relation $T_{n+1} = T_n + n + 1, T_1 = 1$.

a List the first five triangular numbers.

b Express T_n as an explicit function of n.

c Express the sum $T_1 + T_2 + T_3 + T_4 + \ldots + T_n$

i using sigma notation

ii as an explicit function of n.

d Find the sum of the first 100 triangular numbers.

4 A series is generated using the formula $u_n = n^2 - n - 1$.

a Express $\sum_{r=1}^{n} (r^2 - r - 1)$ as an explicit function of n.

b If the nth term of the series is 109, what is the sum to n terms?

5 Express $\sum_{r=1}^{n} \left(\sqrt{r} - \sqrt{r-1}\right)$ as an explicit function of n.

6 Use partial fractions to help you prove by direct means that

$$\sum_{r=2}^{n} \frac{1}{r^2 - 1} = \frac{(n - 1)(3n + 2)}{4n(n + 1)}$$

7 Prove by induction that the sum $\frac{1}{8} + \frac{1}{24} + \frac{1}{48} + \ldots + \frac{1}{4n(n+1)} = \frac{n}{4(n+1)}$.

8 Give the first five non-zero terms in Maclaurin's expansion of

a $f(x) = \cos x$ b $f(x) = \ln(1 + x)$ c $f(x) = \sin x - \cos x$

9 Find the first four terms in the power series for

a $f(x) = x \cos x$ b $f(x) = \sqrt[3]{1 + x}$

10 Find sin 0.5 correct to 3 decimal places using the power series for $\sin x$.

11 Express as a power series

a $\sin\left(2x + \frac{\pi}{3}\right)$ b e^{3x+2}

Summary 10

1 $\sum_{r=a}^{b} f(r) = f(a) + f(a+1) + f(a+2) + \ldots + f(b-1) + f(b)$

2 $\sum_{r=a}^{b} f(r) = \sum_{r=1}^{b} f(r) - \sum_{r=1}^{a-1} f(r)$

3 $\sum_{r=a}^{b} (f(r) + g(r)) = \sum_{r=a}^{b} f(r) + \sum_{r=a}^{b} g(r)$

4 $\sum_{r=1}^{n} (f(r+1) - f(r)) = \sum_{r=1}^{n} f(r+1) - \sum_{r=1}^{n} f(r) = f(n+1) - f(1)$

- Other similar results can be found by expanding the sigma notation.
- Partial fractions can be useful when $f(x)$ is rational.

5 a $\sum_{r=1}^{n} 1 = n$

b $\sum_{r=1}^{n} r = \frac{n}{2}(n+1)$

c $\sum_{r=1}^{n} r^2 = \frac{n}{6}(n+1)(2n+1)$

d $\sum_{r=1}^{n} r^3 = \left[\frac{n}{2}(n+1)\right]^2$

6 It is common for summation formulae to be proved by induction.

7 Maclaurin's theorem: $f(x) = \sum_{r=0}^{\infty} \frac{f^{(r)}(0) \cdot x^r}{r!}$

One has to ascertain over what domain the expansion is valid.

8 Examples of Maclaurin's expansion:

a $e^x = \frac{1}{0!} + \frac{x^1}{1!} + \frac{x^2}{2!} + \frac{x^3}{3!} + \frac{x^4}{4!} + \frac{x^5}{5!} + \ldots = \sum_{r=0}^{\infty} \frac{x^r}{r!}$

b $\sin x = \frac{x^1}{1!} - \frac{x^3}{3!} + \frac{x^5}{5!} - \frac{x^7}{7!} + \frac{x^9}{9!} - \ldots = \sum_{r=0}^{\infty} (-1)^r \frac{x^{2r+1}}{(2r+1)!}$

c $\cos x = \frac{x^0}{0!} - \frac{x^2}{2!} + \frac{x^4}{4!} - \frac{x^6}{6!} + \frac{x^8}{8!} - \ldots = \sum_{r=0}^{\infty} (-1)^n \frac{x^{2n}}{(2n)!}$

11 Applications of calculus

Historical note

Rectilinear motion, motion in a straight line, was studied by the philosophers of ancient Greece. It was, however, in the early 17th century that Galileo Galilei did his famous experiments on free fall, defining acceleration as $a = \frac{v - v_0}{t}$ where t represents the time it takes the velocity to change from v_0 to v.

This gave us the formulae $v = v_0 + at$ and $s = v_0 t + \frac{1}{2}at^2$ where s is the displacement from the origin.

Unit 2: Algebra

11.1 Rectilinear motion

When modelling rectilinear motion we consider a body moving along the x-axis in a straight line.
Its distance, or displacement, from the origin after a time t units is x units.
Note that the *names* of the units have been omitted, however:

- Unless otherwise stated we work in metres (m) and seconds (s).
- The use of units must be consistent: for example with x measured in metres and t in seconds, v is measured in m/s or ms^{-1} and a in m/s^2 or ms^{-2}.

If displacement from the origin is a function of time, that is, $x = f(t)$, then we can apply calculus to derive formulae for the velocity, v, and the acceleration, a, at time t.

Velocity is the rate of change of *displacement* with time: $v = \frac{dx}{dt}$

Acceleration is the rate of change of *velocity* with time: $a = \frac{dv}{dt} = \frac{d^2x}{dt^2}$

The application of integration may be used to determine velocity given acceleration, or displacement given velocity or acceleration.

$$x = \int v \, dt + c_1 \text{ and } v = \int a \, dt + c_2$$

As with any differential equation, initial conditions must also be given so that the constants of integration can be determined.

Example 1

A particle moves along the x-axis such that $x(t) = 2t^3 - 3t + 4$ where x metres is its displacement from the origin t seconds after observations began.

a How far from the origin was the particle when observations began?

b Calculate the velocity and acceleration of the particle after 4 s.

a When $t = 0$, $x(0) = 2 \cdot 0^3 - 3 \cdot 0 + 4 = 4$.

Initially the particle is 4 m from the origin.

b $v = \frac{dx}{dt} = 6t^2 - 3$. At $t = 4$, $v = 6 \cdot 4^2 - 3 = 96 - 3 = 93$. The velocity is 93 ms^{-1}.

$a = \frac{d^2x}{dt^2} = 12t$. At $t = 4$, $a = 12 \cdot 4 = 48$. The acceleration is 48 ms^{-2}.

Example 2

A body travels along a straight line such that $s = t^3 - 9t^2 + 15t - 2$ where s metres is the displacement from the origin t seconds after observations began.

a Find when **i** the velocity is zero **ii** the acceleration is zero.

b When is the distance s increasing?

c When is the velocity of the body decreasing?

---

a **i** $s = t^3 - 9t^2 + 15t - 2 \Rightarrow v = \frac{ds}{dt} = 3t^2 - 18t + 15$

$v = 0 \Rightarrow 3t^2 - 18t + 15 = 0 \Rightarrow 3(t - 1)(t - 5) = 0 \Rightarrow t = 1, 5$

The velocity is zero at the first and fifth seconds.

ii $a = \frac{d^2s}{dt^2} = 6t - 18$

$a = 0 \Rightarrow 6t - 18 = 0 \Rightarrow t = 3$

The acceleration is zero at the third second.

b s increasing $\Rightarrow \frac{ds}{dt} > 0 \Rightarrow 3(t - 1)(t - 5) > 0 \Rightarrow t < 1$ or $t > 5$

The particle was moving away from the origin (s increasing) before the first second and after the fifth second.

c v decreasing $\Rightarrow \frac{d^2s}{dt^2} < 0 \Rightarrow 6t - 18 < 0 \Rightarrow t < 3$

The particle was slowing down before the third second.

Example 3

A particle starts at the origin and, at time t seconds, the velocity in ms^{-1} is given by $v = 3t^2 + 6t - 2$. Determine, at time $t = 3$ s,

a the displacement **b** the velocity **c** the acceleration.

---

a $v = 3t^2 + 6t - 2 \Rightarrow s = \int v\, dt = t^3 + 3t^2 - 2t + c$

When $t = 0, s = 0 \Rightarrow 0 = 0^3 + 3 \cdot 0^2 - 2 \cdot 0 + c \Rightarrow c = 0$

$\Rightarrow s = t^3 + 3t^2 - 2t$

$\Rightarrow s(3) = 3^3 + 3 \cdot 3^2 - 2 \cdot 3 = 27 + 27 - 6 = 48$

At the third second the particle is 48 m from the origin.

b $v(3) = 3 \cdot 3^2 + 6 \cdot 3 - 2 = 27 + 18 - 2 = 43$

At the third second the particle is moving at 43 ms^{-1} away from the origin.

c $a = \frac{d^2s}{dt^2} = 6t + 6$

$\Rightarrow a(3) = 6 \cdot 3 + 6 = 24$

At the third second the particle is accelerating at 24 ms^{-2} away from the origin.

Exercise 11.1

1 Given that particles are moving in a straight line according to the equations given below, calculate for each the velocity and acceleration

i after t seconds ii after 3 s.

a $x = 3t^2 + t + 1$ b $x = \dfrac{2t}{t+1}$ c $x = \sqrt{5t+1}$

d $x = t + e^{3-t}$ e $x = 2\sqrt{2}\sin\dfrac{\pi}{12}t$ f $x = t + \dfrac{1}{t}$

2 The movement of particles can be modelled by the equations below.
Find the displacement and the acceleration the moment each particle comes to rest for the first time ($v = 0$).

a $x = 180t - 3t^2$ b $x = 2t^3 - 24t^2 + 90t + 1$ c $x = 3t + \dfrac{75}{t+3}$

d $x = 5\cos 3t$ e $x = 2t + \dfrac{32}{t}$ f $x = 2t - e^t$

3 A particle is moving in a straight line. Its velocity can be calculated from $v(t) = 3t^2 + 1$ where t is the time in seconds. Initially the particle is 3 m from the origin.

a Find an expression for $x(t)$, the displacement of the particle at time t.

b What is the acceleration of the particle in the third second?

c i Explain why you know that the velocity is always positive.

ii How far did the particle travel between the third and sixth seconds?

4 A particle is moving so that the acceleration in ms^{-2} is modelled by $a = 3\sin 2t$ where t is the time in seconds since observations began.
Initially the particle is at rest and 1 m from the origin.
[That is, at $t = 0$, $v = 0$ and $s = 1$.]

a Find an expression for

i the velocity at time t ii the displacement at time t.

b Calculate the displacement, velocity and acceleration of the particle when t is $\frac{\pi}{4}$ s.

5 The equation of motion of a particle is $x = t^2 - \sin t$.

a Show that the particle is always accelerating.

b After how many seconds is the velocity always in the direction away from the origin?

6 A projectile is fired straight up with an initial velocity of $100\ ms^{-1}$.
Its height, h metres, above the ground after t seconds is given by $h(t) = -5t^2 + 100t$.

a Acceleration due to gravity is a constant.
What is its value in this model?

b Find i the maximum height ii the time at which it is attained.

c i Identify the times when $h = 0$. ii With what velocity does the projectile hit the ground?

7 A car is tested to destruction by propelling it into a wall at the test site.
The equation of motion of the car is $x = 30t^{\frac{3}{2}}$ where x metres is the distance travelled t seconds into the run. The car hits the wall after 9 s.

a How far from the wall did the car start the run?

b What is the velocity at the moment of impact?

c What is the acceleration i after 1 s ii after 4 s iii at the moment of impact?

8 A point on a piston moves up and down in a straight line.
Its motion can be modelled by $s(t) = 10\sin\left(\dfrac{\pi t}{12}\right)$.
The graph shows how s, v and a vary with time.

The x-axis is scaled in seconds. The units of the y-axis depend on the curve being interpreted.
[s m, v ms^{-1}, a ms^{-2}]

a Verify that the acceleration is a maximum/minimum when the displacement is a minimum/maximum.

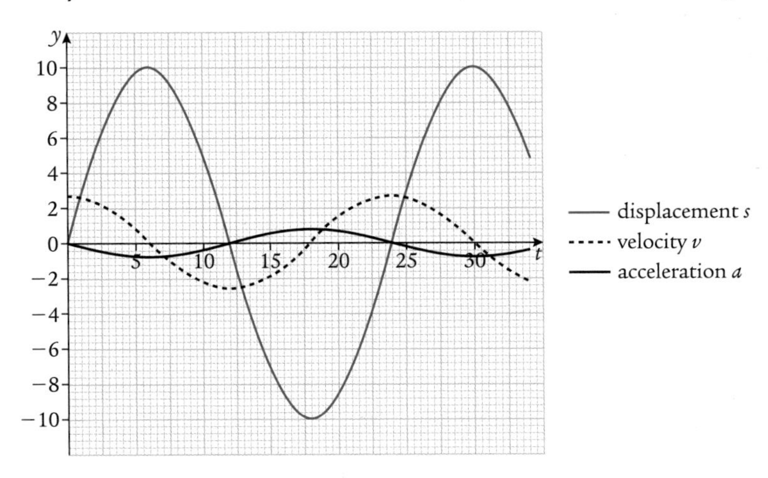

b Verify that the extrema of the velocity correspond to the zeros of the displacement.

c Determine the velocity and acceleration when $t = 0$.

d The graph suggests that at 7 s the velocity and acceleration have the same value.
Is this in fact the case?

e What is the acceleration when the displacement is at a maximum?

9 Viewed from the side, a carriage on a ferris wheel moves with rectilinear motion with equation $x = 6\sin\left(\frac{\pi t}{36}\right) + 9$, where x metres is the height of the carriage above the ground at time t seconds after observations started.

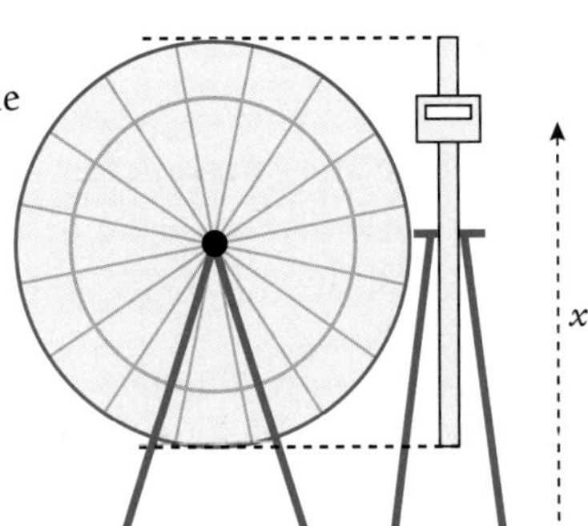

a i What is the radius of the wheel?

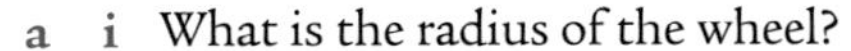

ii How high above the ground is the bottom of the wheel?

b Calculate the velocity and acceleration at the start.

c How long does it take to make one revolution?

d What is the maximum velocity of the carriage?

e What is the acceleration of the carriage when it is 10 m high and rising?

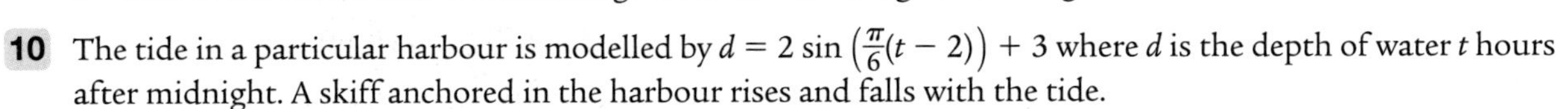

10 The tide in a particular harbour is modelled by $d = 2\sin\left(\frac{\pi}{6}(t-2)\right) + 3$ where d is the depth of water t hours after midnight. A skiff anchored in the harbour rises and falls with the tide.

a What is the vertical velocity of the skiff at 4 a.m.?

b i When, in the morning, is the vertical velocity of the skiff zero?

ii What is the acceleration at these times?

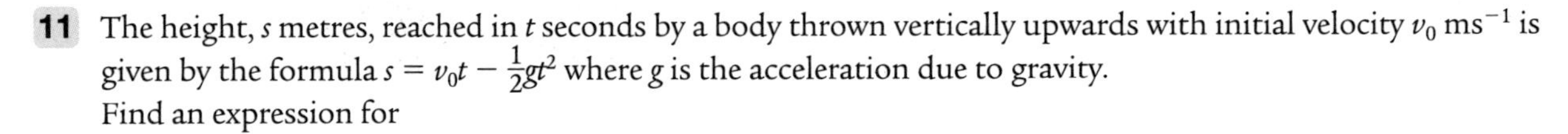

11 The height, s metres, reached in t seconds by a body thrown vertically upwards with initial velocity v_0 ms^{-1} is given by the formula $s = v_0t - \frac{1}{2}gt^2$ where g is the acceleration due to gravity.
Find an expression for

a v_t, the velocity at time t

b the times when $s = 0$ m

c the time when the body reaches its maximum height

d the maximum height.

12 A particle is moving in a straight line so that, at time t, its distance from the origin is x metres. Its acceleration at time t can be calculated by $a = k\cos^2 t$.
Initially the particle is at the origin with a velocity of 5 ms^{-1}.

After 1 second the particle is 8 metres from the origin.

[Remember: $\cos^2 t = \frac{1}{2}(\cos 2t + 1)$]

a Find an expression for the velocity at time t.

b Find the displacement after four seconds (to 3 sf).

13 A car starts from rest and proceeds in a straight line. Its acceleration is given by $a = \frac{1}{8}(30 - t)\ \text{ms}^{-2}$ where t is the time in seconds since the start.

a Find the velocity after 4 s.

b At this instant acceleration ceases and the car continues with constant velocity.
How far has the car travelled in total after 16 s?

c The diagram shows the velocity–time graph for the car's movement.
Calculate the total shaded area and compare this answer with your answer to **b**.

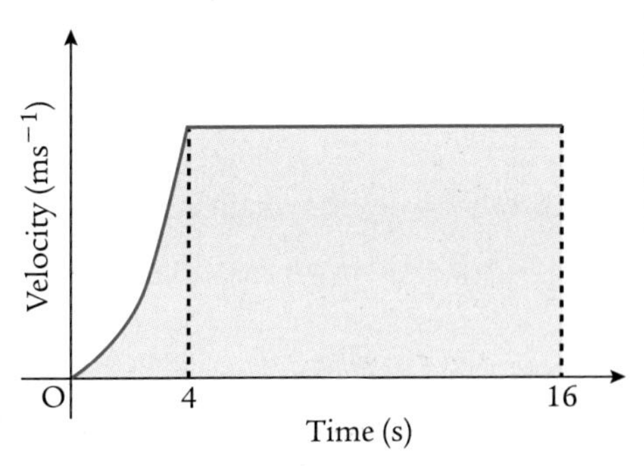

14 A particle, starting from rest, proceeds in a straight line. Its acceleration after t seconds is given by $a = 4\sec^2 t$ unit s^{-2} where $0 \le t \le 1$. Calculate the velocity after 0.5 s and the distance travelled after $\frac{\pi}{4}$ s.

11.2 Motion in a plane

Historical note

It was mainly for this particular field of study, and in particular celestial mechanics, that Sir Isaac Newton developed calculus.

Broadly, in his notation,

Displacement, s, is often expressed as a function of time: $s(t)$

Velocity, v, is the rate of change of displacement with time: $v(t) = s'(t)$

Acceleration, a, is the rate of change of velocity with time: $a(t) = v'(t) = s''(t)$

Definitions

With reference to a suitable set of axes, a particle in motion on a plane is at position $(x(t), y(t))$ at a time t. Let the displacement of the particle from the origin be denoted by $s(t)$.

Displacement

The displacement, $s(t)$, is represented by its position vector, $s(t) = \begin{pmatrix} x(t) \\ y(t) \end{pmatrix}$

or $s(t) = x(t)\mathbf{i} + y(t)\mathbf{j}$ where $\mathbf{i}$ and $\mathbf{j}$ are unit vectors in the x- and y-directions respectively.

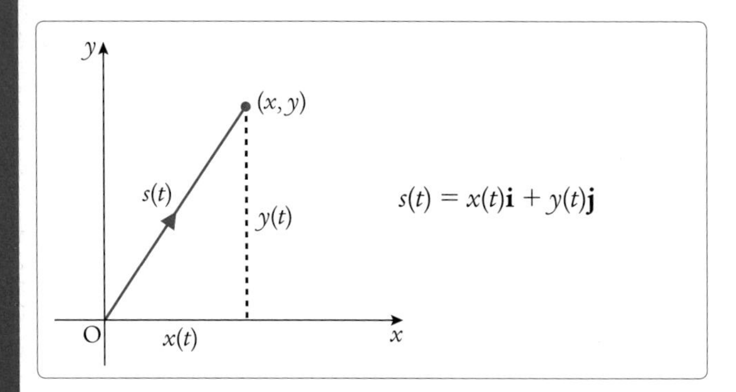

The distance from the origin is the magnitude of the displacement.

$$|s| = \sqrt{x^2 + y^2}$$

Velocity

The velocity, $v(t)$, is represented by the vector $v(t) = s'(t) = \begin{pmatrix} x'(t) \\ y'(t) \end{pmatrix}$

or $v(t) = s'(t) = x'(t)\mathbf{i} + y'(t)\mathbf{j}$.

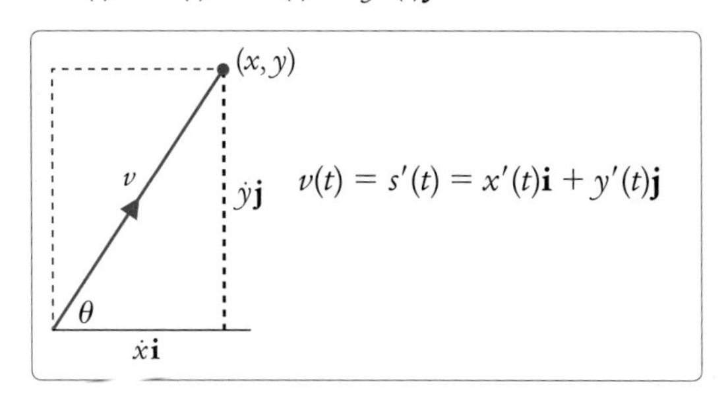

This is often denoted by $v = \dot{x}\mathbf{i} + \dot{y}\mathbf{j}$ where the dot above the variable denotes differentiation with respect to t.

The **speed** of the particle is the magnitude of the velocity: $|v| = \sqrt{\dot{x}^2 + \dot{y}^2}$.
The **direction of motion** at any instant of time can be described with reference to the x-direction.

From the diagram we see that $\tan\theta = \dfrac{\dot{y}}{\dot{x}}$.

This is the same as $\tan\theta = \dfrac{\frac{dy}{dt}}{\frac{dx}{dt}} = \dfrac{dy}{dt} \cdot \dfrac{dt}{dx} = \dfrac{dy}{dx}$.

Acceleration

The acceleration, $a(t)$, is represented by the vector $a(t) = v'(t) = s''(t) = \begin{pmatrix} x''(t) \\ y''(t) \end{pmatrix}$

or $a(t) = v'(t) = s''(t) = x''(t)\mathbf{i} + y''(t)\mathbf{j}$.

This is often denoted by $a = \ddot{x}\mathbf{i} + \ddot{y}\mathbf{j}$ where the double-dot indicates the second derivative with respect to t.

The magnitude of acceleration is $|a| = \sqrt{\ddot{x}^2 + \ddot{y}^2}$ [It does not have a special name.]

Example 4

A flare is fired from a point 200 m above sea level.

Its motion can be modelled by the parametric equations $x = 6t; \quad y = 200 + 10t - t^2$.

Find **a** the speed of the flare after 5 s

b its direction of motion at this time

c the situation after 10 s.

---

a Differentiating with respect to t: $\dot{x} = 6; \quad \dot{y} = 10 - 2t$

After 5 s, $t = 5$: $\dot{x}_{t=5} = 6; \ \dot{y}_{t=5} = 10 - 2 \cdot 5 = 0$

$$\Rightarrow \text{speed} = \sqrt{6^2 - 0^2} = 6 \text{ ms}^{-1}$$

b $\tan\theta = \dfrac{\dot{y}}{\dot{x}} = \dfrac{0}{6} = 0 \Rightarrow \theta = 0 \text{ or } \pi$

Examine the components of the velocity of the flare at $t = 5$:

$x'(5) = 6; y'(5) = 10 - 10 = 0$

It is going to the right at 6 ms^{-1} and not moving vertically.

So $\theta = 0$.

The flare, when $t = 5$, is moving horizontally to the right.

c After 10 s, $t = 10$: $\dot{x}_{t=10} = 6; \ \dot{y}_{t=10} = 10 - 20 = -10$

$$\Rightarrow \text{speed} = \sqrt{6^2 + (-10)^2} = 11.7 \text{ ms}^{-1} \text{ to 3 sf}$$

$$\tan\theta = \frac{\dot{y}}{\dot{x}} = \frac{-10}{6} \Rightarrow \theta = -1.03 \text{ or } \pi + (-1.03) = 2.11$$

It is going to the right at 6 ms^{-1} and going down at 10 ms^{-1}.

So $\theta = -1.03$ radians $= -59.0°$.

Note: A spreadsheet can be used to explore the 'flight' of the flare.

In Column A we record the time, t.

In A2 enter 0; in A3 enter =A2+1; fill down to row 22.

In B2 enter =6*A2; fill down to row 22.

In C2 enter =200+10*A2−A2^2; fill down to row 22.

Select columns B and C only, and insert a chart. [smooth lined scatter]

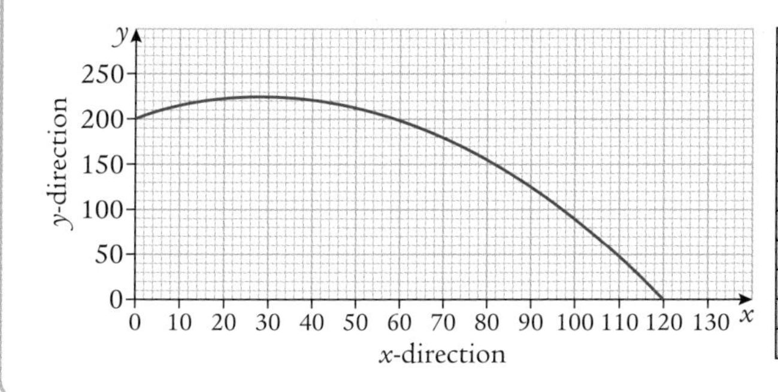

	A	B	C
1	time t	$x = 6t$	$y = 200 + 10t - t^2$
2	0	0	200
3	1	6	209
4	2	12	216
5	3	18	221
6	4	24	224
7	5	30	225
8	6	36	224
9	7	42	221
10	8	48	216

Example 5

The equations of motion of a particle moving in a plane are $x = t^3 - 3t, y = t^2 + t$, where x and y are measured in metres and t in seconds. Find the magnitude and direction of

a the velocity

b the acceleration after 3 s.

a Let v ms^{-1} represent the velocity and let the direction be $\alpha°$ to the x-direction.

$x'(t) = 3t^2 - 3, \quad y'(t) = 2t + 1$

$\Rightarrow x'(3) = 24, \quad y'(3) = 7$

$\Rightarrow |v| = \sqrt{24^2 + 7^2} = 25$: the speed is 25 ms^{-1}.

Also, $\tan \alpha° = \frac{7}{24} \Rightarrow \alpha° = 16.3°$ or $196.3°$

Since $x'(3) > 0$ and $y'(3) > 0$ [first quadrant], then $\alpha° = 16.3°$.

b Let a ms^{-2} represent the acceleration; let the direction be $\beta°$ to the x-direction.

$x''(t) = 6t, \quad y''(t) = 2$

$\Rightarrow x''(3) = 18, \quad y''(3) = 2$

$\Rightarrow |a| = \sqrt{18^2 + 2^2} = 18.1$ to 3 sf

The magnitude of the acceleration is 18.1 ms^{-2}.

Also, $\tan \beta° = \frac{2}{18} \Rightarrow \beta° = 6.3°$ or $186.3°$

Since $x''(3) > 0$ and $y''(3) > 0$ [first quadrant], then $\beta° = 6.3°$.

Example 6

A mill wheel is driven by water passing under it. The movement of a particle on the circumference of the wheel is modelled by $x = 3 \sin t, y = 3 \cos t + 2$.

The x-axis models the water level.

a Find the position of the particle when $t = \frac{\pi}{2}$.

b Find the velocity at this point.

c At what time does the particle dip into the water?

d Find the speed at this point, working to 3 significant figures

---

a When $t = \frac{\pi}{2}$ $x = 3 \sin \frac{\pi}{2} = 3, y = 3 \cos \frac{\pi}{2} + 2 = 2$.

The particle is at point (3, 2).

b $\dot{x} = 3 \cos t \Rightarrow \dot{x}_{t=\frac{\pi}{2}} = 3 \cos \frac{\pi}{2} = 0, \dot{y} = -3 \sin t \Rightarrow \dot{y}_{t=\frac{\pi}{2}} = -3 \sin \frac{\pi}{2} = -3$

$\Rightarrow |v| = \sqrt{0^2 + (-3)^2} = 3; \tan(\alpha°) = \frac{\dot{y}}{\dot{x}} = \frac{-3}{0}$ ... undefined. So velocity is vertical.

Since $\dot{y}_{t=\frac{\pi}{2}} < 0$, the direction is vertically *down*.

The particle is moving vertically downwards at 3 ms^{-1}.

c The particle dips into the water when $y = 0$ [on the x-axis].

$y = 3 \cos t + 2 = 0 \Rightarrow t = \cos^{-1}\left(\frac{-2}{3}\right) \Rightarrow t = 2.30$

After 2.30 s the particle dips into the water.

d $\dot{x} = 3 \cos t \Rightarrow \dot{x}_{t=2.30} = 3 \cos 2.30 = -2.00$,

$\dot{y} = -3 \sin t \Rightarrow \dot{y}_{t=2.30} = -3 \sin 2.30 =$ -2.24

$\Rightarrow |v| = \sqrt{(-2.00)^2 + (-2.24)^2} = 3.00$

The particle is travelling at 3 ms^{-1} when it hits the water.

Note: a spreadsheet can be used to give a clearer picture of the locus of the particle.

With x and y being trigonometric functions of t, it can be useful to make t grow in increments of a fraction of π.

In A2 type: 0; in A3 type: =A2+PI()/12.
The increment is $\frac{\pi}{12}$.
In B2 type: =3*SIN(A2).
In C2 type: =3*COS(A2)+2.
Fill A3 and B2 and C2 down to row 26.
Select B2 to C26 and insert a chart.
Reshape the frame to make the grid 'square'.

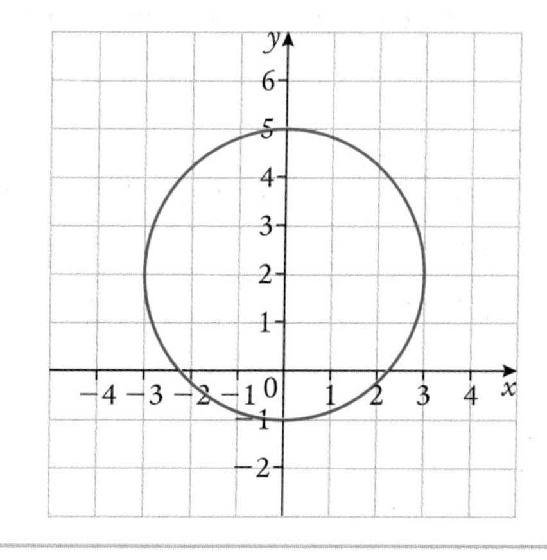

Exercise 11.2

In this exercise

- t represents time in seconds; x and y are distances in metres.
- Work in radian measure when dealing with trigonometric functions.
- Work to 3 significant figures where appropriate.
- Where possible, you should explore the 'paths' generated on a spreadsheet.

1 A particle moves in a plane according to the parametric equations $x = \frac{t^3}{\pi} + \sin t, y = t^2 - \cos t$.

a Find the speed of the particle, and the direction of motion, when $t = \pi$.

b Find the magnitude of the acceleration at the same time.

2 A package of supplies is dropped from a plane.
The locus of its path is given by $x = 2t - 1, y = 224 - 3t - 5t^2$.

a Find the value of y when $x = 11$.

b How far from the drop point would the package land?
[$y = 0$. What is x?]

c A parachute is used to slow the package down.
How fast will the package strike the ground if the parachute does not deploy?

3 A particle moves in a plane according to the equations
$x = \ln(t + 2) - 0.69, y = \ln(t + 3) + 1$

a i Use the chain rule to establish an expression in t for $\frac{dy}{dx}$.

ii Hence show that when $t > 0, \frac{dy}{dx} > 0$, and so the displacement is always increasing.

b How far did the particle travel between the first and fourth seconds?

c Find the magnitude and direction of the velocity at the first second.

d Find the magnitude and direction of the acceleration initially.

4 As it takes off, a light aircraft's movement can be modelled by the equations
$x = t \ln t, y = t^2 \ln t$, for $t > 0$.
Find, when $t = 22$,

a its position and displacement

b the magnitude and direction of the velocity

c the magnitude and direction of the acceleration.

5 A particle is moving so that at time t, the acceleration can be modelled by $\ddot{x} = 6$, $\ddot{y} = 6t$.

a If the velocity initially ($t = 0$) is given by $v_0 = -6\mathbf{i} - 3\mathbf{j}$ find parametric equations to model the velocity at time t.

b Initially the particle is at the origin.
Find parametric equations to model the displacement at time t.

c i Find when the particle is momentarily at rest. [That is when $v = 0$.]

ii Find its position and acceleration at this moment.

6 The London Eye is a tourist attraction on the banks of the Thames.
It is a ferris wheel that travels slow enough to allow people to step on and off without it stopping. The movement of a point on the circumference can be modelled by
$x = 65\cos\left(\frac{\pi t}{15} - \frac{\pi}{2}\right), y = 65\sin\left(\frac{\pi t}{15} - \frac{\pi}{2}\right) + 70$
where t is the number of minutes since the point was last at the bottom of the wheel.

a How high above the ground is the bottom of the wheel?
[That is, what is y when $x = 0$?]

b How long does it take to make a complete revolution?

c i Show that its speed is a constant (that is, independent of t) and give its value.

ii Describe its velocity after 10 min.

d Describe its acceleration after 15 min.

7 At a planetarium, a computer simulates a planet in its elliptical orbit by
$\dot{x} = \frac{\pi}{45}\cos\left(\frac{\pi}{180}t\right), \dot{y} = \frac{\pi}{60}\sin\left(\frac{\pi}{180}t\right)$ where t is the number of days since the equinox.

a On day 90 the planet is at position (4, 0). Use this information to find parametric equations to model the displacement.

b i Find the position of the planet on day 210.

ii Find the velocity, magnitude and direction on this day.

c Find the magnitude and direction of the acceleration on this day.

8 The velocity of a particle can be modelled by $\dot{x} = \frac{e^t - e^{-t}}{2}, \dot{y} = \frac{e^t + e^{-t}}{2}$.

a i Find parametric equations to give the position at time t.

ii Find the position of the particle initially if the constants generated by integration are both zero.

b Express, in terms of e^{2t},

i the speed

ii the tangent of the angle that the direction of motion makes with the x-direction.

c Find the acceleration when $t = 5$.

9 On 14th February, a laser light was made to play on a wall tracing out a design by following the equations of motion $x = \cos^3 t, y = \sin t - \sin^2 t$ where t is the time in tenths of a second and x and y are measured in metres.

a What is the position of the starting point?

b Calculate the velocity when $t = 10$.

10 A particle's motion is described by $x = 1 + \cos t - \sin t, y = 1 - \cos t + \sin t$.

a Show that at all times t, the direction of the velocity and that of the acceleration are the same.

b Show that $|v(t)|^2 + |a(t)|^2 = 4 \;\forall\; t$.

c i Show that $x + y = k$ where k is a constant.

ii Hence sketch the locus of the particle in the domain $0 \leq x \leq 2$.

11.3 Related rates of change

Reminders

- Given that $y = f(x)$ then $\frac{dy}{dx} = \frac{1}{\frac{dx}{dy}}$.
- Given that y is a function of x and that both x and y are functions of u the chain rule tells us that $\frac{dy}{dx} = \frac{dy}{du} \times \frac{du}{dx}$.

  This is equivalent to $\frac{dy}{dx} = \frac{dy}{du} \div \frac{dx}{du}$.

These facts are useful in solving many problems.

Example 7

In car use the application of rates is fairly ubiquitous.

You pay 140 pence per litre, there are 0.22 gallons per litre, you get 60 miles to the gallon...

a At what rate are you using fuel, in gallons per hour, when you travel at

i 50 mph **ii** 70 mph?

b Cruising at 60 mph what is it costing you

i per mile? **ii** per hour?

---

a Let L be volume in litres, P be cost in pence, G be volume in gallons, D be distance in miles and T be time in hours.

The data in the question gives $\frac{dP}{dL} = 140$, $\frac{dG}{dL} = 0.22$, $\frac{dD}{dG} = 60$.

i You are being asked for $\frac{dG}{dt}$ when given $\frac{dD}{dt} = 50$.

$$\frac{dG}{dt} = \frac{dD}{dt} \times \frac{dG}{dD} = \frac{dD}{dt} \div \frac{dD}{dG} = 50 \div 60$$

So you are using $\frac{5}{6}$ gallons per hour when travelling at 50 mph.

ii When $\frac{dD}{dt} = 70$, $\frac{dG}{dt} = \frac{dD}{dt} \div \frac{dD}{dG} = 70 \div 60$.

So you are using $1\frac{1}{6}$ gallons per hour when travelling at 70 mph.

b **i** You need $\frac{dP}{dD}$. Using only what you know, $\frac{dP}{dD} = \frac{dP}{dL} \times \frac{dL}{dG} \times \frac{dG}{dD}$

$$\Rightarrow \frac{dP}{dD} = \frac{dP}{dL} \times \frac{1}{dG/dL} \times \frac{1}{dD/dG} = 140 \times \frac{1}{0.22} \times \frac{1}{60}$$

It is costing you 10.6 pence per mile.

ii You need $\frac{dP}{dt}$.

Using what you know, $\frac{dP}{dt} = \frac{dP}{dD} \times \frac{dD}{dt} = 10.6 \times 60 = 636$.

It is costing you 636 pence per hour.

Example 8

A spherical balloon is being inflated at a constant rate of 200 cm^3 per second.

a At what rate is the radius increasing when it is 10 cm?

b At what rate is the radius increasing after 6 s?

a Let $v(t)$ and $r(t)$ be the volume and radius respectively after t seconds.

We know $\frac{dv}{dt} = 200$ (given) and $v = \frac{4}{3}\pi r^3 \Rightarrow \frac{dv}{dr} = 4\pi r^2$ (theory).

We desire $\frac{dr}{dt}$. Now, $\frac{dr}{dt} = \frac{dr}{dv} \times \frac{dv}{dt} = \frac{1}{dv/dr} \times \frac{dv}{dt}$.

So, $\frac{dr}{dt} = \frac{1}{4\pi r^2} \times 200 = \frac{50}{\pi r^2}$

When $r = 10$, $\frac{dr}{dt} = 0.16$ to 2 sf

The radius is increasing at a rate of 0.16 cms^{-1} when it is 10 cm long.

b After 6 s, the volume is (200×6) $cm^3 = 1200$ cm^3.

The corresponding radius is found from $1200 = \frac{4}{3}\pi r^3 \Rightarrow r = \sqrt[3]{\frac{1200 \times 3}{4\pi}} = 6.59$ (3 sf)

$\Rightarrow \frac{dr}{dt} = \frac{50}{\pi(6.59)^2} = 0.4$

The radius is increasing at a rate of 0.366 cms^{-1} after 6 s.

Example 9

A particle is moving in a circle.
The circle is centred on the origin and has a radius of 5 m. When the particle is at the point (4, 3), the rate of change of the x-coordinate is 21 ms^{-1}.
Find the corresponding rate of change of the y-coordinate.

We desire $\frac{dy}{dt}$. We are given that $\frac{dx}{dt} = 21$ and we have $\frac{dy}{dt} = \frac{dy}{dx} \times \frac{dx}{dt}$.

So now we want $\frac{dy}{dx}$.

The equation of the locus of the particle is $x^2 + y^2 = 25$.

Differentiating with respect to x gives $2x + 2y\frac{dy}{dx} = 0 \Rightarrow \frac{dy}{dx} = -\frac{x}{y}$.

So, $\frac{dy}{dt} = \frac{dy}{dx} \times \frac{dx}{dt} = -\frac{x}{y} \times 21$

When $x = 4, y = 3 \Rightarrow \frac{dy}{dt} = -\frac{4}{3} \times 21 = -28$

The y-coordinate is changing at a rate of -28 ms^{-1}.

Exercise 11.3

1 Density is the rate of change of mass with volume.
Sand with a density of 1440 kgm^{-3} can be dug out and bagged at the rate of 30 m^3h^{-1}.
Bags are filled at the rate of 850 kg per bag.
Sand is sold at 5p per kg.

Let w be the mass in kg, v be the volume in m^3, t be the time in hours, B be the number of bags and P be the cost in pounds.

a State the value of i $\frac{dw}{dv}$ ii $\frac{dv}{dt}$ iii $\frac{dw}{dB}$ iv $\frac{dP}{dw}$

b Find i the volume of 1 kg of sand

ii how much time it takes to bag 1 m^3

iii how much of a bag 1 kg will fill

iv what mass of sand you get for £1.

c Calculate

i the mass that can be bagged per hour, $\frac{dw}{dt}$

ii the money to be made per hour, $\frac{dP}{dt}$.

2 An oil spillage is spreading out on the garage floor.
It is circular in shape and its radius is expanding at the rate of 3 cms^{-1}.
How fast is the area growing when the radius is 50 cm?

3 The motion of a carriage on a ferris wheel can be described using
$x = 15 \sin \frac{\pi t}{30}, y = 15 \cos \frac{\pi t}{30} + 5$.

a Find i $\frac{dx}{dt}$ ii $\frac{dy}{dt}$ iii $\frac{dy}{dx}$

b The carriage is travelling round the circumference at a rate of $\frac{\pi}{2}$ ms^{-1}.

Find the rate of change of the distance travelled with respect to x in the 10th second.

4 A particle is moving in an elliptical orbit with an equation of $\frac{x^2}{9} + \frac{y^2}{4} = 1$.

a Find $\frac{dy}{dx}$.

b The point (1.6, 1.2) lies on the ellipse.
If the x-coordinate is changing at the rate of 27 ms^{-1} at this point, calculate the rate at which the y-coordinate is changing.

5 A man moves away from a lamp post at 2 ms^{-1}.
The lamp post is 6 m tall and the man is 1.5 m.

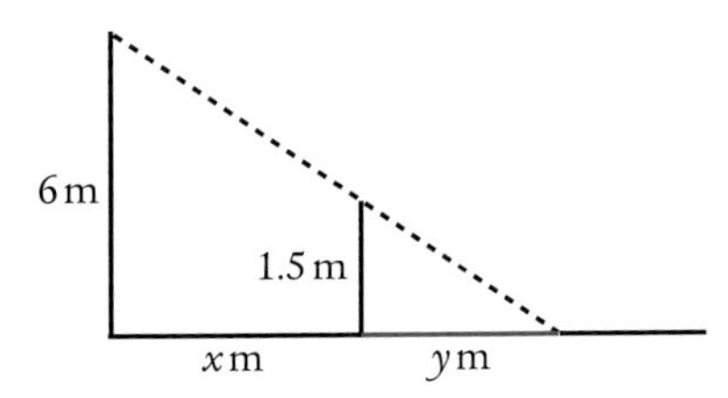

a i If x m is the distance the man is from the lamp post, and y is the length of the shadow, express y in terms of x.

[Hint: using similar triangles, $\frac{y}{x+y} = \frac{1.5}{6}$.]

ii Hence find $\frac{dy}{dx}$.

b Find at what rate the shadow is growing as the man walks away from the lamp post.

6 A metal cube of edges x cm is heated. Each edge expands by 0.003 $cmmin^{-1}$.

a i Express the volume V cm^3 as a function of x.

ii Find an expression for the rate of change of volume with respect to edge length.

b Find the rate at which the volume is expanding with respect to time when the edge is 6 cm long.

7 A plastic sphere is submerged in water. The temperature of the water is T °C.

The volume of the sphere is a function of T such that $V(T) = 100 \times 1.04^T$.

Let V mm³ represent the volume of the sphere and r cm its radius.

a Find i $\frac{dV}{dT}$ ii $\frac{dV}{dr}$

b At the point $r = 1$ and $T = 1$, find

i the rate at which the radius is changing, in mm per degree Celsius;

ii the rate at which the volume is changing with time if the temperature is increased at $2\,°\mathrm{C\,min^{-1}}$.

8 A disc starts from rest and speeds up at a constant rate, measured in revolutions per minute. After t minutes it has rotated through k revolutions where $k = 0.5t^2 + t$.

a Find the speed of the wheel in revolutions per minute, $\frac{dk}{dt}$.

b How long will it take to achieve a speed of 15 rpm?

c A loose particle on the disc moves out from the centre at a constant rate of $2\ \mathrm{mm s^{-1}}$. At how many millimetres per revolution is the particle moving out after i 1 min ii 30 s?

9 According to Boyle's law the volume, $V\ \mathrm{m^3}$, of a fixed mass of gas is inversely proportional to the pressure, $P\ \mathrm{N m^{-2}}$, of the gas.
In one particular case this leads to the relationship $PV = 500$.
The rate of change of the volume of the gas has been measured as $15\ \mathrm{m^3 s^{-1}}$.
Find the rate of change of pressure with respect to time when the volume of the gas is $50\ \mathrm{m^3}$.

10 Climbing a mountain under ideal conditions, the temperature drops at the rate of 9.8 °C per 1000 m.

A climber models his ascent on the equation $h = 5t^2 + 150t$ where h is his height in metres and t is the time in hours.

a Find $\frac{dT}{dt}$ in degrees Celsius per minute.

b At what rate, in degrees Celsius per minute, does he experience the temperature dropping two hours into his ascent?

11 A conical tank has a height of 4 m. Its base radius is 80 cm.
It is being drained at the rate of $0.5\ \mathrm{m^3 min^{-1}}$. At time t minutes, the surface is a circle of radius r metres and the depth of the liquid is h metres.

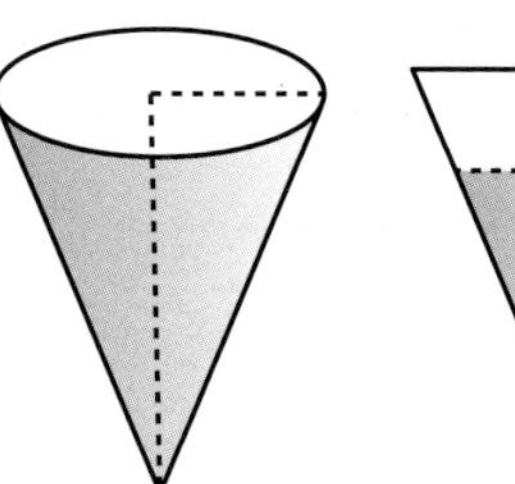

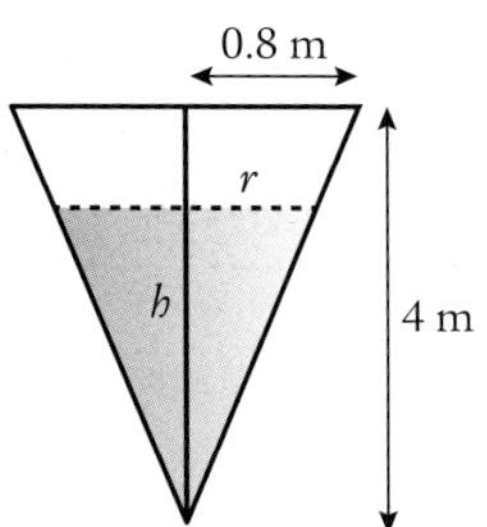

a i Using similar triangles, express h in terms of r.

ii Find an expression for the volume of liquid, $V\ \mathrm{m^3}$, in terms of r and h.

iii Find an expression for the volume of liquid in terms of r alone.

iv Find an expression for $\frac{dV}{dr}$.

b Find the rate at which the radius is decreasing, in metres per minute, when the depth of the liquid is 2 m.

c Find the rate at which the depth is decreasing, in metres per minute, when the depth is 1 m.

12 A hopper for grain is in the shape of an inverted square-based pyramid.
The top is a square of side 2 m. The height is 4 m. The dry grain is poured into the hopper at the rate of $3\ \mathrm{m^3 min^{-1}}$. At any moment treat the surface of the grain in the hopper as a square.
At what rate is the level of the grain rising when

a it is 1 m deep

b its surface is a square of side 1.5 m?

13 A set of stepladders is represented by an isosceles triangle whose equal sides are of length 2 m.
The feet of these lengths are D m apart, and held in place by a rope.
The rope snaps and the feet move apart. D increases by 20 cms^{-1}.
The apex angle is θ radians and its height at time t seconds is h metres.

a Express θ explicitly as a function of D.

b When the feet are 2.4 m apart, calculate the rate at which the angle is opening

  i in radians per second ii in degrees per second.

c Calculate the rate at which the height, h metres, is decreasing when the feet are 3.3 m apart. Express your answer in cms^{-1}.

14 A rocket takes off vertically. The angle of elevation, θ radians, of the rocket when it is at a height of x kilometres above the launch-pad is given by $\theta = \sin^{-1}\left(\frac{x}{y}\right)$ where y is the direct distance in kilometres between the rocket and the observer.
When $x = \frac{8}{5}$ and $y = \frac{5}{2}$, $\frac{dx}{dt} = 10$.

a Find, for these values, $\frac{dy}{dt}$, the speed at which the observer sees the rocket moving away.

b Find, at this instant, the rate at which the angle θ is changing.

11.4 Optimisation

Reminders

- Critical points are points where $f'(x) = 0$ or where $f'(x)$ is undefined, for example at endpoints, cusps, etc.
- Maxima and minima occur at critical points.
- The nature of stationary points can be examined using either a table of signs, or by using the second derivative. $f''(x) > 0$ indicates a minimum; $f''(x) < 0$ indicates a maximum.

Example 10

An open box is made from a 16 cm by 10 cm rectangle of tin.
Congruent squares are cut from each corner and the sides are then folded up to form a cuboid. Find the size of the square which maximises the volume of the resulting box.

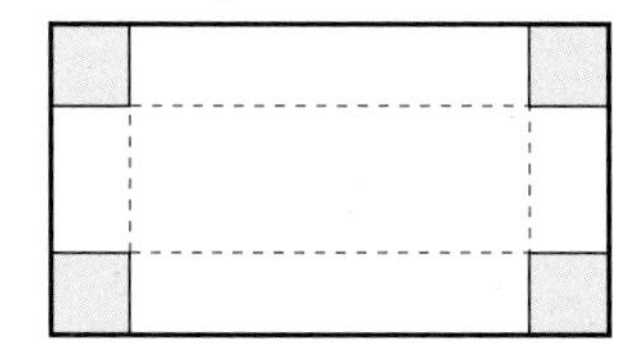

Let x cm be the length of a corner square.
Thus the dimensions of the finished box will be $(16 - 2x)$ cm, $(10 - 2x)$ cm and x cm.

The volume of the box:

$$V(x) = x(16 - 2x)(10 - 2x) \text{ with a practical restriction of } 0 \le x \le 5$$

$$\Rightarrow V(x) = 4x^3 - 52x^2 + 160x$$

$$\Rightarrow V'(x) = 12x^2 - 104x + 160$$

$$\Rightarrow V'(x) = 4(3x - 20)(x - 2)$$

To find maxima and minima we should compare the values of the function at stationary points, $V'(x) = 0$, and at end-points, that is, $V(0)$ and $V(5)$.

$V'(x) = 0 \Rightarrow 4(3x - 20)(x - 2) = 0 \Rightarrow x = \frac{20}{3}$ or $x = 2$

However $x = \frac{20}{3}$ is outside the valid domain for x.

So examine $V(2) = 2 \cdot (16 - 4) \cdot (10 - 4) = 144$; $V(0) = 0$ and $V(5) = 0$

So, by inspection, the maximum value of V in the domain is 144 when $x = 2$.

The minimum value of V is 0 when $x = 0, 5$.

So cut squares of side 2 cm out of the corners.

Example 11

The cost in hundreds of pounds, C, of doing a job is a function of the number of men employed (x men).

$C(x) = \frac{10x^2 + 640}{x}; x \neq 0$

Optimise the number of men.

Here all we know is that we need at least one man – there is no upper limit.

$C(x) = \frac{10x^2 + 640}{x} = 10x + 640x^{-1} \Rightarrow C'(x) = 10 - 640x^{-2}$

Maxima and minima occur at stationary points, $C'(x) = 0$, or end-points, $x = 1$.

$C'(x) = 0 \Rightarrow 10 - 640x^{-2} = 0 \Rightarrow x = 8$ $\quad$ ($x = -8$ is not sensible)

$C(1) = \frac{10.1^2 + 640}{1} = 650;\quad C(8) = \frac{10.8^2 + 640}{8} = 160;\quad C(8) < C(1)$

Because we have no upper limit to the domain, we have to examine the nature of the stationary point using a table of signs or the second derivative:

$C''(x) = 1280x^{-3} \Rightarrow C''(8) = \frac{1280}{\sqrt[3]{8}} = 640 > 0$: $C''(x) > 0 \Rightarrow$ minimum turning point

So the cost is minimised by employing eight men to do the job.

Optimum cost is £16 000.

Exercise 11.4

1 The turning effect, T, of a power boat is given by the formula $T = 12 \cos x \sin^2 x$, $0 < x < \frac{\pi}{2}$, where x is the angle (in radians) between the rudder and the central line of the boat. Find the size of the angle which maximises the turning effect.

2 An underwater cable consists of a core of conductive wire protected by a casing of non-conductive material. Let the ratio of the radius of the core to the thickness of this casing be t.

The speed, V, of the signal passing down the cable is given by $V(t) = kt^2 \ln\left(\frac{1}{t}\right)$, $0 < t < 1$, where k is a positive constant.

a Find the value of t which maximises the speed.

b Find that maximum speed.

3 A particle moves in an elliptical path such that its coordinates are $x = 6 \sin t$, $y = 4 \cos t$ where x and y are measured in metres and t is the time in minutes since the particle was last at the point (0, 4).

At what point(s) will the speed of the particle be at a maximum?

4 A point P is 500 m north of a point Q.
A cyclist, A, leaves P travelling south at 6 ms^{-1}.
At the same time, a cyclist B leaves Q travelling east at 8 ms^{-1}.
At time t seconds, A and B are D metres apart.

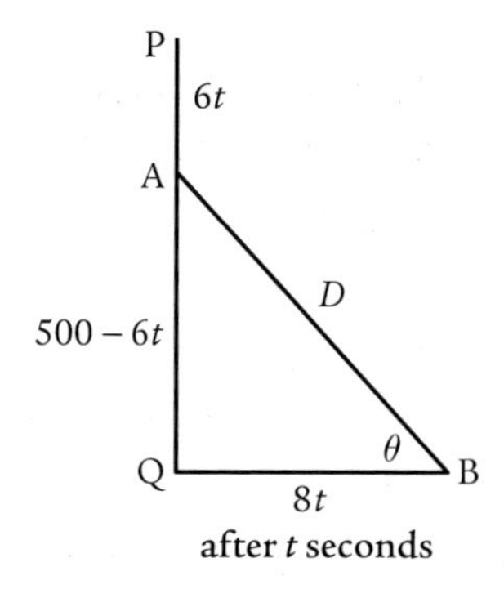

The angle $ABQ = \theta$ radians.

a Verify by substitution that

$$D = \frac{4000}{8\sin\theta + 6\cos\theta}$$

b Find the shortest distance between the two cyclists.
[It may be useful to express the denominator in the form $k\sin(\theta + \alpha)$.]

5 Lorries ferry materials from a quarry to a building site, a round trip of 60 miles. Let the time it takes to make a round trip be t hours.
The drivers get paid £12 per hour.
Diesel costs £1.50 per litre and the lorries burn $\left(\frac{v^2}{169} + 8\right)$ litres per hour, where v miles per hour is the average speed of the lorry.

a Express the time taken for a round trip in terms of v.
b Express what a lorry driver gets paid for a round trip in terms of v.
c Express the cost of the diesel used making a round trip in terms of v.
d The total cost of a round trip is 'driver's wages' + 'cost of diesel'.
What speed should the lorries maintain to minimise the cost of a round trip?

6 A straight line passes through (9, 3) making an acute angle of θ radians with the x-axis. It cuts the y-axis at A and the x-axis at B.

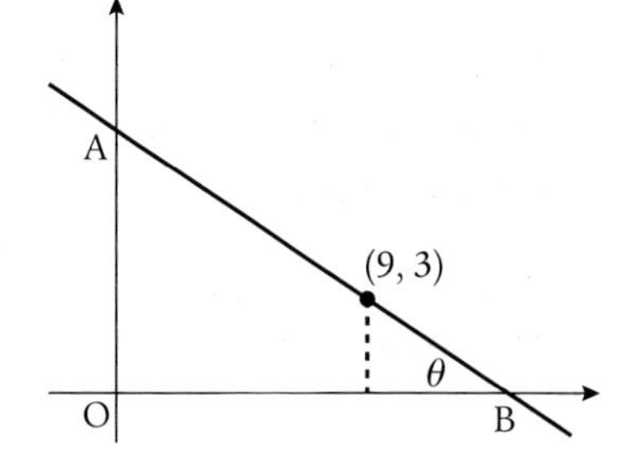

a If AB = d units, express y_A and x_B in terms of d and θ.
b i Use basic trigonometry to show that $\tan\theta = \frac{3}{x_B - 9}$.
ii Hence express d in terms of θ.
c Express $y_A + x_B$ in terms of θ.
d Find the equation of the line that passes through (9, 3) and minimises the sum $y_A + x_B$.

7 A wall, 2.7 m high, is parallel to the side of a house.
It is 6.4 m from the house.
A ladder rests on the ground and the top of the wall, and touches the house.
What is the shortest possible length of the ladder?

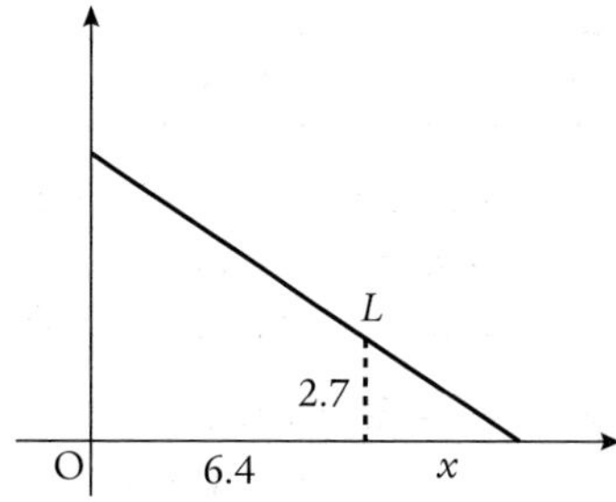

8 A rectangle is 20 cm wide.
Two squares of side x cm are cut from the right-hand corners.
A net is cut out as shown making use of the full width of the card.
The other lengths in the net are constants.
One has been marked as L cm for your convenience.

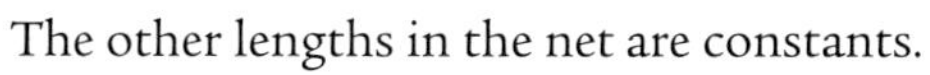

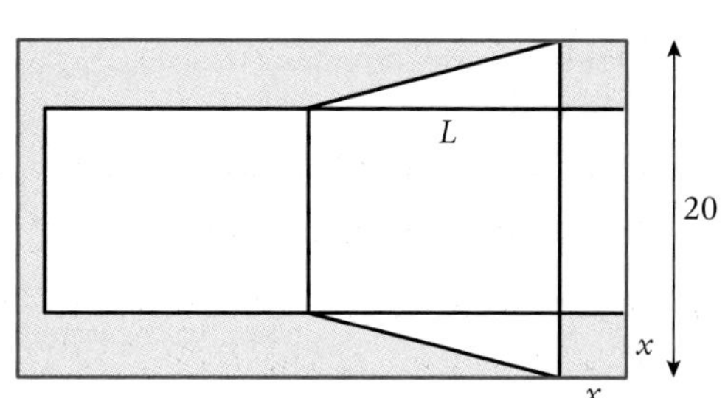

a For what value of x is the volume of the prism a maximum?
b If L is in fact 12, how long should the rectangle of card be, if the waste is kept to a minimum?

9 An open-topped cylinder of volume 228π cm^3 is made with these production costs:

- The base and side cost 30pcm^{-2}.
- The seam around the base costs 10pcm^{-1}.

a Express the height, h cm, of the cylinder in terms of the radius R.

b Express the cost in terms of R.

c Find the dimensions of the cylinder which minimise the cost.

10 A cylinder is inscribed in a cone of height h cm and semi-vertical angle a radians. Find the maximum volume of the cylinder in terms of h and a.

11 A heart-shaped curve is the result of drawing the locus of the parametric equations

$x = \cos^3 t, \quad y = \sin t - \sin^2 t$

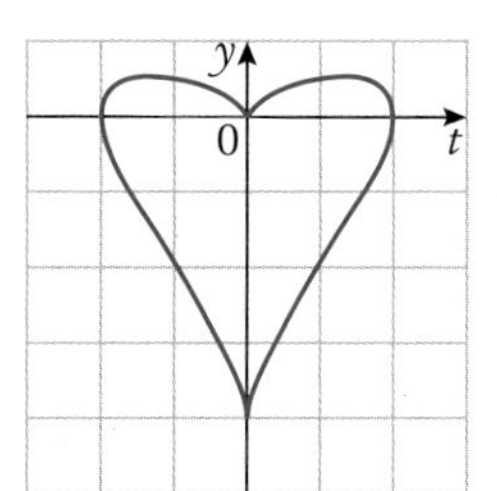

a Calculate the value of x which maximises the value of y.

b Calculate the value of y which maximises the value of x.

12 In engineering an equation of the form $y = 2^{-0.2t} \sin 2t$ might be used to model damped oscillations – like a bouncing weight on a spring coming to rest.

a Use logarithmic differentiation to find $\frac{dy}{dt}$.

b Find the first three maxima of the curve.

13 An isosceles triangle has a perimeter of 20 cm.
What are the lengths of the sides which will maximise its area?
[Hint: let x cm be the lengths of the equal sides; use logarithmic differentiation.]

14 A right-angled triangle has shorter sides x cm and y cm and an hypotenuse of h cm.

a Express h^2 in terms of x and y.

b The sum of the two shorter sides is 10 cm. Use implicit differentiation to find the shortest possible value of h.

Review 11

1 A particle moves on the x-axis with its displacement from the origin, s cm, such that $s = 1 - 2t + t^2$ where t seconds have elapsed since observations began.

a State the displacement in the fourth second.

b What is the velocity when $t = 3$?

c What do we know about the acceleration?

2 A point on a piston moves in a straight line such that its velocity at time t is v ms^{-1} where $v = 3 \cos \frac{\pi t}{3}$.

a i Find an expression for the displacement given that initially it was 2 cm from the origin.

ii What is the displacement when $t = 1$?

b Find the acceleration when $t = 1$.

3 A projectile moves according to the equations $x = 2t$ and $y = 25t - 5t^2$ where t is the time in seconds since the projectile was launched.

a Calculate the displacement from the origin when $t = 4.7$ s.

b **i** Express the velocity in terms of its components.

ii Find the speed and direction of motion when $t = 1$.

c At the top of its flight, the vertical component of the velocity is zero.
At what time does this occur?

d At the end of its flight, the vertical component of the displacement is zero.

i At what time does this occur?

ii At what speed does the projectile hit the ground?

4 A turntable on a record deck for playing vinyl records turns at $33\frac{1}{3}$ rpm.
The motion of a point r centimetres from the centre can be modelled by
$x = r\cos\left(\frac{10\pi}{9}t\right)$, $y = r\sin\left(\frac{10\pi}{9}t\right)$ where t is the time in seconds, measured from when the turntable was switched on.

a What is the starting position of the point?

b **i** Calculate the speed of a point 9 cm from the centre.

ii Calculate the velocity of the point (components and direction) when $t = 10$.

c Calculate the acceleration of a point on the rim, 15 cm from the centre, when $t = 20$.

5 The science tower in Glasgow has an external lift which takes you to an observation platform 105 m up.
The journey takes 2.5 min at a constant rate. Let y metres be the height at time t seconds after the lift has begun its ascent.

a Calculate $\frac{dy}{dt}$.

b It is known that the distance to the horizon is a function of the height of the observer. $D(y) = 3.57\sqrt{y}$ where D kilometres is the distance to the horizon of an observer who is y metres up.
At what rate does the observer see the horizon receding when he is 25 m up ascending in the lift?

c The horizon can be treated as a circle with the observer at the centre.
When he is 100 m up, calculate the rate at which

i the circumference is increasing

ii the area is increasing.

6 Treating the Earth as a sphere of radius 6400 km, the equator is defined as a great circle.
Any other circle parallel to this is called a small circle.
The angle ECP ($\theta°$) measured in *degrees* is the latitude of P and of all points on the small circle.
In the diagram R kilometres is the radius of the Earth, r kilometres is the radius of the small circle, and d kilometres is the distance between the centre of the Earth and the centre of the small circle.
A jet is flying from E to N through P at 1000 kmh^{-1}.

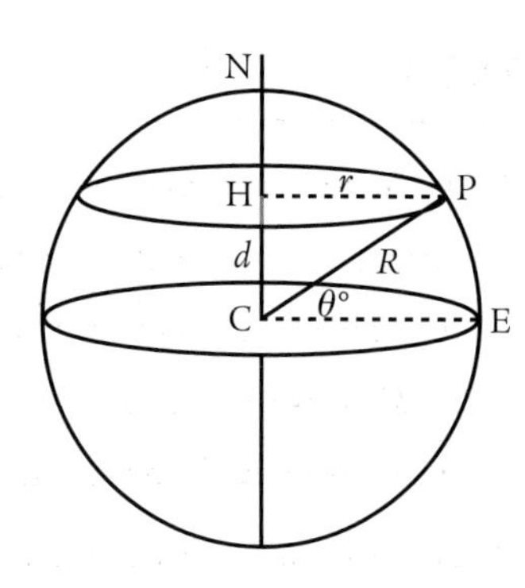

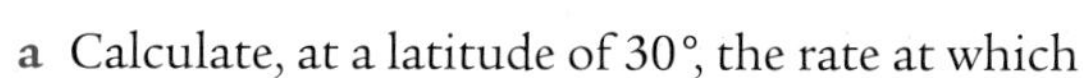

a Calculate, at a latitude of 30°, the rate at which

i the latitude is growing with time

ii the small circle radius is diminishing with respect to latitude

iii the small circle radius is diminishing with respect to time.

b The surface area of the dome which has the small circle as a base is given by $S_{dome} = 2\pi R^2(1 - \sin\theta)$. Calculate the rate at which this area is diminishing with time when the jet is over Edinburgh (latitude: 56°N).

7 A groundsman is to lay out an area in the field, shaped like a rectangle with a semicircle at one end. The perimeter of the area has to be 26 m.

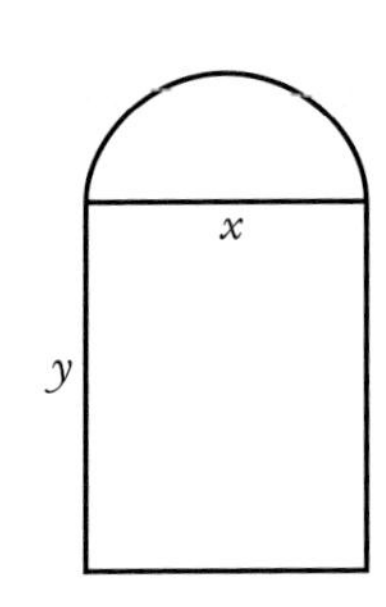

a Find the dimensions of the rectangle which maximises the area.

b How does the situation change if there has to be a semicircle at either end?

8 A right-angled triangle is to have an area of 50 cm^2.
Find its dimensions so that its hypotenuse is the smallest possible.

Summary 11

1 Rectilinear motion

- If displacement from the origin is a function of time, that is, $x = f(t)$, then we can apply calculus to derive formulae for the velocity, v, and the acceleration, a, at time t.
- **Velocity** is the rate of change of *displacement* with time: $v = \dfrac{dx}{dt}$
- **Acceleration** is the rate of change of *velocity* with time: $a = \dfrac{dv}{dt} = \dfrac{d^2x}{dt^2}$
- $x = \int v\,dt + c_1$ and $v = \int a\,dt + c_2$

  Initial conditions must also be given so that the constants of integration can be determined.

2 Motion in a plane

Definitions

- A particle in motion on a plane is at position $(x(t), y(t))$ at a time t.
- The displacement, $s(t)$, is represented by its position vector, $s(t) = \begin{pmatrix} x(t) \\ y(t) \end{pmatrix}$

  or $s(t) = x(t)\mathbf{i} + y(t)\mathbf{j}$ where $\mathbf{i}$ and $\mathbf{j}$ are unit vectors in the x- and y-directions respectively.
- The distance from the origin is the magnitude of the displacement,

  $|s| = \sqrt{x^2 + y^2}$
- The velocity, $v(t)$, is represented by the vector $v(t) = s'(t) = \begin{pmatrix} x'(t) \\ y'(t) \end{pmatrix}$

  or $v(t) = s'(t) = x'(t)\mathbf{i} + y'(t)\mathbf{j}$.

  This is often denoted by $v = \dot{x}\mathbf{i} + \dot{y}\mathbf{j}$ where the dot above the variable denotes differentiation *with respect to t*.
- The **speed** of the particle is the *magnitude* of the velocity: $|v| = \sqrt{\dot{x}^2 + \dot{y}^2}$
- The **direction of motion** at any instant of time can be described as the angle, θ, that it makes with the x-direction,

  $\tan\theta = \dfrac{\dot{y}}{\dot{x}}$

  This is the same as $\tan\theta = \dfrac{dy/dt}{dx/dt} = \dfrac{dy}{dt}\cdot\dfrac{dt}{dx} = \dfrac{dy}{dx}$.
- The acceleration, $a(t)$, is represented by the vector

  $a(t) = v'(t) = s''(t) = \begin{pmatrix} x''(t) \\ y''(t) \end{pmatrix}$

  or $a(t) = v'(t) = s''(t) = x''(t)\mathbf{i} + y''(t)\mathbf{j}$.

  This is often denoted by $a = \ddot{x}\mathbf{i} + \ddot{y}\mathbf{j}$ where the double-dot indicates the second derivative with respect to t.
- The *magnitude* of acceleration is $|a| = \sqrt{\ddot{x}^2 + \ddot{y}^2}$.

3 Related rates of change

- Given that $y = f(x)$ then $\frac{dy}{dx} = \frac{1}{dx/dy}$.
- Given that y is a function of x and that both x and y are functions of u the chain rule tells us that $\frac{dy}{dx} = \frac{dy}{du} \times \frac{du}{dx}$.

  This is equivalent to $\frac{dy}{dx} = \frac{dy}{du} \div \frac{dx}{du}$.

4 Optimisation

- Critical points are points where $f'(x) = 0$ or where $f'(x)$ is undefined, for example at endpoints, cusps, etc.
- Maxima and minima occur at critical points.
- The nature of stationary points can be examined using either a table of signs or the second derivative. $f''(x) > 0$ indicates a minimum; $f''(x) < 0$ indicates a maximum.

12 Complex numbers

Historical note

When two whole numbers are added, the result is another whole number.
The whole numbers are said to be **closed** under addition.

$$a, b \in W \Rightarrow a + b \in W$$

Consider $2 - 3 = -1$: *not* a whole number.
The whole numbers are not closed under subtraction.

Diophantus (around AD 275) called equations which produced negative numbers *absurd.*
By the 16th century negative numbers were becoming acceptable and the set of whole numbers was extended, by the inclusion of negative numbers, to the set of integers.
Consider 2 and 3 as integers: $2 - 3 = -1$, which is an integer.
The integers are closed under subtraction.

$$a, b \in Z \Rightarrow a - b \in Z$$

Consider closure under division and you will see the need for the set of rational numbers.
Consider closure when taking the square root and you will see the need for the set of real numbers.

In 1545 Jerome Cardan tried to find the solution to the problem

What two numbers have a sum of 10 and a product of 40?

His solution involved what he termed as *ficticious* numbers, what we now call **complex** numbers.
In 1637, Descartes used the expressions *real* and *imaginary* in this context and in 1748 Euler used the letter i to stand for the root of the equation $x^2 = -1$.
If we wish to work with $\sqrt{-1}$ we shall need to extend the set of real numbers.

Jerome Cardan

12.1 Arithmetic with complex numbers

Definitions

- i is a number such that $i^2 = -1$; $i \notin R$.
- C is the set of numbers z of the form $z = a + ib$ where a and b are real numbers.[1]
- The members of C are called complex numbers.
- a is called the **real part** of z and we write $a = \Re(z)$ or $a = \text{Re}(z)$.
  b is called the **imaginary part** of z and we write $b = \Im(z)$ or $b = \text{Im}(z)$.
- Given $z_1 = a + bi$ and $z_2 = c + di$,
  addition is defined by $z_1 + z_2 = (a + bi) + (c + di) = (a + c) + (b + d)i$
  multiplication is defined by $z_1z_2 = (a + bi)(c + di) = ac + adi + bci + bdi^2$
  $= (ac - bd) + (ad + bc)i$ since $i^2 = -1$
- If $z_1 = z_2$ then $\Re(z_1) = \Re(z_2)$ and $\Im(z_1) = \Im(z_2)$.
  This is referred to as *equating* real and imaginary parts.

[1] Note that we may write $a + ib$ or $a + bi$, whichever we find more convenient.

Proof

Suppose $z_1 = a + bi$ and $z_2 = c + di$ are equal but $a \neq c$ and $b \neq d$.

Then $\quad a + bi = c + di$

$\Rightarrow \quad a - c = (d - b)i$

$\Rightarrow \quad \dfrac{a - c}{d - b} = i \qquad$ we can divide since $d - b \neq 0$

$\Rightarrow \quad i \in R$ (contradiction)

$\Rightarrow \quad d - b = 0 \quad \Rightarrow \quad d = b$

and $\quad a - c = 0 \quad \Rightarrow \quad a = c$

Addition, Subtraction and Multiplication

Example 1

Given $z_1 = 3 + 2i$ and $z_2 = 4 + 3i$, find **a** $z_1 + z_2$ **b** $z_1 - z_2$ **c** z_1z_2

a $z_1 + z_2 = 3 + 2i + 4 + 3i = 7 + 5i$

b $z_1 - z_2 = 3 + 2i - (4 + 3i) = 3 + 2i - 4 - 3i = -1 - i$

c $z_1z_2 = (3 + 2i)(4 + 3i) = 12 + 9i + 8i + 6i^2 = 12 + 9i + 8i - 6$

$= 6 + 17i$

Example 2

Solve the equation $z^2 - 2z + 5 = 0$.

Using the quadratic formula we get

$$z = \frac{-(-2) \pm \sqrt{(-2)^2 - 4 \times 1 \times 5}}{2 \times 1} = \frac{2 \pm \sqrt{-16}}{2} = 1 \pm \sqrt{-4}$$

$$= 1 \pm \sqrt{4} \times \sqrt{-1}$$

$$= 1 \pm 2i$$

Exercise 12.1

1 Given $z_1 = 2 + i$ and $z_2 = 3 + 4i$ calculate these in the form $a + bi$.

a $z_1 + z_2$ **b** $z_1 z_2$ **c** $3z_1$ **d** $2z_2$ **e** $4z_1 + 3z_2$ **f** z_1^2

g z_1^3 **h** $z_1^3 z_2$ **i** $-z_2$ **j** $z_1 - z_2$ **k** $z_2 - z_1$ **l** $z_1^2 - 2z_2$

2 Simplify these, expressing your answer in the form $a + bi$.

a $(3 + 4i) + (1 + i)$ **b** $(6 - 2i) + (4 + 2i)$ **c** $(1 + i)(1 - i)$

d $(1 + 2i)(1 - 3i)$ **e** $(4 - 3i)^2$ **f** $2(3 - i) - 4(1 + 2i)$

g $3(1 + i) - i(1 + 3i)$ **h** $2i(2 + 3i)(1 - 2i)$ **i** $(3 - i)^2(3 + i)$

3 Solve these quadratic equations giving the roots in the form $z = a \pm bi$.

a $z^2 + 2z + 2 = 0$ **b** $z^2 + 4z + 13 = 0$ **c** $z^2 - 6z + 13 = 0$

d $2z^2 - 4z + 10 = 0$ **e** $3z^2 - 12z + 15 = 0$ **f** $2z^2 + 12z + 36 = 0$

4 Every quadratic equation can be written in the form

$z^2 - (\textit{sum of the roots})z + (\textit{product of the roots}) = 0$

Verify this statement using the equations in Question **3**.

5 Solve Cardan's problem, namely:
Find two numbers which have a sum of 10 and a product of 40.

6 a Simplify each of these.

i $(3 + i)(3 - i)$ ii $(2 + 3i)(2 - 3i)$ iii $(1 + 2i)(1 - 2i)$

b Comment on your answers in each case. Make a conjecture.

c Simplify $(a + ib)(a - ib)$ to prove your conjecture.

7 a $i = i$; $i^2 = -1$; $i^3 = i \times i^2 = -i$; $i^4 = i^2 \times i^2 = 1$
Work out the powers of i up to i^{12}.

b Given that n is an integer, evaluate

i i^{4n-1} ii i^{4n+1} iii i^{4n+2} iv i^{4n} v i^{4n+3}

8 By equating real and imaginary parts, find a and b in each case.

a $a + bi = (3 + i)^2$ b $a + bi = (3 + 2i)^2$ c $a + bi = (2 + i)(3 + 4i)$

12.2 Division and square roots with complex numbers

The complex conjugate

You should have noticed in Question 3 of Exercise 12.1 that the roots of the equations came in pairs of the form $a + bi$ and $a - bi$ where a and b are real numbers.
Such pairs are called **complex conjugates**.

You should also have noticed that the product of this pair of complex numbers is in fact a real number $a^2 + b^2$.

When $z = a + bi$ then its complex conjugate is denoted by $\bar{z} = a - bi$.

$z\bar{z} = a^2 + b^2$

This property is very useful when we wish to do a division.

Division and Square Roots

Example 3

Calculate $(4 + 2i) \div (2 + 3i)$.

$$\frac{(4 + 2i)}{(2 + 3i)} = \frac{(4 + 2i)(2 - 3i)}{(2 + 3i)(2 - 3i)} = \frac{8 - 12i + 4i - 6i^2}{2^2 + 3^2} = \frac{14 - 8i}{13} = \frac{14}{13} - \frac{8}{13}i$$

Note how the complex conjugate is used to make the denominator real.

Example 4

Calculate $\sqrt{5 + 12i}$.

Let $a + bi = \sqrt{5 + 12i}$ where a and b are real.

$\Rightarrow (a + bi)^2 = 5 + 12i$

$\Rightarrow a^2 - b^2 + 2abi = 5 + 12i$

Equating real parts we get $a^2 - b^2 = 5$ (1)

Equating imaginary parts we get $2ab = 12$ (2)

Equation (2) gives $a = \frac{6}{b}$

Substituting into Equation (1) gives	$\left(\frac{6}{b}\right)^2 - b^2 = 5$
Multiply throughout by b^2	$36 - b^4 = 5b^2$
Rearrange	$b^4 + 5b^2 - 36 = 0$
Treat this as a quadratic in b^2	$b^2 = \frac{-5 \pm \sqrt{25 + 144}}{2} = 4$ or -9
Since $b \in \mathbb{R}$	$b = \pm\sqrt{4} = 2$ or -2 and so $a = 3$ or -3
Thus	$\sqrt{5 + 12i} = 3 + 2i$ or $-3 - 2i$

Exercise 12.2

1 Calculate these divisions, expressing your answer in the form $a + ib$ where $a, b \in \mathbb{R}$.

a $(8 + 4i) \div (1 + 3i)$ **b** $(8 + i) \div (3 + 2i)$ **c** $(6 + 2i) \div (4 - 2i)$

d $(-1 - 3i) \div (1 - 2i)$ **e** $8 \div (1 + 2i)$ **f** $(6 + i) \div (3 - i)$

2 In each case below, express z^{-1} in the form $a + ib$ where $a, b \in \mathbb{R}$.

a $z = i$ **b** $z = 1 - i$ **c** $z = 2 + 2i$ **d** $z = 3 + i$ **e** $z = 4 - 2i$

3 Simplify

a $\frac{17 - 7i}{5 + i}$ **b** $\frac{21 + 9i}{2 + 5i}$ **c** $\frac{7 - 3i}{1 + i}$

d $\frac{2 - 5i}{1 + i}$ **e** $\frac{3 - 2i}{1 + 2i}$ **f** $\frac{3}{3 + 4i}$

4 Find a and b in each case so that $(a + ib)^2$ is equal to

a $5 - 12i$ **b** $15 - 8i$ **c** $-24 - 10i$

5 Calculate

a $\sqrt{3 - 4i}$ **b** $\sqrt{21 - 20i}$ **c** $\sqrt{-9 + 40i}$

6 **a** If $z = 2 + 3i$ find, in the form $x + iy$,

i $\bar{z}$ **ii** $\frac{1}{z}$ **iii** $\frac{z}{\bar{z}}$ **iv** $\frac{\bar{z}}{z}$ **v** $\frac{z}{\bar{z}} + \frac{\bar{z}}{z}$ **vi** $\frac{z}{\bar{z}} - \frac{\bar{z}}{z}$

b Repeat these when $z = a + bi$.

7 **a** Show that $\frac{1}{2}(z + \bar{z}) = \Re(z)$.

b Find a similar expression for $\Im(z)$.

8 Given that $z_1 = a + bi$ and $z_2 = x + iy$,

a find expressions for **i** $\bar{z}_1$ **ii** $\bar{z}_2$ **iii** $\overline{z_1 + z_2}$

b state the simple relationship between $\bar{z}_1$, $\bar{z}_2$ and $\overline{z_1 + z_2}$

c identify similar conclusions for **i** $\overline{z_1 - z_2}$ **ii** $\overline{z_1 \times z_2}$ **iii** $\overline{z_1 \div z_2}$.

12.3 A geometric interpretation: Argand diagrams

At the end of the 18th century Caspar Wessel from Norway and Jean Robert Argand from Switzerland independently came up with a geometric interpretation of the complex number $z = x + iy$.

The complex number $z = x + iy$ is represented on the plane by the point $P(x, y)$.
The plane is referred to as the **complex plane**.
Diagrams of this sort are often called **Argand diagrams**.

Any point on the x-axis represents a purely real number.
Any point on the y-axis, except $(0, 0)$, represents a purely imaginary number.

Position vector representation

It can be more useful to consider $z = x + iy$ being represented by $\overrightarrow{OP}$, the position vector of P.

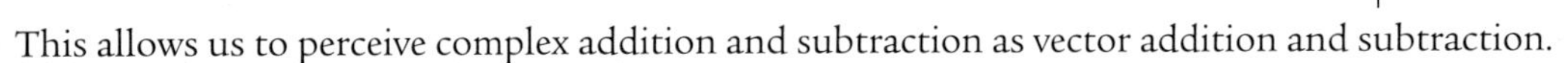

This allows us to perceive complex addition and subtraction as vector addition and subtraction.

$\overrightarrow{OP}$ is considered a vector which has been rotated off the x-axis.
The length of $\overrightarrow{OP}$, r, is called the **modulus** of z and is denoted by $|z|$.

The size of the rotation is called the **amplitude** or **argument** of z.
The size of the rotation could be $\theta \pm 2n\pi$ where n is any integer.
It is often denoted by Arg z.
We refer to the value of Arg z which lies in the range $-\pi < \theta \leq \pi$ as the **principal argument**.

It is denoted by arg z. [Note the lower-case a.]

Polar form

From the diagram above, by Pythagoras' theorem, $r = \sqrt{x^2 + y^2}$.

By simple trigonometry $\qquad \theta = \tan^{-1}\left(\frac{y}{x}\right), -\pi < \theta \leq \pi$

By simple trigonometry $\qquad x = r\cos\theta$

$$y = r\sin\theta$$

Thus $z = x + iy$ can be re-written as $z = r\cos\theta + ir\sin\theta$

$$z = r(\cos\theta + i\sin\theta)$$

This is referred to as the **polar form** of z.

Example 5

Find the modulus and argument of the complex number $z = 3 + 4i$.

$|z| = \sqrt{3^2 + 4^2} = 5$

Arg $z = \tan^{-1}\left(\frac{4}{3}\right) = 0.927 + n\pi$ radians

Check: $(3, 4)$ is in the first quadrant $\Rightarrow n = 0$

$\Rightarrow$ arg $z = 0.927$ radians (3 sf)

Example 6

Find the modulus and argument of the complex number $z = -3 - 4i$.

$|z| = \sqrt{(-3)^2 + (-4)^2} = 5$

Arg $z = \tan^{-1}\left(\frac{-4}{-3}\right) = 0.927 + n\pi$ radians

Check: $(-3, -4)$ is in the *third* quadrant $\Rightarrow n = -1$

arg $z = 0.927 - \pi = -2.21$ (3 sf)

Example 7

Express $z = 2 + 2i$ in the form $r(\cos\theta° + i\sin\theta°)$.

$r = |z| = \sqrt{2^2 + 2^2} = 2\sqrt{2}$

$\theta = \arg z = \tan^{-1}\left(\frac{2}{2}\right) = 45°$ [check quadrant][2]

Hence $z = 2\sqrt{2}(\cos 45° + i\sin 45°)$

Exercise 12.3

1 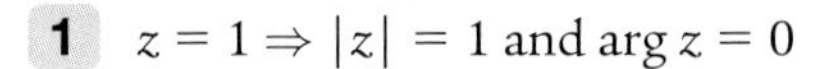
$z = 1 \Rightarrow |z| = 1$ and $\arg z = 0$

Use the diagram to help you make similar statements about

a $z = i$

b $z = -1$

c $z = -i$

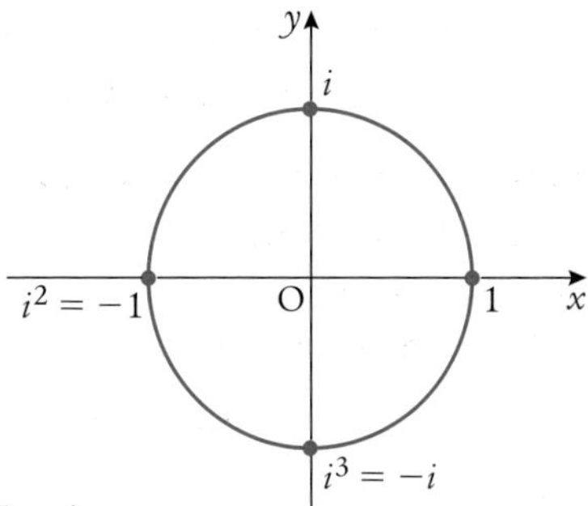

2 a Draw Argand diagrams to illustrate

i $3 + 4i$ and $3 - 4i$ ii $2 + 3i$ and $2 - 3i$ iii $5 + i$ and $5 - i$

b Comment on the Argand diagrams of z and $\bar{z}$.

3 For each of these complex numbers

i plot the number on an Argand diagram

ii find the modulus and argument to 3 significant figures where appropriate.

a $1 + i$ b $2 + 3i$ c $3 + 2i$

d 6 e $3i$ f $-4 - 3i$ (refer to your sketch)

g $-1 + 2i$ h $2 - 3i$ i $4 - i$

4 For each of these expressions

i simplify by writing them in the form $x + iy$

ii find the modulus and argument.

a $\dfrac{3 + 2i}{1 + 5i}$ b $\dfrac{1}{1 + 3i}$ c $(2 + 4i)(1 - i)$

5 a Find the modulus and argument of each expression.

i $10 + 7i$ ii $(10 + 7i)^2$ iii $(10 + 7i)^3$

b Comment on any connection you see.

6 Find the complex number with

a $|z| = 2, \arg z = \frac{\pi}{6}$ b $|z| = 3, \arg z = \frac{\pi}{4}$ c $|z| = 4, \arg z = \frac{\pi}{2}$

d $|z| = 3, \arg z = \frac{\pi}{3}$ e $|z| = 2, \arg z = -\frac{\pi}{4}$ f $|z| = 1, \arg z = -\frac{\pi}{6}$

7 Express each of these complex numbers in polar form. (Give the argument in degrees.)

a $1 + i\sqrt{3}$ b $\sqrt{2} + i\sqrt{2}$ c $-2\sqrt{3} + 2i$

d -1 e $3i$ f $-4 - i4\sqrt{3}$

g $-2\sqrt{3} + 2i$ h $-\sqrt{2} - i\sqrt{2}$ i $-1 - i\sqrt{3}$

[2] We can work in degrees: $-180° < \arg z \leq 180°$.

8 Given that $z_1 = 2 + 3i$ and $z_2 = 3 + i$ the diagram illustrates the sum $z_1 + z_2$ that is, $(2 + 3i) + (3 + i) = 5 + 4i$

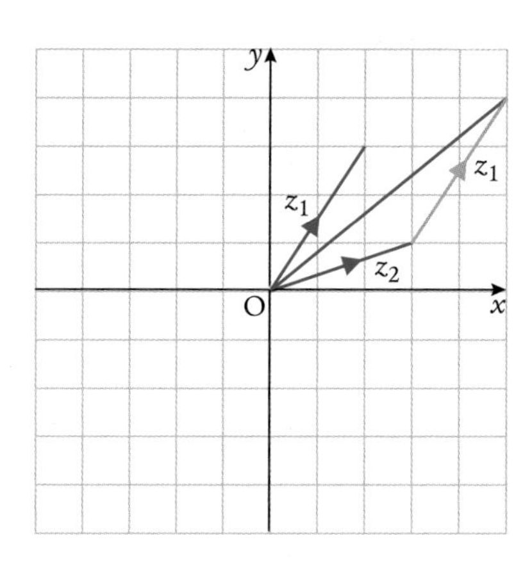

On similar diagrams, illustrate

a $(2 + 3i) + (3 + 2i)$ b $(3 + 3i) + (2 + 2i)$

c $(2 - 3i) + (3 - 2i)$ d $(-2 + 3i) + (-3 - 2i)$

e $(2 + 3i) - (3 + 2i)$ [Hint: $= (2 + 3i) + (-3 - 2i)$]

f $(1 + 3i) - (2 + 4i)$ g $(-3 + i) - (-1 - 2i)$

h $(-1 - 2i) - (4 - 3i)$ i $(-2 - 2i) - (-3 - 3i)$

12.4 Sets of points (loci) on the complex plane

Sometimes we have to find the locus of a point which moves in the complex plane with restrictions placed on its modulus and argument.

Example 8

Given that $z = x + iy$, draw the locus of the point which moves on the complex plane so that a $|z| = 4$ b $|z| \le 4$

$|z| = 4 \Rightarrow \sqrt{x^2 + y^2} = 4 \Rightarrow x^2 + y^2 = 16$

This is a circle, centre the origin, radius 4.

a $|z| = 4$

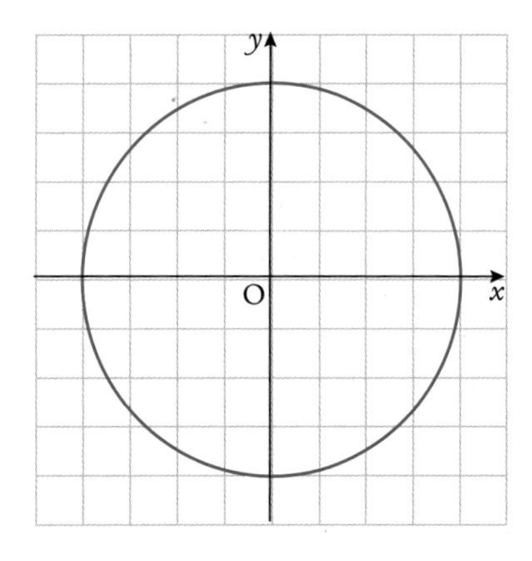

b $|z| \le 4$

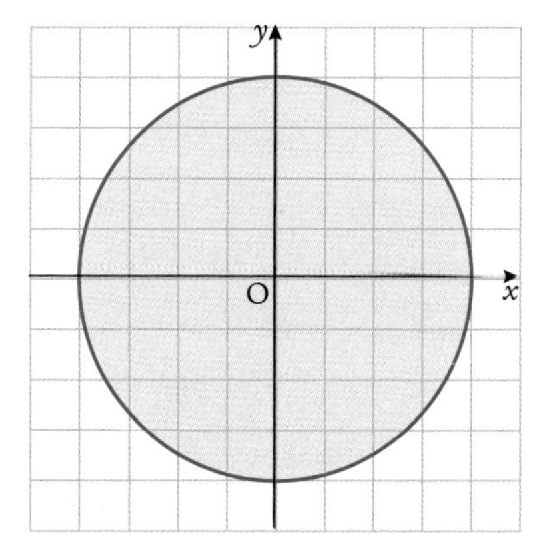

Example 9

If $z = x + iy$

a find the equation of the locus $|z - 2| = 3$

b draw the locus on an Argand diagram.

a $|z - 2| = 3 \Rightarrow |x - 2 + iy| = 3 \Rightarrow \sqrt{(x - 2)^2 + y^2} = 3$

$\Rightarrow (x - 2)^2 + y^2 = 9$

This is a circle with centre (2, 0) and radius 3.

b $|z - 2| = 3$

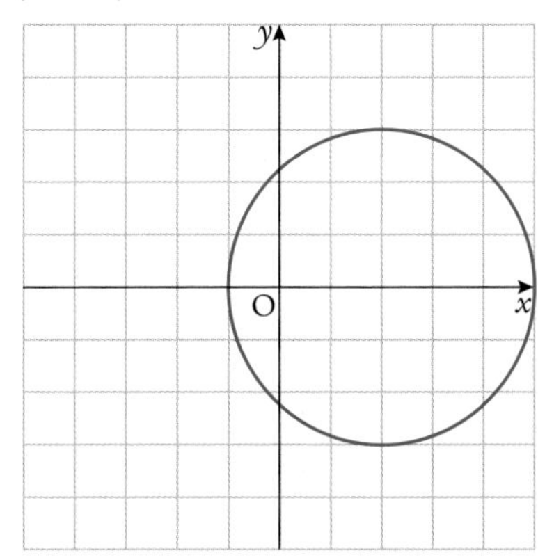

Example 10

If $z = x + iy$ find the equation of the locus $\arg z = \frac{\pi}{3}$.

$\arg z = \frac{\pi}{3} \quad \Rightarrow \tan^{-1}\left(\frac{y}{x}\right) = \frac{\pi}{3}$

$\Rightarrow \frac{y}{x} = \tan\frac{\pi}{3} \Rightarrow \frac{y}{x} = \sqrt{3}$

$\Rightarrow y = \sqrt{3}x$

This is a straight line passing through the origin, gradient $\sqrt{3}$.

Exercise 12.4

1 Given that $z = x + iy$, for each of these equations

i find the equation of the locus ii draw the locus on an Argand diagram.

a $|z| = 5$ b $|z - 3| = 2$ c $|z + 1| = 4$

d $|z + i| = 3$ e $|z - 2i| = 3$ f $|z + 1 + 2i| = 3$

g $|2z + 3i| = 5$ h $|3z - i| = 5$ i $|3z + 3 - 2i| = 4$

j $\arg z = \frac{\pi}{6}$ k $\arg z = \frac{\pi}{4}$ l $\arg z = \frac{2\pi}{3}$

m $\arg z = 1$ n $2 \arg z = \frac{\pi}{4}$ o $\arg z = -\frac{\pi}{3}$

2 Explore the loci of the form

a $|z - a| = b$ b $|z - ai| = b$ c $|z - ai - b| = c$

3 Given that $z = x + iy$ find the equation of the locus in each case.

a $|z - 1| = |z - i|$ b $|z - 2| = |z - i|$

c $|z - 3| = |z - 2i|$ d $|z - a| = |z - bi|$

4 Sketch these loci, given that $z = x + iy$.

a $|z| \leqslant 3$ b $|z - 3| \leqslant 2$ c $|z + 2| \geqslant 5$

A diversion

Using a spreadsheet or the parametric graphing facility on a calculator you can illustrate more complicated loci where the modulus is expressed as a function of the argument.

- A2 contains = −PI()
- A3 contains = A2 + 0.1 * PI()
- A3 is *filled down* to A22.
  This gives us values of the argument θ in the range $-\pi < \theta \leq \pi$.
- Where the argument r is a function of θ that is $r = f(\theta)$, then $= f(\theta)$ is entered in B2.
- B2 is *filled down* to B22.
- C2 contains = B2 * cos (A2) which gives $x = r\cos\theta$.
- D2 contains = B2 * sin (A2) which gives $y = r\sin\theta$.
- C2 and D2 are *filled down* to C22 and D22.
- An X-Y chart is then drawn using columns C and D. [Choose the 'smooth lined scatter'.]

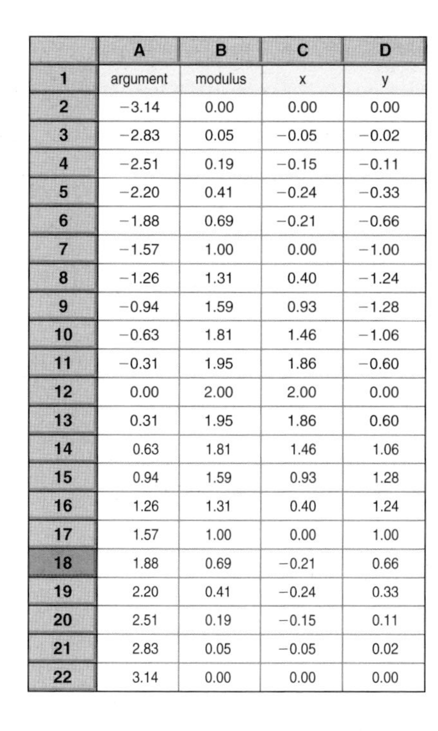

	A	B	C	D
1	argument	modulus	x	y
2	−3.14	0.00	0.00	0.00
3	−2.83	0.05	−0.05	−0.02
4	−2.51	0.19	−0.15	−0.11
5	−2.20	0.41	−0.24	−0.33
6	−1.88	0.69	−0.21	−0.66
7	−1.57	1.00	0.00	−1.00
8	−1.26	1.31	0.40	−1.24
9	−0.94	1.59	0.93	−1.28
10	−0.63	1.81	1.46	−1.06
11	−0.31	1.95	1.86	−0.60
12	0.00	2.00	2.00	0.00
13	0.31	1.95	1.86	0.60
14	0.63	1.81	1.46	1.06
15	0.94	1.59	0.93	1.28
16	1.26	1.31	0.40	1.24
17	1.57	1.00	0.00	1.00
18	1.88	0.69	−0.21	0.66
19	2.20	0.41	−0.24	0.33
20	2.51	0.19	−0.15	0.11
21	2.83	0.05	−0.05	0.02
22	3.14	0.00	0.00	0.00

Better resolution can be achieved by entering a smaller step size in A3, for example

- A3 contains = A2 + 0.05 * PI()
- A3 is *filled down* to A42.

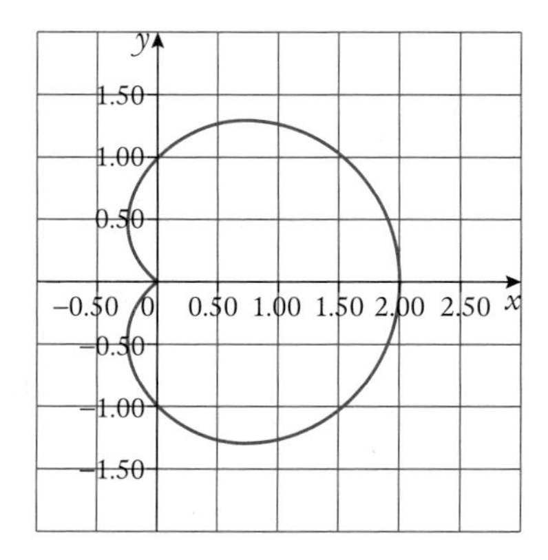

This example is the locus of the points where $|z| = 1 + \cos(\arg z)$ so

- B2 contains = 1 + cos (A2)

The locus is heart-shaped and is called a *cardioid*.

If you have access to a spreadsheet, try these in B2.

1 = cos (2*A2)
Explore cos (a * A2) for different $a \in N$: *rhodonae* (*rose curves*).

2 = sin (2*A2)
Explore sin (a * A2) for different $a \in N$.

3 = 1 + 2 * cos (A2) (*the limaçon*)

4 = 1 + 2 * cos (2 * A2)

5 = A2 ... try this in the range $[0, 2\pi]$ also.

6 = a where a is a constant (*circles*)

7 = 1/(1 + 0.5 * cos (A2)) (*the ellipse*)

A similar exploration can be done on a graphics calculator. You must find how your model performs parametric plotting.

In general, if you wish to graph $|z| = f(\arg z)$

- set the range of the parameter z to run between $-\pi$ and π
- then $x = f(\arg z)^* \cos z$
- and $y = f(\arg z)^* \sin z$

12.5 Polar form and multiplication

Recall that $z = r(\cos\theta + i\sin\theta)$ is the polar form of z.

Consider z_1z_2 where $z_1 = a(\cos A + i\sin A)$ and $z_2 = b(\cos B + i\sin B)$.

$$\begin{aligned} z_1z_2 &= a(\cos A + i\sin A)b(\cos B + i\sin B) \\ &= ab(\cos A\cos B + \cos A \cdot i\sin B + i\sin A\cos B + i^2\sin A\sin B) \\ &= ab([\cos A\cos B - \sin A\sin B] + i[\cos A\sin B + \sin A\cos B]) \\ &= ab(\cos(A + B) + i\sin(A + B)) \end{aligned}$$

We see that

- $|z_1z_2| = |z_1| \times |z_2|$
- $\text{Arg}(z_1z_2) = \text{Arg}\, z_1 + \text{Arg}\, z_2$

but note that the *principal* argument, $\arg(z_1z_2)$, lies in the range $(-\pi, \pi]$ and adjustments have to be made by adding or subtracting 2π as appropriate if $\text{Arg}(z_1z_2)$ goes outside this range during the calculation.

Important notes

- Multiplying $z = r(\cos\theta + i\sin\theta)$ by $\cos A + i\sin A$ gives $r(\cos(\theta + A) + i\sin(\theta + A))$.
  This is equivalent to rotating the vector representing z through an angle of A radians anticlockwise.
- Since $i = \cos\frac{\pi}{2} + i\sin\frac{\pi}{2}$ then multiplying by i is equivalent to rotating z through an angle of $\frac{\pi}{2}$ radians anticlockwise.
- If $z = r(\cos\theta + i\sin\theta)$ then

  $$\frac{1}{z} = \frac{1}{r(\cos\theta + i\sin\theta)} = \frac{(\cos\theta - i\sin\theta)}{r(\cos\theta + i\sin\theta)(\cos\theta - i\sin\theta)}$$

  $$= \frac{1}{r}(\cos\theta - i\sin\theta) = \frac{1}{r}(\cos(-\theta) + i\sin(-\theta))$$

  So $\left|\frac{1}{z}\right| = \frac{1}{|z|}$ and $\arg\left(\frac{1}{z}\right) = -\arg z$

  So $\frac{z_1}{z_2} = z_1 \times \frac{1}{z_2} = \frac{a}{b}[\cos(A - B) + i\sin(A - B)]$

  We see that

  a $\left|\frac{z_1}{z_2}\right| = |z_1| \div |z_2|$

  b $\text{Arg}\left(\frac{z_1}{z_2}\right) = \text{Arg}\, z_1 - \text{Arg}\, z_2$

  but note that the *principal* argument lies in the range $(-\pi, \pi]$
  and adjustments have to be made by adding or subtracting 2π
  as appropriate if $\text{Arg}\left(\frac{z_1}{z_2}\right)$ goes outside this range during the calculation.

Exercise 12.5

1 Simplify these expressions.

a $3\left(\cos\frac{\pi}{3} + i\sin\frac{\pi}{3}\right) \times 4\left(\cos\frac{\pi}{2} + i\sin\frac{\pi}{2}\right)$

b $2\left(\cos\frac{\pi}{4} + i\sin\frac{\pi}{4}\right) \times 5\left(\cos\frac{\pi}{6} + i\sin\frac{\pi}{6}\right)$

c $2\left(\cos\frac{\pi}{3} + i\sin\frac{\pi}{3}\right) \times 4\left(\cos\frac{\pi}{3} - i\sin\frac{\pi}{3}\right)$

Hint: remember $\left(\cos\frac{\pi}{3} - i\sin\frac{\pi}{3}\right) = \left(\cos\left(-\frac{\pi}{3}\right) + i\sin\left(-\frac{\pi}{3}\right)\right)$

d $\left(\cos\frac{\pi}{2} - i\sin\frac{\pi}{2}\right) \times 2\left(\cos\frac{\pi}{3} - i\sin\frac{\pi}{3}\right)$

e $5\left(\cos\frac{\pi}{5} - i\sin\frac{\pi}{5}\right) \times 2\left(\cos\frac{\pi}{6} + i\sin\frac{\pi}{6}\right)$

f $4\left(\cos\frac{\pi}{2} + i\sin\frac{\pi}{2}\right) \div 2\left(\cos\frac{\pi}{3} + i\sin\frac{\pi}{3}\right)$

g $5\left(\cos\frac{\pi}{4} + i\sin\frac{\pi}{4}\right) \div 2\left(\cos\frac{\pi}{8} + i\sin\frac{\pi}{8}\right)$

h $9\left(\cos\frac{\pi}{2} + i\sin\frac{\pi}{2}\right) \div 3\left(\cos\frac{\pi}{6} + i\sin\frac{\pi}{6}\right)$

i $8\left(\cos\frac{\pi}{7} - i\sin\frac{\pi}{7}\right) \div 2\left(\cos\frac{2\pi}{7} - i\sin\frac{2\pi}{7}\right)$

2 Convert each complex number to polar form then state the product, z_1z_2, and quotient, $\frac{z_1}{z_2}$, of each pair. (Work to 3 significant figures.)

a $z_1 = 3 + 4i, \quad z_2 = 1 + i$ b $z_1 = 2 + 3i, \quad z_2 = 3 - i$

c $z_1 = 1 - i, \quad z_2 = -1 - i$ d $z_1 = -4 + i, \quad z_2 = -2 + 2i$

3 Given that $z = r\left(\cos\frac{\pi}{3} + i\sin\frac{\pi}{3}\right)$ calculate

a $z^2 \left[= r^2\left(\cos\frac{\pi}{3} + i\sin\frac{\pi}{3}\right)^2 = r^2\left(\cos\frac{\pi}{3} + i\sin\frac{\pi}{3}\right)\left(\cos\frac{\pi}{3} + i\sin\frac{\pi}{3}\right)\right]$

b z^3 $[= z^2z]$

c z^4 [remember to bring the argument back into the range $(-\pi, \pi)$]

d z^5 e z^6 f z^7

4 Repeat Question **3** using

i $z = r\left(\cos\frac{\pi}{2} + i\sin\frac{\pi}{2}\right)$ ii $z = r\left(\cos\frac{2\pi}{3} + i\sin\frac{2\pi}{3}\right)$

iii $z = r\left(\cos\frac{3\pi}{4} + i\sin\frac{3\pi}{4}\right)$ iv $z = r(\cos\theta + i\sin\theta)$

5 a Use the binomial theorem to expand $(3 + 4i)^4$.

b i Express $z = 3 + 4i$ in polar form (to 3 sf).

ii Use the notion developed in Questions **3** and **4** to find $z^4 = (3 + 4i)^4$ in polar form.

iii Use your calculator to help you express z^4 in the form $a + bi$.

c Which method, **a** or **b**, would be preferable when calculating $(3 + 4i)^{20}$?

12.6 De Moivre's theorem

Historical note

Abraham De Moivre (1667–1754) was a French mathematician who, after fleeing religious persecution, spent most of his life in London. A friend of Halley, Newton and Stirling, he made important contributions to probability and discovered a deep connection between complex numbers and trigonometry.

Questions **3** and **4** above suggest that

if $z = r(\cos\theta + i\sin\theta)$ then $z^n = r^n(\cos n\theta + i\sin n\theta)$.

The result is called De Moivre's theorem who proved it for integer values of n. Later Euler proved it true for all $n \in R$.

Proof (for $n \in N$)

Suppose that there exists a natural number $n = k$ for which the theorem is true.
Then, given $z = r(\cos\theta + i\sin\theta)$, we have $z^k = r^k(\cos k\theta + i\sin k\theta)$.

$$z^{k+1} = r^k(\cos k\theta + i\sin k\theta) \times r(\cos\theta + i\sin\theta)$$
$$= r^{k+1}(\cos(k\theta + \theta) + i\sin(k\theta + \theta))$$
$$= r^{k+1}(\cos(k+1)\theta + i\sin(k+1)\theta)$$

Thus, if it is true for $n = k$ then it is true for $n = k + 1$.
We know, however, that it *is* true for $n = 1$.

Thus, by induction, it is true for all $n \geqslant 1, n \in N$.

Proof for all $n \in R$ is beyond the scope of this course but it can be illustrated and verified by suitable examples.

For example, given $z = r(\cos\theta + i\sin\theta)$ and $z_1 = \sqrt{r}\left(\cos\frac{\theta}{2} + i\sin\frac{\theta}{2}\right)$ then

$\Rightarrow z_1{}^2 = (\sqrt{r})^2\left(\cos\frac{\theta}{2} + i\sin\frac{\theta}{2}\right)^2$

$\Rightarrow z_1{}^2 = r\left(\cos\frac{2\theta}{2} + i\sin\frac{2\theta}{2}\right)$ by De Moivre's theorem

$\quad = r(\cos\theta + i\sin\theta) = z$

$\Rightarrow z_1 = \sqrt{z}$

It would appear that De Moivre's theorem holds for $n = \frac{1}{2}$.

That is, $[r(\cos\theta + i\sin\theta)]^{\frac{1}{2}} = r^{\frac{1}{2}}\left(\cos\frac{\theta}{2} + i\sin\frac{\theta}{2}\right)$

Can you show that it holds when $n = -1$?

Example 11

Given $z = 1 + i\sqrt{3}$, find **a** z^2 **b** z^5 **c** z^7 **d** z^{10}

$|z| = \sqrt{1^2 + (\sqrt{3})^2} = 2$, $\arg z = \arg z = \tan^{-1}\left(\frac{\sqrt{3}}{1}\right) = \frac{\pi}{3}$

Thus $z = 2\left(\cos\frac{\pi}{3} + i\sin\frac{\pi}{3}\right)$

a $z^2 = 2^2\left(\cos\frac{\pi}{3} + i\sin\frac{\pi}{3}\right)^2 = 4\left(\cos\frac{2\pi}{3} + i\sin\frac{2\pi}{3}\right)$

$\quad = 4\left(-\frac{1}{2} + i\frac{\sqrt{3}}{2}\right) = -2 + i2\sqrt{3}$

b $z^5 = 2^5\left(\cos\frac{\pi}{3} + i\sin\frac{\pi}{3}\right)^5 = 32\left(\cos\frac{5\pi}{3} + i\sin\frac{5\pi}{3}\right)$

The argument must be brought into range $(-\pi, \pi]$ by subtracting 2π.

$\quad = 32\left(\cos\left(-\frac{\pi}{3}\right) + i\sin\left(-\frac{\pi}{3}\right)\right) = 32\left(\cos\frac{\pi}{3} - i\sin\frac{\pi}{3}\right)$

$\quad = 32\left(\frac{1}{2} - i\frac{\sqrt{3}}{2}\right) = 16 - i16\sqrt{3}$

c $z^7 = 128\left(\cos\frac{7\pi}{3} + i\sin\frac{7\pi}{3}\right)$

The argument must be brought into range $(-\pi, \pi]$ by subtracting 2π.

$\quad = 128\left(\cos\left(\frac{\pi}{3}\right) + i\sin\left(\frac{\pi}{3}\right)\right)$

$\quad = 128\left(\frac{1}{2} + i\frac{\sqrt{3}}{2}\right) = 64 + i64\sqrt{3}$

d $z^{10} = 1024\left(\cos\frac{10\pi}{3} + i\sin\frac{10\pi}{3}\right)$

The argument must be brought into range $(-\pi, \pi]$ by subtracting 2π *twice*.

$\quad = 1024\left(\cos\left(-\frac{2\pi}{3}\right) + i\sin\left(-\frac{2\pi}{3}\right)\right) = 1024\left(\cos\frac{2\pi}{3} - i\sin\frac{2\pi}{3}\right)$

$\quad = 1024\left(-\frac{1}{2} - i\frac{\sqrt{3}}{2}\right) = -512 - i512\sqrt{3}$

Example 12

Given $z = 2 + i$, calculate z^4.

[Work to 3 dp and round final answer to nearest integer.]

$|z| = \sqrt{2^2 + 1^2} = \sqrt{5}$, $\arg z = \arg z = \tan^{-1}\left(\frac{1}{2}\right) = 0.464$ (3 dp)

Thus $z = \sqrt{5}(\cos 0.464 + i\sin 0.464)$

So $z^4 = (\sqrt{5})^4(\cos 0.464 + i\sin 0.464)^4 = 25(\cos 1.856 + i\sin 1.856)$

$= 25(-0.281 + i \cdot 0.960)$

$= -7 + 24i$ (nearest integer)

Exercise 12.6

1 For each of these complex numbers,

- express it in polar form
- express each of the required powers in polar form, bringing the argument into the range $(-\pi, \pi]$
- finally express your answer in the form $a + ib$.

a Given $z = 2\sqrt{3} + 2i$ find i z^2 ii z^5 iii z^{10}

b Given $z = \sqrt{3} - i$ find i z^3 ii z^4 iii z^8

c Given $z = 1 + i$ find i z^3 ii z^6 iii z^{12}

2 Simplify these expressions, giving your answers correct to 3 significant figures.

a $\left[3\left(\cos\frac{\pi}{5} + i\sin\frac{\pi}{5}\right)\right]^3$

b $\left[2\left(\cos\frac{\pi}{6} + i\sin\frac{\pi}{6}\right)\right]^8$

c $\left(\cos\frac{\pi}{4} + i\sin\frac{\pi}{4}\right)^2\left(\cos\frac{3\pi}{4} + i\sin\frac{3\pi}{4}\right)^2$

d $\left(\cos\frac{2\pi}{7} + i\sin\frac{2\pi}{7}\right)^3\left(\cos\frac{3\pi}{7} + i\sin\frac{3\pi}{7}\right)^4$

3 In each of these work to 3 decimal places where necessary then round the components of your final answers to the nearest whole number.

a Given $z = 2 + 3i$, calculate z^3.

b Given $z = -1 + 4i$, calculate z^5.

c Given $z = -2 - 3i$, calculate z^4.

d Given $z = 2 - 2i$, calculate z^7.

4 The argument can be given in degrees.
The same laws apply and the range of the argument is $(-180°, 180°]$.
Simplify these expressions.

a $(\cos 10° + i\sin 10°)(\cos 30° + i\sin 30°)$

b $(\cos 50° + i\sin 50°)(\cos 145° + i\sin 145°)$

c $(\cos 25° + i\sin 25°)(\cos 20° - i\sin 20°)$

d $(\cos 150° - i\sin 150°)(\cos 40° - i\sin 40°)$

e $(\cos 30° + i\sin 30°) \div (\cos 10° + i\sin 10°)$

f $(\cos 4° + i\sin 4°) \div (\cos 10° + i\sin 10°)$

g $(\cos 20° + i\sin 20°)^3(\cos 30° + i\sin 30°)^2$

h $(\cos 125° - i\sin 125°)^4(\cos 15° - i\sin 15°)^3$

i $\dfrac{(\cos 40° + i\sin 40°)^3}{(\cos 10° + i\sin 10°)^2}$ j $\dfrac{(\cos 6° + i\sin 6°)^5}{(\cos 3° + i\sin 3°)^2}$

k $\dfrac{(\cos 25° + i\sin 25°)^4}{(\cos 7° + i\sin 7°)(\cos 3° + i\sin 3°)}$ l $\dfrac{(\cos 32° + i\sin 32°)^4}{(\cos 16° + i\sin 16°)^3(\cos 4° - i\sin 4°)^2}$

5 a Expand $(\cos\theta + i\sin\theta)^2$

i using the binomial theorem ii using De Moivre's theorem.

b i By equating the *real* parts express $\cos 2\theta$ in terms of $\sin\theta$ and $\cos\theta$.

ii By equating the *imaginary* parts express $\sin 2\theta$ in terms of $\sin\theta$ and $\cos\theta$.

6 a Expand $(\cos\theta + i\sin\theta)^3$

i using the binomial theorem ii using De Moivre's theorem.

b i By equating the *real* parts express $\cos 3\theta$ in terms of $\sin\theta$ and $\cos\theta$.

ii Use the identity $\sin^2\theta + \cos^2\theta = 1$ to help you express $\cos 3\theta$ in terms of $\cos\theta$ only.

c Express $\sin 3\theta$ in terms of $\sin\theta$.

d Hence, express $\sin^3\theta$ in terms of $\sin\theta$ and $\sin 3\theta$.

7 a By considering the expansion of $(\cos\theta + i\sin\theta)^4$ express

i $\cos 4\theta$ in terms of $\cos\theta$

ii $\sin 4\theta$ in terms of $\sin\theta$ and $\cos\theta$

iii $\cos^4\theta$ in terms of $\cos\theta$ and $\cos 4\theta$.

b Express

i $\cos 5\theta$ in terms of $\cos\theta$

ii $\sin 5\theta$ in terms of $\sin\theta$

iii $\cos^5\theta$ in terms of $\cos\theta$ and $\cos 5\theta$.

8 $z_1 = \cos\frac{11\pi}{6} - i\sin\frac{11\pi}{6}$, $z_2 = \cos\frac{5\pi}{6} - i\sin\frac{5\pi}{6}$, $z_3 = \cos\frac{\pi}{6} + i\sin\frac{\pi}{6}$,

$z_4 = \cos\frac{7\pi}{6} + i\sin\frac{7\pi}{6}$

a Find expressions for i ${z_1}^2$ ii ${z_2}^2$ iii ${z_3}^2$ iv ${z_4}^2$

b i Reduce each argument so that it lies in the range $(-\pi, \pi]$.

ii How many distinct answers are obtained?

c i Reduce the arguments of z_1, z_2, z_3 and z_4.

ii If asked for $z \in C$ such that $z^2 = \cos\frac{\pi}{3} + i\sin\frac{\pi}{3}$ what would be a complete answer?

iii Illustrate the set of solutions on an Argand diagram.

9 $z_1 = \cos\frac{13\pi}{12} - i\sin\frac{13\pi}{12}$, $z_2 = \cos\frac{5\pi}{12} - i\sin\frac{5\pi}{12}$, $z_3 = \cos\frac{\pi}{4} + i\sin\frac{\pi}{4}$,

$z_4 = \cos\frac{11\pi}{12} + i\sin\frac{11\pi}{12}$, $z_5 = \cos\frac{19\pi}{12} + i\sin\frac{19\pi}{12}$

a Verify in each case that $z^3 = \cos\frac{3\pi}{4} + i\sin\frac{3\pi}{4}$.

b i Reduce the arguments of z_1, z_2, z_3, z_4 and z_5 to lie in the range $(-\pi, \pi]$.

ii If asked for $z \in C$ such that $z^3 = \cos\frac{3\pi}{4} + i\sin\frac{3\pi}{4}$, what would be a complete answer?

iii Illustrate the set of solutions on an Argand diagram.

12.7 Roots of a complex number

Square roots

Question 8 of Exercise 12.6 explored solutions of the equation $z^2 = \cos\frac{\pi}{3} + i\sin\frac{\pi}{3}$.

Two solutions were found, namely $z_2 = \cos\frac{5\pi}{6} - i\sin\frac{5\pi}{6}$ and $z_3 = \cos\frac{\pi}{6} + i\sin\frac{\pi}{6}$.

On an Argand diagram we can see z, z_2 and z_3:

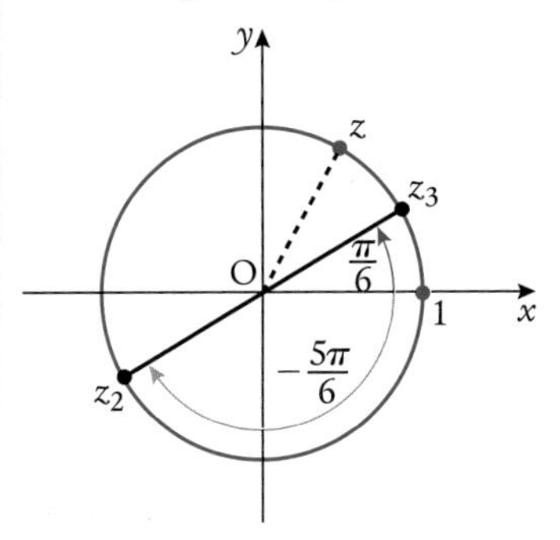

Note:

- Starting with the position vector of 1 on the x-axis, a rotation of $\frac{\pi}{6}$ takes us to z_3 – then a second rotation of $\frac{\pi}{6}$ takes us to z.
- Starting with the position vector of 1 on the x-axis, a rotation of $\frac{-5\pi}{6}$ takes us to z_2 – then a second rotation of $\frac{-5\pi}{6}$ takes us to z.
- The position vectors of the two solutions are $\frac{2\pi}{2}$ radians apart.
- Both solutions take the form $z = \left[\cos\left(\frac{\pi}{3} + 2k\pi\right) + i\sin\left(\frac{\pi}{3} + 2k\pi\right)\right]^{\frac{1}{2}}$ where $k = 0, 1$.

  Check: by De Moivre's theorem,

$$z = \left[\cos\frac{1}{2}\left(\frac{\pi}{3} + 2k\pi\right) + i\sin\frac{1}{2}\left(\frac{\pi}{3} + 2k\pi\right)\right]$$

$$= \left[\cos\left(\frac{\pi}{6} + k\pi\right) + i\sin\left(\frac{\pi}{6} + k\pi\right)\right]$$

  When $k = 0$ we get z_3; when $k = 1$ we get z_2 if we remember to bring the argument into the range $(-\pi, \pi]$.

Cube roots

Question 9 considered solutions of the equation $z^3 = \left(\cos\frac{3\pi}{4} + i\sin\frac{3\pi}{4}\right)$.

Three solutions were found, namely

$z_2 = \left(\cos\frac{5\pi}{12} - i\sin\frac{5\pi}{12}\right)$, $z_3 = \left(\cos\frac{\pi}{4} + i\sin\frac{\pi}{4}\right)$, $z_4 = \left(\cos\frac{11\pi}{12} + i\sin\frac{11\pi}{12}\right)$

On an Argand diagram we have

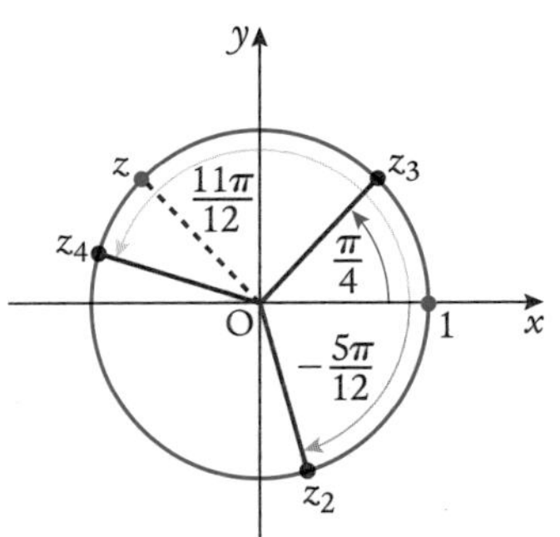

Note:

- Starting with the position vector of 1 on the x-axis, a rotation of $\frac{\pi}{4}$ takes us to z_3 – then two more rotations of $\frac{\pi}{4}$ take us to z.
- Starting with the position vector of 1 on the x-axis, a rotation of $\frac{-5\pi}{12}$ takes us to z_2 – then two more rotations of $\frac{-5\pi}{12}$ take us to z.
- Starting with the position vector of 1 on the x-axis, a rotation of $\frac{11\pi}{12}$ takes us to z_4 – then two more rotations of $\frac{11\pi}{12}$ take us to z.
- The position vectors of the three solutions are $\frac{2\pi}{3}$ radians apart.
- All three solutions are of the form $z = \left[\cos\left(\frac{3\pi}{4} + 2k\pi\right) + i\sin\left(\frac{3\pi}{4} + 2k\pi\right)\right]^{\frac{1}{3}}$ where $k = 0, 1, 2$.

  Check: by De Moivre's theorem,

$$z = \left[\cos\frac{1}{3}\left(\frac{3\pi}{4} + 2k\pi\right) + i\sin\frac{1}{3}\left(\frac{3\pi}{4} + 2k\pi\right)\right]$$

$$= \left[\cos\left(\frac{\pi}{4} + \frac{2k\pi}{3}\right) + i\sin\left(\frac{\pi}{4} + \frac{2k\pi}{3}\right)\right]$$

  When $k = 0$ we get z_3; when $k = 1$ we get z_4; when $k = 2$ we get z_2 – if we remember to bring the argument into the range $(-\pi, \pi]$.

The general case: *n*th roots

By De Moivre's theorem, when finding the nth root of a complex number we are effectively dividing the argument by n.

We should therefore study arguments in the range $(-n\pi, n\pi]$ so that we have all the solutions in the range $(-\pi, \pi]$ after division by n.

If $z = r(\cos\theta + i\sin\theta)$ then the n solutions of the equation $z_1{}^n = z$ are given by

$$z_1 = r^{\frac{1}{n}}\left(\cos\left(\frac{\theta + 2k\pi}{n}\right) + i\sin\left(\frac{\theta + 2k\pi}{n}\right)\right) \text{ where } k = 0, 1, 2, 3, ..., n - 1.$$

The position vectors of the solutions will divide the circle of radius r, centre the origin, into n equal sectors.

Example 13

Solve the equation $z^3 = 4 + i\,4\sqrt{3}$.

First convert to polar form.

$$|z^3| = \sqrt{4^2 + (4\sqrt{3})^2} = 8; \arg(z^3) = \tan^{-1}\frac{4\sqrt{3}}{4} = \frac{\pi}{3} \Rightarrow z^3 = 8\left(\cos\frac{\pi}{3} + i\sin\frac{\pi}{3}\right)$$

Solutions are of the form

$$z = 8^{\frac{1}{3}}\left(\cos\frac{1}{3}\left(\frac{\pi}{3} + 2k\pi\right) + i\sin\frac{1}{3}\left(\frac{\pi}{3} + 2k\pi\right)\right) \text{where } k = 0, 1, 2$$

$k = 0$ gives $z = 2\left(\cos\frac{\pi}{9} + i\sin\frac{\pi}{9}\right)$

$k = 1$ gives $z = 2\left(\cos\frac{7\pi}{9} + i\sin\frac{7\pi}{9}\right)$

$k = 2$ gives $z = 2\left(\cos\frac{13\pi}{9} + i\sin\frac{13\pi}{9}\right)$

$$= 2\left(\cos\frac{-5\pi}{9} + i\sin\frac{-5\pi}{9}\right)$$

$$= 2\left(\cos\frac{5\pi}{9} - i\sin\frac{5\pi}{9}\right)$$

Example 14

Solve the equation $z^5 = 1$.

First convert to polar form.

$|z^5| = \sqrt{1^2 + 0^2} = 1$; $\arg(z^5) = \tan^{-1}\frac{0}{1} = 0 \Rightarrow z^5 = 1(\cos 0 + i \sin 0)$

Solutions are of the form

$z = 1^{\frac{1}{5}}\left(\cos\frac{1}{5}(0 + 2k\pi) + i\sin\frac{1}{5}(0 + 2k\pi)\right)$ where $k = 0, 1, 2, 3, 4$

$k = 0$ gives $z = (\cos 0 + i\sin 0) = 1$

$k = 1$ gives $z = \left(\cos\frac{2\pi}{5} + i\sin\frac{2\pi}{5}\right)$

$k = 2$ gives $z = \left(\cos\frac{4\pi}{5} + i\sin\frac{4\pi}{5}\right)$

$k = 3$ gives $z = \left(\cos\frac{6\pi}{5} + i\sin\frac{6\pi}{5}\right) = \left(\cos\frac{-4\pi}{5} + i\sin\frac{-4\pi}{5}\right) = \cos\frac{4\pi}{5} - i\sin\frac{4\pi}{5}$

$k = 4$ gives $z = \left(\cos\frac{8\pi}{5} + i\sin\frac{8\pi}{5}\right) = \left(\cos\frac{-2\pi}{5} + i\sin\frac{-2\pi}{5}\right) = \cos\frac{2\pi}{5} - i\sin\frac{2\pi}{5}$

These solutions are often referred to as the fifth roots of unity. When raised to the power 5, each number produces the answer 1.

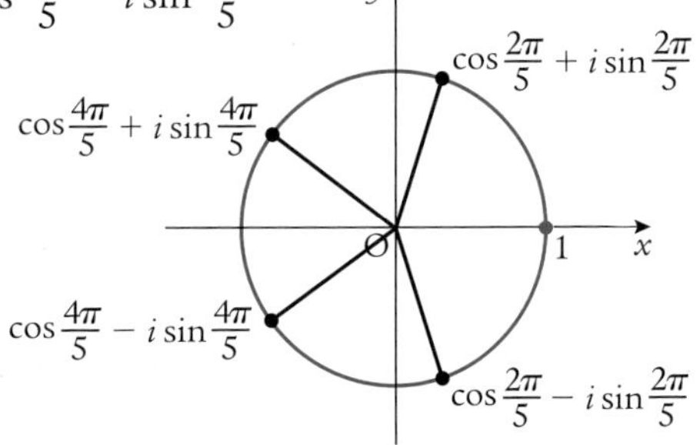

Exercise 12.7

1 For each of these

i solve the equation, leaving your answers in polar form.

ii draw an Argand diagram to illustrate the solutions.

a $z^3 = 8\left(\cos\frac{\pi}{4} + i\sin\frac{\pi}{4}\right)$ **b** $z^4 = \left(\cos\frac{\pi}{5} + i\sin\frac{\pi}{5}\right)$

c $z^5 = 32\left(\cos\frac{\pi}{7} + i\sin\frac{\pi}{7}\right)$ **d** $z^3 = 64\left(\cos\frac{2\pi}{3} + i\sin\frac{2\pi}{3}\right)$

e $z^5 = 32\left(\cos\frac{\pi}{7} - i\sin\frac{\pi}{7}\right)$ **f** $z^3 = 64\left(\cos\frac{2\pi}{3} - i\sin\frac{2\pi}{3}\right)$

g $z^4 = -2 - 2i$ **h** $z^5 = -3 + 3\sqrt{3}\,i$

i $z^4 = -2 + 2i$ **j** $z^5 = -3 - 3\sqrt{3}\,i$

2 **a** Solve $z^3 = 1$ to find the cube roots of unity. [Hint: $z^3 = 1(\cos 0 + i\sin 0)$]

b Solve $z^4 = 1$ to find the fourth roots of unity.

c Find the sixth roots of unity.

d Solve the equation $z^4 = 81$.

e Find the complex numbers which satisfy the equation

i $z^5 = -1$ **ii** $z^5 = i$ **iii** $z^5 = -i$

f Find in polar form the solutions of

i $z^3 = -64$ **ii** $z^4 = 625i$ **iii** $z^5 = -\frac{i}{32}$

12.8 Polynomials

In 1799 Gauss proved that every polynomial equation with complex coefficients, $f(z) = 0$, where $z \in C$, has at least one root in the set of complex numbers.

He later called this theorem **The Fundamental Theorem of Algebra**.

We restrict ourselves in this course to real coefficients.
The Fundamental Theorem of Algebra still applies since real numbers are also complex.

Theorem 1

If the root of a polynomial equation with real coefficients is non-real, that is, of the form $r(\cos\theta + \mathrm{i}\sin\theta)$, $r\sin\theta \neq 0$, then its conjugate, $r(\cos\theta - \mathrm{i}\sin\theta)$, is also a root.

Proof

Suppose $F(z) = a_n z^n + a_{n-1}z^{n-1} + a_{n-2}z^{n-2} + \ldots + a_2 z^2 + a_1 z^1 + a_0$.

If $z = r(\cos\theta + i\sin\theta)$ is a root then

$$a_n r^n(\cos\theta + i\sin\theta)^n + a_{n-1}r^{n-1}(\cos\theta + i\sin\theta)^{n-1} + \ldots + a_2 r^2(\cos\theta + i\sin\theta)^2 + a_1 r(\cos\theta + i\sin\theta)^1 + a_0 = 0$$

Using De Moivre's theorem and then equating real and imaginary parts:

- $a_n r^n \cos n\theta + a_{n-1}r^{n-1}\cos(n-1)\theta + \ldots + a_1 r^1 \cos\theta + a_0 = 0$ (1)
- $a_n r^n \sin n\theta + a_{n-1}r^{n-1}\sin(n-1)\theta + \ldots + a_1 r^1 \sin\theta = 0$ (2)

Now

$\bar{z} = r(\cos\theta - i\sin\theta)$

$$\begin{aligned}F(\bar{z}) &= a_n r^n(\cos\theta - i\sin\theta)^n + a_{n-1}r^{n-1}(\cos\theta - i\sin\theta)^{n-1} + \ldots + a_1 r^1(\cos\theta - i\sin\theta)^1 + a_0\\ &= a_n r^n(\cos n\theta - i\sin n\theta) + a_{n-1}r^{n-1}(\cos(n-1)\theta - i\sin(n-1)\theta) + \ldots + a_1(\cos\theta - i\sin\theta) + a_0\\ &= \left[a_n r^n\cos n\theta + a_{n-1}r^{n-1}\cos(n-1)\theta + \ldots + a_1 r^1\cos\theta + a_0\right]\\ &\quad - i\left[a_n r^n\sin n\theta + a_{n-1}r^{n-1}\sin(n-1)\theta + \ldots + a_1 r^1\sin\theta\right]\end{aligned}$$

So, by (1) and (2) above we have

$F(\bar{z}) = 0 - i0 = 0$

Hence $\bar{z} = r(\cos\theta - i\sin\theta)$ is also a root.

Theorem 2

A polynomial of degree n will have n complex roots.

Proof

Given that $F(z) = 0$ is a polynomial equation of degree n then by the fundamental theorem of algebra a root exists. Call this root k_n. By the factor theorem $(z - k_n)$ is a factor and $F(z) = (z - k_n)G(z)$ where $G(z)$ is a polynomial of degree $n - 1$. Since $F(z) = 0$ then $G(z) = 0$.

By the Fundamental Theorem of Algebra a root for this polynomial equation also exists.
Call this root k_{n-1}. By the factor theorem $(z - k_{n-1})$ is a factor and $F(z) = (z - k_n)(z - k_{n-1})H(z)$ where $H(z)$ is a polynomial of degree $n - 2$. Since $F(z) = 0$ then $H(z) = 0$.
Proceeding in this manner we get $F(z) = (z - k_n)(z - k_{n-1})\ldots(z - k_2)(z - k_1)$
Thus a polynomial of degree n will have n complex roots.

Theorem 3

A polynomial of degree n, with real coefficients, can be reduced to the product of real linear factors and real irreducible quadratic factors.

Proof

Either a root k is real, leading to a linear factor $(z - k)$, or it is non-real, leading to the non-real linear factors $(z - k)$ and $(z - \bar{k})$.
The product of these two factors leads to a real quadratic factor which is irreducible in R.

Example 15

Given $f(z) = z^4 - 6z^3 + 18z^2 - 30z + 25$,

a show that $z = 1 + 2i$ is a root of the equation $f(z) = 0$

b hence find the other roots of the polynomial.

a $f(1 + 2i) = (1 + 2i)^4 - 6(1 + 2i)^3 + 18(1 + 2i)^2 - 30(1 + 2i) + 25$

$= (-7 - 24i) - 6(-11 - 2i) + 18(-3 + 4i) - 30(1 + 2i) + 25$

$= -7 - 24i + 66 + 12i - 54 + 72i - 30 - 60i + 25$

$= 0$

Thus $z = 1 + 2i$ is a root.

b If $z = 1 + 2i$ is a root then, since $f(z)$ has real coefficients, the conjugate, $1 - 2i$, is also a root.
Thus $(z - (1 + 2i))$ and $(z - (1 - 2i))$ are complex factors of $f(z)$.
These multiply to give the real quadratic factor $(z - 1 - 2i))(z - 1 + 2i) = z^2 - 2z + 5$.

By division...

$$\begin{array}{r|l} & z^2 - 4z + 5 \\ \hline z^2 - 2z + 5 & z^4 - 6z^3 + 18z^2 - 30z + 25 \\ & z^4 - 2z^3 + 5z^2 \\ \hline & -4z^3 + 13z^2 - 30z + 25 \\ & -4z^3 + 8z^2 - 20z \\ \hline & 5z^2 - 10z + 25 \\ & 5z^2 - 10z + 25 \\ \hline & 0 \end{array}$$

We find that the complementary real factor is $z^2 - 4z + 5$.

Equating this to zero and using the quadratic formula,

$$z = \frac{4 \pm \sqrt{16 - 20}}{2} = 2 \pm i$$

We now have all four roots, which are $1 + 2i$, $1 - 2i$, $2 + i$ and $2 - i$.

Exercise 12.8

1 Use the quadratic formula to find the two complex roots of each equation.

a $z^2 - 2z + 10 = 0$

b $z^2 - 4z + 5 = 0$

c $z^2 - 6z + 25 = 0$

d $4z^2 - 16z + 17 = 0$

e $2z^2 + 2z + 1 = 0$

f $5z^2 + 4z + 8 = 0$

2 For each cubic equation, a real root has been identified.
Find the remaining two complex roots.

a $z^3 + 2z^2 + z + 2 = 0$; $z = -2$

b $z^3 - z^2 - z - 15 = 0$; $z = 3$

c $z^3 + 6z^2 + 37z + 58 = 0$; $z = -2$

d $z^3 - 11z - 20 = 0$; $z = 4$

e $4z^3 + 8z^2 + 14z + 10 = 0$; $z = -1$

f $2z^3 + 11z^2 + 20z - 13 = 0$; $z = \frac{1}{2}$

3 For each cubic equation, a factor has been given.
Find the roots of the equation.

a $z^3 + z^2 - 7z - 15 = 0$; $z - 3$

b $z^3 - 6z^2 + 13z - 20 = 0$; $z - 4$

c $2z^3 + 5z^2 + 8z + 20 = 0$; $z - 2i$

d $2z^3 + 7z^2 + 26z + 30 = 0$; $z + 1 + 3i$

e $4z^3 - 4z^2 + 9z - 9 = 0$; 2 $z - 3i$

f $2z^3 + 13z^2 + 46z + 65 = 0$; $z + 2 - 3i$

4 Given $f(z) = z^4 - z^3 - 2z^2 + 6z - 4$ and given that $z = 1 + i$ is a root of the equation $f(z) = 0$ find the real factors of the polynomial.

5 $1 + 2i$ is a root of the equation $z^4 - 5z^3 + 13z^2 - 19z + 10$.
Find the real factors of the polynomial.

6 For each of these

i show that the given complex number is a zero of the given polynomial

ii find all the remaining roots.

a $z = 2 + i$; $f(z) = z^4 - 2z^3 - z^2 + 2z + 10$

b $z = 3 + 2i$; $f(z) = z^4 - 8z^3 + 30z^2 - 56z + 65$

c $z = 1 + 3i$; $f(z) = 2z^4 - 3z^3 + 17z^2 + 12z - 10$

7 In each case the given complex number is a zero of the given polynomial.
Find all the roots.

a $z = 4 + i$; $f(z) = z^4 - 8z^3 + 13z^2 + 32z - 68$

b $z = 2 - 3i$; $f(z) = 6z^4 - 31z^3 + 108z^2 - 99z + 26$

c $z = 4 + 2i$; $f(z) = 2z^4 - 25z^3 + 107z^2 - 140z - 100$

8 $z^2 + 4z + 5$ is a factor of $z^5 + 7z^4 + 21z^3 + 33z^2 + 28z + 10$.
Find all the roots of the equation $z^5 + 7z^4 + 21z^3 + 33z^2 + 28z + 10 = 0$.

Historical note

In the 18th century a Cambridge mathematician, Roger Cotes (1682–1716), developed a third form in which to express a complex number.
He discovered that $z = r(\cos\theta + i\sin\theta) = re^{i\theta}$
where r is the modulus, θ is the argument of z and $e = 2.718...$

Maclaurin's theorem can be used to prove this.
It does, however, produce a few curiosities worthy of mention here.

When $z = -1, r = 1$ and $\theta = \pi$ which leads to a famous result: $e^{i\pi} = -1$.

When $z = i, r = 1$ and $\theta = \frac{\pi}{2}: i = e^{\frac{i\pi}{2}} \Rightarrow i^i = \left(e^{\frac{i\pi}{2}}\right)^i = e^{-\frac{\pi}{2}} \Rightarrow i^i \in R$!!!

Review 12

1 Given $z_1 = 5 - 12i$ and $z_2 = 3 + 4i$ calculate

a $z_1 + z_2$ b $z_1 - z_2$ c $z_1 \times z_2$ d $\bar{z}_1$ e $\dfrac{z_1}{z_2}$ f $\sqrt{z_1}$ g $2z_1 + z_2^2$

2 If $(2 + bi)(a + 3i) = 1 + 8i$, $a, b \in N$, find a and b by equating real and imaginary parts.

3 Express $z = 5 + 12i$ in polar form.

4 Calculate the modulus and argument of $\dfrac{4 - 3i}{1 + i}$ correct to 3 significant figures where appropriate.

5 Draw an Argand diagram to illustrate the sum $z_1 + z_2$ where $z_1 = 1 + 3i$ and $z_2 = 4 + 2i$.

6 Given $z = x + iy$,

a find the equation of the locus $|z + 1| = 5$

b draw the locus on an Argand diagram.

7 For $z_1 = 2\left(\cos\frac{\pi}{3} + i\sin\frac{\pi}{3}\right)$ and $z_2 = 3\left(\cos\frac{\pi}{6} + i\sin\frac{\pi}{6}\right)$ calculate

a z_1z_2 b $\dfrac{z_1}{z_2}$ c z_1^3

8 Use De Moivre's theorem to simplify $(-1 + \sqrt{3}i)^8$ giving your answer

a in polar form b in the form $a + ib$.

9 a Expand $(\cos\theta + i\sin\theta)^5$

i using the binomial theorem

ii using De Moivre's theorem.

b By equating imaginary parts, express $\sin 5\theta$ in terms of $\sin\theta$.

10 a Solve $z^3 = 125\left(\cos\frac{\pi}{4} + i\sin\frac{\pi}{4}\right)$, leaving your answers in polar form.

b Illustrate the roots on an Argand diagram.

11 Find the fifth roots of unity and illustrate them on an Argand diagram.

12 Find the real factors of $f(z) = z^4 - z^3 + 13z^2 + 21z - 34$ given that $1 + 4i$ is a zero of $f(z)$.

13 Solve $z^4 - 6z^3 + 26z^2 - 46z + 65 = 0$ for all its complex roots given that $2 + 3i$ is one root.

Summary 12

1 a $i^2 = -1$; $i \notin R$

b C is the set of numbers z of the form $z = a + bi$ where $a, b \in R$.

c The members of C are called **complex numbers**.

d a is called the **real part** of z and we write $a = \Re(z)$.

b is called the **imaginary part** of z and we write $b = \Im(z)$.

e Given $z_1 = a + bi$ and $z_2 = c + di$

addition is defined by

$$z_1 + z_2 = (a + bi) + (c + di) = (a + c) + (b + d)i$$

multiplication is defined by

$$z_1z_2 = (a + bi)(c + di) = ac + adi + bci + bdi^2$$
$$= (ac - bd) + (ad + bc)i \text{ since } i^2 = -1$$

f If $z_1 = z_2$ then $\Re(z_1) = \Re(z_2)$ and $\Im(z_1) = \Im(z_2)$.

If $z = a + bi$ then its **complex conjugate** is $\bar{z} = a - bi$.

Divisions are simplified by multiplying numerator and denominator by the complex conjugate of the denominator.

$$\frac{a + bi}{c + di} = \frac{(a + bi)(c - di)}{(c + di)(c - di)} = \frac{(a + bi)(c - di)}{c^2 + d^2}$$

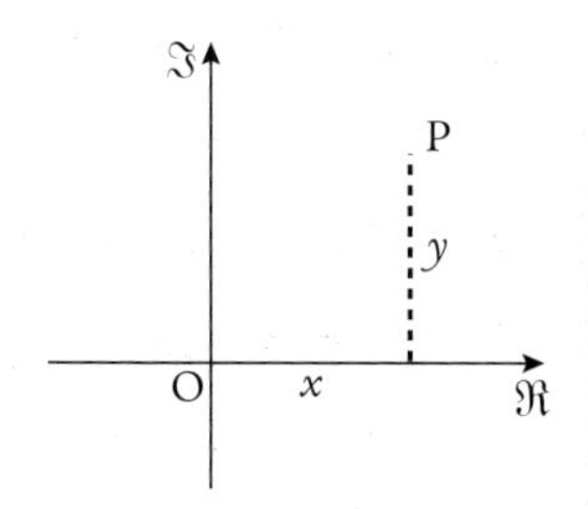

A complex number z can be represented on the complex plane by the point P or its position vector $\overrightarrow{OP}$.

Such a diagram is often referred to as an **Argand diagram**.

The angle through which OP has rotated is called the **argument** of z.
$\text{Arg } z = \theta + n\pi$

The **principal argument** lies in the range $(-\pi, \pi]$ and is denoted by $\arg z$.

The distance OP, r, is known as the **modulus** of z.

This is denoted by $|z|$.

$r = \sqrt{x^2 + y^2}$ and $\theta = \tan^{-1}\left(\frac{y}{x}\right)$ remembering that one should also check in which quadrant P is to be found.

$x = r\cos\theta$ and $y = r\sin\theta$

$z = r(\cos\theta + \sin\theta)$ is the **polar form** of z.

$|z_1z_2| = |z_1| \times |z_2|$; $\text{Arg}(z_1z_2) = \text{Arg}(z_1) + \text{Arg}(z_2)$

$\left|\frac{z_1}{z_2}\right| = |z_1| \div |z_2|$; $\text{Arg}\left(\frac{z_1}{z_2}\right) = \text{Arg}(z_1) - \text{Arg}(z_2)$

Note: the argument may have to be adjusted by adding or subtracting 2π to bring it back into the range $(-\pi, \pi]$.

De Moivre's theorem

$z = r(\cos\theta + i\sin\theta) \Rightarrow z^n = r^n(\cos\theta + i\sin\theta)^n = r^n(\cos n\theta + i\sin n\theta)$

$z^n = r(\cos\theta + i\sin\theta) \Rightarrow z = r^{\frac{1}{n}}\left(\cos\left(\frac{\theta + 2k\pi}{n}\right) + i\sin\left(\frac{\theta + 2k\pi}{n}\right)\right)$;

$k = 0, 1, 2, 3, ..., n - 1$

As a special case, $z = 1, r = 1$ and $\theta = 0$, $z^n = 1$ has roots
$\left(\cos\left(\frac{2k\pi}{n}\right) + i\sin\left(\frac{2k\pi}{n}\right)\right)$; $k = 0, 1, 2, 3, ..., n - 1$.
These are the nth roots of unity.

Every polynomial equation with complex coefficients, $f(z) = 0$, where $z \in C$, has at least one root in the set of complex numbers.
This is called **The Fundamental Theorem of Algebra**.

If the root is non-real, that is of the form $r(\cos\theta + i\sin\theta)$, $r\sin\theta \neq 0$, then its conjugate, $r(\cos\theta - i\sin\theta)$, is also a root.

A polynomial of degree n will have n complex roots.

A polynomial of degree n with real coefficients can be reduced to a product of real linear factors and real irreducible quadratic factors.

13 Matrices

Historical note

Arthur Cayley

The first use of the term 'matrix' was by the English mathematician James Sylvester in 1850.
Before this, in 1841, his friend Arthur Cayley had been developing determinants and their uses in solving equations. After many conversations with Sylvester, Cayley went on to develop a formal algebra for matrix operations.
Most of the current notation for matrices and determinants is due to Cayley. His first paper was published in 1855 and dealt with the use of matrices to describe transformations of the plane.

James Sylvester

13.1 Definitions

- A **matrix** is a *table* or **array** of numbers, referred to as **elements** or **entries**, arranged in **rows** and **columns**.
- The order of a matrix is given by stating its dimensions:
  number of rows × number of columns.
  For example the matrix A below is of order 2×3 since it has two rows and three columns.

$$A = \begin{pmatrix} 2 & 4 & 1 \\ 3 & 1 & 2 \end{pmatrix}$$

- The element of A in the ith row and jth column is denoted by a_{ij}
  for example $a_{12} = 4$, $a_{21} = 3$ and $a_{23} = 2$.
- Some matrices are categorised and named according to their shape.
  For example

B is a 3×1 column matrix

$$B = \begin{pmatrix} 1 \\ -2 \\ 2 \end{pmatrix}$$

C is a 1×4 row matrix

$$C = \begin{pmatrix} 1 & 2 & 5 & -1 \end{pmatrix}$$

D is a square matrix of order 2

$$D = \begin{pmatrix} 2 & 0 \\ 1 & 1 \end{pmatrix}$$

Basic Properties and operations on matrices

A matrix can be used to summarise a table of values where the context is known.
For example:

- A theatre has three areas for which you can book seats.
- Adults and children are charged differently.

A booking clerk might enter bookings in a spreadsheet like this.

	A	B	C	D
1	Area	A	B	C
2	Adult	3	4	5
3	Child	2	1	3

or summarise it in a matrix like this:

$$\begin{pmatrix} 3 & 4 & 5 \\ 2 & 1 & 3 \end{pmatrix}$$

as long as he knows what each row and column means.

Using this context as an example we can consider various operations on matrices.

Equality of matrices

Two matrices are defined to be equal only if they are of the same order and their corresponding entries are equal. Note, for example, that

$$\begin{pmatrix} 2 & 1 \\ 3 & 5 \end{pmatrix} \neq \begin{pmatrix} 2 & 1 & 0 \\ 3 & 5 & 0 \end{pmatrix}$$

In the context above, two booking clerks can only claim to have equal bookings if they have the same patterns of adults and children in the same areas.

Addition of matrices

Area	A	B	C
Adult	3	4	5
Child	2	1	3
Bookings by Clerk 1			

Area	A	B	C
Adult	2	1	2
Child	3	1	6
Bookings by Clerk 2			

Area	A	B	C
Adult	5	5	7
Child	5	2	9
Total Bookings			

In the same way we can pool the results of two booking clerks, we can add two matrices. The matrices are said to be **compatible for addition** only if they have the same order. The addition is accomplished by adding corresponding entries.

$$A + B = C \Leftrightarrow a_{ij} + b_{ij} = c_{ij}$$

For example

$$\begin{pmatrix} 3 & 4 & 5 \\ 2 & 1 & 3 \end{pmatrix} + \begin{pmatrix} 2 & 1 & 2 \\ 3 & 1 & 6 \end{pmatrix} = \begin{pmatrix} 3+2 & 4+1 & 5+2 \\ 2+3 & 1+1 & 3+6 \end{pmatrix} = \begin{pmatrix} 5 & 5 & 7 \\ 5 & 2 & 9 \end{pmatrix}$$

Scalar multiplication

Any matrix can be multiplied by a scalar (number) by considering the definition of addition. For example

$$3\begin{pmatrix} 2 & 1 \\ 3 & 5 \end{pmatrix} = \begin{pmatrix} 2 & 1 \\ 3 & 5 \end{pmatrix} + \begin{pmatrix} 2 & 1 \\ 3 & 5 \end{pmatrix} + \begin{pmatrix} 2 & 1 \\ 3 & 5 \end{pmatrix}$$

$$= \begin{pmatrix} 2+2+2 & 1+1+1 \\ 3+3+3 & 5+5+5 \end{pmatrix} = \begin{pmatrix} 3\times 2 & 3\times 1 \\ 3\times 3 & 3\times 5 \end{pmatrix} = \begin{pmatrix} 6 & 3 \\ 9 & 15 \end{pmatrix}$$

Thus a matrix is multiplied by a scalar by multiplying each entry by the scalar.

$$E = kD \Leftrightarrow e_{ij} = kd_{ij}$$

Negative of a matrix

A cancellation could be recorded by the clerk as a negative entry.
Here the clerk has cancelled all his bookings.

Area	A	B	C
Adult	−3	−4	−5
Child	−2	−1	−3

The negative of a matrix, G, is denoted by $-G$.

$$H = -G \Leftrightarrow h_{ij} = -g_{ij}$$

This is the same as multiplying the matrix by -1.

$$\begin{pmatrix} 3 & 4 & 5 \\ 2 & 1 & 3 \end{pmatrix} + \begin{pmatrix} -3 & -4 & -5 \\ -2 & -1 & -3 \end{pmatrix} = \begin{pmatrix} 0 & 0 & 0 \\ 0 & 0 & 0 \end{pmatrix}$$

Note that $\begin{pmatrix} 0 & 0 & 0 \\ 0 & 0 & 0 \end{pmatrix}$ is referred to as the 2×3 zero matrix

or the 2×3 identity matrix for addition.
Each order of matrix will have its own zero matrix.

Subtraction of matrices

Subtracting matrix B from matrix A can be accomplished by adding the negative of B. This is, of course, equivalent to subtracting corresponding entries.

$$A - B = C \Leftrightarrow a_{ij} - b_{ij} = c_{ij}$$

Note that two matrices are **compatible for subtraction** only if they have the same order.

The transpose of a matrix

It is sometimes convenient to switch rows and columns when dealing with tables.

Area	A	B	C
Adult	3	4	5
Child	2	1	3

Area	Adult	Child
A	3	2
B	4	1
C	5	3

When the rows and columns of a matrix A are interchanged, the resulting matrix is called the **transpose** of A and is denoted by A' or A^{T}; thus $a'_{ij} = a_{ji}$. For example

$$B = \begin{pmatrix} 3 & 4 & 5 \\ 2 & 1 & 3 \end{pmatrix} \Leftrightarrow B' = \begin{pmatrix} 3 & 2 \\ 4 & 1 \\ 5 & 3 \end{pmatrix} \text{ and } \begin{pmatrix} 2 \\ 4 \\ 1 \end{pmatrix}^{\mathrm{T}} = (2 \;\; 4 \;\; 1)$$

Symmetric and skew-symmetric matrices

A matrix A is **symmetric** if $A^{\mathrm{T}} = A$ and thus $a_{ij} = a_{ji}$, for example

$$\begin{pmatrix} 1 & 3 & 5 \\ 3 & 2 & -1 \\ 5 & -1 & 7 \end{pmatrix}$$

Note that the matrix is symmetric about the **leading diagonal**.

A matrix A is **skew-symmetric** if $A^{\mathrm{T}} = -A$ and thus $a_{ij} = -a_{ji}$, for example

$$\begin{pmatrix} 0 & -3 & -5 \\ 3 & 0 & 1 \\ 5 & -1 & 0 \end{pmatrix}$$

Note that there can only be zeros in the leading diagonal.

Exercise 13.1

1 $A = \begin{pmatrix} 2 & 1 \\ 3 & -4 \end{pmatrix}$ $B = \begin{pmatrix} 3 & 2 & -4 \\ -1 & 0 & 5 \end{pmatrix}$ $C = \begin{pmatrix} 1 & 0 & 3 \\ 2 & 7 & 6 \\ 5 & -1 & 4 \\ 8 & 12 & -2 \end{pmatrix}$ $D = \begin{pmatrix} 1 \\ -3 \\ 4 \end{pmatrix}$

a How many rows has the matrix C?

b How many columns has the matrix B?

c State the order of the matrix A.

d State the order of the matrix D.

e List the entries in the second column of B.

f List the entries in the first row of C.

g Write the element in the first row and second column of A.

h Write the element in the second row and first column of B.

i Write the entry in the third row and second column of C.

j State the value of **i** a_{21} **ii** b_{22} **iii** c_{23} **iv** d_{11} **v** b_{13} **vi** c_{12}

2 Write the order of each of these matrices.

a $\begin{pmatrix} 1 & 2 \\ 2 & -1 \end{pmatrix}$ **b** $\begin{pmatrix} 1 \\ 1 \\ 1 \end{pmatrix}$ **c** $\begin{pmatrix} 0 & 1 & 0 \\ 1 & 1 & -1 \end{pmatrix}$

d $\begin{pmatrix} 2 & 1 & 2 & 1 \\ 2 & 3 & 5 & 2 \\ 8 & 6 & -1 & 3 \end{pmatrix}$ **e** $\begin{pmatrix} 1 & -3 & 0 \end{pmatrix}$ **f** $\begin{pmatrix} 2 & 1 & 2 \\ 0 & 0 & 1 \\ 4 & 5 & 8 \end{pmatrix}$

3 Find the value of x in each case.

a $\begin{pmatrix} 2 \\ 2x \end{pmatrix} = \begin{pmatrix} 2 \\ 6 \end{pmatrix}$ **b** $\begin{pmatrix} 2x \\ x \\ -x \end{pmatrix} = \begin{pmatrix} 6 \\ 3 \\ -3 \end{pmatrix}$ **c** $\begin{pmatrix} 0 & 4x+1 & 2x-3 \\ 1 & 1 & 5 \end{pmatrix} = \begin{pmatrix} 0 & 21 & 7 \\ 1 & 1 & 5 \end{pmatrix}$

4 Find the values of x and y in each case.

a $\begin{pmatrix} 3x \\ 12 \end{pmatrix} = \begin{pmatrix} 6 \\ y \end{pmatrix}$ **b** $\begin{pmatrix} x-y & y \end{pmatrix} = \begin{pmatrix} 8 & 7 \end{pmatrix}$ **c** $\begin{pmatrix} 1 & 3 \\ 4 & 2 \end{pmatrix} = \begin{pmatrix} x & 1-y \\ 4 & 2x \end{pmatrix}$

d $\begin{pmatrix} x+y \\ 2x \end{pmatrix} = \begin{pmatrix} 7 \\ 8 \end{pmatrix}$ **e** $\begin{pmatrix} 2x+3y \\ x+2y \end{pmatrix} = \begin{pmatrix} 8 \\ 5 \end{pmatrix}$ **f** $\begin{pmatrix} 2 & 3x+y \\ 4x-3y & 5 \end{pmatrix} = \begin{pmatrix} 2 & 3 \\ 17 & 5 \end{pmatrix}$

5 **a** Prove that $\begin{pmatrix} x \\ y \\ x+y \end{pmatrix} \neq \begin{pmatrix} 3 \\ -2 \\ 5 \end{pmatrix}$.

b For each pair of matrices, find, where this is possible, the values of x and y which make them equal.

i $\begin{pmatrix} 2x \\ y \\ x+2y \end{pmatrix}, \begin{pmatrix} 6 \\ 1 \\ 5 \end{pmatrix}$ **ii** $\begin{pmatrix} x+y \\ x-y \\ x+3y \end{pmatrix}, \begin{pmatrix} 1 \\ 3 \\ -1 \end{pmatrix}$

iii $\begin{pmatrix} 3x+2y \\ 2x+y \\ xy \end{pmatrix}, \begin{pmatrix} 4 \\ 3 \\ 3 \end{pmatrix}$ **iv** $\begin{pmatrix} x+2y \\ x+y^2 \\ xy \end{pmatrix}, \begin{pmatrix} 5 \\ 4 \\ 3 \end{pmatrix}$

6 Simplify

a $\begin{pmatrix} 2 \\ 1 \end{pmatrix} + \begin{pmatrix} 5 \\ 3 \end{pmatrix}$ **b** $\begin{pmatrix} 6 \\ -8 \end{pmatrix} + \begin{pmatrix} -1 \\ 9 \end{pmatrix}$ **c** $\begin{pmatrix} p+q \\ p-q \end{pmatrix} + \begin{pmatrix} -p \\ q \end{pmatrix}$

d $\begin{pmatrix} 2x & y \end{pmatrix} + \begin{pmatrix} 3x & -3y \end{pmatrix}$ **e** $\begin{pmatrix} 5k & -k \end{pmatrix} + \begin{pmatrix} -3k & 8k \end{pmatrix} + \begin{pmatrix} 4 & 1 \end{pmatrix}$ **f** $\begin{pmatrix} 4 & 1 \\ 2 & 3 \\ 4 & 5 \end{pmatrix} + \begin{pmatrix} 1 & 6 \\ 2 & 5 \\ 3 & 3 \end{pmatrix}$

g $\begin{pmatrix} 3 & 0 \\ 0 & 5 \\ 4 & 1 \end{pmatrix} + \begin{pmatrix} 2 & 3 \\ 1 & 4 \\ 5 & 5 \end{pmatrix} + \begin{pmatrix} -4 & 2 \\ 3 & -3 \\ 4 & -9 \end{pmatrix}$

h $\begin{pmatrix} 3 & 4 & 2 \\ 2 & 1 & 6 \end{pmatrix} + \begin{pmatrix} 2 & 1 & -1 \\ -3 & 0 & 4 \end{pmatrix}$

i $\begin{pmatrix} 4 & 1 & 3 \\ 2 & 0 & 0 \\ -2 & 1 & -1 \end{pmatrix} + \begin{pmatrix} 2 & 0 & 2 \\ 1 & 0 & 0 \\ 0 & 2 & -3 \end{pmatrix}$

j $\begin{pmatrix} 5 & -3 & 2 \\ -2 & -1 & 3 \\ 0 & 2 & -2 \end{pmatrix} + \begin{pmatrix} -5 & 3 & -2 \\ 2 & 1 & -3 \\ 0 & -2 & 2 \end{pmatrix}$

k $\begin{pmatrix} 3 \\ 2 \end{pmatrix} - \begin{pmatrix} 1 \\ 3 \end{pmatrix}$

l $\begin{pmatrix} 4 \\ -2 \end{pmatrix} - \begin{pmatrix} -2 \\ 6 \end{pmatrix}$

m $\begin{pmatrix} a + 2b \\ 2a - b \end{pmatrix} - \begin{pmatrix} a + b \\ 3a - b \end{pmatrix}$

n $(4a \;\; 2b) - (-a \;\; -b)$

o $(3m \;\; -2n) + (-m \;\; 4n) - (5m \;\; 3n)$

p $\begin{pmatrix} 2 & 5 \\ 1 & -4 \\ -1 & 3 \end{pmatrix} - \begin{pmatrix} -2 & 4 \\ 3 & 1 \\ 4 & -1 \end{pmatrix}$

q $\begin{pmatrix} -1 & 1 \\ 1 & -1 \\ -1 & 1 \end{pmatrix} + \begin{pmatrix} 3 & 1 \\ -1 & 1 \\ 3 & 1 \end{pmatrix} - \begin{pmatrix} -3 & 1 \\ 3 & -3 \\ 3 & -1 \end{pmatrix}$

r $5\begin{pmatrix} 1 & -4 & -6 \\ 3 & -3 & -1 \end{pmatrix}$

s $-3\begin{pmatrix} -1 & 3 & 1 \\ -4 & 2 & 0 \\ -5 & -1 & -3 \end{pmatrix}$

t $3\begin{pmatrix} 4 & 1 & -2 \\ -1 & 0 & -2 \\ 5 & 1 & 1 \end{pmatrix} - 2\begin{pmatrix} 3 & -4 & -1 \\ 3 & 2 & 0 \\ 1 & 0 & -3 \end{pmatrix}$

7 A, B, C, D, E and F are matrices. Solve these equations to find them.

a $A + \begin{pmatrix} 1 & 1 \\ 2 & 3 \end{pmatrix} = \begin{pmatrix} 4 & 7 \\ 1 & 5 \end{pmatrix}$

b $\begin{pmatrix} 3 & 1 \\ 2 & 5 \end{pmatrix} + B = \begin{pmatrix} 1 & 2 \\ 1 & 3 \end{pmatrix}$

c $\begin{pmatrix} 3 & 2 \\ -1 & 4 \end{pmatrix} + C = \begin{pmatrix} 4 & 7 \\ 1 & 3 \end{pmatrix}$

d $D - \begin{pmatrix} 2 & 3 \\ 1 & 4 \end{pmatrix} = \begin{pmatrix} 3 & 1 \\ 4 & 6 \end{pmatrix}$

e $\begin{pmatrix} 3 & 2 & 1 \\ 4 & 0 & 6 \end{pmatrix} = \begin{pmatrix} 4 & 2 & 1 \\ 3 & 1 & 4 \end{pmatrix} - E$

f $F - \begin{pmatrix} 2 & 1 \\ 3 & 4 \\ 5 & 7 \end{pmatrix} = \begin{pmatrix} 1 & 3 \\ 4 & 2 \\ 9 & 8 \end{pmatrix}$

8 Given $A = \begin{pmatrix} 1 & -1 & 0 \\ 2 & 1 & 2 \end{pmatrix}$, $B = \begin{pmatrix} 0 & 1 & -1 \\ 3 & 2 & 1 \end{pmatrix}$ and $C = \begin{pmatrix} 4 & 1 & 2 \\ -5 & 0 & 2 \end{pmatrix}$ evaluate

a $2A + 3B - C$ b $3A - 2B + C$ c $A - 2B + 3C$ d $2(A + B + C)$

9 Solve these matrix equations.

a $3A = \begin{pmatrix} 6 & -3 \\ 0 & 9 \end{pmatrix}$ b $2B + \begin{pmatrix} 1 & 4 \\ 5 & 7 \end{pmatrix} = \begin{pmatrix} 5 & 6 \\ 1 & 9 \end{pmatrix}$ c $2C - 3\begin{pmatrix} 1 & 1 & 2 \\ 2 & -1 & 0 \end{pmatrix} = \begin{pmatrix} 7 & 5 & 1 \\ 6 & -2 & 3 \end{pmatrix}$

10 a Write the transpose of each of these matrices.

i $\begin{pmatrix} 3 & 4 & 1 \\ -7 & 9 & 5 \end{pmatrix}$ ii $\begin{pmatrix} 3 & -6 & 0 \\ -4 & 7 & 1 \\ 7 & 3 & -2 \end{pmatrix}$ iii $\begin{pmatrix} 2 & -1 \\ -1 & 2 \end{pmatrix}$ iv $\begin{pmatrix} 0 & 1 & -5 \\ -1 & 0 & 2 \\ 5 & -2 & 0 \end{pmatrix}$

b Comment on your answers for **iii** and **iv**.

13.2 Algebraic properties of matrices

The algebra of matrices is in many respects similar to the algebra of numbers – with some noteable differences. The next exercise explores some of the properties of matrices.

Exercise 13.2

1 a Given $A = \begin{pmatrix} a_{11} & a_{12} \\ a_{21} & a_{22} \end{pmatrix}$ and $B = \begin{pmatrix} b_{11} & b_{12} \\ b_{21} & b_{22} \end{pmatrix}$ evaluate

i $A + B$ ii $B + A$

b Make a comment about the addition of 2×2 matrices.

c Can this comment be generalised to any pair of compatible matrices?

d Evaluate i $A - B$ ii $B - A$

Comment on the subtraction of matrices.

2 a Given $A = \begin{pmatrix} a_{11} & a_{12} \\ a_{21} & a_{22} \end{pmatrix}$, $B = \begin{pmatrix} b_{11} & b_{12} \\ b_{21} & b_{22} \end{pmatrix}$ and $C = \begin{pmatrix} c_{11} & c_{12} \\ c_{21} & c_{22} \end{pmatrix}$ evaluate

i $(A + B) + C$ ii $A + (B + C)$ iii $(A - B) - C$ iv $A - (B - C)$

b Comment on the associative properties of matrices.

3 a Given $A = \begin{pmatrix} a_{11} & a_{12} \\ a_{21} & a_{22} \end{pmatrix}$ and $B = \begin{pmatrix} b_{11} & b_{12} \\ b_{21} & b_{22} \end{pmatrix}$ and the scalar x, evaluate

i xA ii xB iii $x(A + B)$ iv $xA + xB$

b Comment on the distributive properties of scalar multiplication over the addition of matrices.

4 a Given $A = \begin{pmatrix} a_{11} & a_{12} \\ a_{21} & a_{22} \end{pmatrix}$ and the zero matrix, $O = \begin{pmatrix} 0 & 0 \\ 0 & 0 \end{pmatrix}$, evaluate

i $A + O$ ii $O + A$ iii $A - O$ iv $O - A$

b Comment on the properties of the zero matrix with respect to addition and subtraction.

c Comment on the value of xO where x is a scalar.

5 Given $A = \begin{pmatrix} a_{11} & a_{12} \\ a_{21} & a_{22} \end{pmatrix}$ and $B = \begin{pmatrix} b_{11} & b_{12} \\ b_{21} & b_{22} \end{pmatrix}$ evaluate

a $A + B$ b A' c B' d $A' + B'$

e $(A + B)'$ f $(A')'$ g $(B')'$ h kA

i kA' j $(kA)'$

Make any relevant observations you can about the transpose of a matrix.

6 a Given that $A = \begin{pmatrix} 1 & -4 & 7 \\ -2 & 3 & 2 \\ 1 & 0 & -6 \end{pmatrix}$ find A'.

b Work out i $A + A'$ ii $A - A'$

c i Comment on your results.

ii Can this be generalised?

d Show that any square matrix A can be expressed as the sum of a symmetric and a skew-symmetric matrix.

Summary

- A zero matrix, O, has all entries equal to zero. For example the 2×2 zero matrix is $\begin{pmatrix} 0 & 0 \\ 0 & 0 \end{pmatrix}$.
- $A + B = O \Leftrightarrow A = -B$
- The commutative law holds for addition, but not subtraction:

  $A + B = B + A$ but $A - B \neq B - A$
- The associative law hold for addition: $(A + B) + C = A + (B + C) = A + B + C$
- Scalar multiplication is distributive over matrix addition:

  $k(A + B) = kA + kB$
- $(A')' = A$
- $(A + B)' = A' + B'$
- $(kA)' = kA'$

13.3 Matrix multiplication

Consider the booking clerk once again. Suppose the clerk makes these bookings:

Area	A	B	C
Adult	3	4	5
Child	2	1	3

and these are the charges (in pounds).

Costs	Adult	Child
Morning	2	1
Afternoon	4	2
Evening	6	4

These two tables can be combined to form another table which shows the money made per area depending on whether these are morning, afternoon or evening bookings.

If it is a morning booking,

area A would collect £8 $\quad £2 \times 3 + £1 \times 2$

area B would collect £9 $\quad £2 \times 4 + £1 \times 1$

area C would collect £13 $\quad £2 \times 5 + £1 \times 3$

If it is an afternoon booking,

area A would collect £16 $\quad £4 \times 3 + £2 \times 2$

area B would collect £18 $\quad £4 \times 4 + £2 \times 1$

area C would collect £26 $\quad £4 \times 5 + £2 \times 3$

If it is an evening booking,

area A would collect £26 $\quad £6 \times 3 + £4 \times 2$

area B would collect £28 $\quad £6 \times 4 + £4 \times 1$

area C would collect £42 $\quad £6 \times 5 + £4 \times 3$

This gives the combined result

Area	A	B	C
Morning	8	9	13
Afternoon	16	18	26
Evening	26	28	42

In context, we have seen a matrix multiplication taking place, namely

$$\begin{pmatrix} 2 & 1 \\ 4 & 2 \\ 6 & 4 \end{pmatrix}\begin{pmatrix} 3 & 4 & 5 \\ 2 & 1 & 3 \end{pmatrix} = \begin{pmatrix} 8 & 9 & 13 \\ 16 & 18 & 26 \\ 26 & 28 & 42 \end{pmatrix}$$

Note that in this context it does not matter whether the *costs* table is 3×2 or 2×3, we would interpret the product appropriately. However, to conform with the following definitions, we have been careful to select the 3×2 format.

Definitions

- Let us define the product of a row and a column as the **scalar product** of the two vectors which can be represented by the row and column. For example

$$(2 \;\; 5 \;\; -1)\begin{pmatrix} -3 \\ 1 \\ 4 \end{pmatrix} = 2 \times (-3) + 5 \times 1 + (-1) \times 4 = -5$$

- If the matrix $C = AB$ is the product of two matrices, A and B, with order $m \times n$ and $n \times p$ respectively, then

$$c_{ij} = (i\text{th row of } A) \cdot (j\text{th column of } B)$$

$$= (a_{i1}\ a_{i2}\ a_{i3} \dots a_{in}) \begin{pmatrix} b_{1j} \\ b_{2j} \\ b_{3j} \\ \vdots \\ b_{nj} \end{pmatrix}$$

$$= a_{i1}b_{1j} + a_{i2}b_{2j} + a_{i3}b_{3j} + \dots + a_{in}b_{nj}$$

$$= \sum_{k=1}^{n} a_{ik}b_{kj}$$

This definition will only work when the number of columns in A is the same as the number of rows of B.

This is a necessary condition for A and B to be compatible for multiplication.

A and B might be compatible to form the product AB yet not compatible to form the product BA.

The product of an $m \times n$ with an $n \times p$ matrix is an $m \times p$ matrix.
for example the product of a 2×3 with a 3×1 matrix is a 2×1 matrix.
This is often likened to matching dominoes:

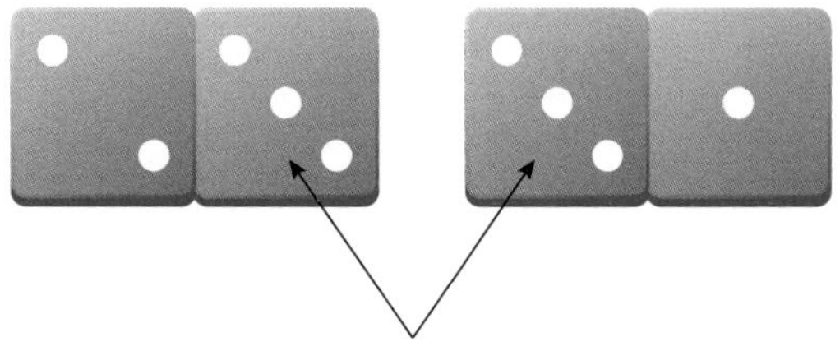

These have to be the same to match dominoes

which effectively produces this.

Example 1

Evaluate $\begin{pmatrix} 8 & 6 \\ -1 & 3 \end{pmatrix} \begin{pmatrix} 2 & 4 & 5 \\ 7 & 1 & -2 \end{pmatrix}$.

Note that the matrices, a $2 \times \mathbf{2}$ and a $\mathbf{2} \times 3$, are compatible and that the product will be a 2×3 matrix.

$$\begin{pmatrix} 8 & 6 \\ -1 & 3 \end{pmatrix} \begin{pmatrix} 2 & 4 & 5 \\ 7 & 1 & -2 \end{pmatrix} = \begin{pmatrix} 8 \times 2 + 6 \times 7 & 8 \times 4 + 6 \times 1 & 8 \times 5 + 6 \times (-2) \\ (-1) \times 2 + 3 \times 7 & (-1) \times 4 + 3 \times 1 & (-1) \times 5 + 3 \times (-2) \end{pmatrix}$$

$$= \begin{pmatrix} 58 & 38 & 28 \\ 19 & -1 & -11 \end{pmatrix}$$

Exercise 13.3

1 Evaluate

a $(2\ \ 1)\begin{pmatrix} 1 \\ 3 \end{pmatrix}$

b $(6\ \ 2)\begin{pmatrix} -1 \\ 5 \end{pmatrix}$

c $(1\ \ 2\ \ 3)\begin{pmatrix} 3 \\ 2 \\ 1 \end{pmatrix}$

d $(2\ \ 1\ \ 0)\begin{pmatrix} 0 \\ 1 \\ 2 \end{pmatrix}$

e $(2\ \ 2\ \ 3\ \ -1)\begin{pmatrix} -1 \\ -1 \\ 0 \\ 1 \end{pmatrix}$

f $(6\ \ 8\ \ 4\ \ 2)\begin{pmatrix} 1 \\ 3 \\ 5 \\ 7 \end{pmatrix}$

g $(2\ \ 3)\begin{pmatrix} x \\ y \end{pmatrix}$

h $(2\ \ 3\ \ -4)\begin{pmatrix} x \\ y \\ z \end{pmatrix}$

2 Evaluate each matrix product.

a $\begin{pmatrix}2 & 1\\3 & 4\end{pmatrix}\begin{pmatrix}1\\2\end{pmatrix}$ b $\begin{pmatrix}3 & 1\\4 & 3\end{pmatrix}\begin{pmatrix}-1\\2\end{pmatrix}$ c $\begin{pmatrix}2 & -1\\4 & 3\end{pmatrix}\begin{pmatrix}-2\\1\end{pmatrix}$

d $\begin{pmatrix}0 & 1\\1 & 0\end{pmatrix}\begin{pmatrix}2\\5\end{pmatrix}$ e $\begin{pmatrix}1 & 1\\0 & -1\end{pmatrix}\begin{pmatrix}3\\5\end{pmatrix}$ f $\begin{pmatrix}2 & 3\\4 & -1\end{pmatrix}\begin{pmatrix}5\\-7\end{pmatrix}$

g $\begin{pmatrix}2 & 3\\-1 & 5\end{pmatrix}\begin{pmatrix}x\\y\end{pmatrix}$ h $\begin{pmatrix}2 & -1\\3 & 7\end{pmatrix}\begin{pmatrix}p\\q\end{pmatrix}$ i $\begin{pmatrix}1 & 2\\-1 & 1\end{pmatrix}\begin{pmatrix}2 & -2\\2 & -1\end{pmatrix}$

j $\begin{pmatrix}2 & 0\\4 & 1\end{pmatrix}\begin{pmatrix}0 & -2\\1 & 2\end{pmatrix}$ k $\begin{pmatrix}2 & 1 & 3\\3 & 1 & 2\end{pmatrix}\begin{pmatrix}2\\1\\1\end{pmatrix}$ l $\begin{pmatrix}3 & 1 & 1\\-1 & 1 & 2\end{pmatrix}\begin{pmatrix}1 & 0\\-1 & 2\\0 & 1\end{pmatrix}$

m $\begin{pmatrix}1 & 3 & 2\\-2 & 0 & 1\\4 & 2 & 3\end{pmatrix}\begin{pmatrix}1\\-1\\2\end{pmatrix}$ n $\begin{pmatrix}1 & 1 & 0\\2 & 0 & 1\\3 & 4 & 5\end{pmatrix}\begin{pmatrix}2\\-2\\1\end{pmatrix}$ o $\begin{pmatrix}1 & 1 & 0\\2 & 0 & 1\\3 & 4 & 5\end{pmatrix}\begin{pmatrix}2 & 1\\-2 & 2\\1 & 0\end{pmatrix}$

p $\begin{pmatrix}1 & 0 & 0\\0 & 1 & 0\\0 & 0 & 1\end{pmatrix}\begin{pmatrix}p\\q\\r\end{pmatrix}$

3 Simplify these matrix expressions.

a $\begin{pmatrix}\cos\theta & \sin\theta\\\sin\theta & -\cos\theta\end{pmatrix}\begin{pmatrix}\cos\theta\\\sin\theta\end{pmatrix}$ b $\begin{pmatrix}\cos\theta & -\sin\theta\\\sin\theta & \cos\theta\end{pmatrix}\begin{pmatrix}\sin\theta\\\cos\theta\end{pmatrix}$ c $\begin{pmatrix}\cos\theta & \sin\theta\\\sin\theta & -\cos\theta\end{pmatrix}\begin{pmatrix}\cos\theta & \sin\theta\\\sin\theta & -\cos\theta\end{pmatrix}$

4 Given that $A = \begin{pmatrix}1 & 2\\-1 & 1\end{pmatrix}$ calculate a A^2 b A^3

5 Express each product as a single matrix.

a $\begin{pmatrix}1 & 2\\2 & 1\end{pmatrix}\begin{pmatrix}3 & 1\\-1 & 2\end{pmatrix}$ b $\begin{pmatrix}1 & 2\\4 & -1\end{pmatrix}\begin{pmatrix}2 & -1\\1 & 3\end{pmatrix}$ c $\begin{pmatrix}1 & 2\\5 & 7\end{pmatrix}\begin{pmatrix}-1 & 2\\3 & -2\end{pmatrix}$

d $\begin{pmatrix}0 & 1\\2 & 1\end{pmatrix}\begin{pmatrix}1 & 2\\-1 & 3\end{pmatrix}$ e $\begin{pmatrix}0 & 1\\1 & 0\end{pmatrix}\begin{pmatrix}2 & 7\\1 & 3\end{pmatrix}$ f $\begin{pmatrix}1 & 3\\2 & -1\end{pmatrix}\begin{pmatrix}a & b\\c & d\end{pmatrix}$

13.4 Properties of matrix multiplication

The following exercise explores the properties of matrix multiplication.

Exercise 13.4

1 Express each product as a single matrix.

a i $\begin{pmatrix}1 & 3\\0 & 2\end{pmatrix}\begin{pmatrix}2 & 1\\-1 & 1\end{pmatrix}$ ii $\begin{pmatrix}2 & 1\\-1 & 1\end{pmatrix}\begin{pmatrix}1 & 3\\0 & 2\end{pmatrix}$

b i $\begin{pmatrix}2 & 0\\0 & 2\end{pmatrix}\begin{pmatrix}3 & 1\\1 & -1\end{pmatrix}$ ii $\begin{pmatrix}3 & 1\\1 & -1\end{pmatrix}\begin{pmatrix}2 & 0\\0 & 2\end{pmatrix}$

c i $\begin{pmatrix}4 & -2\\1 & 2\end{pmatrix}\begin{pmatrix}3 & -2\\0 & -3\end{pmatrix}$ ii $\begin{pmatrix}3 & -2\\0 & -3\end{pmatrix}\begin{pmatrix}4 & -2\\1 & 2\end{pmatrix}$

d i $\begin{pmatrix}1 & 0\\0 & -1\end{pmatrix}\begin{pmatrix}-1 & 0\\0 & 1\end{pmatrix}$ ii $\begin{pmatrix}-1 & 0\\0 & 1\end{pmatrix}\begin{pmatrix}1 & 0\\0 & -1\end{pmatrix}$

2 a In general, does the commutative law hold for 2×2 matrix multiplication?

b In general, does the commutative law hold for matrix multiplication?

c Are there any matrices for which $AB = BA$?

3 $B = \begin{pmatrix}2 & 1\\-1 & 1\end{pmatrix}$ and $A = \begin{pmatrix}3 & 1\\0 & 1\end{pmatrix}$

a When we form the product AB, we call it **pre-multiplying** B by A.
Find this product.

b Forming the product BA is called **post-multiplying** B by A.
Find this product also.

c Confirm, for 2×2 matrices, that pre-multiplying B by A and post-multiplying B by A are in general different by considering the matrices

$$A = \begin{pmatrix} a_{11} & a_{12} \\ a_{21} & a_{22} \end{pmatrix} \text{ and } B = \begin{pmatrix} b_{11} & b_{12} \\ b_{21} & b_{22} \end{pmatrix}$$

4 Express each of these as a single matrix.

a **i** $\begin{pmatrix} 1 & 0 \\ 0 & 1 \end{pmatrix}\begin{pmatrix} 2 & 3 \\ -5 & 6 \end{pmatrix}$ **ii** $\begin{pmatrix} 2 & 3 \\ -5 & 6 \end{pmatrix}\begin{pmatrix} 1 & 0 \\ 0 & 1 \end{pmatrix}$

b **i** $\begin{pmatrix} 1 & 0 \\ 0 & 1 \end{pmatrix}\begin{pmatrix} 4 & 0 \\ 5 & -1 \end{pmatrix}$ **ii** $\begin{pmatrix} 4 & 0 \\ 5 & -1 \end{pmatrix}\begin{pmatrix} 1 & 0 \\ 0 & 1 \end{pmatrix}$

c **i** $\begin{pmatrix} 1 & 0 \\ 0 & 1 \end{pmatrix}\begin{pmatrix} a_{11} & a_{12} \\ a_{21} & a_{22} \end{pmatrix}$ **ii** $\begin{pmatrix} a_{11} & a_{12} \\ a_{21} & a_{22} \end{pmatrix}\begin{pmatrix} 1 & 0 \\ 0 & 1 \end{pmatrix}$

5 **a** From the results of Question 4 we see that $\begin{pmatrix} 1 & 0 \\ 0 & 1 \end{pmatrix}$ is the identity element for 2×2 matrix multiplication.

By considering the matrix $\begin{pmatrix} a_{11} & a_{12} & a_{13} \\ a_{21} & a_{22} & a_{23} \\ a_{31} & a_{32} & a_{33} \end{pmatrix}$ show that $\begin{pmatrix} 1 & 0 & 0 \\ 0 & 1 & 0 \\ 0 & 0 & 1 \end{pmatrix}$ is the identity element for 3×3 matrix multiplication.

b Suggest the corresponding element for the 4×4 matrices and test it on a suitable matrix.

6 **a** Given $A = \begin{pmatrix} 1 & 2 \\ 0 & 1 \end{pmatrix}$, $B = \begin{pmatrix} 3 & 5 \\ 1 & 6 \end{pmatrix}$ and $C = \begin{pmatrix} 2 & -1 \\ 8 & 3 \end{pmatrix}$, evaluate

i AB **ii** $(AB)C$ **iii** BC **iv** $A(BC)$

b Comment on the associative law and 2×2 matrix multiplication.

c Prove it indeed holds for any 2×2 matrix by considering

$A = \begin{pmatrix} a_{11} & a_{12} \\ a_{21} & a_{22} \end{pmatrix}$ etc.

7 **a** Given that $A = \begin{pmatrix} 3 & 1 \\ 4 & 5 \end{pmatrix}$ and $B = \begin{pmatrix} 1 & -2 \\ 1 & 3 \end{pmatrix}$ evaluate

i A' **ii** B' **iii** AB **iv** $(AB)'$ **v** $B'A'$ **vi** $(BA)'$

b Complete the equation $(AB)' = \ldots$

c Show that this is generally true for 2×2 matrices using

$$A = \begin{pmatrix} a_{11} & a_{12} \\ a_{21} & a_{22} \end{pmatrix} \text{ and } B = \begin{pmatrix} b_{11} & b_{12} \\ b_{21} & b_{22} \end{pmatrix}$$

8 **a** Using $A = \begin{pmatrix} 1 & 5 \\ 3 & 2 \end{pmatrix}$, $B = \begin{pmatrix} 2 & 0 \\ 4 & 1 \end{pmatrix}$ and $C = \begin{pmatrix} 1 & -1 \\ 2 & 4 \end{pmatrix}$ demonstrate that $A(B + C) = AB + AC$.

b Working with general 2×2 matrices, prove that matrix multiplication is distributive over matrix addition.

Summary

- $AB \neq BA$: the commutative law does not hold in general for matrix multiplication.
- $(AB)' = B'A'$: a transpose reversal rule.
- $A(BC) = (AB)C = ABC$: the associative law holds for matrix multiplication.
- $A(B + C) = AB + AC$: the distributive law holds.
- The identity element is denoted by I.

$$I_{2\times2} = \begin{pmatrix} 1 & 0 \\ 0 & 1 \end{pmatrix} \text{ and } I_{3\times3} = \begin{pmatrix} 1 & 0 & 0 \\ 0 & 1 & 0 \\ 0 & 0 & 1 \end{pmatrix}$$

13.5 Further properties of matrix multiplication

Example 2

Simplify $A(A + B) - B(B - A)$.

$$A(A + B) - B(B - A) = AA + AB - BB + BA$$
$$= A^2 + AB - B^2 + BA$$

No further simplification is possible as $AB \neq BA$ in general.

Example 3

If $Q = \begin{pmatrix} 2 & -1 \\ 3 & 5 \end{pmatrix}$

a show that $Q^2 = aQ + bI$ for some $a, b \in R$

b hence show that $Q^3 = 36Q - 91I$.

a $Q^2 = \begin{pmatrix} 2 & -1 \\ 3 & 5 \end{pmatrix}\begin{pmatrix} 2 & -1 \\ 3 & 5 \end{pmatrix} = \begin{pmatrix} 1 & -7 \\ 21 & 22 \end{pmatrix}$ also $Q^2 = a\begin{pmatrix} 2 & -1 \\ 3 & 5 \end{pmatrix} + b\begin{pmatrix} 1 & 0 \\ 0 & 1 \end{pmatrix} = \begin{pmatrix} 2a + b & -a \\ 3a & 5a + b \end{pmatrix}$

Equating matrices, and hence entries, gives $-a = -7 \Leftrightarrow a = 7$; $2a + b = 1 \Leftrightarrow b = -13$ $\quad Q^2 = 7Q - 13I$

b $Q^3 = Q \cdot Q^2 = Q(7Q - 13I) = 7Q^2 - 13QI$ $\quad$ Using result from part **a**

$= 7(7Q - 13I) - 13Q = 49Q - 91I - 13Q$ $\quad$ Using result again

$= 36Q - 91I$

This technique can be used, repeatedly, to find powers of a matrix.

Example 4

A matrix A is said to be **orthogonal** if $A'A = I = AA'$.

Prove that $A = \begin{pmatrix} 0.8 & 0.6 \\ -0.6 & 0.8 \end{pmatrix}$ is orthogonal.

$A = \begin{pmatrix} 0.8 & 0.6 \\ -0.6 & 0.8 \end{pmatrix} \Rightarrow A' = \begin{pmatrix} 0.8 & -0.6 \\ 0.6 & 0.8 \end{pmatrix}$

$A'A = \begin{pmatrix} 0.8 & -0.6 \\ 0.6 & 0.8 \end{pmatrix}\begin{pmatrix} 0.8 & 0.6 \\ -0.6 & 0.8 \end{pmatrix} = \begin{pmatrix} 1 & 0 \\ 0 & 1 \end{pmatrix} = I$

$\Rightarrow A$ is orthogonal.

Exercise 13.5

1 Simplify

a $\begin{pmatrix} 4 & 1 & 5 \\ 2 & 1 & 3 \end{pmatrix}\begin{pmatrix} 1 & 3 \\ 3 & 2 \\ 3 & 1 \end{pmatrix}$ **b** $\begin{pmatrix} 3 & 1 & 4 \\ 1 & 2 & 5 \end{pmatrix}\begin{pmatrix} 4 & 1 & 2 \\ 1 & 3 & 1 \\ 7 & 4 & 3 \end{pmatrix}$ **c** $\begin{pmatrix} 1 & 0 & -1 \\ 1 & 1 & -1 \\ -1 & 1 & 0 \end{pmatrix}\begin{pmatrix} 2 & -1 & -1 \\ 2 & 1 & -1 \\ 0 & 2 & 2 \end{pmatrix}$

2 Given $A = \begin{pmatrix} 4 & 2 & 1 \\ 3 & 0 & -2 \\ 6 & 5 & 1 \end{pmatrix}$, $B = \begin{pmatrix} 4 & 7 & 2 \\ 1 & -1 & 0 \\ 2 & 3 & -1 \end{pmatrix}$, $C = \begin{pmatrix} 2 & 1 & 3 \\ 0 & 1 & -1 \\ -2 & 3 & 0 \end{pmatrix}$ and

$D = \begin{pmatrix} 2 & 1 & 0 \\ 3 & 0 & -1 \\ 2 & 4 & 7 \end{pmatrix}$ evaluate **a** AB **b** CD **c** $AB + D^2$ **d** C^2 **e** C^3 **f** $AB + CD$

3 a Given that $R = \begin{pmatrix} 2 & -1 & 1 \\ -3 & 4 & -3 \\ -5 & 5 & -4 \end{pmatrix}$ and $S = \begin{pmatrix} -1 & 1 & -1 \\ 3 & -3 & 3 \\ 5 & -5 & 5 \end{pmatrix}$, show that $RS = O$.

b Does $SR = O$?

4 Given that $A = \begin{pmatrix} 2 & 1 \\ -1 & 3 \end{pmatrix}$ and $B = \begin{pmatrix} 3 & 1 \\ -2 & 4 \end{pmatrix}$ find which of these are true.

a $AB = BA$

b $A^2 - B^2 = (A + B)(A - B)$

c $(A + B)^2 = A^2 + 2AB + B^2$

d $(A - B)^2 = A^2 - 2AB + B^2$

5 Explore the claim that for any matrix A, both AA' and $A'A$ are symmetric.

6 a Given that $A = \begin{pmatrix} 1 & 2 \\ 3 & 1 \end{pmatrix}$ and $I = \begin{pmatrix} 1 & 0 \\ 0 & 1 \end{pmatrix}$ show that $A^2 = 5I + 2A$.

b Multiplying this equation by A, express A^3 in the form $aI + bA$.
[Hint: you know an expression for A^2.]

7 a If $A = \begin{pmatrix} 3 & 4 \\ 2 & 1 \end{pmatrix}$ show that $A^2 = 4A + 5I$.

b Hence show that $A^3 = 21A + 20I$.

8 a If $B = \begin{pmatrix} 2 & 3 \\ -1 & 2 \end{pmatrix}$ show that $B^2 = 4B - 7I$.

b Express B^3 in the form $aB + bI$ where $a, b \in R$.

9 a Show that $B^2 = \begin{pmatrix} 17 & 8 \\ 16 & 9 \end{pmatrix}$ where $B = \begin{pmatrix} 3 & 2 \\ 4 & 1 \end{pmatrix}$.

b By considering the equation $a\begin{pmatrix} 1 & 0 \\ 0 & 1 \end{pmatrix} + b\begin{pmatrix} 3 & 2 \\ 4 & 1 \end{pmatrix} = \begin{pmatrix} 17 & 8 \\ 16 & 9 \end{pmatrix}$
show that $B^2 = aI + bB$ and find the values of a and b.

c Use this to express B^3, B^4 and B^5 in terms of I and B only.

10 Given $C = \begin{pmatrix} 2 & 5 \\ -3 & 1 \end{pmatrix}$ find p and q such that $C^2 = pC + qI$.

11 Given $A = \begin{pmatrix} a_{11} & a_{12} \\ a_{21} & a_{22} \end{pmatrix}$ and the fact that $A^2 = pI + qA$, express p and q in terms of the entries of A.

12 $E = \begin{pmatrix} 1 & 2 & 3 \\ 2 & 1 & 0 \\ 1 & 0 & 1 \end{pmatrix}$

a Calculate the entries of the first row of E^2.

b Find expressions for the first row of the matrix defined by $aI + bE$ where $a, b \in$ R.

c By considering the second row, show that $E^2 \neq aI + bE$, for any values of a and b.

d Find E^3 and show that $E^3 - 3E^2 - 4E + 6I = O$ (the zero matrix).

13 Given $F = \begin{pmatrix} 1 & 1 & 1 \\ 1 & 1 & 0 \\ 1 & 0 & 0 \end{pmatrix}$, find F^2, F^3 and $a, b, c \in$ R such that $F^3 = aF^2 + bF + cI$.

14 If $G = \begin{pmatrix} a^2 & ab & ac \\ ab & b^2 & bc \\ ac & bc & c^2 \end{pmatrix}$ and $a^2 + b^2 + c^2 = 1$, prove that $G^2 = G$.

15 Given $I = \begin{pmatrix} 1 & 0 \\ 0 & 1 \end{pmatrix}$, $J = \begin{pmatrix} 0 & 1 \\ 1 & 0 \end{pmatrix}$, $K = \begin{pmatrix} 1 & 0 \\ 0 & -1 \end{pmatrix}$ and $L = \begin{pmatrix} 0 & 1 \\ -1 & 0 \end{pmatrix}$

a show that each of I, J, K and L is orthogonal.

b show that $JK = -L$ and similarly evaluate KL, LJ, KJ, LK, JL.

16 Show that if A and B are orthogonal then so is AB.

13.6 The determinant of a 2 × 2 matrix

Consider the system of equations

$$ax + by = e \qquad (1)$$
$$cx + dy = f \qquad (2)$$

$$(1) \times \frac{c}{a} \quad cx + \frac{cb}{a}y = \frac{ce}{a} \qquad (3)$$

$$(2) - (3) \quad 0 + dy - \frac{cb}{a}y = f - \frac{ce}{a}$$

$$\Rightarrow \left(\frac{ad - bc}{a}\right)y = \frac{af - ce}{a}$$

$$\Rightarrow y = \frac{af - ce}{ad - bc}$$

Substitute this into Equation (1) and we get $x = \frac{de - bc}{ad - bc}$.

The system can be expressed as a matrix equation

$$\begin{pmatrix} ax + by \\ cx + dy \end{pmatrix} = \begin{pmatrix} e \\ f \end{pmatrix}$$ Equal entries implies equal matrices.

Using the definition of matrix multiplication we get

$$\begin{pmatrix} a & b \\ c & d \end{pmatrix}\begin{pmatrix} x \\ y \end{pmatrix} = \begin{pmatrix} e \\ f \end{pmatrix}$$

Now look at the solution to the system: $x = \frac{de - bc}{ad - bc}, y = \frac{af - ce}{ad - bc}$.

We can see that a solution to the system $\begin{pmatrix} a & b \\ c & d \end{pmatrix}\begin{pmatrix} x \\ y \end{pmatrix} = \begin{pmatrix} e \\ f \end{pmatrix}$ exists if and only if $ad - bc \neq 0$.

Caley called this number, $ad - bc$, the **determinant** of the matrix $\begin{pmatrix} a & b \\ c & d \end{pmatrix}$.

The determinant of the matrix A is denoted by $\det(A)$ or by $|A|$.

The determinant of $A = \begin{pmatrix} a & b \\ c & d \end{pmatrix}$ is written as $\begin{vmatrix} a & b \\ c & d \end{vmatrix} = ad - bc$.

Exercise 13.6

1 Calculate the determinant of each matrix.

a $\begin{pmatrix} 3 & 1 \\ -2 & 4 \end{pmatrix}$ b $\begin{pmatrix} 12 & 3 \\ 8 & 2 \end{pmatrix}$ c $\begin{pmatrix} 5 & -2 \\ -3 & -1 \end{pmatrix}$ d $\begin{pmatrix} 1 & 0 \\ 3 & 7 \end{pmatrix}$

e $\begin{pmatrix} -4 & -5 \\ 2 & -1 \end{pmatrix}$ f $\begin{pmatrix} 0 & 1 \\ 1 & 1 \end{pmatrix}$ g $\begin{pmatrix} 7 & 1 \\ -2 & -1 \end{pmatrix}$ h $\begin{pmatrix} \sin x & -\cos x \\ \cos x & \sin x \end{pmatrix}$

2 Find x in each case.

a $\begin{vmatrix} 2 & 1 \\ 1 & x \end{vmatrix} = 7$ b $\begin{vmatrix} 3 & -1 \\ 2x & 4 \end{vmatrix} = 26$ c $\begin{vmatrix} 3x & 1 \\ 1 & x \end{vmatrix} = 47$ d $\begin{vmatrix} 2x & x \\ -3 & x \end{vmatrix} = 2$

e $\begin{vmatrix} x & x \\ 3 & x \end{vmatrix} = 10$ f $\begin{vmatrix} \sin x^\circ & -1 \\ 1 & 1 \end{vmatrix} = 0, 0 \leq x \leq 360$ g $\begin{vmatrix} e^x & e \\ 1 & e^x \end{vmatrix} = 0$

3 For each of these systems of equations

i express the system of equations as a matrix equation of the form $AX = B$ where $X = \begin{pmatrix} x \\ y \end{pmatrix}$

ii by considering $\det(A)$, determine whether the system has a solution.

a $x + y = 1$
$3x + 2y = 4$

b $4x + y = 2$
$8x + 2y = 3$

c $5x - 2y = 2$
$10x - 4y = 1$

d $5x - y = 1$
$3x - 2y = 0$

4 Study each system of equations and say for what value(s) of k the system has no solution.

a $3x + ky = 3$
$x + 2y = 1$

b $5x - 2ky = 4$
$3x + 6y = -2$

c $6x - 2ky = -1$
$kx - 12y = 0$

d $kx + (k - 4)y = 5$
$2x + ky = 3$

13.7 The inverse of a 2 × 2 matrix

Under *addition* the set of 2×2 matrices has an identity element, namely $O = \begin{pmatrix} 0 & 0 \\ 0 & 0 \end{pmatrix}$, because

$$\begin{pmatrix} 0 & 0 \\ 0 & 0 \end{pmatrix} + \begin{pmatrix} a & b \\ c & d \end{pmatrix} = \begin{pmatrix} a & b \\ c & d \end{pmatrix} + \begin{pmatrix} 0 & 0 \\ 0 & 0 \end{pmatrix} = \begin{pmatrix} a & b \\ c & d \end{pmatrix}$$

Also, each element $A = \begin{pmatrix} a & b \\ c & d \end{pmatrix}$ has an **additive inverse**, namely $-A = \begin{pmatrix} -a & -b \\ -c & -d \end{pmatrix}$, because $A + (-A) = O$.

Under *multiplication* the set of 2×2 matrices has an identity element, namely $I = \begin{pmatrix} 1 & 0 \\ 0 & 1 \end{pmatrix}$, because

$$\begin{pmatrix} 1 & 0 \\ 0 & 1 \end{pmatrix}\begin{pmatrix} a & b \\ c & d \end{pmatrix} = \begin{pmatrix} a & b \\ c & d \end{pmatrix}\begin{pmatrix} 1 & 0 \\ 0 & 1 \end{pmatrix} = \begin{pmatrix} a & b \\ c & d \end{pmatrix}$$

Does a **multiplicative inverse** for $\begin{pmatrix} a & b \\ c & d \end{pmatrix}$ exist?

Is there a matrix $\begin{pmatrix} p & q \\ r & s \end{pmatrix}$ such that

$$\begin{pmatrix} a & b \\ c & d \end{pmatrix}\begin{pmatrix} p & q \\ r & s \end{pmatrix} = \begin{pmatrix} p & q \\ r & s \end{pmatrix}\begin{pmatrix} a & b \\ c & d \end{pmatrix} = I?$$

Such a matrix would satisfy the equation $\begin{pmatrix} a & b \\ c & d \end{pmatrix}\begin{pmatrix} p & q \\ r & s \end{pmatrix} = \begin{pmatrix} 1 & 0 \\ 0 & 1 \end{pmatrix}$.

Thus $\begin{pmatrix} ap + br & aq + bs \\ cp + dr & cq + ds \end{pmatrix} = \begin{pmatrix} 1 & 0 \\ 0 & 1 \end{pmatrix}$ and equating entries gives the system of equations

$$\begin{aligned} ap + br &= 1 \quad (1) \\ aq + bs &= 0 \quad (2) \\ cp + dr &= 0 \quad (3) \\ cq + ds &= 1 \quad (4) \end{aligned}$$

which we solve for p, q, r and s in terms of a, b, c and d.

If $c \neq 0$, equation (3) gives $p = -\frac{dr}{c}$.

Substituting in equation (1) we get $-\frac{adr}{c} + br = 1$ so

$$\boxed{r = -\frac{c}{ad - bc} \text{ and } p = \frac{d}{ad - bc},\ ad - bc \neq 0}$$

If $c = 0$, equation (3) gives $r = 0 = -\frac{c}{ad - bc}$ and equation (1) gives $p = \frac{1}{a} = \frac{d}{ad - bc}$

($ad - bc \neq 0$ and $c = 0$ requires $d \neq 0$)

If $a \neq 0$, equation (2) gives $q = -\frac{bs}{a}$.

Substituting in equation (4) we get $-\frac{bcs}{a} + ds = 1$ so

$$\boxed{s = \frac{a}{ad - bc} \text{ and } q = -\frac{b}{ad - bc},\ ad - bc \neq 0}$$

If $a = 0$, equation (2) gives $s = 0 = \frac{a}{ad - bc}$ and equation (4) gives $q = \frac{1}{c} = -\frac{b}{ad - bc}$

($ad - bc \neq 0$ and $a = 0$ requires $b \neq 0$)

Thus $\begin{pmatrix} p & q \\ r & s \end{pmatrix} = \begin{pmatrix} \frac{d}{ad-bc} & -\frac{b}{ad-bc} \\ -\frac{c}{ad-bc} & \frac{a}{ad-bc} \end{pmatrix} = \frac{1}{ad-bc}\begin{pmatrix} d & -b \\ -c & a \end{pmatrix}$, $ad - bc \neq 0$

When $ad - bc \neq 0$ the matrix $A = \begin{pmatrix} a & b \\ c & d \end{pmatrix}$ has an inverse denoted by A^{-1}

such that $A^{-1} = \frac{1}{ad-bc}\begin{pmatrix} d & -b \\ -c & a \end{pmatrix}$.

Notes

- The matrix $\begin{pmatrix} d & -b \\ -c & a \end{pmatrix}$ is called the **adjoint** or **adjugate** of A, denoted by adj(A).
  Thus we may write $A^{-1} = \frac{\text{adj}(A)}{\det(A)}$.
- When $|A| = ad - bc = 0$ the inverse is undefined.
  The matrix is then called **singular**.
  When $|A| \neq 0$ then A is non-singular and invertible because the inverse is defined.

Example 5

Find the inverse of the matrix $A = \begin{pmatrix} 2 & 4 \\ 1 & 3 \end{pmatrix}$.

$\det(A) = 2 \times 3 - 1 \times 4 = 2$ ($\neq 0$ and so an inverse exists)

$\text{adj}(A) = \begin{pmatrix} 3 & -4 \\ -1 & 2 \end{pmatrix}$ and thus $A^{-1} = \frac{1}{2}\begin{pmatrix} 3 & -4 \\ -1 & 2 \end{pmatrix} = \begin{pmatrix} \frac{3}{2} & -2 \\ -\frac{1}{2} & 1 \end{pmatrix}$

Example 6

A non-singular matrix B satisfies the equation $B^2 = 3B - 2I$.

Show that $B^{-1} = \frac{3}{2}I - \frac{1}{2}B$.

$B^2 = 3B - 2I \Rightarrow B^{-1}B^2 = 3B^{-1}B - 2B^{-1}I$

$\Rightarrow B^{-1}BB = 3I - 2B^{-1}$

$\Rightarrow IB = 3I - 2B^{-1}$

$\Rightarrow 2B^{-1} = 3I - B$

$\Rightarrow B^{-1} = \frac{3}{2}I - \frac{1}{2}B$

Example 7

Use matrix multiplication to solve the system of equations

$2x + 3y = 1$

$x - y = 3$

Expressing the system in matrix form we get

$\begin{pmatrix} 2x + 3y \\ x - y \end{pmatrix} = \begin{pmatrix} 1 \\ 3 \end{pmatrix} \Rightarrow \begin{pmatrix} 2 & 3 \\ 1 & -1 \end{pmatrix}\begin{pmatrix} x \\ y \end{pmatrix} = \begin{pmatrix} 1 \\ 3 \end{pmatrix}$

The inverse of $\begin{pmatrix} 2 & 3 \\ 1 & -1 \end{pmatrix}$ is $-\frac{1}{5}\begin{pmatrix} -1 & -3 \\ -1 & 2 \end{pmatrix}$.

Pre-multiplying both sides of the equation by the inverse of $\begin{pmatrix} 2 & 3 \\ 1 & -1 \end{pmatrix}$ we get

$-\frac{1}{5}\begin{pmatrix} -1 & -3 \\ -1 & 2 \end{pmatrix}\begin{pmatrix} 2 & 3 \\ 1 & -1 \end{pmatrix}\begin{pmatrix} x \\ y \end{pmatrix} = -\frac{1}{5}\begin{pmatrix} -1 & -3 \\ -1 & 2 \end{pmatrix}\begin{pmatrix} 1 \\ 3 \end{pmatrix}$

$\Rightarrow \begin{pmatrix} 1 & 0 \\ 0 & 1 \end{pmatrix} \begin{pmatrix} x \\ y \end{pmatrix} = -\frac{1}{5} \begin{pmatrix} -1 + (-9) \\ -1 + 6 \end{pmatrix}$

$\Rightarrow \begin{pmatrix} x \\ y \end{pmatrix} = \begin{pmatrix} 2 \\ -1 \end{pmatrix}$

giving the solution $x = 2, y = -1$.

Exercise 13.7

1 Find A^{-1}, the inverse of the matrix $A = \begin{pmatrix} 2 & 1 \\ 3 & 2 \end{pmatrix}$, and verify that $A^{-1}A = I = AA^{-1}$.

2 Find B^{-1}, the inverse of the matrix $B = \begin{pmatrix} 4 & 2 \\ 5 & 3 \end{pmatrix}$, and verify that $B^{-1}B = I = BB^{-1}$.

3 Find the inverse, where it exists, of each of these matrices.

a $\begin{pmatrix} 2 & 4 \\ 3 & 6 \end{pmatrix}$ b $\begin{pmatrix} 5 & 4 \\ 4 & 3 \end{pmatrix}$ c $\begin{pmatrix} 9 & 6 \\ 3 & 2 \end{pmatrix}$ d $\begin{pmatrix} 4 & -2 \\ -7 & 3 \end{pmatrix}$ e $\begin{pmatrix} 9 & 2 \\ 13 & 3 \end{pmatrix}$

f $\begin{pmatrix} 5 & 2 \\ 7 & 3 \end{pmatrix}$ g $\begin{pmatrix} 4 & -11 \\ -1 & 3 \end{pmatrix}$ h $\begin{pmatrix} -3 & 4 \\ 8 & -11 \end{pmatrix}$ i $\begin{pmatrix} 3 & 1 \\ 7 & 3 \end{pmatrix}$ j $\begin{pmatrix} 4 & 1 \\ 5 & 3 \end{pmatrix}$

k $\begin{pmatrix} 3 & 5 \\ 2 & 3 \end{pmatrix}$ l $\begin{pmatrix} 4 & 8 \\ 3 & 5 \end{pmatrix}$ m $\begin{pmatrix} 2 & 1 \\ 8 & 4 \end{pmatrix}$ n $\begin{pmatrix} 3 & -2 \\ 6 & 1 \end{pmatrix}$ o $\begin{pmatrix} 2 & 3 \\ -1 & 4 \end{pmatrix}$

p $\begin{pmatrix} 3 & -4 \\ -6 & 8 \end{pmatrix}$ q $\begin{pmatrix} -2 & -6 \\ 0 & -2 \end{pmatrix}$ r $\begin{pmatrix} 5 & -4 \\ -3 & 3 \end{pmatrix}$ s $\begin{pmatrix} -3 & -6 \\ 1 & -2 \end{pmatrix}$ t $\begin{pmatrix} 3 & -5 \\ -2 & 1 \end{pmatrix}$

4 Given $P = \begin{pmatrix} 4 & 3 \\ 1 & 1 \end{pmatrix}$ and $Q = \begin{pmatrix} 2 & 5 \\ -2 & -4 \end{pmatrix}$, evaluate

a PQ b QP c P^{-1} d Q^{-1}

e $(PQ)^{-1}$ f $P^{-1}Q^{-1}$ g $Q^{-1}P^{-1}$ h $(QP)^{-1}$

5 Given that $A = \begin{pmatrix} 2 & 5 \\ 1 & 3 \end{pmatrix}$ and $B = \begin{pmatrix} 7 & 2 \\ 4 & 1 \end{pmatrix}$, show that

a $A^{-1}B^{-1} = (BA)^{-1}$ b $(AB)^{-1} = B^{-1}A^{-1}$ c $|A|\,|B| = |AB|$

6 a Given that A and B are square matrices, simplify

i $A^{-1}B^{-1}BA$ ii $BAA^{-1}B^{-1}$ iii $B^{-1}A^{-1}AB$ iv $ABB^{-1}A^{-1}$

b What can be concluded from your answers?

7 Find the inverse of

a $\begin{pmatrix} a & -a \\ -a & 2a \end{pmatrix}$ b $\begin{pmatrix} 3x & 5x \\ 2x & 4x \end{pmatrix}$ c $\begin{pmatrix} 3t & t^3 \\ 2 & t^2 \end{pmatrix}$

d $\begin{pmatrix} \cos\theta & -\sin\theta \\ \sin\theta & \cos\theta \end{pmatrix}$ e $\begin{pmatrix} 1-x & x \\ -x & 1+x \end{pmatrix}$ f $\begin{pmatrix} a & a+1 \\ a-1 & a \end{pmatrix}$

8 For what values of k are these matrices singular?

a $\begin{pmatrix} 2 & 2 \\ 4 & k \end{pmatrix}$ b $\begin{pmatrix} 1 & 2k \\ 3 & 6 \end{pmatrix}$ c $\begin{pmatrix} 1-k & -1 \\ 3 & 1+k \end{pmatrix}$ d $\begin{pmatrix} 2+k & -6 \\ 4 & 3-k \end{pmatrix}$

9 Show that these matrices are their own inverse (that is, $A^{-1} = A$).

a $\begin{pmatrix} 1 & 0 \\ 0 & 1 \end{pmatrix}$ b $\begin{pmatrix} 0 & 1 \\ 1 & 0 \end{pmatrix}$ c $\begin{pmatrix} 1 & 0 \\ 0 & -1 \end{pmatrix}$ d $\begin{pmatrix} -1 & 0 \\ 0 & 1 \end{pmatrix}$ e $\begin{pmatrix} 0 & -1 \\ -1 & 0 \end{pmatrix}$

f $\begin{pmatrix} \sin\theta & \cos\theta \\ \cos\theta & -\sin\theta \end{pmatrix}$ g $\begin{pmatrix} \frac{4}{5} & \frac{3}{5} \\ \frac{3}{5} & -\frac{4}{5} \end{pmatrix}$

10 $A = \begin{pmatrix} 2 & 3 \\ 7 & 11 \end{pmatrix}$

a Show that $A^2 = 13A - I$.

b Hence show (without evaluating A^3 or A^{-1}) that

i $A^3 = 168A - 13I$ ii $A^{-1} = 13I - A$

11 For each of these systems of equations

i express the system of equations in the form $AX = B$

ii find the inverse of the matrix A

iii hence solve the system for x and y.

a $2x + y = 9$, $3x + 2y = 16$

b $4x - 3y = 11$, $x + y = 1$

c $5x + 4y = 10$, $4x - 3y = 39$

d $7x + 4y = -1$, $3x + 2y = 1$

e $11x + 4y = 17$, $2x + y = 5$

f $5x - 2y = 34$, $3x - 2y = 18$

12 Solve these matrix equations for X where X is the 2×1 column matrix $\begin{pmatrix} x \\ y \end{pmatrix}$.

a $\begin{pmatrix} 3 & 2 \\ 4 & 3 \end{pmatrix}X = \begin{pmatrix} 1 \\ 2 \end{pmatrix}$

b $\begin{pmatrix} 5 & 3 \\ 3 & 2 \end{pmatrix}X = \begin{pmatrix} 5 \\ 2 \end{pmatrix}$

c $\begin{pmatrix} 4 & 5 \\ 2 & 3 \end{pmatrix}X = \begin{pmatrix} 7 \\ 5 \end{pmatrix}$

d $\begin{pmatrix} 5 & 1 \\ 7 & 2 \end{pmatrix}X = \begin{pmatrix} -9 \\ -6 \end{pmatrix}$

13.8 Further properties of matrices

The following exercises explores further properties of matrices.

Exercise 13.8

1 $B = \begin{pmatrix} 5 & 4 \\ 6 & 5 \end{pmatrix}$

a Show that $B^2 = 10B - I$.

b Hence show (without evaluating B^3 or B^{-1}) that

i $B^3 = 99B - 10I$ ii $B^{-1} = 10I - B$

2 Prove that $C^2 = 4C - 3I \Rightarrow C^{-1} = \frac{4}{3}I - \frac{1}{3}C$

3 Find the two possible 2×2 matrices A for which $|A| = 1$ and $A = A^{-1}$.

4 Find the four possible 2×2 matrices A, with integer entries, for which $|A| = 1$ and $A^T = A^{-1}$.

5 $P = \begin{pmatrix} 4 & 2 \\ 13 & 6 \end{pmatrix}$

a Find P^{-1}.

b Show that P^2 is the inverse of $(P^{-1})^2$.

6 Solve these matrix equations for the 2×2 matrix X.

a $\begin{pmatrix} 3 & 1 \\ 2 & 1 \end{pmatrix}X = \begin{pmatrix} 1 & 0 \\ 4 & 1 \end{pmatrix}$

b $\begin{pmatrix} 3 & -5 \\ -1 & 2 \end{pmatrix}X = \begin{pmatrix} 2 & -1 \\ 3 & 2 \end{pmatrix}$

c $\begin{pmatrix} 2 & -1 \\ 2 & 5 \end{pmatrix}X = \begin{pmatrix} 3 & 6 \\ 9 & -3 \end{pmatrix}$

d $X\begin{pmatrix} 3 & 4 \\ 1 & 3 \end{pmatrix} = \begin{pmatrix} 5 & 10 \\ -1 & -3 \end{pmatrix}$

e $X\begin{pmatrix} 6 & 8 \\ 1 & 2 \end{pmatrix} = \begin{pmatrix} 13 & 18 \\ -3 & -2 \end{pmatrix}$

f $X\begin{pmatrix} 2 & 1 \\ 0 & 3 \end{pmatrix} = \begin{pmatrix} 2 & 13 \\ -4 & 13 \end{pmatrix}$

7 Solve for X, where X is a matrix.

a $\begin{pmatrix} 3 & 2 \\ 1 & 0 \end{pmatrix}X - \begin{pmatrix} 6 & 20 \\ 4 & 10 \end{pmatrix} = \begin{pmatrix} -2 & 6 \\ -2 & -2 \end{pmatrix}$

b $\begin{pmatrix} 2 & 2 \\ -2 & -3 \end{pmatrix}X + \begin{pmatrix} -5 & -18 \\ 8 & 20 \end{pmatrix} = \begin{pmatrix} 5 & 10 \\ -6 & -17 \end{pmatrix}$

c $\begin{pmatrix} 16 & 15 \\ 14 & 13 \end{pmatrix} - X\begin{pmatrix} 3 & 2 \\ 3 & 3 \end{pmatrix} = \begin{pmatrix} 1 & 2 \\ -1 & 2 \end{pmatrix}$

d $\begin{pmatrix} 3 & 1 \\ -2 & -5 \end{pmatrix} + X\begin{pmatrix} 3 & 5 \\ 2 & 3 \end{pmatrix} = \begin{pmatrix} 3 & 4 \\ 4 & 6 \end{pmatrix}$

8 $A = \begin{pmatrix} 2 & 5 \\ 4 & 1 \end{pmatrix}$. For what values of k is the matrix $A - kI$ singular?

9 $B = \begin{pmatrix} 3 & 5 \\ 4 & 2 \end{pmatrix}$. For what values of k is the matrix $B - kI$ singular?

10 a $A = \begin{pmatrix} a_{11} & a_{12} \\ a_{21} & a_{22} \end{pmatrix}$, $B = \begin{pmatrix} b_{11} & b_{12} \\ b_{21} & b_{22} \end{pmatrix}$. Find AB and show that $|AB| = |A||B|$.

b Show that $|A'| = |A|$.

c Hence show that if A is orthogonal, then $|A| = \pm 1$.

11 Prove that if A is orthogonal, then so is A^{-1}.

12 Make X the subject of each of these matrix equations where all the matrices are non-singular 2×2 matrices.

a $AX = B$ b $XA = C$ c $AXA = D$ d $A + X + B = C$

e $AX + B = C$ f $XA + D = E$ g $AXA + F = G$ h $AXB = C$

i $ABX = D$ j $XAB = E$ k $ABXC = D$ l $AXBC = E$

13 Cayley proved in 1846 that if S is a skew-symmetric matrix, then $I + S$ is non-singular and $A = (I - S)(I + S)^{-1}$ is orthogonal.

Find A when $S = \begin{pmatrix} 0 & 3 \\ -3 & 0 \end{pmatrix}$ and show that it is orthogonal.

14 The matrix $A = \begin{pmatrix} a & b \\ c & d \end{pmatrix}$ is orthogonal with $|A| = 1$.

Use the definition $A'A = I$ and $|A| = 1$ to prove that

A must either be of the form $\begin{pmatrix} \cos\theta & \sin\theta \\ -\sin\theta & \cos\theta \end{pmatrix}$ or $\begin{pmatrix} \cos\theta & -\sin\theta \\ \sin\theta & \cos\theta \end{pmatrix}$.

15 Show that

a if A is symmetric, then so is BAB'

b if A and B are symmetric, then $(AB - BA)$ is skew-symmetric

c $(A^{-1})' = (A')^{-1}$ [Hint: start from $AA^{-1} = I$]

d (hence) if A is symmetric and invertible, then A^{-1} is symmetric

e if A and B are invertible (non-singular), then $A^{-1} + B^{-1} = A^{-1}(A + B)B^{-1}$

f a symmetric matrix of order $n \times n$ has at most $\frac{1}{2}n(n + 1)$ distinct elements

g a skew-symmetric matrix of order $n \times n$ has at most $\frac{1}{2}n(n - 1)$ distinct elements.

Summary

- $(AB)^{-1} = B^{-1}A^{-1}$

The proof is independent of the order of the matrices.

Proof

$(B^{-1}A^{-1})(AB)$	$= B^{-1}(A^{-1}A)B$	(The associative law)
	$= B^{-1}IB$	(The defining property of the inverse)
	$= B^{-1}(IB)$	(The associative law)
	$= B^{-1}B$	(The defining property of the identity)
	$= I$	(The defining property of the inverse)

Hence $(B^{-1}A^{-1}) = (AB)^{-1}$.

- $|AB| = |A|\,|B|$.

This is proved in the 2×2 case in Question **10** of Exercise **13.8**. We have only defined 2×2 determinants so far.

- $(A^{-1})' = (A')^{-1}$

13.9 The determinant of a 3 × 3 matrix

Consider the 3 × 3 system of equations

$ax + by + cz = r$ (1)

$dx + ey + fz = s$ (2)

$gx + hy + iz = t$ (3)

where x, y and z are the variables and the other letters represent known coefficients. We find the solution to the system when we express x, y and z in terms of $a, b, c, d, e, f, g, h, i, r, s$ and t.

Consider the steps taken when solving for z.

$(1) \times \frac{d}{a}$ $\quad dx + \frac{bd}{a}y + \frac{cd}{a}z = \frac{dr}{a};\ a \neq 0$ (4)

$(2) - (4)$ eliminates x $\quad \left(e - \frac{bd}{a}\right)y + \left(f - \frac{cd}{a}\right)z = s - \frac{dr}{a}$

Simplification gives $\quad (ae - bd)y + (af - cd)z = as - dr$ (5)

In a similar fashion

$(1) \times \frac{g}{a}$ $\quad gx + \frac{bg}{a}y + \frac{cg}{a}z = \frac{gr}{a}$ (6)

$(3) - (6)$ again eliminates x $\quad \left(h - \frac{bg}{a}\right)y + \left(i - \frac{cg}{a}\right)z = t - \frac{gr}{a}$

Simplification gives $\quad (ah - bg)y + (ai - cg)z = at - gr;\ a \neq 0$ (7)

Considering (5) and (7), we now have a 2 × 2 system of equations

$(5) \times \frac{ah - bg}{ae - bd}$ $\quad (ah - bg)y + \frac{(ah - bg)(af - cd)}{(ae - bd)}z = \frac{(ah - bg)(as - dr)}{(ae - bd)};\ ae - bd \neq 0$ (8)

$(7) - (8)$ eliminates y $\quad \left((ai - cg) - \frac{(ah - bg)(af - cd)}{(ae - bd)}\right)z = (at - gr) - \frac{(ah - bg)(as - dr)}{(ae - bd)}$

Simplifying gives

$$((ai - cg)(ae - bd) - (ah - bg)(af - cd))z = (ae - bd)(at - gr) - (ah - bg)(as - dr)$$

$$\Rightarrow z = \frac{(ae - bd)(at - gr) - (ah - bg)(as - dr)}{(ai - cg)(ae - bd) - (ah - bg)(af - cd)}$$

This is a solution as long as $(ai - cg)(ae - bd) - (ah - bg)(af - cd) \neq 0$

Expanding the brackets we get

$$a^2ei - abdi - aceg + bcdg - a^2fh + acdh + abfg - bcdg = a(aei - bdi - ceg - afh + cdh + bfg)$$

So a solution exists if $a \neq 0$, $ae - bd \neq 0$ and $aei - bdi - ceg - afh + cdh + bfg \neq 0$.

This latter expression is called the determinant of the 3 × 3 matrix of coefficients.

So given $A = \begin{pmatrix} a & b & c \\ d & e & f \\ g & h & i \end{pmatrix}$, $\det(A) = aei - bdi - ceg - afh + cdh + bfg$.

At this stage we can collect like terms in different ways, for example

$\det(A) = a(ei - fh) - b(di - fg) + c(dh - eg)$

Using the notation developed earlier that $\begin{vmatrix} a & b \\ c & d \end{vmatrix} = ad - bc$, we have

$$\det(A) = \begin{vmatrix} a & b & c \\ d & e & f \\ g & h & i \end{vmatrix} = a\begin{vmatrix} e & f \\ h & i \end{vmatrix} - b\begin{vmatrix} d & f \\ g & i \end{vmatrix} + c\begin{vmatrix} d & e \\ g & h \end{vmatrix}$$

Of course we could have collected our terms differently obtaining alternative expressions for $\det(A)$

namely $\begin{vmatrix} a & b & c \\ d & e & f \\ g & h & i \end{vmatrix} = -d\begin{vmatrix} b & c \\ h & i \end{vmatrix} + e\begin{vmatrix} a & c \\ g & i \end{vmatrix} - f\begin{vmatrix} a & b \\ g & h \end{vmatrix}$

or $\begin{vmatrix} a & b & c \\ d & e & f \\ g & h & i \end{vmatrix} = g\begin{vmatrix} b & c \\ e & g \end{vmatrix} - h\begin{vmatrix} a & c \\ d & f \end{vmatrix} + i\begin{vmatrix} a & b \\ d & e \end{vmatrix}$

When trying to remember the three ways of expressing the determinant two new definitions are useful.

Consider the matrix $A = \begin{pmatrix} a_{11} & a_{12} & a_{13} \\ a_{21} & a_{22} & a_{23} \\ a_{31} & a_{32} & a_{33} \end{pmatrix}$.

1 The **minor** of entry a_{ij}, denoted by M_{ij}, is the value of the determinant resulting from the deletion of row i and column j, for example

$M_{21} = \begin{vmatrix} a_{12} & a_{13} \\ a_{32} & a_{33} \end{vmatrix} = a_{12}a_{33} - a_{32}a_{13}$

$\begin{pmatrix} a_{11} & a_{12} & a_{13} \\ a_{21} & a_{22} & a_{23} \\ a_{31} & a_{32} & a_{33} \end{pmatrix}$

2 The **signed minor** or **cofactor** of entry a_{ij}, denoted by A_{ij}, is defined as $A_{ij} = (-1)^{i+j} M_{ij}$

The determinant can now be expressed in one of three ways:

a $\det(A) = a_{11}A_{11} + a_{12}A_{12} + a_{13}A_{13}$

b $\det(A) = a_{21}A_{21} + a_{22}A_{22} + a_{23}A_{23}$

c $\det(A) = a_{31}A_{31} + a_{32}A_{32} + a_{33}A_{33}$

Picking a row which contains zeros will cut down on the work.

Notes

- The matrix created by replacing each entry of A^T, the transpose of A, by its cofactor is called the **adjoint** or **adjugate** of A.
- As with 2×2 matrices, the inverse of A can be calculated using the formula $A^{-1} = \frac{\text{adj}(A)}{\det(A)}$. However, working out the adjoint and the determinant can be very laborious and other methods of finding the inverse, when it exists, are known. A useful method is described in the chapter on Gaussian elimination (Section 14.2). Having said that, evaluating the determinant is still the best test of invertibility, namely $\det(A) \neq 0$ implies that A is invertible.

Example 8

Given $A = \begin{pmatrix} 1 & 2 & 1 \\ 4 & -2 & 3 \\ 2 & 1 & -1 \end{pmatrix}$, calculate

a the minor M_{23} **b** the cofactor A_{31} **c** $\det(A)$

a $M_{23} = \begin{vmatrix} 1 & 2 \\ 2 & 1 \end{vmatrix} = 1 \times 1 - 2 \times 2 = -3$

b $A_{31} = (-1)^{3+1}\begin{vmatrix} 2 & 1 \\ -2 & 3 \end{vmatrix} = 1(6 + 2) = 8$

$\begin{pmatrix} 1 & 2 & 1 \\ 4 & -2 & 3 \\ 2 & 1 & -1 \end{pmatrix}$

c Using row 1 as the basis:

$\det(A) = 1\begin{vmatrix} -2 & 3 \\ 1 & -1 \end{vmatrix} - 2\begin{vmatrix} 4 & 3 \\ 2 & -1 \end{vmatrix} + 1\begin{vmatrix} 4 & -2 \\ 2 & 1 \end{vmatrix}$

$= 1(2 - 3) - 2(-4 - 6) + 1(4 - (-4))$

$= -1 + 20 + 8$

$= 27$

Exercise 13.9

1 Given $A = \begin{pmatrix} 2 & 3 & 5 \\ 1 & -1 & 2 \\ -3 & 4 & 1 \end{pmatrix}$ calculate

a the minor of **i** a_{11} **ii** a_{22} **iii** a_{33}

b i A_{11} **ii** A_{22} **iii** A_{33}

c i M_{12} **ii** M_{31} **iii** M_{32}

2 Given $B = \begin{pmatrix} 3 & -2 & 2 \\ 1 & 0 & 4 \\ -1 & 2 & 3 \end{pmatrix}$ calculate

a the cofactor of **i** b_{12} **ii** b_{31} **iii** b_{32}

b the cofactor of **i** b_{11} **ii** b_{22} **iii** b_{33}

c adj(B)

3 Given $C = \begin{pmatrix} a & b & c \\ d & e & f \\ g & h & i \end{pmatrix}$ write expressions for

a the minor of **i** a **ii** g **iii** f

b the cofactor of **i** c **ii** e **iii** h

4 Evaluate each determinant.

a $\begin{vmatrix} 2 & 1 & 3 \\ 4 & -2 & 5 \\ 3 & 6 & 8 \end{vmatrix}$ b $\begin{vmatrix} -1 & 2 & 1 \\ 3 & 4 & 5 \\ 2 & -7 & 3 \end{vmatrix}$ c $\begin{vmatrix} 4 & 1 & 3 \\ 1 & 3 & 2 \\ 2 & -1 & 1 \end{vmatrix}$ d $\begin{vmatrix} 1 & 1 & 1 \\ 2 & -2 & 3 \\ -1 & -1 & -1 \end{vmatrix}$

5 Simplify each determinant.

a $\begin{vmatrix} a & b & c \\ 4 & 7 & -1 \\ 3 & -2 & 0 \end{vmatrix}$ b $\begin{vmatrix} p & 2 & 4 \\ q & -1 & 3 \\ r & 1 & -2 \end{vmatrix}$ c $\begin{vmatrix} 1 & k & 2 \\ 4 & m & -1 \\ -3 & n & 2 \end{vmatrix}$ d $\begin{vmatrix} 1 & 0 & 1 \\ 0 & x & 0 \\ 1 & 0 & 1 \end{vmatrix}$

6 Write an expression for the determinant of

a the symmetric matrix $\begin{pmatrix} a & h & g \\ h & b & f \\ g & f & c \end{pmatrix}$

b the skew-symmetric matrix $\begin{pmatrix} 0 & -h & -g \\ h & 0 & -f \\ g & f & 0 \end{pmatrix}$

7 $A = \begin{pmatrix} a & b & c \\ d & e & f \\ g & h & i \end{pmatrix}$

a Write the matrix A^{T}.

b Write expressions for **i** $|A|$ **ii** $|A^{\mathrm{T}}|$.

c Comment on the results.

8 a $P = \begin{pmatrix} 1 & 2 \\ 3 & 4 \end{pmatrix}$

i Calculate $|P|$. **ii** Write $2P$ and evaluate $|2P|$.

b $Q = \begin{pmatrix} 3 & 5 \\ 1 & 3 \end{pmatrix}$

i Calculate $|Q|$. **ii** Write $3Q$ and evaluate $|3Q|$.

c Given that $|R| = \begin{vmatrix} 2 & 1 & 3 \\ 4 & -2 & 5 \\ 3 & 6 & 8 \end{vmatrix} = -19$,

write $2R$ and evaluate $|2R|$.

d Given that $|S| = \begin{vmatrix} -1 & 2 & 1 \\ 3 & 4 & 5 \\ 2 & -7 & 3 \end{vmatrix} = -74$

write $3S$ and evaluate $|3S|$.

e Given that $|K| = \begin{pmatrix} 1 & 0 & 1 \\ 2 & 1 & -1 \\ -1 & 0 & 1 \end{pmatrix}$

i calculate $|K|$ **ii** write aK and evaluate $|aK|$.

f If A is a square matrix of order n, make a conjecture about the relationship between $|A|$ and $|xA|$ where $x \in R$.

13.10 Transformation matrices

Computer animation has become a fixture in our culture.

An object may be drawn by joining lists of points, defined by their coordinates, in a fixed order. Computers accomplish animation by transforming each point according to some rule and redrawing the object.

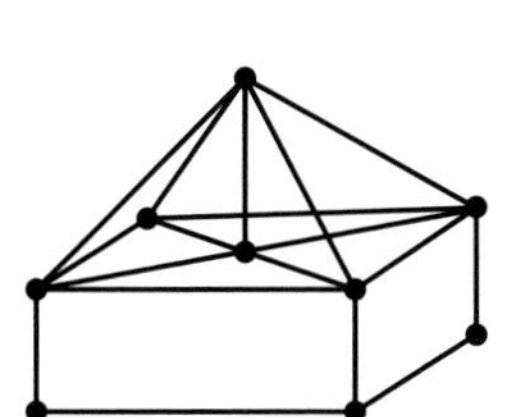

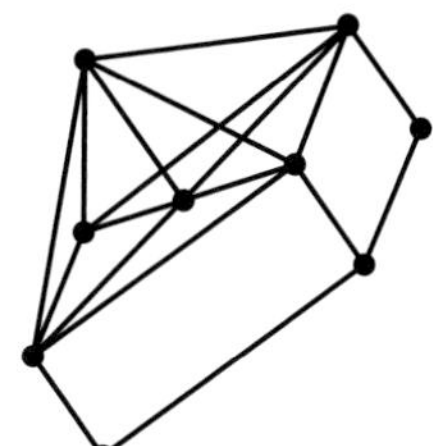

Persistence of vision completes the illusion of movement.

Being performed on a two-dimensional computer screen, the transformations can all be modelled on the (x, y)-plane. In this section we will be studying some such transformations – the linear transformations.

A linear transformation can be described as any mapping of the form

$(x, y) \rightarrow (ax + by, cx + dy)$ for $a, b, c, d \in \mathrm{R}$

Consider that, under the above transformation, the point $\mathrm{P}(x, y)$ has an image $\mathrm{P}'(x', y')$: then

$$\begin{matrix} x' = ax + by \\ y' = cx + dy \end{matrix} \Rightarrow \begin{pmatrix} x' \\ y' \end{pmatrix} = \begin{pmatrix} ax + by \\ cx + dy \end{pmatrix} \Rightarrow \begin{pmatrix} x' \\ y' \end{pmatrix} = \begin{pmatrix} a & b \\ c & d \end{pmatrix} \begin{pmatrix} x \\ y \end{pmatrix}$$

The position vector of P′ is obtained by pre-multiplying the position vector of P by $\begin{pmatrix} a & b \\ c & d \end{pmatrix}$. We say that $\begin{pmatrix} a & b \\ c & d \end{pmatrix}$ is the matrix associated with the transformation $(x, y) \rightarrow (ax + by, cx + dy)$.

Example 9

A triangle has vertices O(0, 0), A(2, 5), B(4, 0).

Find its image under the transformation with associated matrix $\begin{pmatrix} 2 & 1 \\ 0 & 2 \end{pmatrix}$.

Arrange the position vectors of the points together in one matrix and pre-multiply: $\begin{pmatrix} 2 & 1 \\ 0 & 2 \end{pmatrix} \begin{pmatrix} 0 & 2 & 4 \\ 0 & 5 & 0 \end{pmatrix} = \begin{pmatrix} 0 & 9 & 8 \\ 0 & 10 & 0 \end{pmatrix}$ giving the images O′(0, 0), A′(9, 10), B′(8, 0).

In a linear transformation straight lines are transformed into straight lines. The line OA becomes O′A′ and the triangle OAB becomes the triangle O′A′B′.

Note that O is its own image under this transformation.

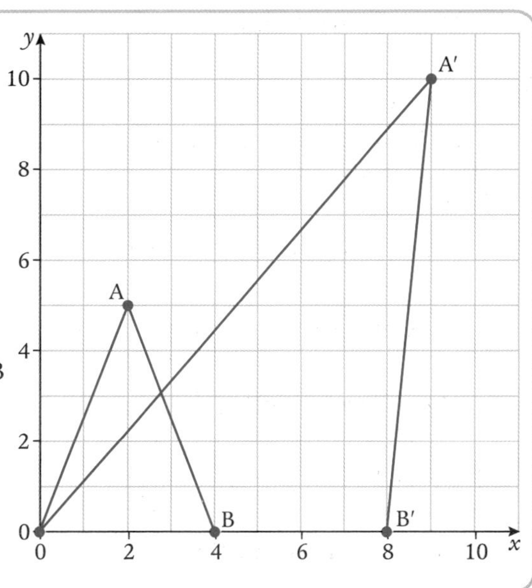

Constructing a transformation matrix

Method 1

Consider the images of (1, 0) and (0, 1) under the transformation defined by $\begin{pmatrix} a & b \\ c & d \end{pmatrix}$.

$$\begin{pmatrix} a & b \\ c & d \end{pmatrix}\begin{pmatrix} 1 & 0 \\ 0 & 1 \end{pmatrix} = \begin{pmatrix} a & b \\ c & d \end{pmatrix}$$

The point (1, 0) has an image (a, c) and the point (0, 1) has an image (b, d).

To find the matrix associated with a particular transformation, we need only find the images of (1, 0) and (0, 1) under that transformation.

Method 2

Where it is not possible to get the images of (1, 0) and (0, 1), the images of any two points will allow you to deduce the corresponding transformation matrix.

Let $(x_1, y_1) \rightarrow (X_1, Y_1)$ and $(x_2, y_2) \rightarrow (X_2, Y_2)$ under the transformation defined by $\begin{pmatrix} a & b \\ c & d \end{pmatrix}$.

Then $\begin{pmatrix} a & b \\ c & d \end{pmatrix}\begin{pmatrix} x_1 & x_2 \\ y_1 & y_2 \end{pmatrix} = \begin{pmatrix} X_1 & X_2 \\ Y_1 & Y_2 \end{pmatrix}$

$$\Rightarrow \begin{pmatrix} ax_1 + by_1 & ax_2 + by_2 \\ cx_1 + dy_1 & cx_2 + dy_2 \end{pmatrix} = \begin{pmatrix} X_1 & X_2 \\ Y_1 & Y_2 \end{pmatrix}$$

We can find a and b by solving the system of equations $\begin{cases} ax_1 + by_1 = X_1 \\ ax_2 + by_2 = X_2 \end{cases}$

We can find c and d by solving the system of equations $\begin{cases} cx_1 + dy_1 = Y_1 \\ cx_2 + dy_2 = Y_2 \end{cases}$

Example 10

a Find R, the matrix associated with reflection in the line $y = -x$.

b Calculate the coordinates of the image of the typical point $P(x, y)$ under this transformation. [Note that straight lines reflect as straight lines: the transformation is linear.]

---

a The diagram shows that under the transformation

- $(1, 0) \rightarrow (0, -1)$ giving $a = 0$ and $c = -1$
- $(0, 1) \rightarrow (-1, 0)$ giving $b = -1$ and $d = 0$

Thus $R = \begin{pmatrix} 0 & -1 \\ -1 & 0 \end{pmatrix}$.

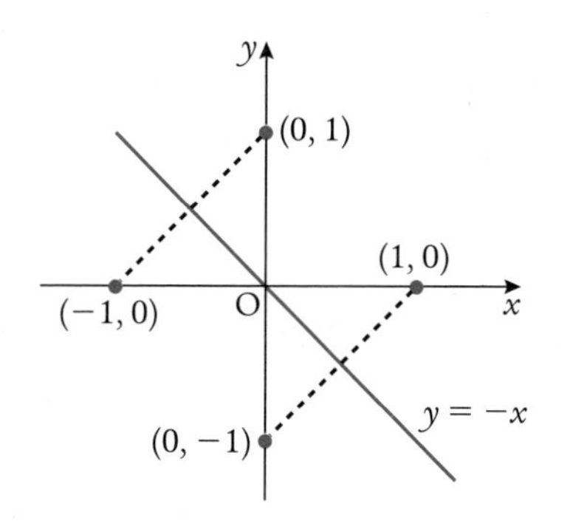

b $\begin{pmatrix} x' \\ y' \end{pmatrix} = \begin{pmatrix} 0 & -1 \\ -1 & 0 \end{pmatrix}\begin{pmatrix} x \\ y \end{pmatrix} = \begin{pmatrix} -y \\ -x \end{pmatrix}$

Thus the image is $P'(-y, -x)$.

Example 11

a Find K, the matrix associated with anticlockwise rotation of $\theta°$ about the origin, O.

b Calculate the coordinates of the image of the point P(2, 4) under a 60° rotation about the origin.

a The diagram shows that under the transformation

- $(1, 0) \rightarrow (\cos\theta°, \sin\theta°)$ giving $a = \cos\theta°$ and $c = \sin\theta°$
- $(0, 1) \rightarrow (-\sin\theta°, \cos\theta°)$ giving $b = -\sin\theta°$ and $d = \cos\theta°$

Thus $K = \begin{pmatrix}\cos\theta° & -\sin\theta° \\ \sin\theta° & \cos\theta°\end{pmatrix}$.

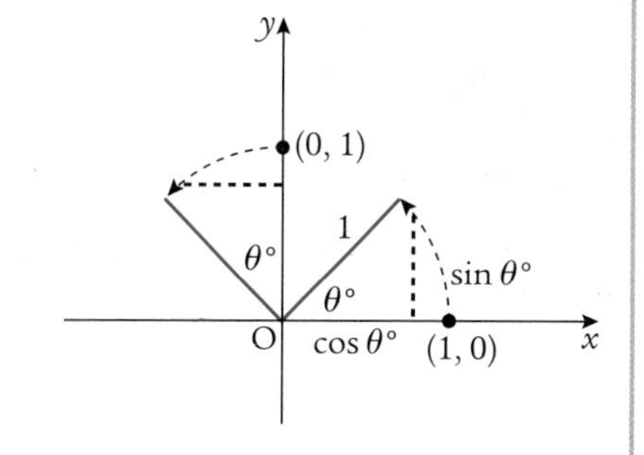

b $\begin{pmatrix}x' \\ y'\end{pmatrix} = \begin{pmatrix}\cos 60° & -\sin 60° \\ \sin 60° & \cos 60°\end{pmatrix}\begin{pmatrix}2 \\ 4\end{pmatrix} = \begin{pmatrix}\frac{1}{2} & -\frac{\sqrt{3}}{2} \\ \frac{\sqrt{3}}{2} & \frac{1}{2}\end{pmatrix}\begin{pmatrix}2 \\ 4\end{pmatrix} = \begin{pmatrix}1 - 2\sqrt{3} \\ \sqrt{3} + 2\end{pmatrix}$

Thus the image is $P'(1 - 2\sqrt{3}, 2 + \sqrt{3})$.

Exercise 13.10

1 In each of these, find the image of the point P under the transformation with the associated matrix A.

a $P(1, 2); A = \begin{pmatrix}1 & 0 \\ 2 & 1\end{pmatrix}$ b $P(3, 4); A = \begin{pmatrix}1 & 1 \\ 2 & 0\end{pmatrix}$ c $P(-1, 2); A = \begin{pmatrix}3 & -4 \\ 4 & 3\end{pmatrix}$

2 The triangle ABC has vertices A(1, 1), B(2, 3) and C(−1, 4).
Work out its image under the transformation associated with each of these matrices.

a $\begin{pmatrix}0 & 1 \\ 1 & 0\end{pmatrix}$ reflection in $y = x$ b $\begin{pmatrix}-1 & 0 \\ 0 & 1\end{pmatrix}$ reflection in $x = 0$ c $\begin{pmatrix}1 & 0 \\ 0 & -1\end{pmatrix}$ reflection in $y = 0$

d $\begin{pmatrix}-1 & 0 \\ 0 & -1\end{pmatrix}$ reflection in O(0, 0) e $\begin{pmatrix}2 & 0 \\ 0 & 2\end{pmatrix}$ enlargement (× 2) f $\begin{pmatrix}\frac{1}{2} & 0 \\ 0 & \frac{1}{2}\end{pmatrix}$ reduction $\left(\times \frac{1}{2}\right)$

3 A transformation maps (a, b) onto (a', b').

$(a, b) \rightarrow (a', b')$ where $a' = 2a + 3b, b' = a - 2b$

The matrix associated with such a mapping is $\begin{pmatrix}2 & 3 \\ 1 & -2\end{pmatrix}$.

In a similar way, find the matrix associated with each of these mappings.

a $(a, b) \rightarrow (a', b')$ where $a' = 2a + b, b' = -2a + b$

b $(a, b) \rightarrow (a', b')$ where $a' = 3a - 4b, b' = 2a + 3b$

c $(a, b) \rightarrow (5a + 3b, 3a - 2b)$

d $(a, b) \rightarrow (a + b, a - b)$

e $(a, b) \rightarrow (-b, -a)$

4 Write the mapping associated with each of these matrices in the form
$(a, b) \rightarrow (pa + qb, ra + sb)$ where $p, q, r, s \in \mathbb{R}$.

a $\begin{pmatrix}2 & 1 \\ 1 & -2\end{pmatrix}$ b $\begin{pmatrix}3 & 0 \\ 1 & 4\end{pmatrix}$ c $\begin{pmatrix}0 & 1 \\ 1 & 0\end{pmatrix}$ d $\begin{pmatrix}0 & 0 \\ 0 & 1\end{pmatrix}$ e $\begin{pmatrix}1 & 0 \\ 1 & 0\end{pmatrix}$ f $\begin{pmatrix}0 & 0 \\ 0 & 0\end{pmatrix}$

5 a i Work out the image of the points A(1, 0) and B(0, 1) under reflection in the x-axis.

ii Hence write the matrix associated with this linear transformation.

b Repeat this to find the matrix associated with

i reflection in the y-axis ii reflection in $y = x$

iii reflection in the origin iv a half turn about the origin

v a quarter turn about the origin vi a 30° rotation about the origin.

6 Describe in words the transformation associated with

a $\begin{pmatrix} -1 & 0 \\ 0 & -1 \end{pmatrix}$ b $\begin{pmatrix} 0 & -1 \\ -1 & 0 \end{pmatrix}$ c $\begin{pmatrix} 0 & 1 \\ -1 & 0 \end{pmatrix}$ d $\begin{pmatrix} 1 & 0 \\ 0 & 1 \end{pmatrix}$ e $\begin{pmatrix} 1 & 0 \\ 1 & 0 \end{pmatrix}$ f $\begin{pmatrix} 0 & 0 \\ 0 & 0 \end{pmatrix}$

7 **Dilatation** is a transformation where the image shape is mathematically similar to the original. In the illustration the point C is called the centre of dilatation and the image is twice the original (a scale factor of 2).

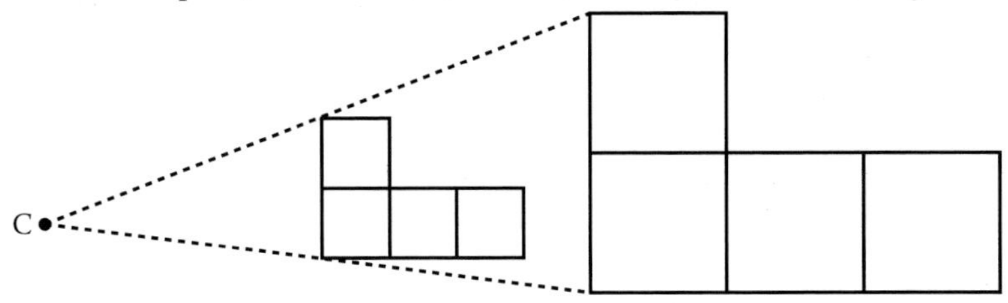

When the centre is the origin then matrices of the form $\begin{pmatrix} k & 0 \\ 0 & k \end{pmatrix}$ are associated with dilatation.

By considering the rectangle ABCD given by the points A(1, 1), B(6, 1), C(6, 4) and D(1, 4) examine the cases when

a $0 < k < 1$ b $k = 1$ c $k > 1$ d $-1 < k < 0$ e $k = 0$ f $k < -1$ g $k = -1$

8 A square has vertices P(1, 0), Q(2, 0), R(2, 1) and S(1, 1).

It undergoes reflection in the line $y = x$.

a Write the matrix B associated with this transformation.

b Find the image of PQRS.

c Calculate the area of i PQRS ii its image.

d Calculate $\det(B)$.

13.11 Properties of transformation matrices

Inverse transformation matrices

The effects of a transformation can be reversed by pre-multiplying the position vector of the image by the inverse of the matrix associated with the transformation.

When the transformation matrix is *orthogonal*, its transpose equals its inverse. Examples 10 and 11 illustrate orthogonal matrices.

Invariant points

If, under a transformation, a point P is its own image then it is called invariant under the transformation.

Example 12

Find all the invariant points under the transformation with associated matrix $\begin{pmatrix} 2 & 1 \\ 2 & 3 \end{pmatrix}$.

Considering the typical invariant point (x, y), we have

$$\begin{pmatrix} 2 & 1 \\ 2 & 3 \end{pmatrix}\begin{pmatrix} x \\ y \end{pmatrix} = \begin{pmatrix} x \\ y \end{pmatrix} \Rightarrow \begin{pmatrix} 2x + y \\ 2x + 3y \end{pmatrix} = \begin{pmatrix} x \\ y \end{pmatrix}$$

Hence, equating entries we get

$2x + y = x \Rightarrow x + y = 0$ ①

$2x + 3y = y \Rightarrow 2x + 2y = 0$ ②

This system of equations has an infinite set of solutions, namely $x + y = 0$.

All points on the line $x + y = 0$ are invariant under the transformation.

Transformation of loci

How do we calculate the equation of the image of a curve?

Example 13

Find the equation of the image of the curve with equation $y = 3x^2$ under the transformation with associated matrix $A = \begin{pmatrix} 1 & 2 \\ 2 & 3 \end{pmatrix}$

Let the image of the point (a, b) on the curve be (x, y).
We know the relation between a and b: $b = 3a^2$ since (a, b) lies on the curve.
But what is the relation between x and y?

Since (x, y) is the image of (a, b) we have $\begin{pmatrix} 1 & 2 \\ 2 & 3 \end{pmatrix}\begin{pmatrix} a \\ b \end{pmatrix} = \begin{pmatrix} x \\ y \end{pmatrix}$.

Make $\begin{pmatrix} a \\ b \end{pmatrix}$ the subject.

$\begin{pmatrix} a \\ b \end{pmatrix} = A^{-1}\begin{pmatrix} x \\ y \end{pmatrix} = -\frac{1}{1}\begin{pmatrix} 3 & -2 \\ -2 & 1 \end{pmatrix}\begin{pmatrix} x \\ y \end{pmatrix} = \begin{pmatrix} -3x + 2y \\ 2x - y \end{pmatrix}$

Equating entries gives $a = 2y - 3x$ and $b = 2x - y$.

Substituting in $b = 3a^2$ we get $2x - y = 3(2y - 3x)^2$.

This is the equation of the transformed curve stated implicitly.

Exercise 13.11

1 Find all the invariant points of the transformation associated with these matrices.

a $A = \begin{pmatrix} 2 & 1 \\ 1 & 2 \end{pmatrix}$ b $B = \begin{pmatrix} 3 & 4 \\ 2 & 5 \end{pmatrix}$ c $C = \begin{pmatrix} 2 & 1 \\ 7 & 8 \end{pmatrix}$ d $D = \begin{pmatrix} 4 & 5 \\ 3 & 6 \end{pmatrix}$ e $E = \begin{pmatrix} 3 & 4 \\ 3 & 7 \end{pmatrix}$

2 Find the equation of the image of each curve under the mapping with the given associated matrix.

a $y = x^2,\ A = \begin{pmatrix} 1 & 0 \\ 2 & 2 \end{pmatrix}$ b $y = 2x + 1,\ B = \begin{pmatrix} 2 & 1 \\ 1 & 3 \end{pmatrix}$

c $y^2 = x - 1,\ C = \begin{pmatrix} 1 & -1 \\ 2 & -1 \end{pmatrix}$ d $3x + 4y = 5,\ D = \begin{pmatrix} 4 & 5 \\ 2 & 3 \end{pmatrix}$

3 a A triangle has vertices K(0, 0), L(6, 0) and M(4, 6). It undergoes a transformation with associated matrix $A = \begin{pmatrix} 3 & 2 \\ 0 & 3 \end{pmatrix}$.

i Calculate the images of K, L and M.

ii Calculate the area of KLM and its image. By what factor has the area increased?

iii Calculate det(A).

b Repeat part **a** using a rectangle with vertices P(1, 1), Q(4, 1), R(4, 6) and S(1, 6) which is transformed to a parallelogram by the matrix $B = \begin{pmatrix} 4 & 0 \\ 2 & 1 \end{pmatrix}$.

c A circle, centre N(1, 1), passes through the point T(7, 1).

It is transformed by the matrix $D = \begin{pmatrix} 4 & 0 \\ 0 & 4 \end{pmatrix}$. Its image is a circle.

Compare the increase in area with det(D).

4 The examples in Question **3** illustrate a theorem that the enlargement factor for area when a shape undergoes a transformation is equal to the magnitude of the determinant of the associated matrix.

a A circle centre F(2, 4) passes through the point T(5, 4).

It is transformed by the matrix $E = \begin{pmatrix} 4 & 1 \\ 5 & 2 \end{pmatrix}$ into an ellipse.

Calculate the area of the ellipse.

b Prove that the transformation associated with the matrix $M = \begin{pmatrix} \sin\theta & \cos\theta \\ -\cos\theta & \sin\theta \end{pmatrix}$ conserves area.

5 The matrix $D = \begin{pmatrix} 1 & 0 \\ 2 & 0 \end{pmatrix}$ has a determinant of zero.

It is therefore singular.

a The area of any shape transformed by this matrix must collapse to zero.

By examining the square P(0, 0), Q(5, 0), R(5, 5) and S(0, 5) find why this is so.

b Every point on the plane when transformed by this matrix will lie on the same line.

By considering $\begin{pmatrix} 1 & 0 \\ 2 & 0 \end{pmatrix}\begin{pmatrix} x \\ y \end{pmatrix}$ find the equation of this line.

Note that this transformation is irreversible. The matrix has no inverse. Compare this with the notion of a shadow. Every point in an object maps onto a shadow. Knowing the object and the source of light allows us to construct the shadow. However, looking at the shadow we cannot reconstruct the object.

6 Each of these matrices is associated with a collapse onto a straight line.

Find, in each case, the equation of the line.

a $\begin{pmatrix} 3 & 0 \\ 2 & 0 \end{pmatrix}$ **b** $\begin{pmatrix} 2 & 3 \\ 0 & 0 \end{pmatrix}$ **c** $\begin{pmatrix} 0 & 0 \\ 3 & 0 \end{pmatrix}$ **d** $\begin{pmatrix} 0 & 1 \\ 0 & 1 \end{pmatrix}$

7 Find the matrix associated with each of these transformations.

a a half turn about the origin, O

b a positive quarter turn about O

c a negative quarter turn about O

d a 360° rotation about O

e an enlargement, centre O, scale factor 5

f a reduction, centre O, scale factor 0.5.

8 These transformations and their associated matrices can be applied to the complex plane equally well.
For example, the diagram illustrates how the complex conjugate $\bar{z} = x - iy$ is the reflection of $z = x + iy$ in the x-axis.
The matrix associated with this transformation, namely $\begin{pmatrix} 1 & 0 \\ 0 & -1 \end{pmatrix}$, can be used to compute conjugates.

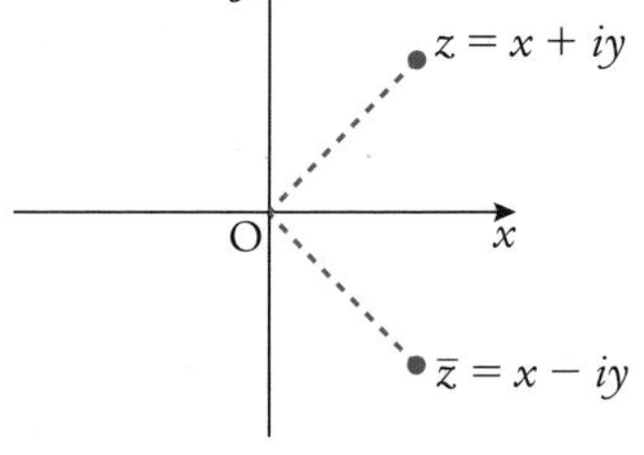

a Make sketches to study the effect of these transformations on the complex plane.

i Reflection in the x-axis.

ii A half turn about the origin, O.

iii Reflection in the y-axis.

iv Reflection in the line $y = x$.

v Reflection in the line $y = -x$.

vi A positive quarter turn about O.

b In the complex plane a point is interpreted as a complex number and rotation of $\theta°$ about the origin is interpreted as multiplying by $z = \cos\theta° + i\sin\theta°$.

Write a matrix associated with multiplying a complex number by $z = \cos 60° + i\sin 60°$.

c The matrix multiplication $\begin{pmatrix} \frac{1}{\sqrt{2}} & -\frac{1}{\sqrt{2}} \\ \frac{1}{\sqrt{2}} & \frac{1}{\sqrt{2}} \end{pmatrix}\begin{pmatrix} 1 & 1 & 3 & 2 \\ 2 & 4 & -1 & -3 \end{pmatrix}$, when interpreted in the context of the complex plane, represents the multiplication of four different complex numbers by the same complex factor. Identify the four numbers and the factor.

d If we consider $z = x + iy$ then the product $\begin{pmatrix} \frac{1}{\sqrt{2}} & -\frac{1}{\sqrt{2}} \\ \frac{1}{\sqrt{2}} & \frac{1}{\sqrt{2}} \end{pmatrix}\begin{pmatrix} x \\ y \end{pmatrix}$ represents a function of z.

In this case $f(z) = z(\cos 45° + i \sin 45°) = \frac{z}{\sqrt{2}}(1 + i)$.

Find functions associated with the matrix

i $\begin{pmatrix} \frac{3}{5} & -\frac{4}{5} \\ \frac{4}{5} & \frac{3}{5} \end{pmatrix}$ **ii** $\begin{pmatrix} \frac{5}{13} & -\frac{12}{13} \\ \frac{12}{13} & \frac{5}{13} \end{pmatrix}$ **iii** $\begin{pmatrix} 3 & -4 \\ 4 & 3 \end{pmatrix}$

13.12 Composition of transformations

Often we wish to combine transformations.

We may, for instance, wish to reflect $P(a, b)$ in the x-axis and then in the line $y = x$.

$X = \begin{pmatrix} 1 & 0 \\ 0 & -1 \end{pmatrix}$ is the matrix associated with reflection in the x-axis.

The image of P, $XP = \begin{pmatrix} 1 & 0 \\ 0 & -1 \end{pmatrix}\begin{pmatrix} a \\ b \end{pmatrix}$.

We can refer to the transformation itself by X.

$L = \begin{pmatrix} 0 & 1 \\ 1 & 0 \end{pmatrix}$ is the matrix associated with reflection in the line $y = x$.

We wish to perform L once we have performed X. This can be written as LXP.

Using matrices we get $LXP = \begin{pmatrix} 0 & 1 \\ 1 & 0 \end{pmatrix}\begin{pmatrix} 1 & 0 \\ 0 & -1 \end{pmatrix}\begin{pmatrix} a \\ b \end{pmatrix} = \begin{pmatrix} 0 & -1 \\ 1 & 0 \end{pmatrix}\begin{pmatrix} a \\ b \end{pmatrix}$.

So the composite transformation, LX, is associated with the matrix $\begin{pmatrix} 0 & -1 \\ 1 & 0 \end{pmatrix}$.

We obtain the matrix for the composite transformation by multiplying the matrices for the individual transformations bearing in mind the order of multiplication.

Exercise 13.12

1 Let X denote reflection in the x-axis, and Y denote reflection in the y-axis.

a Write the matrix associated with **i** X **ii** Y **iii** XY **iv** YX

b Write the image of $P(a, b)$ after the transformation **i** XY **ii** YX

c Considering the geometry, is it a surprise that the image is the same in both cases?

2 Let A denote reflection in the line $y = x$ and B denote reflection in the line $y = -x$.

a Describe **i** BA **ii** AB as a single transformation.

b If P is (a, b), state the coordinates of its image under **i** BA **ii** AB

c Write the matrices associated with **i** A **ii** B **iii** AB **iv** BA

d A triangle has vertices O(0, 0), P(6, 0) and Q(3, 5).
Find its image after BA.

3 Let F denote reflection in the x-axis, and G denote reflection in the line $y - x$.

a Find the matrix associated with **i** GF **ii** FG

b Explain briefly (geometrically) why $GF \neq FG$.

4 As already stated, the matrix $\begin{pmatrix} \cos\theta° & -\sin\theta° \\ \sin\theta° & \cos\theta° \end{pmatrix}$ is associated with an anticlockwise rotation of $\theta°$ about the origin.

a Write the matrices P, Q and R respectively associated with an anticlockwise rotation about the origin of

i $A°$ **ii** $B°$ **iii** $(A+B)°$

b By expanding PQ and equating its entries with those of R, find well-known expansions for $\sin(A+B)$ and $\cos(A+B)$.
Explain why equating entries is valid.

5 Let X denote reflection in the x-axis and Y denote reflection in the y-axis in the complex plane.
Find the image of the complex number $z = a + ib$ under

i X **ii** Y **iii** XY **iv** YX

6 a Find the matrix associated with reflection in the line $y = x$, and show that the image of $y = 2x$ under this reflection is $x = 2y$.

b Find the image of the line $y = x$ under a rotation, anticlockwise, of 30° about the origin.

Review 13

Throughout this review we shall use the matrices

$$A = \begin{pmatrix} 1 & 2 \\ 4 & 3 \end{pmatrix} \quad B = \begin{pmatrix} 3 & -2 \\ 1 & 4 \end{pmatrix} \quad C = \begin{pmatrix} 0 & 1 \\ 5 & -1 \end{pmatrix}$$

$$P = \begin{pmatrix} 2 & 1 & 0 \\ 3 & 2 & 4 \\ 1 & -2 & 3 \end{pmatrix} \quad Q = \begin{pmatrix} 3 & -1 & 4 \\ 2 & 1 & -3 \\ 5 & 1 & 6 \end{pmatrix} \quad R = \begin{pmatrix} 1 & 1 & 4 \\ 1 & -2 & 2 \\ 0 & 3 & 1 \end{pmatrix}$$

1 Evaluate a $2A + 3B - C$ b $A - kI$

2 Evaluate a $P + 2Q - R'$ b $3P - 2I$

3 Complete the matrix $X = \begin{pmatrix} 1 & \cdot & -1 \\ 4 & 2 & 0 \\ \cdot & \cdot & 3 \end{pmatrix}$ if X is symmetric.

4 Complete the matrix $Y = \begin{pmatrix} \cdot & \cdot & 1 \\ 2 & \cdot & \cdot \\ \cdot & 3 & \cdot \end{pmatrix}$ if Y is skew-symmetric.

5 Evaluate a $|A|$ b $|P|$

6 Obtain B^{-1} using the formula $B^{-1} = \dfrac{\text{adj}(B)}{\det(B)}$

and verify that $B^{-1}B = I = BB^{-1}$.

7 Given that D is an invertible matrix such that $D^2 = 3D - I$ show that

a $D^3 = 8D - 3I$ b $D^{-1} = 3I - D$

8 a Find the matrices U, V and W associated respectively with

i a half turn about the origin

ii reflection in the x-axis

iii reflection in the y-axis.

b Show that U, V and W are orthogonal.

c Show that $VU = W$.

9 A linear transformation maps the point $(1, 0)$ to $(3, 4)$ and the point $(0, 1)$ to $(-1, 2)$.

a Obtain the matrix associated with this transformation.

b Find the image of $(5, 6)$.

10 Prove that if D and E are orthogonal, then

a DE is orthogonal

b $(DED^{-1})^{\mathrm{T}} = (DED^{\mathrm{T}})^{-1}$

Summary 13

1 Definitions and notation

a a_{ij} is the element in the ith row and jth column of A.

b **Addition** and **subtraction** are defined by
$A \pm B = C \Leftrightarrow c_{ij} = a_{ij} \pm b_{ij}$

c $O = \begin{pmatrix} 0 & 0 \\ 0 & 0 \end{pmatrix}$ is the 2×2 **identity matrix** for *addition* (or zero matrix).

d **Scalar multiplication** by $k \in \mathrm{R}$ is defined by $E = kD \Leftrightarrow e_{ij} = kd_{ij}$.

e The **transpose** of a matrix X, denoted by X' or X^{T}, is obtained by interchanging the rows and columns of X, that is, $x'_{ij} = x_{ji}$.

f A matrix M is **symmetric** if $M^{\mathrm{T}} = M$, that is, $m_{ij} = m_{ji}$.

g A matrix M is **skew-symmetric** if $M^{\mathrm{T}} = -M$, that is, $m_{ij} = -m_{ji}$.

2 Matrix multiplication

a If $C = AB$ then $c_{ij} =$ (the ith row of A) $\cdot$ (the jth column of B)

$$c_{ij} = \sum_{k=1}^{n} a_{ik}b_{kj}$$

b As $AB \neq BA$, AB is called pre-multiplication of B by A or post-multiplication of A by B.

c $I = \begin{pmatrix} 1 & 0 \\ 0 & 1 \end{pmatrix}$ is the 2×2 **identity matrix** for *multiplication*.

d A matrix A is orthogonal if $A^{\mathrm{T}}A = I = AA^{\mathrm{T}}$.

3 The determinant of a 2×2 matrix

a $A = \begin{pmatrix} a & b \\ c & d \end{pmatrix} \Rightarrow |A| = \det(A) = \begin{vmatrix} a & b \\ c & d \end{vmatrix} = ad - bc$

b The **inverse** of the matrix A is B if and only if $BA = I = AB$.

The inverse is denoted by A^{-1}.

c The matrix A is **singular** if $|A| = 0$; then A^{-1} is undefined.

d The matrix A is **non-singular** if $|A| \neq 0$; then A^{-1} exists and A is called **invertible**.

4 The determinant of a 3×3 matrix

a $A = \begin{vmatrix} a & b & c \\ d & e & f \\ g & h & i \end{vmatrix} \Rightarrow |A| = \begin{vmatrix} a & b & c \\ d & e & f \\ g & h & i \end{vmatrix} = a\begin{vmatrix} e & f \\ h & i \end{vmatrix} - b\begin{vmatrix} d & f \\ g & i \end{vmatrix} + c\begin{vmatrix} d & e \\ g & h \end{vmatrix}$

$= a(ei - hf) - b(di - gf) + c(dh - ge) = aei - afh - bdi + bfg + cdh - ceg$

This expansion was based on row 1 of the matrix.
We may have begun with the second row,

$= -d\begin{vmatrix} b & c \\ h & i \end{vmatrix} + e\begin{vmatrix} a & c \\ g & i \end{vmatrix} - f\begin{vmatrix} a & b \\ g & h \end{vmatrix}$

or the third: $= g\begin{vmatrix} b & c \\ e & f \end{vmatrix} - h\begin{vmatrix} a & c \\ d & f \end{vmatrix} + i\begin{vmatrix} a & b \\ d & e \end{vmatrix}$.

b The **minor**, M_{ij}, of a_{ij} is the determinant created by omitting the ith row and jth column.

c The **cofactor** A_{ij} of a_{ij} is $(-1)^{i+j} M_{ij}$.

5 Transformation matrices

a The matrix associated with the transformation $p \to p'$ is A such that $Ap = p'$.

b The matrix A associated with the transformation

$(a, b) \to (pa + qb, ra + sb)$ is $A = \begin{pmatrix} p & q \\ r & s \end{pmatrix}$.

6 Matrix properties

- $(A')' = A$
- $A + (B + C) = (A + B) + C$
- $(kA)' = kA'$
- $(AB)' = B'A'$
- $A(B + C) = AB + AC$
- $(AB)^{-1} = B^{-1}A^{-1}$
- $|AB| = |A|\,|B|$
- $(A^{-1})' = (A')^{-1}$
- $|kA| = k^n|A|$ where A has order $n \times n$, $n = 2, 3$
- $A + B = B + A$
- $(A + B)' = A' + B'$
- $AB \neq BA$
- $A(BC) = (AB)C$
- $A = \begin{pmatrix} a & b \\ c & d \end{pmatrix} \Rightarrow A^{-1} = \dfrac{1}{ad - bc}\begin{pmatrix} d & -b \\ -c & a \end{pmatrix}$
- $|A^{T}| = |A|$
- $|A^{-1}| = \dfrac{1}{|A|}$
- $(A^{-1})' = (A')^{-1}$
- $(kA)^{-1} = \frac{1}{k}A^{-1}$

14 Systems of linear equations

14.1 Reminders

Equations and solutions

- An equation is a mathematical sentence, containing '=', whose truth depends on the value(s) of the variable(s) in the sentence.
- The values of variables which make the sentence true are called solutions of the equation.
- The equation $3x + 2y = 5$ has infinitely many solutions, for example $(1, 1)$, $(9, -11)$ ... In fact for any value of x, $\left(x, \dfrac{(5 - 3x)}{2}\right)$ is a solution.
- This type of equation is called a linear equation: all solutions, when plotted on the Cartesian plane, lie in a straight line.

Example 1

In 1973
Two second-class and three first-class stamps cost a total of 21 pence.
Three second-class and two first-class stamps cost a total of 19 pence.
What was the cost of one of each?

Situations like this lead to systems of linear equations

$2x + 3y = 21 \quad (1)$

$3x + 2y = 19 \quad (2)$

where x represents the cost of a second-class stamp and y, the cost of a first-class stamp in pence.

Finding the solution is a fairly standard procedure.

Equation (1) $\times$ 3	$6x + 9y = 63$	(3)
Equation (3) $\times$ 2	$6x + 4y = 38$	(4)
Equation (4) $-$ Equation (3)	$-5y = -25$	(5)
Equation (5) $\div$ (-5)	$y = 5$	

Substitute this value back into equation (3): $6x + 45 = 63$

$\Rightarrow \quad 6x = 18$

$\Rightarrow \quad x = 3$

The cost of a second-class stamp was 3 pence.
The cost of a first-class stamp was 5 pence.

This system of equations is known as a 2×2 system of linear equations because there are two linear equations and two variables.

Not every pair of 2×2 linear equations produces a unique solution like Example 1, as the next two sets of equations show.

Redundancy

$3x + 3y = 6$
$4x + 4y = 8$

These equations are equivalent and when any attempt to eliminate a variable is undertaken, the resulting unhelpful truism occurs.

$0 = 0$

One of the equations is said to be **redundant**.

There is in fact an infinite number of solutions, that is, for any value of x, $(x, 2 - x)$ is a solution.

Consider this system of 3×2 equations.

$x + 2y = 7$
$2x + y = 5$
$7x + 8y = 31$

The third equation is redundant since the solution, which does satisfy it, can be deduced from the first two equations only.

A redundant equation can be *built* from the sum of multiples of the other equations in the system.

Inconsistency

$x + 4y = 6$
$2x + 8y = 10$

If we attempt to eliminate a variable by doubling equation ① we get $0 = 2$ which is clearly impossible.
The equations are said to be **inconsistent**.

There are no solutions.

Consider this system of 3×2 equations.

$x + 2y = 7$
$2x + y = 5$
$7x + 8y = 30$

The third equation is inconsistent with the other two since a solution based on the first two does not satisfy the third.
The system has no solution.

Exercise 14.1

1 For each of these systems of equations either

- solve it for its unique solution
- declare one of the equations redundant and give the solution in the form $(x, ax + b)$ where a and b are constants, or
- declare the system inconsistent and that there are no solutions.

a $2x + y = 6$
$x + 2y = 9$

b $2x + 3y = 9$
$10x + 6y = 16$

c $4x + y = 3$
$8x + 2y = 6$

d $x - 3y = 2$
$6y - 2x = 1$

e $3x + 2y = 4$
$2x + 5y = -1$

f $6x = 2y - 4$
$y = 2 - 3x$

2 In each of these systems, decide the relationship between the third equation and the other two. State the solution where appropriate.

a $2x + y = 7$
$x + 3y = 6$
$2x + 3y = 9$

b $x - 2y = -5$
$x + y = 1$
$3x + 4y = 4$

c $x + 3y = 2$
$3x + y = 3$
$x + 5y = 1$

d $4x - 2y = -2$
$x - 3y = 2$
$2x - y = -1$

3 Comment on this system of equations.

$2x + 3y = 5$
$4x + 6y = 10$
$10x + 15y = 25$

4 In the Greasy Spoon Café, an order of one cola and three teas cost £3.60.
The bill for an order of two colas and two teas came to £4.
A third order, three colas and two teas, cost £5.

a Form a system of equations.

b Use the first two equations to find prices which satisfy both.

c Comment on the third order.

14.2 Matrices and 2 × 2 systems; the augmented matrix

In this chapter we will be studying systems of equations of different sizes and so are looking for a more compact way of organising and recording our working.

We saw in Section **10.1** that a system of equations can be expressed as a matrix equation of the form $AX = B$
For example, the system of equations used in the postage stamp problem can be represented by

$$\begin{pmatrix} 2 & 3 \\ 3 & 2 \end{pmatrix} \begin{pmatrix} x \\ y \end{pmatrix} = \begin{pmatrix} 21 \\ 19 \end{pmatrix}$$

where A is a 2×2 matrix for the coefficients of the variables, column 1 for the x-coefficients and column 2 for the y-coefficients.

X is a 2×1 matrix for the variables, commonly called a vector in this context;

B is a 2×1 matrix for the constants on the right-hand side.

An even more compact representation is attained by combining matrices A and B into a bigger matrix known as the **augmented** matrix:

$$\left(\begin{array}{cc|c} 2 & 3 & 21 \\ 3 & 2 & 19 \end{array}\right)$$

This contains all the data needed to calculate a solution.

Exercise 14.2

1 Rewrite each system of equations

i in the matrix form $AX = B$

ii in the augmented matrix form.

a $x + 2y = 4$
$3x - y = 5$

b $2x + 4y = 8$
$x - 2y = -4$

c $3x - 2y = 7$
$x - y = 2$

d $3x = -6$
$4x + y = -7$

e $0.5x + 2y = 3$
$x - 1.5y = -5$

f $0.4x + 0.6y = 0.2$
$0.1x - 0.2y = 0.4$

2 Write out in full the systems of equations which are represented by these augmented matrices.

a $\left(\begin{array}{cc|c} 2 & 4 & 42 \\ 1 & 5 & 57 \end{array}\right)$

b $\left(\begin{array}{cc|c} 0 & 1 & 5 \\ 2 & -1 & 4 \end{array}\right)$

c $\left(\begin{array}{cc|c} 4 & 1 & 5 \\ 3 & 0 & 3 \end{array}\right)$

d $\left(\begin{array}{cc|c} 3 & 0 & 5 \\ 0 & 4 & 3 \end{array}\right)$

14.3 Elementary row operations

When solving a system of equations there are several simple alterations that can be made to the system to produce a new system with the same solutions:

- The order of equations can be switched (the solution does not depend on the order).
- An equation of the system can be multiplied by a constant (if $A = B$ then $aA = aB$).
- One equation can be added to or subtracted from another (if $A = B$ and $C = D$ then $A \pm C = B \pm D$).

We would obviously be on the look-out for alterations which produced a simpler system. For example in the case of the postage stamp problem, the system

$$\begin{aligned} 2x + 3y &= 21 \\ 3x + 2y &= 19 \end{aligned} \quad \text{became} \quad \begin{aligned} 6x + 9y &= 63 \\ 6x + 4y &= 38 \end{aligned} \quad \text{then} \quad \begin{aligned} 6x + 9y &= 63 \\ -5y &= -25 \end{aligned}$$

In this final simple form, it is easily deduced that $y = 5$, from the second equation.
By substitution back into the first equation we get $6x + 45 = 63$, and hence $x = 3$.

When working with the system in the augmented matrix form, the three simple alterations become what are known as the **elementary row operations**. (EROs):

- two rows can be interchanged
- a row can be multiplied by a constant
- one row can have another row added to it

EROs can be combined to create more complex row operations, for example you may subtract a multiple of one row from another.

A simple shorthand can be used to record the operations.

$R1 \leftrightarrow R2$	'interchange row 1 and row 2'
$R1 \rightarrow a \times R1$	'row 1 becomes a times row 1'
$R1 \rightarrow R1 + R2$	'row 1 becomes row 1 plus row 2'
$R1 \rightarrow R1 - 5\,R2$	'row 1 becomes row 1 minus 5 times row 2'

Let us re-examine the postage stamp problem using the augmented matrix format

$$\left(\begin{array}{cc|c} 2 & 3 & 21 \\ 3 & 2 & 19 \end{array}\right)$$

$$\begin{array}{l} R1 \rightarrow 3 \times R1 \\ R2 \rightarrow 2 \times R2 \end{array} \quad \left(\begin{array}{cc|c} 6 & 9 & 63 \\ 6 & 4 & 38 \end{array}\right)$$

$$R2 \rightarrow R2 - R1 \quad \left(\begin{array}{cc|c} 6 & 9 & 63 \\ 0 & -5 & -25 \end{array}\right)$$

At this stage the non-zero entries in the left-hand side of the augmented matrix form a triangle. This is often referred to as the **upper triangular form**. We can re-interpret the matrix as a system of equations $6x + 9y = 63$ and $-5y = -25$ and proceed to solve as before, or we could continue

$$R2 \rightarrow -\tfrac{1}{5}R2 \quad \left(\begin{array}{cc|c} 6 & 9 & 63 \\ 0 & 1 & 5 \end{array}\right)$$

$$R1 \rightarrow R1 - 9R2 \quad \left(\begin{array}{cc|c} 6 & 0 & 18 \\ 0 & 1 & 5 \end{array}\right)$$

$$R1 \rightarrow \tfrac{1}{6}R1 \quad \left(\begin{array}{cc|c} 1 & 0 & 3 \\ 0 & 1 & 5 \end{array}\right)$$

Re-interpretation now gives us $x = 3, y = 5$.

Exercise 14.3

1 **i** Express each of these systems of equations in augmented matrix form.

ii Reduce it to upper triangular form using row operations.

iii Re-express this simplified form as a system of equations and solve.

a $2x + y = 6$
$x - y = 1$

b $2x + 3y = -1$
$x - 2y = -4$

c $4x - 3y = 22$
$2x + 5y = -2$

d $2x - y = -1$
$3x - 5y = -4$

2 **i** Express each of these systems of equations in augmented matrix form.

ii Reduce to the form $\left(\begin{array}{cc:c} 1 & 0 & p \\ 0 & 1 & q \end{array}\right)$ using row operations.

iii Hence solve.

a $3x - 5y = -8$
$2x - y = -3$

b $4x + 7y = 5$
$3x - 4y = 13$

c $2x - 5y = -4$
$5x - 2y = -10$

d $6x - 4y = -36$
$9x + 2y = -6$

3 Each of these systems contains an equation which is redundant.

a $2x - y = 1$
$6x - 3y = 3$

b $x + 3y = 7$
$4x + 12y = 28$

i Express each in augmented matrix form.

ii Use row operations to simplify it.

iii Comment on what happens to the matrix when redundancy exists.

4 Each of these systems is inconsistent.

a $3x - 2y = 1$
$6x - 4y = 3$

b $4x + 2y = 5$
$2x + y = 3$

i Express each in augmented matrix form.

ii Use row operations to simplify it.

iii Comment on what happens to the matrix when inconsistency exists.

5 Relative to a certain set of axes, and using suitable units, the flight of a golf ball can be modelled by an equation of the form $y = ax - bx^2$ where y is the height and x is the distance from the tee, and a and b are constants. It is noted that when $x = 1$ then $y = 9$, and when $x = 4, y = 12$.

a Form two equations in a and b.

b Solve the system by first expressing it in augmented matrix form.

c How many units of distance from the tee is the ball when it lands ($y = 0$)?

6 In a computer simulation, the routes of four ferries in an estuary have been modelled by the four straight lines:

Aberline ferry	$3x + y = 10$
Balfour ferry	$5x - 2y = -9$
Clanaig ferry	$9x + 3y = 30$
Dunmuir ferry	$6x + 2y = 21$

a Create a suitable augmented matrix to help you find where the Aberline route crosses the Balfour route.

b Attempt to do the same with

i the Aberline/Clanaig routes

ii the Aberline/Dunmuir routes.

c Comment on the geometric interpretation of

i redundancy

ii inconsistency.

14.4 The 3 × 3 system and matrices

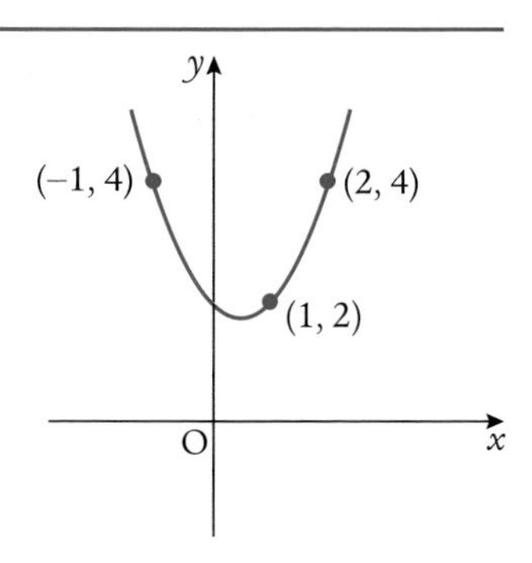

The parabola shown has an equation of the form

$$y = ax^2 + bx + c$$

It passes through the points $(-1, 4)$, $(1, 2)$ and $(2, 4)$.

How do we find the constants a, b, c?

Use the points passed through to help you form a system of equations

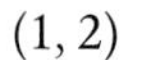

(1, 2)	$a + b + c = 2$
(2, 4)	$4a + 2b + c = 4$
(−1, 4)	$a - b + c = 4$

Three equations, three unknowns: a 3 × 3 system

This system can be reduced to the matrix form $AX = B$

$$\begin{pmatrix} 1 & 1 & 1 \\ 4 & 2 & 1 \\ 1 & -1 & 1 \end{pmatrix} \begin{pmatrix} a \\ b \\ c \end{pmatrix} = \begin{pmatrix} 2 \\ 4 \\ 4 \end{pmatrix}$$

or further reduced to the augmented matrix form

$$\left(\begin{array}{ccc|c} 1 & 1 & 1 & 2 \\ 4 & 2 & 1 & 4 \\ 1 & -1 & 1 & 4 \end{array}\right)$$

Row operations will reduce this to upper triangular form.

$$\begin{array}{l} \\ R2 \rightarrow R2 - 4R1 \\ R3 \rightarrow R3 - R1 \end{array} \left(\begin{array}{ccc|c} 1 & 1 & 1 & 2 \\ 0 & -2 & -3 & -4 \\ 0 & -2 & 0 & 2 \end{array}\right) \text{ the object being to make } a_{21} = a_{31} = 0$$

For the sake of reference, the entry in the ith row and jth column will be referred to as a_{ij}. As row operations are enacted, the entry will generally change its value.

$$R2 \leftrightarrow R3 \quad \left(\begin{array}{ccc|c} 1 & 1 & 1 & 2 \\ 0 & -2 & 0 & 2 \\ 0 & -2 & -3 & -4 \end{array}\right) \text{ a simple switch which saves some work}$$

$$R3 \rightarrow R3 - R2 \quad \left(\begin{array}{ccc|c} 1 & 1 & 1 & 2 \\ 0 & -2 & 0 & 2 \\ 0 & 0 & -3 & -6 \end{array}\right) \text{ making } a_{32} = 0$$

Row 3 gives $-3c = -6 \quad \Rightarrow \quad c = 2$

Row 2 gives $-2b = 2 \quad \Rightarrow \quad b = -1$

Row 1 gives $a + b + c = 2 \quad \Rightarrow \quad a - 1 + 2 = 2 \Rightarrow a = 1$

In general, back-substitution will be used when dealing with both rows 1 *and* 2.

So the equation of the parabola is $y = x^2 - x + 2$.

Historical note

This technique of solving a system of equations by expressing the system in augmented matrix form, reducing it to upper triangular form and then performing back-substitution, is called *Gaussian elimination*. However, in Europe, it was Sir Isaac Newton who first explained how to solve simultaneous equations after noting that it was missing from the algebra text books of his day.

It is named after the famous German mathematician, Carl Friedrich Gauss, 1777–1855, who devised it.

Gauss contributed to many branches of mathematics, physics and astronomy. Indeed it was while working on the problem of the orbit of the newly discovered asteroid, Ceres, that he began to explore numerical analysis and the theory of errors.

Exercise 14.4

1 For each system of equations

 i express it as an augmented matrix

 ii reduce the matrix, using row operations, to upper triangular form

 iii using back-substitution, work out the values of the variables.

a $x + 2y + z = 8$
$3x + y - 2z = -1$
$x + 5y - z = 8$

b $2x + 3y - z = -1$
$x - 3y - 2z = 4$
$5x + y + 3z = 4$

c $3x + y = 5$
$x + 2y - 3z = -12$
$x + 2z = 10$

d $3x - 4y + z = 24$
$x - 2y - 2z = 7$
$x + y + z = 4$

e $4x + 2y + z = 3$
$x + 3y + 5z = 3$
$2x + 3z = 5$

f $x + y + 5z = 0$
$4x + y - 6z = -17$
$x - y - z = 0$

2 A parabola passes through the points (1, 2), (2, 7) and (3, 14).
It has an equation of the form $y = ax^2 + bx + c$.

 a Use the information to form a 3×3 system of equations.

 b Solve the system by Gaussian elimination.

 c Write the equation of the parabola.

3 An archaeological dig discovers the remains of a circular Roman amphitheatre. Using a suitable set of axes and convenient units, the archaeologists positively identify three points on its circumference:
$(-2, -1)$, $(-1, 2)$ and $(6, 3)$.

 a Assuming the perimeter has an equation of the form $x^2 + y^2 + 2gx + 2fy + c = 0$ form a system of equations in g, f and c.

 b Solve the system and identify the equation of the perimeter.

 c What is the radius of the amphitheatre?

4 A set of traffic lights is phased so that the Stop periods and the Go periods are separated by Cautionary periods. The pattern runs thus: S - C - G - C - S - C - G - C ...
Each period lasts a fixed length of time, but each type is of different length.

Three observations were made by a traffic warden:

1 S - C - G lasted for 185 s

2 S - C - G - C - S - C - G - C - S lasted 460 s

3 S - C - G - C - S - C - G lasted 375 s.

a Form a set of equations in s, c and g, where these are fittingly named variables, and solve it to find the length of each period.

b At the start of an hour the light turns to STOP.
What kind of period will it be in when the hour ends?

14.5 Back-substitution using the matrix

Once a matrix has been reduced to upper triangular form, you can continue the row operations until the solution is apparent within the matrix. Returning to the example from the start of Section 14.4.

$$\left(\begin{array}{ccc:c} 1 & 1 & 1 & 2 \\ 0 & -2 & 0 & 2 \\ 0 & 0 & -3 & -6 \end{array}\right)$$

$R2 \to -\frac{1}{2}R2$, $R3 \to -\frac{1}{3}R3$

$$\left(\begin{array}{ccc:c} 1 & 1 & 1 & 2 \\ 0 & 1 & 0 & -1 \\ 0 & 0 & 1 & 2 \end{array}\right)$$

Make the leading non-zero entry in each row equal to 1 by suitable multiplications.

$R1 \to R1 - R3$

$$\left(\begin{array}{ccc:c} 1 & 1 & 0 & 0 \\ 0 & 1 & 0 & -1 \\ 0 & 0 & 1 & 2 \end{array}\right)$$

Make the third entry in rows 1 and 2 equal to zero.

$R1 \to R1 - R2$

$$\left(\begin{array}{ccc:c} 1 & 0 & 0 & 1 \\ 0 & 1 & 0 & -1 \\ 0 & 0 & 1 & 2 \end{array}\right)$$

Make the second entry in row 1 equal to zero.

The solution can now be read off.

Exercise 14.5

1 For each system of equations

i represent it by an augmented matrix

ii reduce this to the form $\left(\begin{array}{ccc:c} 1 & 0 & 0 & p \\ 0 & 1 & 0 & q \\ 0 & 0 & 1 & r \end{array}\right)$

iii write the solution to the system of equations.

a $x + 2y + z = 4$
$2x - y - z = 0$
$3x + 2y + z = 6$

b $5x - 2y + z = 10$
$3x - 4y - z = 10$
$x - 2y - 2z = 3$

c $7x - 2y + 3z = -13$
$x + 4y + 3z = 11$
$x + 2y + z = 5$

d $4x + 3y - 2z = 16$
$x - 2y - 3z = -9$
$3x - 5y - 2z = -4$

e $x - y - 3z = 1$
$2x + y - 2z = 9$
$x - 2y + 2z = 5$

f $y + 3z = 3$
$2x + 3z = 10$
$3x + 2y = 0$

2 Working with convenient units, the supporting arch of a bridge can be modelled by the equation $y = a + bx - cx^2$.

Three points on this arch have been accurately measured as $(1, -3)$, $(2, -28)$ and $(-1, -13)$.

a Use the data to form a system of equations.

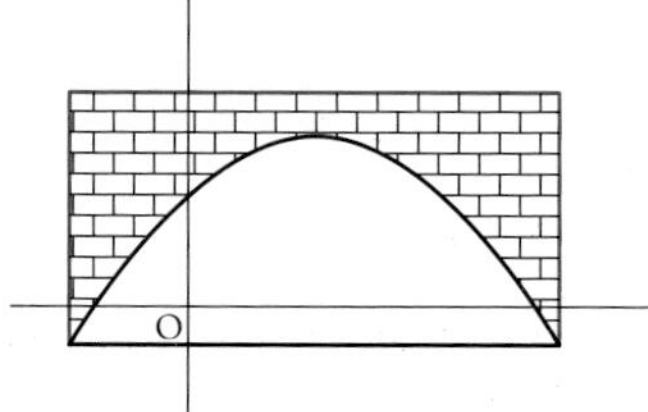

b Solve the system by reducing the augmented matrix to the form $\left(\begin{array}{ccc|c} 1 & 0 & 0 & p \\ 0 & 1 & 0 & q \\ 0 & 0 & 1 & r \end{array}\right)$.

c Write the equation of the arch.

14.6 Redundancy and inconsistency in a 3 × 3 system

Consider the system of equations

$$\begin{aligned} x + 2y + 2z &= 11 \\ x - y + 3z &= 8 \\ 4x - y + 11z &= 35 \end{aligned}$$

$$\left(\begin{array}{ccc|c} 1 & 2 & 2 & 11 \\ 1 & -1 & 3 & 8 \\ 4 & -1 & 11 & 35 \end{array}\right)$$

R2 → R2 − R1
R3 → R3 − 4R1 $\left(\begin{array}{ccc|c} 1 & 2 & 2 & 11 \\ 0 & -3 & 1 & -3 \\ 0 & -9 & 3 & -9 \end{array}\right)$

R3 → R3 − 3R2 $\left(\begin{array}{ccc|c} 1 & 2 & 2 & 11 \\ 0 & -3 & 1 & -3 \\ 0 & 0 & 0 & 0 \end{array}\right)$

The row of zeros tells us that this equation is *redundant*, so there is not a unique solution to the system. There is in fact an infinite number of solutions.

Given any z, then from row 2 $y = \dfrac{z + 3}{3}$

from row 1 $x = 11 - 2z - 2y$

which simplifies to $x = \dfrac{27 - 8z}{3}$

The general solution can be quoted as $x = \dfrac{27 - 8z}{3}$; $y = \dfrac{z + 3}{3}$; $z = z$.

A particular solution can be found by assigning a value to z.

For example, if $z = 3$ the solution would be $x = 1$; $y = 2$; $z = 3$.

Consider the system of equations

$$\begin{aligned} x + 2y + 2z &= 11 \\ 2x - y + z &= 8 \\ 3x + y + 3z &= 18 \end{aligned}$$

$$\left(\begin{array}{ccc|c} 1 & 2 & 2 & 11 \\ 2 & -1 & 1 & 8 \\ 3 & 1 & 3 & 18 \end{array}\right)$$

$$\left(\begin{array}{ccc|c} 1 & 2 & 2 & 11 \\ 0 & -5 & -3 & -14 \\ 0 & -5 & -3 & -15 \end{array}\right)$$

$$\left(\begin{array}{ccc|c} 1 & 2 & 2 & 11 \\ 0 & -5 & -3 & -14 \\ 0 & 0 & 0 & 1 \end{array}\right)$$

Row 3 suggests that $0 = 1$, which tells us that the system of equations is in fact *inconsistent* and that there are no solutions.

Exercise 14.6

1 Attempt to reduce each of these systems of equations to upper triangular form.

- Where this is possible quote the unique solution.
- Where there is a redundant equation, find a general solution.
- Where there is inconsistency, declare that there are no solutions.

a $3x + 2y + 5z = 0$
$2x + y - 2z = 5$
$7x + 4y + z = 10$

b $x + y - z = 4$
$2x - y + 2z = -2$
$x - 3y - 4z = -1$

c $2x - y + 3z = 6$
$x + y + 2z = 7$
$4x + y + 7z = 9$

d $2x - 3y + z = 2$
$x + y - 3z = 7$
$5x - 2y - z = 14$

e $x + 2y - z = 3$
$x + 3z = 5$
$4x + 2y + 8z = 10$

f $5x - 3y - z = -12$
$2x + y + 3z = 3$
$20x - y + 13z = -9$

2 The system of equations

$x + 2y - z = 8$
$3x + y + 2z = -1$
$x + y + kz = -6$

has no solutions. What is the value of k?

3 Find the value of k that makes the system of equations

$x + y + z = 1$
$2x + 3y - 2z = -1$
$x - y + kz = 7$

have infinitely many solutions.

4 For what values of d and e will the three equations

$x + 3y - 2z = 8$
$2x + y - 3z = 5$
$7x - 4y + dz = e$

have **a** no solution

b infinitely many solutions

c a unique solution?

14.7 Automatic processes

The beauty of Gaussian elimination is that, since it is completely systematic, it can be easily programmed into calculators or into spreadsheets.

It can also be very easily adapted to suit larger systems, for example 4×4, 5×5 etc.

Many real-life applications involve large systems. Many real-life applications involve coefficients given correct to, say, 3 decimal places.

In either case, solving such systems by hand becomes impractical.

Solving an $n \times n$ system

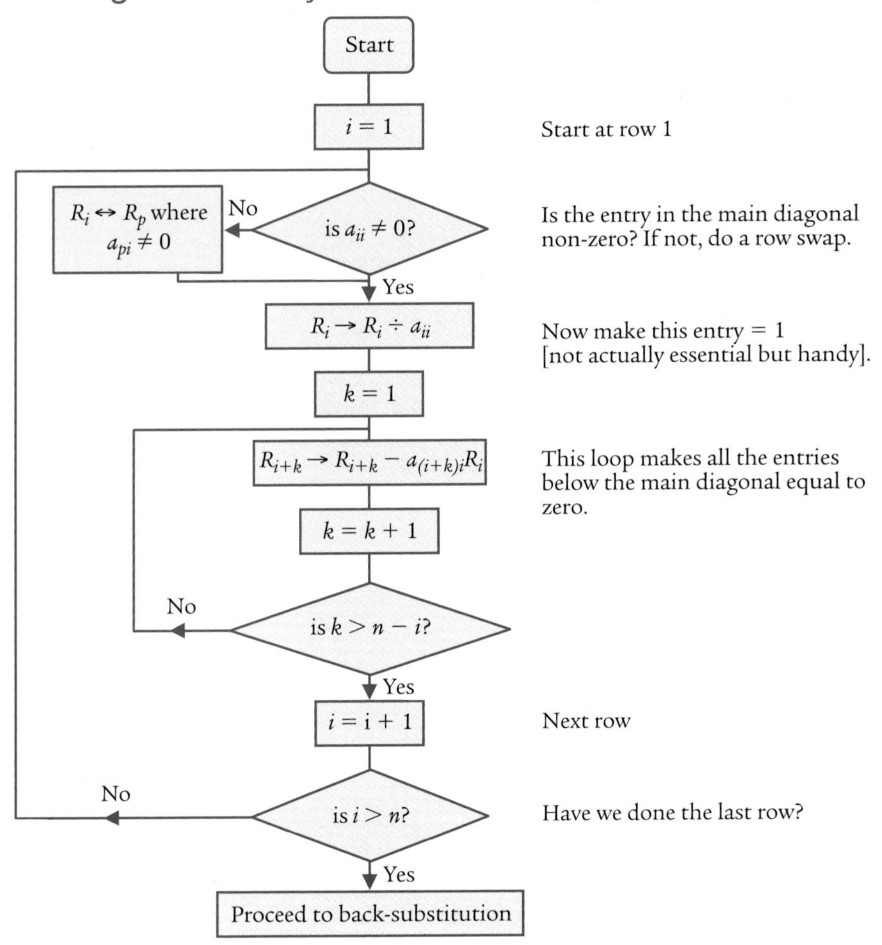

This flowchart should help explain how one can take an $n \times n$ matrix and systematically reduce it to upper triangular form, with the added feature that the main diagonal entries are all equal to 1.

In the next exercise some of the examples can be done by hand, but the rest should be tackled using an appropriate calculator or a spreadsheet.

Exercise 14.7

1 Use Gaussian elimination to solve these systems then check your answer, if you can, using a graphics calculator or spreadsheet.

a
$$\begin{aligned} w + x + y + z &= 5 \\ 2w + 3x + y + 2z &= 9 \\ w - x - y + 3z &= 1 \\ 2w - x + 2y - z &= 4 \end{aligned}$$

b
$$\begin{aligned} 2w - x + 2y + z &= -1 \\ w + 2x - 3y + 2z &= 3 \\ -w + x - 5y - z &= 2 \\ 2w - 2x + 2y + 3z &= -5 \end{aligned}$$

c
$$\begin{aligned} w + x + y + z &= 14 \\ w - x - y + z &= -8 \\ w - x + y - z &= 0 \\ w - x - y - z &= -12 \end{aligned}$$

d
$$\begin{aligned} w + x + y &= 9 \\ w + y + z &= 7 \\ w + x + z &= 5 \\ x + y + z &= 9 \end{aligned}$$

2 a The sum of the first n whole numbers, $1 + 2 + 3 + ... + n$, can be found using a formula of the form $S_n = an^2 + bn + c$.

From the fact that $S_1 = 1, S_2 = 3$ and $S_3 = 6$, form a system of equations and solve it to find the formula.

b The sum of the first n square numbers, $1^2 + 2^2 + 3^2 + ... + n^2$, can be found using a formula of the form $S_n = an^3 + bn^2 + cn + d$.

From the fact that $S_1 = 1, S_2 = 5, S_3 = 14$ and $S_4 = 30$, form a system of equations and solve it to find the formula.

c The sum of the first n cubes, $1^3 + 2^3 + 3^3 + ... + n^3$, can be found using a formula of the form $S_n = an^4 + bn^3 + cn^2 + dn$.

Find the formula.

3 The rotor blade of a helicopter moves in such a way that the distance, y metres, from its tip to the back of the craft can be calculated using a formula of the form

$$y = a \sin x° + b \cos x° + c$$

where y is the distance, $x°$ is the angle rotated through measured from a certain starting position and a, b and c are constants.

Measuring to 3 significant figures this table was constructed.

$x°$	y (m)
30	11.0
100	8.26
120	6.60

a Use the data to form a system of equations.
Work to 3 significant figures.

b Use Gaussian elimination to solve the system and hence construct the formula.

c What is the range of the function $y(x)$?

d Using a calculator, explore the above situation.

How does altering the number of significant figures in the working affect the solution?

14.8 Approximate data

When a measurement is made, or rounding takes place, the resulting data takes on a *fuzziness*.

For example, when we say $x = 51$ to the nearest whole number we mean $50.5 \leq x < 51.5$

This is often quoted as $x = 51 \pm 0.5$: the 0.5 is called the **absolute error** in the measurement.

The size of the error is often quoted as a percentage of the associated measurement.

An error of 0.5 in 51 represents approximately a 1% error in the measurement.

This **percentage error** is a better way of judging just how bad the error is.

Similarly $y = 50$ to the nearest whole number means $49.5 \leq y < 50.5$

The sum $x + y$, which should be 101, could be as low as $50.5 + 49.5 = 100$ or as high as $51.5 + 50.5 = 102$.
That is $100 \leq x + y < 102$ or $x + y = 101 \pm 1$.

The sum has an error of 1% which is acceptable in many situations.

The difference $x - y$, which should be 1, could be as low as $50.5 - 50.5 = 0$ or as high as $51.5 - 49.5 = 2$.
That is $0 \leq x - y < 2$ or $x - y = 1 \pm 1$.

The difference has an error of 100%. The result of such a subtraction has no meaning.

When rounded numbers close to each other in value are subtracted, an unacceptable error builds up. This situation is to be avoided!

When working with equations in real-life situations we must watch out for such occasions.

A metal rod, 51 mm measured to the nearest mm, is cooled down and contracts.

Its length is then measured as 50 mm, again working to the nearest mm.

By how much has it contracted?

The equation $51 - x = 50$ has to be solved.

This means that $x = 51 - 50$ ... but this is exactly the situation above!

$x = 1 \pm 1$ mm, a 100% error.

No useful result can be gleaned from this equation.

Exercise 14.8

1 Each of these measurements has been rounded.

State **i** the range of possible values the measurement can take

ii the absolute error

iii the percentage error.

a $x = 12$ **b** $y = 25$ **c** $z = 46$

d $p = 2.4$ **e** $q = 7.7$ **f** $r = 9.1$

g $a = 0.45$ **h** $b = 0.36$ **i** $c = 0.03$

2 For each pair of values

i state the highest and lowest value of the sum and difference $x + y$ and $x - y$

ii state the absolute error in each result

iii express the error as a percentage of the expected answer

iv comment on the errors you feel are unacceptably large.

a $x = 28, y = 7$ **b** $x = 78, y = 77$ **c** $x = 6.4, y = 6.3$

d $x = 0.81, y = 0.03$ **e** $x = 1.25, y = 1.00$ **f** $x = 0.010, y = 0.011$

3 The numbers in these equations are rounded.

Quote the solutions in the form $x \pm e$, where e is the absolute error in the answer.

a $x - 34 = 12$ **b** $x - 1.4 = 0.9$ **c** $x + 78 = 79$

d $x + 7 = 92$ **e** $x - 1 = 1$ **f** $x + 0.5 = 0.6$

14.9 Gaussian elimination on a spreadsheet

For the next section we wish to be able to study changes to the coefficients in a system of equations and the effect these changes have on the solution.
To this end, this spreadsheet has been devised.

	A	B	C	D	E	F	G
1		1	1	1	19	x=	=E21
2		3	16	1	95	y=	=E22
3		2	9	1	59	z=	=E23
4							
5	R1=R1/a11	=B1/$B$1	=C1/$B$1	=D1/$B$1	=E1/$B$1		
6	R2=R2−a21*R1	=B2−$B$2*B5	=C2−$B$2*C5	=D2−$B$2*D5	=E2−$B$2*E5		
7	R3=R3−a31*R1	=B3−$B3*B5	=C3−$B3*C5	=D3−$B3*D5	=E3−$B3*E5		
8							
9	R1	=B5	=C5	=D5	=E5		
10	R2=R2/a22	=B6/$C$6	=C6/$C$6	=D6/$C$6	=E6/$C$6		
11	R3=R3−a32*R2	=B7−$C$7*B10	=C7−$C$7*C10	=D7−$C$7*D10	=E7−$C$7*E10		
12							
13	R1	=B9	=C9	=D9	=E9		
14	R2	=B10	=C10	=D10	=E10		
15	R3=R3/a33	=B11/$D$11	=C11/$D$11	=D11/$D$11	=E11/$D$11		
16	Going Up						
17	R1=R1−a13/R3	=B13−$D$13*B19	=C13−$D$13*C19	=D13−$D$13*D19	=E13−$D$13*E19		
18	R2=R2−a23*R3	=B14−$D$14*B19	=C14−$D$14*C19	=D14−$D$14*D19	=E14−$D$14*E19		
19	R3	=B15	=C15	=D15	=E15		
20							
21	R1=R1−a12*R2	=B17−$C$17*B22	=C17−$C$17*C22	=D17−$C$17*D22	=E17−$C$17*E22		
22	R2	=B18	=C18	=D18	=E18		
23	R3	=B15	=C15	=D15	=E15		

- The augmented matrix occupies cells B1 to E3.
- Column A records the row operations.
- B5 to E7 give the transformed matrix after one sweep of operations.
- B9 to E11 give the transformed matrix after a second sweep of operations.
- B13 to E15 give the matrix in upper triangular form.
- B17 to E19 give the first step of back-substitution.
- B21 to E23 give the final step of back-substitution.
- Cells F1 to G3 display the solution for convenience beside the original system.

	A	B	C	D	E	F	G
1		1	1	1	19	x=	8.00
2		3	16	1	95	y=	4.00
3		2	9	1	59	z=	7.00
4							
5	R1=R1/a11	1.00	1.00	1.00	19.00		
6	R2=R2−a21*R1	0.00	13.00	−2.00	38.00		
7	R3=R3−a31*R1	0.00	7.00	−1.00	21.00		
8							
9	R1	1.00	1.00	1.00	19.00		
10	R2=R2/a22	0.00	1.00	−0.15	2.92		
11	R3=R3−a32*R2	0.00	0.00	0.08	0.54		
12							
13	R1	1.00	1.00	1.00	19.00		
14	R2	0.00	1.00	−0.15	2.92		
15	R3=R3/a33	0.00	0.00	1.00	7.00		
16	Going Up						
17	R1=R1−a13/R3	1.00	1.00	0.00	12.00		
18	R2=R2−a23*R3	0.00	1.00	0.00	4.00		
19	R3	0.00	0.00	1.00	7.00		
20							
21	R1=R1−a12*R2	1.00	0.00	0.00	8.00		
22	R2	0.00	1.00	0.00	4.00		
23	R3	0.00	0.00	1.00	7.00		

The illustrated example shows the solution of the system

$$\begin{aligned} x + y + z &= 19 \\ 3x + 16y + z &= 95 \\ 2x + 9y + z &= 59 \end{aligned}$$

Note the final form of the augmented matrix

$$\left(\begin{array}{ccc|c} 1 & 0 & 0 & 8 \\ 0 & 1 & 0 & 4 \\ 0 & 0 & 1 & 7 \end{array}\right)$$

The cells have been formatted to show 2 decimal places.

Ill-conditioning

Consider this story.

Two bags of mixed screws are weighed, to the nearest gram.
The bags are then sorted out and it is discovered that the situation can be modelled by the system of equations

Bag 1	$19x + 18y = 55$	19 of type X + 18 of type Y weighs 55 g
Bag 2	$20x + 19y = 58$	20 of type X + 19 of type Y weighs 58 g

where x and y are the weights of each type of screw, measured in grams.

Solving this system leads to the conclusion that type X weigh 1 g each and type Y weigh 2 g each.

However, the 55 g measurement represents 55 ± 0.5 g and the 58 g measurement represents 58 ± 0.5 g, giving percentage errors of around 1%. The table below shows the values of x and y as we explore these ranges.

		The weight of bag 2		
		57.5	**58**	**58.5**
The weight of bag 1	**54.5**	(0.5, 2.5)	(−8.5, 12)	(−17.5, 21.5)
	55	(10, −7.5)	(1, 2)	(−8, 11.5)
	55.5	(19.5, −17.5)	(10.5, −8)	(1.5, 1.5)

From the table we see $-17.5 \leq x \leq 19.5$ or $x = 1 \pm 18.5$ ... over 1000% error
and $-17.5 \leq y \leq 21.5$ or $y = 2 \pm 19.5$ ... 975% error

The actual result is being *swamped* by the error.

Geometrically, when solving a pair of simultaneous equations, we are finding where two lines intersect. If these lines are almost parallel then a slight shift in the position of even one line will result in a big shift in the point of intersection.
[The gradients of the above lines are −1.1111... and −1.0555...]

When a small change in any of the values in a system of equations leads to a disproportionate change in the solutions then the equations are said to be **ill-conditioned**.
When this occurs we have no confidence in the results obtained from such a system.

Similar effects occur in larger systems of equations, for example, this 3×3 system of equations.

$$11x + 12y + 3z = 44$$
$$10x + 10y + z = 33$$
$$42x + 43y + 6z = 146$$

As it stands, the solution is $x = 1, y = 2, z = 3$. However suppose 44 is actually 44 ± 1; exploring this *fuzziness* gives,

Altering Equation 1 to $11x + 12y + 3z = 43.5$ gives $x = -7.5, y = 11, z = -2$
Altering Equation 1 to $11x + 12y + 3z = 44.5$ gives $x = 9.5, y = -7, z = 8$

So at the very least we have $x = 1 \pm 8.5$ ... a percentage error of 850%.

If you have access to a calculator or spreadsheet, explore the parameters of this system.

Exercise 14.9

1 For each of these systems of equations

i copy and complete the table

ii identify the range for both x- and y-values

iii work out the percentage errors

iv say whether you think the system is ill-conditioned or not.

a $3x + 5y = 17$
$6x + 11y = 35$

	34.5	35	35.5
16.5			
17			
17.5			

b $x + 6y = 13$
$2x + y = 4$

	3.5	4	4.5
12.5			
13			
13.5			

c $7x + 4y = 26$
$5x + 3y = 19$

	18.5	19	19.5
25.5			
26			
26.5			

2 Identify which of these systems you feel are ill-conditioned.

a $2x + 9y = 17$
$3x - 5y = 7$

b $9x + 8y = 1$
$8x + 7y = 1$

c $8x + 13y = 18$
$3x + 5y = 7$

d $9x - 10y = 91$
$8x - 9y = 82$

3 At a crossroads, traffic lights automatically contol the flow of two streams of traffic. An observer times the changes.
10 turns for the eastbound traffic plus 10 turns for the northbound traffic took 1700 s.
10 turns for the eastbound traffic plus 11 turns for the northbound traffic took 1790 s.

a Form a system of equations using x and y seconds to represent the time it takes for one turn of the eastbound and northbound traffic respectively.

b Solve the system to find a value for x and y.

c Assuming the original timings were made to the nearest second, explore the confidence you can place in your solutions.

4 The spreadsheet on page 272 examines the system of equations

$$x + y + z = 19$$
$$3x + 16y + z = 95$$
$$2x + 9y + z = 59$$

By considering small changes to the values on the right-hand side of the equations, decide whether or not the system is ill-conditioned

5 Explore the augmented matrix where the left-hand side is a 4×4 symmetric matrix called Wilson's matrix.

$$\left(\begin{array}{cccc|c} 10 & 7 & 8 & 7 & 1 \\ 7 & 5 & 6 & 5 & 1 \\ 8 & 6 & 10 & 9 & 1 \\ 7 & 5 & 9 & 8 & 1 \end{array}\right)$$

a Change just one of the entries in the right-hand column and note the resulting change in the solution of the related system of equations.

b Examine different right-hand columns.

14.10 The inverse of a 3 × 3 matrix using EROs

The strategy for solving a system of equations by Gaussian elimination depends on the reduction of the matrix equation $AX = B$ by successive elementary row operations to the form $IX = A^{-1}B$.

The same operations which have reduced AX to IX have also reduced IB to $A^{-1}B$.
In other words, the EROs which convert A to I also convert I to A^{-1}.
This leads to a useful method of finding the inverse of a 3×3 matrix.

- Place A and I side-by-side on the page, with A on the left.
- Perform suitable EROs on the left-hand matrix with a view to reducing it to I.
- Simultaneously perform the same operations on the right-hand matrix.
- When the left-hand matrix is reduced to I, the right-hand matrix will be A^{-1}.

Example 2

$A = \begin{pmatrix} 1 & 1 & 1 \\ 2 & -3 & -1 \\ 5 & 2 & 3 \end{pmatrix}$ is a non-singular 3×3 matrix. Find its inverse.

$$\begin{pmatrix} 1 & 1 & 1 \\ 2 & -3 & -1 \\ 5 & 2 & 3 \end{pmatrix}\begin{pmatrix} 1 & 0 & 0 \\ 0 & 1 & 0 \\ 0 & 0 & 1 \end{pmatrix}$$

$R2 \to R2 - 2R1$, $R3 \to R3 - 5R1$

$$\begin{pmatrix} 1 & 1 & 1 \\ 0 & -5 & -3 \\ 0 & -3 & -2 \end{pmatrix}\begin{pmatrix} 1 & 0 & 0 \\ -2 & 1 & 0 \\ -5 & 0 & 1 \end{pmatrix}$$

The main diagonal entry in row 1 = 1. Make the entries below it 0.

$R2 \to R2 \div (-5)$, $R3 \to R3 + 3R2$

$$\begin{pmatrix} 1 & 1 & 1 \\ 0 & 1 & \frac{3}{5} \\ 0 & 0 & -\frac{1}{5} \end{pmatrix}\begin{pmatrix} 1 & 0 & 0 \\ \frac{2}{5} & -\frac{1}{5} & 0 \\ -\frac{19}{5} & -\frac{3}{5} & 1 \end{pmatrix}$$

Make main diagonal entry in row 2 = 1. Make the entry below it 0.

$R3 \to R3 \div \left(-\frac{1}{5}\right)$

$$\begin{pmatrix} 1 & 1 & 1 \\ 0 & 1 & \frac{3}{5} \\ 0 & 0 & 1 \end{pmatrix}\begin{pmatrix} 1 & 0 & 0 \\ \frac{2}{5} & -\frac{1}{5} & 0 \\ 19 & 3 & -5 \end{pmatrix}$$

Make main diagonal entry in row 3 = 1.

$R1 \to R1 - R3$, $R2 \to R2 - \frac{3}{5}R3$

$$\begin{pmatrix} 1 & 1 & 0 \\ 0 & 1 & 0 \\ 0 & 0 & 1 \end{pmatrix}\begin{pmatrix} -18 & -3 & 5 \\ -11 & -2 & 3 \\ 19 & 3 & -5 \end{pmatrix}$$

Make the entries above the main diagonal entry in row 3 become 0.

$R1 \to R1 - R2$

$$\begin{pmatrix} 1 & 0 & 0 \\ 0 & 1 & 0 \\ 0 & 0 & 1 \end{pmatrix}\begin{pmatrix} -7 & -1 & 2 \\ -11 & -2 & 3 \\ 19 & 3 & -5 \end{pmatrix}$$

Make the entries above the main diagonal entry in row 2 become 0.

The left-hand matrix has been reduced to I, so the right-hand matrix is the inverse

$$A^{-1} = \begin{pmatrix} -7 & -1 & 2 \\ -11 & -2 & 3 \\ 19 & 3 & -5 \end{pmatrix}$$

This method is mechanical in its approach and is readily adapted to find the inverses of higher-order matrices. However, calculations become tiresome, so the use of a spreadsheet is useful. If you have access to a spreadsheet, then programming it to do the above would be an instructive exercise.

Exercise 14.10

1 Using elementary row operations, find the inverse of each of these non-singular matrices.

a $\begin{pmatrix} 1 & 0 & 2 \\ 4 & 1 & 1 \\ 3 & 1 & 0 \end{pmatrix}$ **b** $\begin{pmatrix} 1 & 1 & 2 \\ 1 & 0 & 2 \\ 1 & 1 & 1 \end{pmatrix}$ **c** $\begin{pmatrix} 1 & -1 & 1 \\ -2 & 2 & -3 \\ 4 & -5 & 6 \end{pmatrix}$

d $\begin{pmatrix} 3 & 2 & -2 \\ 2 & 1 & 1 \\ 4 & 2 & 1 \end{pmatrix}$ **e** $\begin{pmatrix} 5 & 10 & 2 \\ 1 & 5 & 2 \\ 4 & 3 & -1 \end{pmatrix}$ **f** $\begin{pmatrix} 0 & -1 & -1 \\ 1 & 2 & 1 \\ 1 & -1 & -1 \end{pmatrix}$

2 For each of these matrices A

i show that A is invertible [by showing $|A| \neq 0$]

ii find the inverse matrix, A^{-1}, by using elementary row operations.

a $\begin{pmatrix} 0 & 1 & 0 \\ 0 & 0 & 1 \\ 1 & 0 & 0 \end{pmatrix}$ b $\begin{pmatrix} 0 & 0 & 1 \\ 0 & 1 & 0 \\ 1 & 0 & 0 \end{pmatrix}$ c $\begin{pmatrix} 1 & -1 & 1 \\ 0 & -1 & -1 \\ 0 & 0 & 1 \end{pmatrix}$

d $\begin{pmatrix} 1 & 0 & 0 \\ 3 & 1 & 0 \\ 2 & 1 & 4 \end{pmatrix}$ e $\begin{pmatrix} 1 & 3 & 5 \\ 0 & 1 & 4 \\ 0 & 0 & 1 \end{pmatrix}$ f $\begin{pmatrix} 1 & 0 & 0 \\ 2 & 1 & 0 \\ 3 & 4 & 1 \end{pmatrix}$

g $\begin{pmatrix} 3 & 2 & 1 \\ 5 & 6 & 4 \\ 7 & 2 & 3 \end{pmatrix}$ h $\begin{pmatrix} -1 & 4 & 1 \\ 2 & -3 & 1 \\ 1 & 2 & -1 \end{pmatrix}$

3 Find the unique solution of each of these systems of equations by first finding the inverse of the matrix of coefficients using elementary row operations.

a
$$\begin{aligned} x + y - z &= 1 \\ 3x + 2y + z &= 16 \\ 4x - y - 2z &= 15 \end{aligned}$$

b
$$\begin{aligned} x - 2y - z &= 2 \\ 2x + 4y + z &= 11 \\ 3x + 2y - 3z &= 10 \end{aligned}$$

c
$$\begin{aligned} 2x + 3y - z &= 1 \\ 3x - 4y + 2z &= 17 \\ 5x + y - 3z &= 8 \end{aligned}$$

4 Solve this system of equations using matrices:.
$$\begin{aligned} 2x + 3y &= 12 \\ x + 7y &= 17 \end{aligned}$$

5 Solve these systems of equations.

a
$$\begin{aligned} 3x + 2y \quad\;\; &= 1 \\ x + 2y + 4z &= 7 \\ 2x + y + 3z &= 7 \end{aligned}$$

b
$$\begin{aligned} x + y + z &= 6 \\ 2x + 3y + 7z &= 28 \\ x - y + 8z &= 25 \end{aligned}$$

6 Use elementary row operations to find the inverse of $A = \begin{pmatrix} 1 & 0 & 0 & 1 \\ 2 & 1 & 2 & 0 \\ 0 & 2 & 0 & 1 \\ 3 & 0 & 3 & -1 \end{pmatrix}$.

Review 14

1 Solve this 2×2 system of equations

a by elimination

b by using a matrix.

$$\begin{aligned} 2x + y &= 1 \\ 3x - 2y &= 5 \end{aligned}$$

2 a Express this 3×3 system of equations as

i a matrix equation (in the form $AX = B$)

ii in augmented matrix form.

$$\begin{aligned} 2x + y + z &= 2 \\ 3x + 2y - z &= 6 \\ x - y \quad\;\; &= 0 \end{aligned}$$

b Reduce the matrix to upper triangular form.

c Solve the system with the aid of back-substitution.

3 Solve this system of equations using Gaussian elimination.

$$\begin{aligned} x + y + z &= 1 \\ 2x - y - z &= 14 \\ x - 2y + z &= 4 \end{aligned}$$

4 In 1804 the first asteroid, Ceres, was discovered. Gauss, using a very small number of observations, was able to compute its elliptical orbit, sparking off *his* interest in numerical analysis and other people's interest in his methods.

Using suitable axes, an ellipse has the equation $ax^2 + by^2 + cx - 8y + 1 = 0$.
It passes through the points $(3, 1)$, $(-1, 1)$ and $(1, 2)$.

a Form a 3×3 system of equations using the data.

b Solve the system using Gaussian elimination.

c Write the equation of the ellipse.

5 Examine this system of equations.

$$\begin{aligned} x + y + z &= 2 \\ x + y \quad &= 5 \\ y + z &= -2 \end{aligned}$$

a Reduce the associated augmented matrix to the form $= \left(\begin{array}{ccc|c} 1 & 0 & 0 & p \\ 0 & 1 & 0 & q \\ 0 & 0 & 1 & r \end{array}\right)$.

b Hence declare the solution of the system.

6 Under what conditions does the system of equations

$$\begin{aligned} 2x + y + z &= 1 \\ x + 2y + 2z &= 1 \\ 3x + y + pz &= q \end{aligned}$$

a have no solution

b have infinitely many solutions?

7 Which system would you consider ill-conditioned?

a $\begin{aligned} 2x + 7y &= 5 \\ 3x + 10y &= 6 \end{aligned}$ **b** $\begin{aligned} 2x - 7y &= 5 \\ 3x + 10y &= 6 \end{aligned}$

8 Find the inverse of each matrix using elementary row operations.

a $\begin{pmatrix} 1 & 1 & 1 \\ 2 & 1 & 3 \\ 1 & -1 & -1 \end{pmatrix}$ **b** $\begin{pmatrix} 3 & 1 & 2 \\ 1 & 1 & 2 \\ 4 & 1 & 6 \end{pmatrix}$

Summary 14

1 A system of equations can be represented by a matrix equation of the form $AX = B$. For example

$$\begin{aligned} 2x + 3y + z &= 6 \\ 3x + y + 3z &= 7 \\ x + 2y + z &= 4 \end{aligned}$$

can be represented by $\begin{pmatrix} 2 & 3 & 1 \\ 3 & 1 & 3 \\ 1 & 2 & 1 \end{pmatrix} \begin{pmatrix} x \\ y \\ z \end{pmatrix} = \begin{pmatrix} 6 \\ 7 \\ 4 \end{pmatrix}$.

2 This form can be further compacted into the augmented matrix form

$$\left(\begin{array}{ccc|c} 2 & 3 & 1 & 6 \\ 3 & 1 & 3 & 7 \\ 1 & 2 & 1 & 4 \end{array}\right)$$

3 There are three elementary row operations (EROs) which can be performed on a matrix:

a Two rows can be interchanged $\quad R1 \leftrightarrow R2$

b A row can be multiplied by a constant $\quad R1 \rightarrow aR1$

c One row can have another row added to it $\quad R1 \rightarrow R1 + R2$

4 A combination of EROs can produce another row operation. For example one row can have a multiple of another row added to it $\quad R1 \rightarrow R1 + aR2$

5 a If a system of equations has a unique solution then the augmented matrix can be reduced to upper triangular form by row operations.

b If an $n \times n$ system has infinitely many solutions then, when simplified, the augmented matrix will contain at least one row of zero entries.

c If a system has no solutions then at least one row will suggest that $0 = a$ where a is non-zero.

6 When a system has a unique solution, it can be systematically worked out by reducing the augmented matrix to triangular form and then performing back-substitution. This technique is called **Gaussian elimination**.

7 When small changes in the coefficients produce disproportionately large changes in the solution the system is said to be **ill-conditioned**.

When the data used is rounded data and the system is ill-conditioned then no confidence can be put on the results obtained.

8 To find the inverse of a 3×3 matrix, A:
Place A and I side-by-side on the page, with A on the left.
Perform suitable EROs on the left-hand matrix with a view to reducing it to I.
Simultaneously perform the same operations on the right-hand matrix.
When the left-hand matrix is reduced to I, the right-hand matrix will be A^{-1}.

15 Vectors

Historical note

William Rowan Hamilton, Ireland's greatest scientist, tried to construct an algebra of vectors and rotation in three-dimensional space.

He knew that the multiplication of complex numbers could be interpreted as a rotation in two dimensions. His considerations led him to develop a new set of numbers of the form $a + bi + cj + dk$ called quaternions. Initial problems multiplying such numbers were overcome when Hamilton had a flash of inspiration while walking along the banks of the Royal Canal in Dublin. He was so exited about his solution that he carved it in the stone of Brougham Bridge under which he was then walking.

A plaque can be found there today to commemorate the moment. What he wrote was

$$i^2 = j^2 = k^2 = ijk = -1$$

The real number a was called the scalar part of the quaternion and $ib + jc + kd$ was called the vector part. As time passed the algebra of vectors became separate from the theory of quaternions. The mathematical physicist James Clerk Maxwell (1831–1879) was the main character in its development in Britain.

15.1 Reminders and definitions

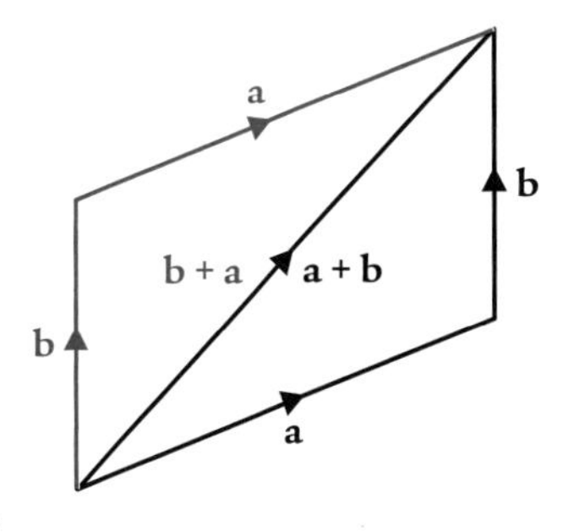

1 The addition of vectors is **commutative**.
This means that $\mathbf{a} + \mathbf{b} = \mathbf{b} + \mathbf{a}$.

2 The triangle inequality gives $|\mathbf{a} + \mathbf{b}| \leq |\mathbf{a}| + |\mathbf{b}|$ where $|\mathbf{a}|$ represents the magnitude of $\mathbf{a}$.

3 The addition of vectors is **associative**.
This means $\mathbf{a} + (\mathbf{b} + \mathbf{c}) = (\mathbf{a} + \mathbf{b}) + \mathbf{c}$.
Thus it is acceptable to write $\mathbf{a} + \mathbf{b} + \mathbf{c}$ without brackets.

4 The **negative** of a vector $\mathbf{u}$ has the same magnitude and direction as $\mathbf{u}$, but the opposite *sense*.
Subtraction of vectors can be defined by $\mathbf{a} - \mathbf{b} = \mathbf{a} + (-\mathbf{b})$.

5 If a vector $\mathbf{u}$ is multiplied by a scalar k, then the product $k\mathbf{u}$ is a vector in the same direction as $\mathbf{u}$ but k times the magnitude.

If $|k| > 1$, then the magnitude is increased.

If $|k| < 1$, then the magnitude is decreased.

If $k > 0$, then $k\mathbf{u}$ has the same sense as $\mathbf{u}$.

If $k < 0$, then $k\mathbf{u}$ has the opposite sense to $\mathbf{u}$.

6 Multiplication of a vector by a scalar is **distributive** over addition.

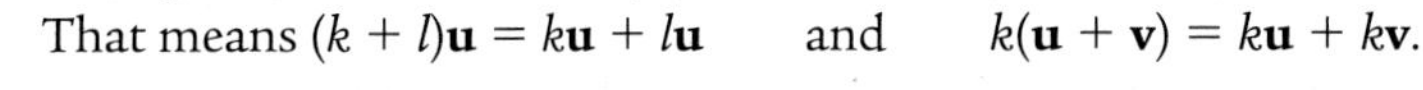

That means $(k + l)\mathbf{u} = k\mathbf{u} + l\mathbf{u}$ and $k(\mathbf{u} + \mathbf{v}) = k\mathbf{u} + k\mathbf{v}$.

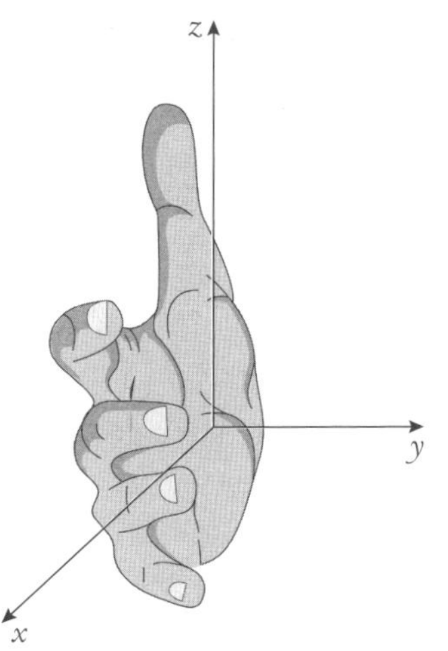

7 A three-dimensional coordinate system can be either right-handed or left-handed.

For a right-handed system... holding your right hand out as in preparation for a handshake, the x-direction is indicated by the fingers, the y-direction by the palm of the hand and the z-direction by the thumb.

The left-handed version can be described in a similar fashion.
Most applications work with right-handed systems.

8 Given the point A(a_1, a_2, a_3) then the vector $\boldsymbol{a} = \begin{pmatrix} a_1 \\ a_2 \\ a_3 \end{pmatrix}$ is called the position vector of A.

By convention an upper-case letter represents a point and the corresponding lower-case letter, its position vector.

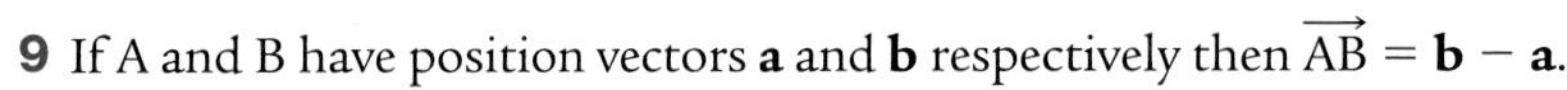

9 If A and B have position vectors **a** and **b** respectively then $\overrightarrow{AB} = \mathbf{b} - \mathbf{a}$.

10 If P divides $\overrightarrow{AB}$ in the ratio $m : n$ then $\dfrac{|\overrightarrow{AP}|}{|\overrightarrow{PB}|} = \dfrac{m}{n}$.

Using position vectors leads to $\mathbf{p} = \dfrac{m\mathbf{b} + n\mathbf{a}}{m + n}$.

11 The **magnitude** of vector $\mathbf{u} = \begin{pmatrix} u_1 \\ u_2 \\ u_3 \end{pmatrix}$ is denoted by $|\mathbf{u}| = \sqrt{u_1^2 + u_2^2 + u_3^2}$.

12 A **unit vector** is a vector with a magnitude of 1. A unit vector in the same direction as vector **a** is often denoted by $\mathbf{u}_a$. Obviously, $\mathbf{u}_a = \dfrac{1}{|\mathbf{a}|}\mathbf{a}$.

13 Unit vectors in the x-direction, y-direction and z-direction are denoted by **i**, **j** and **k** respectively.

Thus $\mathbf{i} = \begin{pmatrix} 1 \\ 0 \\ 0 \end{pmatrix}, \mathbf{j} = \begin{pmatrix} 0 \\ 1 \\ 0 \end{pmatrix}, \mathbf{k} = \begin{pmatrix} 0 \\ 0 \\ 1 \end{pmatrix}$.

14 Any vector can be expressed in terms of **i**, **j** and **k**.

For example $\begin{pmatrix} 2 \\ 3 \\ -5 \end{pmatrix} = \begin{pmatrix} 2 \\ 0 \\ 0 \end{pmatrix} + \begin{pmatrix} 0 \\ 3 \\ 0 \end{pmatrix} + \begin{pmatrix} 0 \\ 0 \\ -5 \end{pmatrix} = 2\begin{pmatrix} 1 \\ 0 \\ 0 \end{pmatrix} + 3\begin{pmatrix} 0 \\ 1 \\ 0 \end{pmatrix} + (-5)\begin{pmatrix} 0 \\ 0 \\ 1 \end{pmatrix}$

$= 2\mathbf{i} + 3\mathbf{j} - 5\mathbf{k}$

15 The **projection** of a point P on a plane is the point P′ at the foot of the perpendicular to the plane passing through P.

16 The projection of a line PQ on a plane is the line P′Q′ which joins the projections of P and Q on the plane.

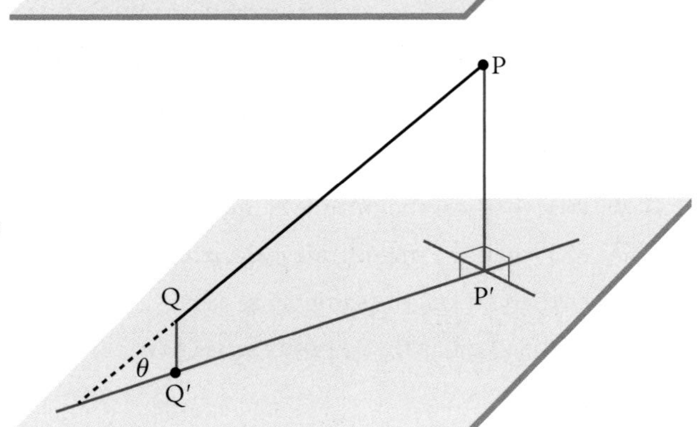

17 The angle between a line and a plane, θ, is the angle between the line and its projection on the plane.

18 In a similar fashion the projection of a point P on a line and of a line segment on a line can be defined.

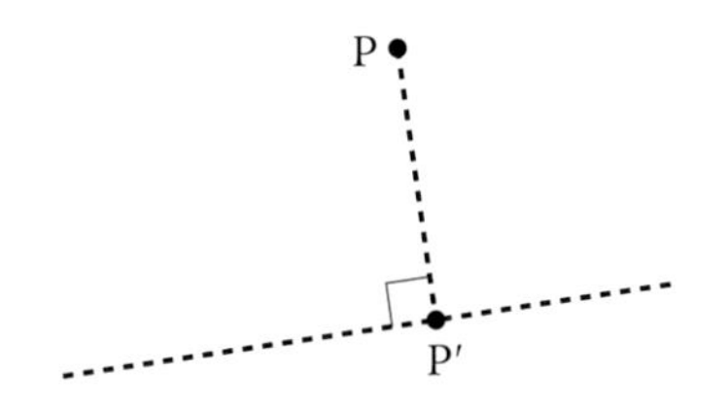

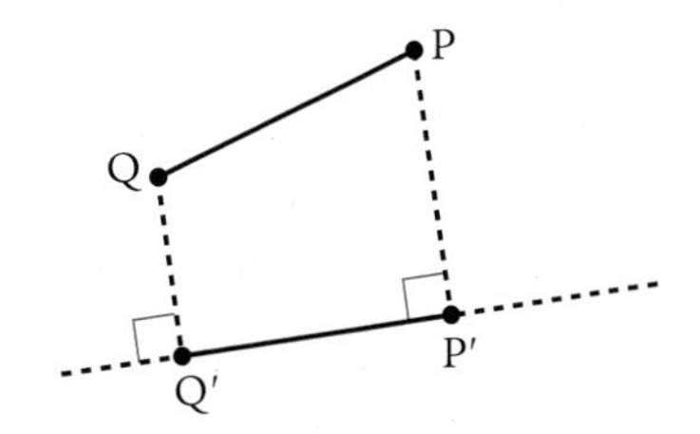

19 When the representatives of vectors **a** and **b** are positioned tail-to-tail they make an angle of θ. The magnitude of the projection of **b** on **a** is given by $|\mathbf{b}|\cos\theta$.

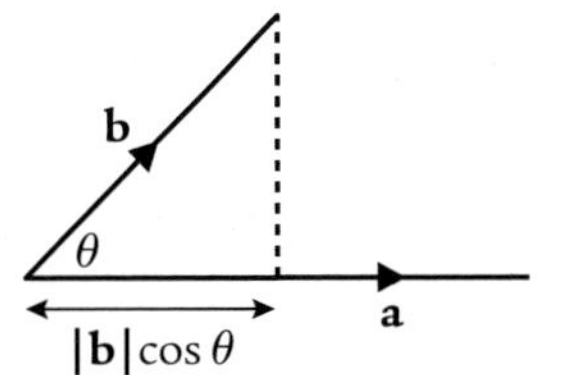

20 A definition:

The product $|\mathbf{a}|\,|\mathbf{b}|\cos\theta$ is called the **scalar product** of **a** and **b** and is denoted by $\mathbf{a}\cdot\mathbf{b}$. Because of the notation, it is often referred to as the **dot product**.

a $\mathbf{a}\cdot\mathbf{b}$ is a scalar.

b $\mathbf{a}\cdot\mathbf{a} = |\mathbf{a}|\,|\mathbf{a}|\cos 0 = |\mathbf{a}|^2$

c $\mathbf{a}\cdot\mathbf{b} = \mathbf{b}\cdot\mathbf{a}$ (the scalar product is commutative)

d $\mathbf{a}\cdot(\mathbf{b}+\mathbf{c}) = \mathbf{a}\cdot\mathbf{b} + \mathbf{a}\cdot\mathbf{c}$ (the scalar product is distributive over addition)

e $\mathbf{a}\cdot\mathbf{b} = 0$ and $\mathbf{a} \neq 0$ and $\mathbf{b} \neq 0 \Leftrightarrow$ **a** and **b** are perpendicular

f $\mathbf{i}\cdot\mathbf{i} = \mathbf{j}\cdot\mathbf{j} = \mathbf{k}\cdot\mathbf{k} = 1\cdot 1\cdot\cos 0° = 1$ and $\mathbf{i}\cdot\mathbf{j} = \mathbf{j}\cdot\mathbf{k} = \mathbf{k}\cdot\mathbf{i} = 1\cdot 1\cdot\cos 90° = 0$

g Given that

$$\mathbf{a} = \begin{pmatrix} a_1 \\ a_2 \\ a_3 \end{pmatrix} = a_1\mathbf{i} + a_2\mathbf{j} + a_3\mathbf{k} \text{ and } \mathbf{b} = \begin{pmatrix} b_1 \\ b_2 \\ b_3 \end{pmatrix} = b_1\mathbf{i} + b_2\mathbf{j} + b_3\mathbf{k}$$

$$\mathbf{a}\cdot\mathbf{b} = (a_1\mathbf{i} + a_2\mathbf{j} + a_3\mathbf{k})(b_1\mathbf{i} + b_2\mathbf{j} + b_3\mathbf{k}) = a_1b_1 + a_2b_2 + a_3b_3$$

h The angle θ can be determined using

$$\cos\theta = \frac{\mathbf{a}\cdot\mathbf{b}}{|\mathbf{a}|\,|\mathbf{b}|} = \frac{a_1b_1 + a_2b_2 + a_3b_3}{\sqrt{a_1^2 + a_2^2 + a_3^2}\sqrt{b_1^2 + b_2^2 + b_3^2}}$$

Exercise 15.1

1 Show that the points P(7, −2, 11), Q(9, 0, 7) and R(12, 3, 1) are collinear, stating the ratio PQ : QR.

2 Show that the three points P(1, −2, −8), Q(5, 0, −2) and R(11, 3, 7) are collinear, and find the ratio in which Q divides PR.

3 OADBCEFG is a parallelepiped.

$\overrightarrow{OA} = \mathbf{i} + 2\mathbf{j} + 3\mathbf{k}$, $\overrightarrow{OB} = 3\mathbf{i} + \mathbf{j}$, $\overrightarrow{OC} = 5\mathbf{i} + 7\mathbf{j}$.

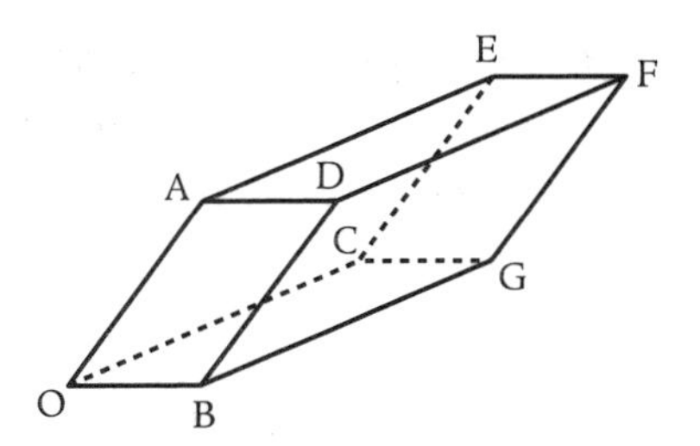

Find the components of

a $\overrightarrow{OG}$ b $\overrightarrow{OF}$ c $\overrightarrow{CF}$

d $\overrightarrow{ED}$ e $\overrightarrow{GE}$ f $\overrightarrow{BE}$

g $\overrightarrow{AG}$ h $\overrightarrow{OH}$, where H is the mid-point of BC.

4 VABCD is a right pyramid with a rectangular base.

$\overrightarrow{AV} = \begin{pmatrix} 18 \\ 14 \\ 2 \end{pmatrix}$, $\overrightarrow{AD} = \begin{pmatrix} -4 \\ 16 \\ 8 \end{pmatrix}$, $\overrightarrow{AB} = \begin{pmatrix} 8 \\ -4 \\ 12 \end{pmatrix}$

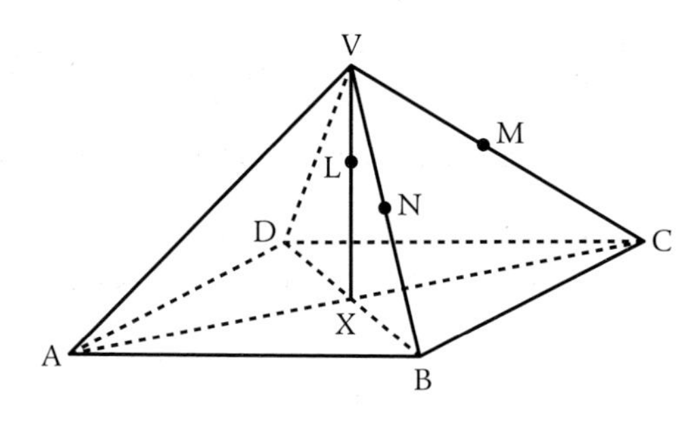

X is the centre of the base.

M is the mid-point of VC.

N is the mid-point of VB.

L lies three-quarters of the way up XV.

Find the components of **a** $\overrightarrow{AM}$ **b** $\overrightarrow{DN}$ **c** $\overrightarrow{CL}$

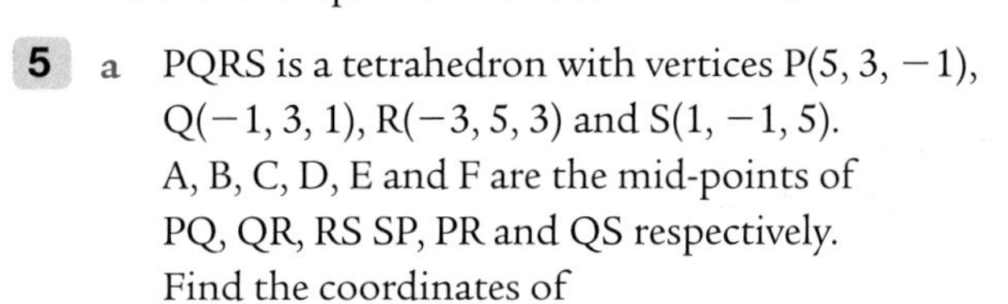

5 **a** PQRS is a tetrahedron with vertices P(5, 3, −1), Q(−1, 3, 1), R(−3, 5, 3) and S(1, −1, 5).
A, B, C, D, E and F are the mid-points of PQ, QR, RS SP, PR and QS respectively.
Find the coordinates of

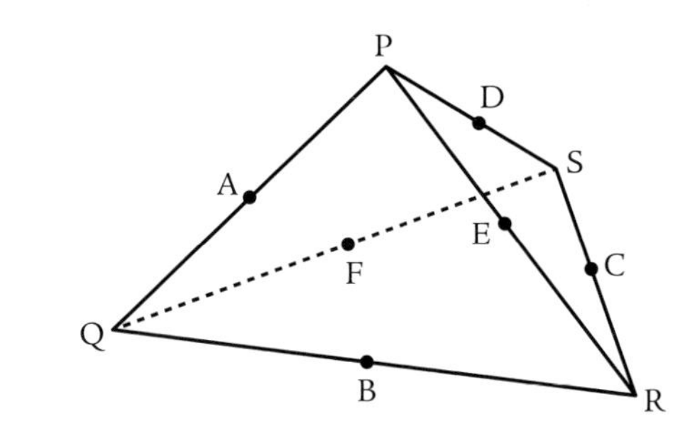

i W, the mid-point of EF

ii X, the mid-point of AC

iii Y, the mid-point of BD.

b Show that if PQRS is *any* tetrahedron with mid-points labelled as above, then W, X and Y are coincident points.

6 **a** K is the point (5, −1, 4) and L is (10, 4, −1).
Find the coordinates of the point M which divides KL internally in the ratio 3 : 2.

b Find the coordinates of X which divides YZ internally in the ratio 2 : 1, where Y is the point (1, 0, 1) and Z is (4, 6, 10).

c Given the points A(2, −1, 1) and B(6, 11, −7),
find the coordinates of P which divide AB *externally* in the ratio 1 : 3.
$\left[\text{Hint: } \dfrac{|\overrightarrow{AP}|}{|\overrightarrow{PB}|} = -\dfrac{1}{3}\right]$

7 Calculate the size of the angle between the vectors

a $\mathbf{u} = 12\mathbf{i} + 24\mathbf{j} + 3\mathbf{k}$ and $\mathbf{v} = 10\mathbf{i} - 5\mathbf{j} + 10\mathbf{k}$

b $\mathbf{r} = 6\mathbf{i} + 6\mathbf{j} - 7\mathbf{k}$ and $\mathbf{s} = 4\mathbf{i} - 7\mathbf{j} - 4\mathbf{k}$.

8 S and T are the points (6, 2, 3) and (2, −9, 6).
Calculate the size of angle SOT.

9 Find the value of t for which $2\mathbf{i} + 3\mathbf{j} - 9\mathbf{k}$ is perpendicular to $3\mathbf{i} - 4\mathbf{j} - t\mathbf{k}$.

10 **a** Prove that the vectors $\mathbf{a} = 2\mathbf{i} + 4\mathbf{j} + 5\mathbf{k}$ and $\mathbf{b} = 3\mathbf{i} - 4\mathbf{j} + 2\mathbf{k}$ are perpendicular.

b Find the value of k for which the vectors
$\mathbf{s} = k\mathbf{i} - 2\mathbf{j} + 3\mathbf{k}$ and $\mathbf{t} = \mathbf{i} + 2\mathbf{j} - \mathbf{k}$ are perpendicular.

11 The vectors $\mathbf{p}$ and $\mathbf{q}$ are inclined at 60° to each other, with $|\mathbf{p}| = 3$ and $|\mathbf{q}| = 8$.
Evaluate $\mathbf{p} \cdot (\mathbf{p} + \mathbf{q})$.

12 K, L and M are the points (1, 2, 3), (0, 6, 11) and (−4, −2, 10) respectively. Show that $\cos \angle KLM = \frac{4}{9}$.

15.2 The vector product

Two vectors can be combined by a binary operation, the scalar product, to produce a number (or scalar).

It is also possible to define an operation where two vectors, **a** and **b**, *multiply* to produce a vector.
This is referred to as the **vector product**, or **cross product**, and is denoted by $\mathbf{a} \times \mathbf{b}$.

Any two non-parallel vectors, **a** and **b**, define a plane.
Let **n** be a *unit* vector perpendicular to this plane (a normal to the plane) so that **a**, **b** and **n** form a right-handed system of vectors.

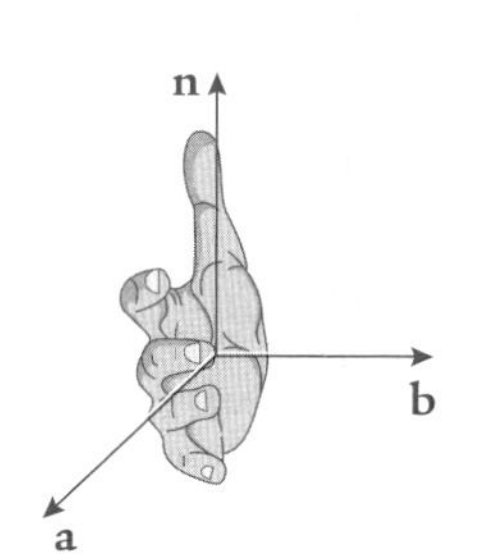

Note:
a along the fingers
b from the palm of the hand
n along the thumb
The angle between **a** and **b** need not be 90°

The vector product is defined as $\mathbf{a} \times \mathbf{b} = \mathbf{n}|\mathbf{a}|\,|\mathbf{b}|\sin\theta$
where θ is the angle between the positive directions of **a** and **b**.

If either $\mathbf{a} = \mathbf{0}$ or $\mathbf{b} = \mathbf{0}$ then **n** is not defined and $\mathbf{a} \times \mathbf{b}$ is defined as **0**.

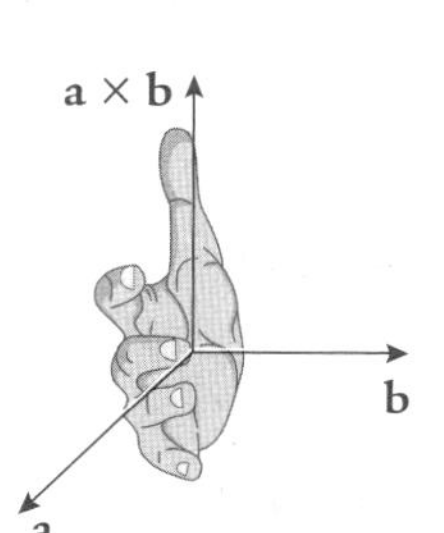

These properties follow directly from the definition.

- $\mathbf{a} \times \mathbf{b}$ is a vector with the same sense and direction as **n**
- $|\mathbf{a} \times \mathbf{b}| = |\mathbf{a}|\,|\mathbf{b}|\sin\theta$
  which is the area of the parallelogram defined by **a** and **b**
- $|\mathbf{a} \times \mathbf{a}| = |\mathbf{a}|\,|\mathbf{a}|\sin 0 = 0$

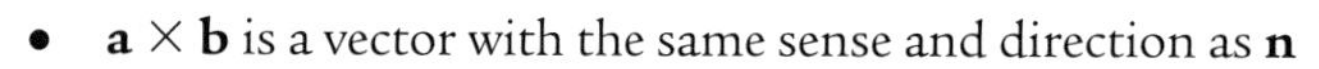

- $|\mathbf{a} \times k\mathbf{a}| = |\mathbf{a}|\,|k\mathbf{a}|\sin 0 = 0$ – parallel vectors have a vector product of zero
- $\mathbf{a} \neq 0$ and $\mathbf{b} \neq 0$ and $|\mathbf{a} \times \mathbf{b}| = 0 \Rightarrow$ **a** and **b** are parallel vectors
- $\mathbf{a} \times \mathbf{b} = -(\mathbf{b} \times \mathbf{a})$ – the vector product is *not* commutative
- **i**, **j** and **k** form a right-handed system so
  $\mathbf{i} \times \mathbf{j} = \mathbf{k}|\mathbf{i}|\,|\mathbf{j}|\sin 90° = \mathbf{k}$ and, similarly, $\mathbf{j} \times \mathbf{k} = \mathbf{i}$, $\mathbf{k} \times \mathbf{i} = \mathbf{j}$
- $\mathbf{j} \times \mathbf{i} = -\mathbf{k}$, $\mathbf{k} \times \mathbf{j} = -\mathbf{i}$, $\mathbf{i} \times \mathbf{k} = -\mathbf{j}$

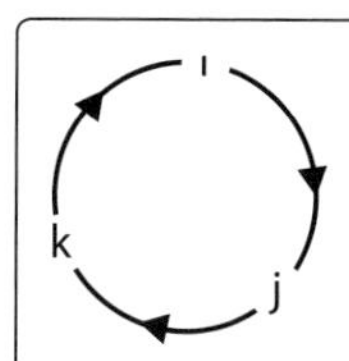

These six results can be memorised using this diagram. Clock-wise gives a positive result, anti-clockwise a negative one.

- The vector product is distributive over addition
  $\mathbf{a} \times (\mathbf{b} + \mathbf{c}) = \mathbf{a} \times \mathbf{b} + \mathbf{a} \times \mathbf{c}$ and $(\mathbf{a} + \mathbf{b}) \times \mathbf{c} = \mathbf{a} \times \mathbf{c} + \mathbf{b} \times \mathbf{c}$
  The proof is too long to include at this stage.

Example 1

Copy the diagram and on it indicate the magnitude and direction of the vector product

a $\mathbf{a} \times \mathbf{b}$ b $\mathbf{b} \times \mathbf{a}$

[Note: an ambiguity is caused by trying to represent 3D in 2D. To clarify in this case, **b** is running into the page and **a** is coming out. We might equally say that **a** is nearer the reader.]

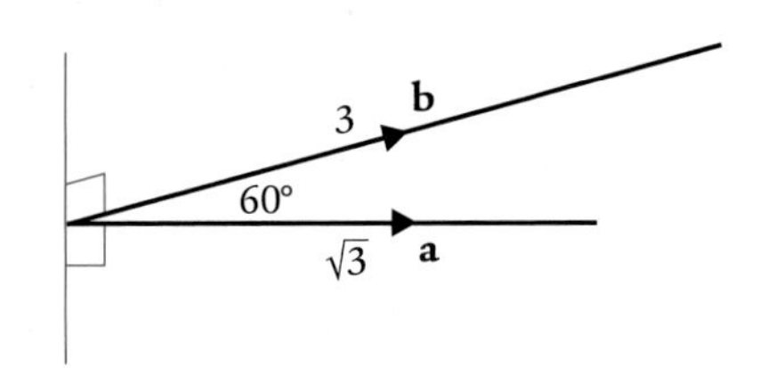

a Magnitude: $|\mathbf{a} \times \mathbf{b}| = \sqrt{3} \times 3 \times \sin 60° = 3 \times \sqrt{3} \times \frac{\sqrt{3}}{2} = \frac{9}{2}$

Direction: imagining the right-hand fingers along **a**, and **b** coming out of the palm of the hand, then the thumb would be pointing upwards, giving

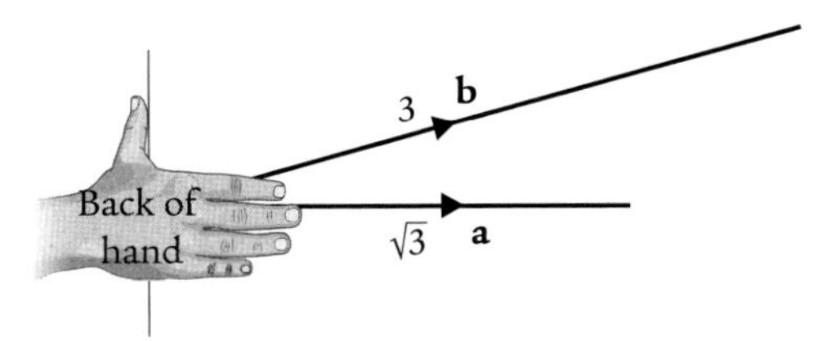

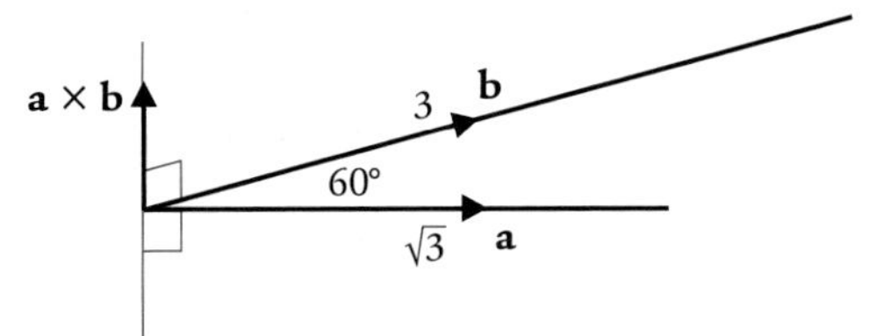

b Magnitude: $|\mathbf{b} \times \mathbf{a}| = 3 \times \sqrt{3} \times \sin 60° = 3 \times \sqrt{3} \times \frac{\sqrt{3}}{2} = \frac{9}{2}$

Direction: imagining the right-hand fingers along **b**, and **a** coming out of the palm of the hand, then the thumb would be pointing downwards, giving

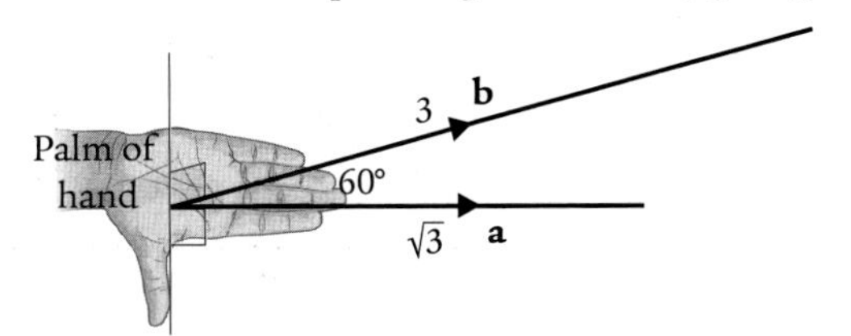

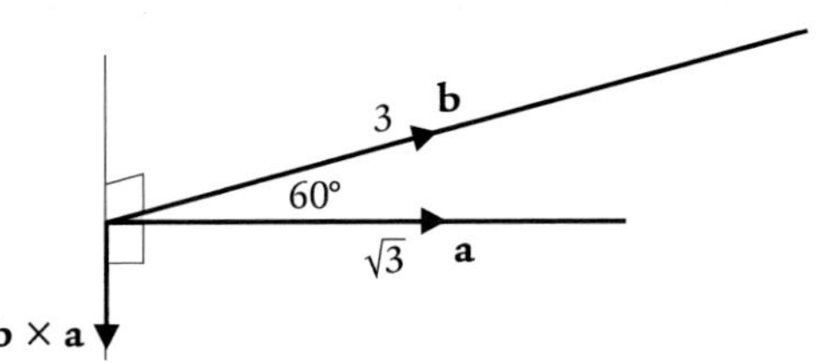

Note that as expected $\mathbf{a} \times \mathbf{b}$ and $\mathbf{b} \times \mathbf{a}$ have the same magnitude and direction but the opposite sense.

Exercise 15.2

1 Copy each diagram and add $\mathbf{a} \times \mathbf{b}$ in each case, indicating the magnitude and direction clearly. The *normal* to the plane occupied by **a** and **b** is indicated in each case and a statement is included to clarify the ambiguity caused by optical illusion.

a

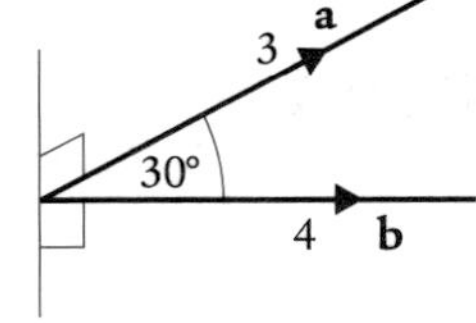

b is nearer

b

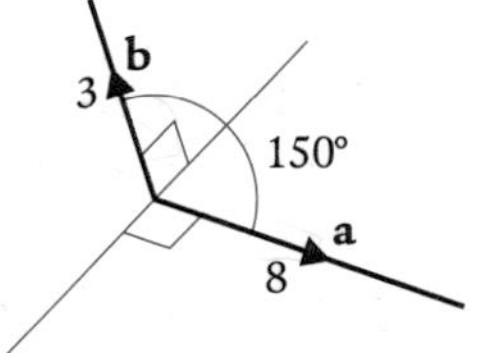

b comes out of the page

c

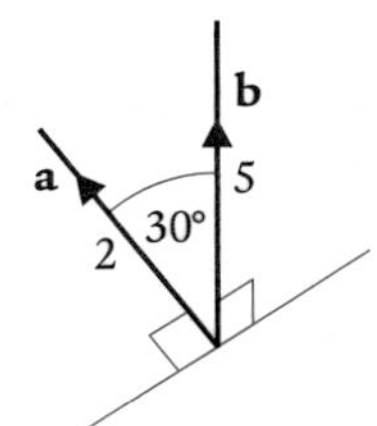

b is nearer

d

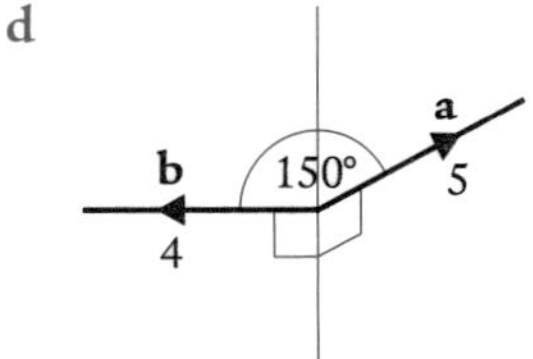

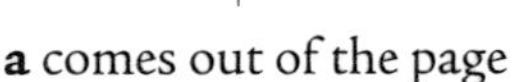

a comes out of the page

e

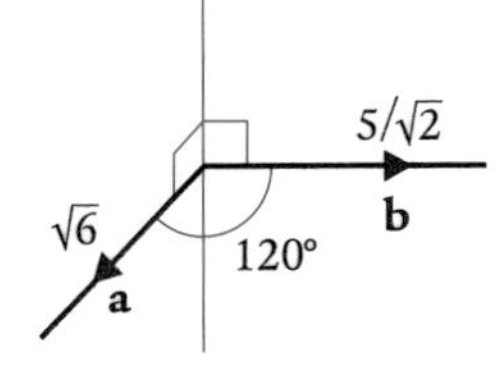

a comes out of the page

f

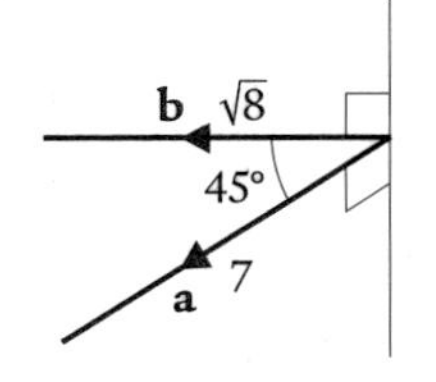

a comes out of the page

2 Let A, B be the points A(3, 4, 0) and B(5, 12, 0).

a By considering the scalar product $\overrightarrow{OA} \cdot \overrightarrow{OB}$, find the exact value of $\cos \angle AOB$.

b Given that $\angle AOB$ is acute, find the exact value of $\sin \angle AOB$.

c Give the magnitude and direction of $\overrightarrow{OA} \times \overrightarrow{OB}$.

3 For each pair of points, work out the magnitude and direction of the vector product of the related position vectors, by first finding their scalar product.

a P(6, 0, 8) and Q(16, 0, 12) b R(0, 5, 12) and T(0, 9, 12)

c W(6, −8, 0) and V(10, −24, 0) d M(0, 0, 4) and N(0, 8, 15)

4 By considering the strategy used in Questions 2 and 3 prove that $|\mathbf{a} \times \mathbf{b}|^2 = (|\mathbf{a}|\,|\mathbf{b}|)^2 - (\mathbf{a} \cdot \mathbf{b})^2$.

5 Use the fact that the vector product is distributive over addition to show that

$(\mathbf{a} - \mathbf{b}) \times (\mathbf{a} + \mathbf{b}) = 2(\mathbf{a} \times \mathbf{b})$

6 By considering the definition of $\mathbf{a} \times \mathbf{b}$ prove that $k(\mathbf{a} \times \mathbf{b}) = (k\mathbf{a}) \times \mathbf{b} = \mathbf{a} \times (k\mathbf{b})$.

7 If **a**, **b** and **c** form the triangle shown, prove that

$\mathbf{a} \times \mathbf{b} = \mathbf{b} \times \mathbf{c} = \mathbf{c} \times \mathbf{a}$

[Hint: consider the obvious relation between **a**, **b** and **c** then construct suitable vector products.]

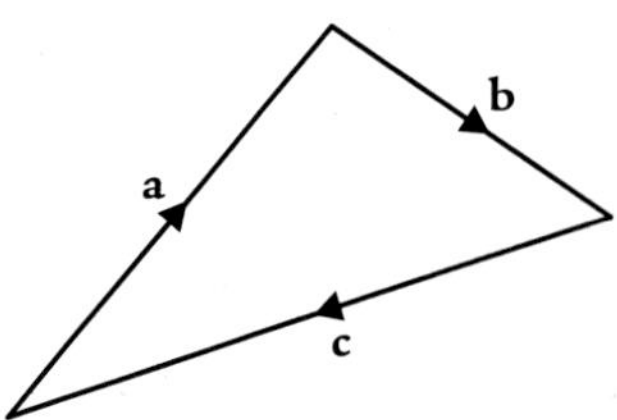

8 The point M is the midpoint of BC, that is, AM is a median of the triangle ABC.
$\overrightarrow{AB} = \mathbf{c}$ and $\overrightarrow{AC} = \mathbf{b}$

Express the vector product $\overrightarrow{MB} \times \overrightarrow{MA}$ in terms of **b** and **c**.

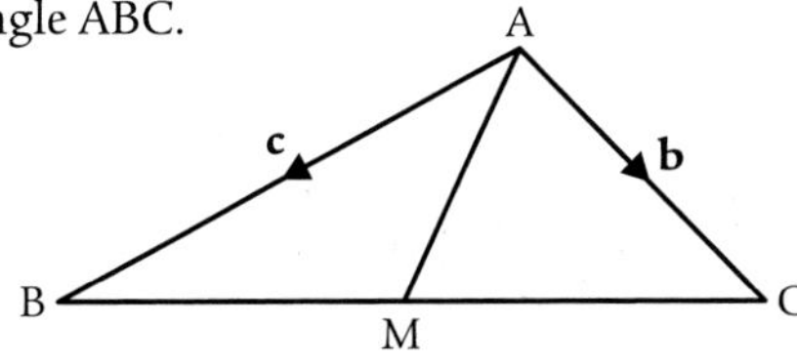

9 The point P lies on the side BC of △ABC such that $\overrightarrow{BP} = \mathbf{t}$ and $\overrightarrow{CP} = \mathbf{w}$.

If $\overrightarrow{AB} = \mathbf{u}$ and $\overrightarrow{AC} = \mathbf{v}$, prove that $\mathbf{u} \times \mathbf{v} = \mathbf{u} \times \mathbf{t} + \mathbf{w} \times \mathbf{v}$.

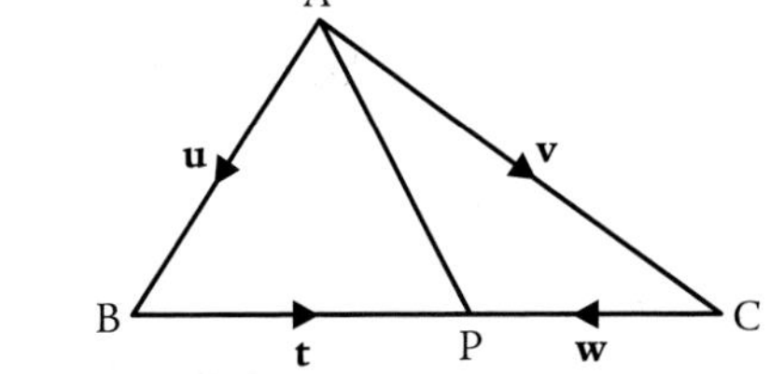

10 Non-zero non-parallel vectors **a**, **b** and **c** are such that $\mathbf{b} \times \mathbf{c} = \mathbf{c} \times \mathbf{a}$.

Prove that $\mathbf{a} + \mathbf{b} = k\mathbf{c}$ for some scalar k.

11 Prove that if the numbers p, q, r and s satisfy $ps = qr$, then $(p\mathbf{a} + q\mathbf{b}) \times (r\mathbf{a} + s\mathbf{b}) = \mathbf{0}$.

15.3 Component form of the vector product

Suppose $\mathbf{a} = \begin{pmatrix} a_1 \\ a_2 \\ a_3 \end{pmatrix}$ and $\mathbf{b} = \begin{pmatrix} b_1 \\ b_2 \\ b_3 \end{pmatrix}$, then $\mathbf{a} \times \mathbf{b} = (a_1\mathbf{i} + a_2\mathbf{j} + a_3\mathbf{k}) \times (b_1\mathbf{i} + b_2\mathbf{j} + b_3\mathbf{k})$.

Using the distributive law

$$\begin{aligned}\mathbf{a} \times \mathbf{b} = {} & a_1b_1(\mathbf{i} \times \mathbf{i}) + a_1b_2(\mathbf{i} \times \mathbf{j}) + a_1b_3(\mathbf{i} \times \mathbf{k}) \\ & + a_2b_1(\mathbf{j} \times \mathbf{i}) + a_2b_2(\mathbf{j} \times \mathbf{j}) + a_2b_3(\mathbf{j} \times \mathbf{k}) \\ & + a_3b_1(\mathbf{k} \times \mathbf{i}) + a_3b_2(\mathbf{k} \times \mathbf{j}) + a_3b_3(\mathbf{j} \times \mathbf{k})\end{aligned}$$

$$\begin{aligned}\mathbf{a} \times \mathbf{b} = {} & \mathbf{0} + a_1b_2\mathbf{k} + a_1b_3(-\mathbf{j}) \\ & + a_2b_1(-\mathbf{k}) + \mathbf{0} + a_2b_3\mathbf{i} \\ & + a_3b_1\mathbf{j} + a_3b_2(-\mathbf{i}) + \mathbf{0}\end{aligned}$$

$\mathbf{a} \times \mathbf{b} = (a_2b_3 - a_3b_2)\mathbf{i} - (a_1b_3 - a_3b_1)\mathbf{j} + (a_1b_2 - a_2b_1)\mathbf{k}$

Using the matrix notation developed in Chapter 13 we have

$$\mathbf{a} \times \mathbf{b} = \begin{vmatrix} \mathbf{i} & \mathbf{j} & \mathbf{k} \\ a_1 & a_2 & a_3 \\ b_1 & b_2 & b_3 \end{vmatrix}$$

Example 2

Calculate the area of the triangle whose vertices are A(2, −1, 3), B(5, −1, 2) and C(2, 3, 4).

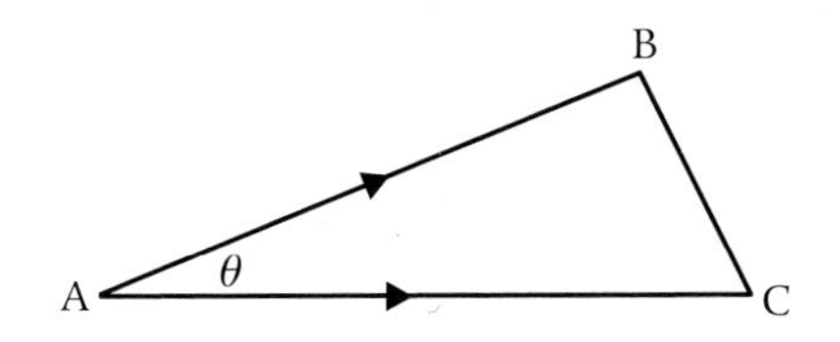

Area of $\triangle ABC = \frac{1}{2}|\overrightarrow{AB}||\overrightarrow{AC}|\sin\theta = \frac{1}{2}|\overrightarrow{AB} \times \overrightarrow{AC}|$

$$\overrightarrow{AB} = \begin{pmatrix} 5-2 \\ -1-(-1) \\ 2-3 \end{pmatrix} = \begin{pmatrix} 3 \\ 0 \\ -1 \end{pmatrix}$$

$$\overrightarrow{AC} = \begin{pmatrix} 2-2 \\ 3-(-1) \\ 4-3 \end{pmatrix} = \begin{pmatrix} 0 \\ 4 \\ 1 \end{pmatrix}$$

$$\text{Area of } \triangle ABC = \frac{1}{2}\left|\begin{pmatrix} 3 \\ 0 \\ -1 \end{pmatrix} \times \begin{pmatrix} 0 \\ 4 \\ 1 \end{pmatrix}\right| = \frac{1}{2}\begin{vmatrix} \mathbf{i} & \mathbf{j} & \mathbf{k} \\ 3 & 0 & -1 \\ 0 & 4 & 1 \end{vmatrix}$$

$$= \tfrac{1}{2}|(0 \times 1 - 4 \times (-1))\mathbf{i} - (3 \times 1 - 0 \times (-1))\mathbf{j} + (3 \times 4 - 0 \times 0)\mathbf{k}|$$

$$= \tfrac{1}{2}|4\mathbf{i} - 3\mathbf{j} + 12\mathbf{k}|$$

$$= \tfrac{1}{2}\sqrt{4^2 + (-3)^2 + 12^2}$$

$$= \tfrac{13}{2} \text{ square units}$$

Note:

We can quickly check our arithmetic. Both vectors must be perpendicular to their cross product. So the dot product of each of the vectors with the cross product is zero.

$$\begin{pmatrix} 4 \\ -3 \\ 12 \end{pmatrix} \cdot \begin{pmatrix} 3 \\ 0 \\ -1 \end{pmatrix} = 0 = \begin{pmatrix} 4 \\ -3 \\ 12 \end{pmatrix} \cdot \begin{pmatrix} 0 \\ 4 \\ 1 \end{pmatrix}$$

Exercise 15.3

1 Evaluate

a $\left|\begin{pmatrix} 1 \\ 0 \\ 0 \end{pmatrix} \times \begin{pmatrix} 0 \\ 1 \\ 0 \end{pmatrix}\right|$ b $\left|\begin{pmatrix} 1 \\ 2 \\ 3 \end{pmatrix} \times \begin{pmatrix} 4 \\ 5 \\ 6 \end{pmatrix}\right|$ c $\left|\begin{pmatrix} 3 \\ -1 \\ 2 \end{pmatrix} \times \begin{pmatrix} 5 \\ 7 \\ 0 \end{pmatrix}\right|$ d $\left|\begin{pmatrix} 5 \\ -7 \\ -2 \end{pmatrix} \times \begin{pmatrix} 8 \\ 4 \\ -1 \end{pmatrix}\right|$

2 Express $\overrightarrow{PQ} \times \overrightarrow{PR}$ in component form for each set of coordinates.

a P(1, −1, 0), Q(2, 1, −1), R(3, 0, 3)
b P(4 0, 2), Q(1, 3, 2), R(−1, −2, 0)
c P(0, 5, 3), Q(−1, 2, −1), R(6, 0, 0)
d P(−4 0, 4), Q(0, 3, 2), R(−6, 5, −3)

3 a Simplify the expression $(\mathbf{a} + 2\mathbf{b}) \times (2\mathbf{a} + \mathbf{b})$.

b Express in component form when $\mathbf{a} = \begin{pmatrix} 3 \\ 1 \\ 1 \end{pmatrix}$ and $\mathbf{b} = \begin{pmatrix} 0 \\ 2 \\ -1 \end{pmatrix}$.

4 If $\mathbf{a} = \begin{pmatrix} 2 \\ 1 \\ -1 \end{pmatrix}$, $\mathbf{b} = \begin{pmatrix} 1 \\ -1 \\ -1 \end{pmatrix}$ and $\mathbf{c} = \begin{pmatrix} 1 \\ 2 \\ 2 \end{pmatrix}$, verify that

$(\mathbf{c} - \mathbf{a}) \times (\mathbf{b} - \mathbf{a}) = (\mathbf{b} - \mathbf{c}) \times (\mathbf{a} - \mathbf{c})$

5 For $\mathbf{a} = \begin{pmatrix} 3 \\ 2 \\ -1 \end{pmatrix}$, $\mathbf{b} = \begin{pmatrix} 1 \\ -1 \\ -2 \end{pmatrix}$ and $\mathbf{c} = \begin{pmatrix} 4 \\ -3 \\ 4 \end{pmatrix}$, verify that

$\mathbf{a} \times (\mathbf{b} \times \mathbf{c}) \neq (\mathbf{a} \times \mathbf{b}) \times \mathbf{c}$

6 Given $\mathbf{u} = \begin{pmatrix} 2 \\ 2 \\ -1 \end{pmatrix}$, $\mathbf{v} = \begin{pmatrix} 3 \\ -1 \\ -2 \end{pmatrix}$ and $\mathbf{w} = \begin{pmatrix} 2 \\ -3 \\ 4 \end{pmatrix}$, evaluate

a $(\mathbf{u} \times \mathbf{v}) \cdot (\mathbf{u} \times \mathbf{w})$ b $(\mathbf{u} \times \mathbf{v}) \cdot (\mathbf{v} \times \mathbf{w})$ c $[\mathbf{u} \times (\mathbf{u} \times \mathbf{v})] \cdot \mathbf{w}$

7 Find the area of the triangle whose vertices are

a $(2, -1, 4)$, $(-1, 0, 2)$ and $(4, 4, 0)$ b $(-3, 1, 1)$, $(1, -1, 0)$ and $(2, 0, 3)$

8 **p**, **q** and **n** form a right-handed system of vectors. Find the unit vector in the direction of **n** when **p** and **q** are given by

a $\mathbf{p} = \begin{pmatrix} 1 \\ 1 \\ -1 \end{pmatrix}$, $\mathbf{q} = \begin{pmatrix} 1 \\ -1 \\ 1 \end{pmatrix}$

b $\mathbf{p} = \begin{pmatrix} 3 \\ -1 \\ -1 \end{pmatrix}$, $\mathbf{q} = \begin{pmatrix} 1 \\ 2 \\ -2 \end{pmatrix}$

c $\mathbf{p} = \begin{pmatrix} 2 \\ 3 \\ 0 \end{pmatrix}$, $\mathbf{q} = \begin{pmatrix} 1 \\ -1 \\ 0 \end{pmatrix}$

9 a Use the vector product to calculate the exact value of the sine of the angle between each pair of vectors

i $4\mathbf{i} + \mathbf{j}$, $2\mathbf{i} - \mathbf{j}$ ii $\mathbf{i} + \mathbf{j} + \mathbf{k}$, $\mathbf{i} - \mathbf{j} - \mathbf{k}$ iii $4\mathbf{i}$, $\mathbf{i} + \mathbf{j} + \mathbf{k}$

b For the vectors in part **a** **ii** use the scalar product to find the exact value of the cosine of the angle between them and show that these values satisfy $\cos^2 x + \sin^2 x = 1$.

10 By expressing the vectors **a**, **b** and **c** in terms of their components, show that

$\mathbf{a} \cdot (\mathbf{b} \times \mathbf{c}) = (\mathbf{a} \times \mathbf{b}) \cdot \mathbf{c}$

11 Find the areas of the parallelograms whose *diagonals* represent

a $2\mathbf{i} - \mathbf{k}, \mathbf{i} + 2\mathbf{j} + \mathbf{k}$ b $4\mathbf{i} + 2\mathbf{j} - 6\mathbf{k}, 2\mathbf{i} - \mathbf{j} - \mathbf{k}$

[Hint: the area, A, of a parallelogram with diagonals d_1 and d_2 which intersect at an angle of $\theta°$ is given by $A = \frac{1}{2} d_1 d_2 \sin \theta$.]

12 If $\mathbf{a} = 3\mathbf{i} + \mathbf{j} + 2\mathbf{k}$, $\mathbf{b} = 2\mathbf{j} - \mathbf{k}$, $\mathbf{c} = \mathbf{i} + \mathbf{j} + \mathbf{k}$ and $\mathbf{d} = \mathbf{b} \times (\mathbf{c} \times \mathbf{a}) + (\mathbf{a} \cdot \mathbf{c})\,\mathbf{a}$, prove that **b** and **d** are perpendicular.

15.4 The scalar triple product

A parallelepiped is a region of three-dimensional space bounded by three pairs of parallel planes.
Its volume can be calculated by multiplying the area of one plane in a pair and the perpendicular distance between the planes.

$$V = Ah$$

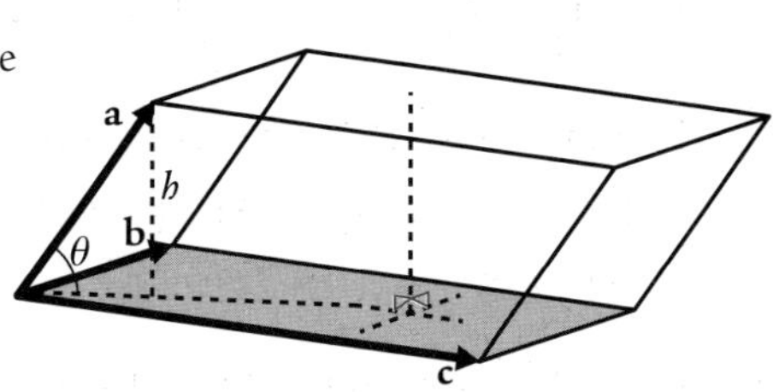

Suppose that the parallelepiped is defined by the three vectors **a**, **b** and **c** which form a right-handed system.

The area of the base $A = |\mathbf{b} \times \mathbf{c}|$

The distance between planes $h = |\mathbf{a}| \cos \theta$

Thus $V = |\mathbf{b} \times \mathbf{c}| \cdot |\mathbf{a}| \cos \theta = \mathbf{a} \cdot (\mathbf{b} \times \mathbf{c})$

Now, any of the three pairs of parallel planes could have been used to find the volume giving

$V = \mathbf{a} \cdot (\mathbf{b} \times \mathbf{c}) = \mathbf{b} \cdot (\mathbf{c} \times \mathbf{a}) = \mathbf{c} \cdot (\mathbf{a} \times \mathbf{b})$

- $\mathbf{a} \cdot (\mathbf{b} \times \mathbf{c})$ is a *number*, not a vector
- $\mathbf{a} \cdot (\mathbf{b} \times \mathbf{c}) = (\mathbf{a} \times \mathbf{b}) \cdot \mathbf{c}$
- $\mathbf{a} \cdot (\mathbf{b} \times \mathbf{c})$ is called the **scalar triple product** and is often denoted by $[\mathbf{a}, \mathbf{b}, \mathbf{c}]$.
- If any of **a**, **b** or **c** is zero then $\mathbf{a} \cdot (\mathbf{b} \times \mathbf{c})$ is defined as 0.
- If any two of **a**, **b** and **c** are parallel then $\mathbf{a} \cdot (\mathbf{b} \times \mathbf{c})$ is defined as 0.
- Since $\mathbf{a} \cdot \mathbf{b}$ is a scalar then $(\mathbf{a} \cdot \mathbf{b}) \times \mathbf{c}$ has no meaning and $\mathbf{a} \cdot (\mathbf{b} \times \mathbf{c})$ may be written as $\mathbf{a} \cdot \mathbf{b} \times \mathbf{c}$ without ambiguity.
- The vector triple product, $\mathbf{a} \times (\mathbf{b} \times \mathbf{c})$, also exists but is beyond the scope of the course.

Component form of the Scalar triple product

$$\mathbf{a} = \begin{pmatrix} a_1 \\ a_2 \\ a_3 \end{pmatrix}, \mathbf{b} = \begin{pmatrix} b_1 \\ b_2 \\ b_3 \end{pmatrix}, \mathbf{c} = \begin{pmatrix} c_1 \\ c_2 \\ c_3 \end{pmatrix}$$

$$\Rightarrow \mathbf{b} \times \mathbf{c} = \begin{pmatrix} b_2c_3 - b_3c_2 \\ b_3c_1 - b_1c_3 \\ b_1c_2 - b_2c_1 \end{pmatrix}$$

$$\Rightarrow \mathbf{a} \cdot (\mathbf{b} \times \mathbf{c}) = \begin{pmatrix} a_1 \\ a_2 \\ a_3 \end{pmatrix} \cdot \begin{pmatrix} b_2c_3 - b_3c_2 \\ b_3c_1 - b_1c_3 \\ b_1c_2 - b_2c_1 \end{pmatrix} = a_1(b_2c_3 - b_3c_2) + a_2(b_3c_1 - b_1c_3) + a_3(b_1c_2 - b_2c_1)$$

Expressed using determinants we get $\mathbf{a} \cdot (\mathbf{b} \times \mathbf{c}) = \begin{vmatrix} a_1 & a_2 & a_3 \\ b_1 & b_2 & b_3 \\ c_3 & c_3 & c_3 \end{vmatrix}$.

Example 3

Given $\mathbf{a} = \mathbf{i} - \mathbf{j} + \mathbf{k}$, $\mathbf{b} = 2\mathbf{i} + 3\mathbf{j} + 4\mathbf{k}$, $\mathbf{c} = 3\mathbf{i} - 2\mathbf{j} + \mathbf{k}$ and $\mathbf{d} = -2\mathbf{i} + \mathbf{j} + 3\mathbf{k}$ verify that $\mathbf{a} \cdot (\mathbf{b} \times [\mathbf{c} + \mathbf{d}]) = \mathbf{a} \cdot (\mathbf{b} \times \mathbf{c}) + \mathbf{a} \cdot (\mathbf{b} \times \mathbf{d})$.

$$\mathbf{a} = \begin{pmatrix} 1 \\ -1 \\ 1 \end{pmatrix}, \mathbf{b} = \begin{pmatrix} 2 \\ 3 \\ 4 \end{pmatrix}, \mathbf{c} = \begin{pmatrix} 3 \\ -2 \\ 1 \end{pmatrix}, \mathbf{d} = \begin{pmatrix} -2 \\ 1 \\ 3 \end{pmatrix} \Rightarrow \mathbf{c} + \mathbf{d} = \begin{pmatrix} 1 \\ -1 \\ 4 \end{pmatrix}$$

$$\mathbf{a} \cdot (\mathbf{b} \times [\mathbf{c} + \mathbf{d}]) = \begin{vmatrix} 1 & -1 & 1 \\ 2 & 3 & 4 \\ 1 & -1 & 4 \end{vmatrix} = 1\begin{vmatrix} 3 & 4 \\ -1 & 4 \end{vmatrix} - (-1)\begin{vmatrix} 2 & 4 \\ 1 & 4 \end{vmatrix} + 1\begin{vmatrix} 2 & 3 \\ 1 & -1 \end{vmatrix}$$

$$= 1 \cdot (12 + 4) + 1 \cdot (8 - 4) + 1 \cdot (-2 - 3) = 16 + 4 - 5$$

$$= 15$$

$$\mathbf{a} \cdot (\mathbf{b} \times \mathbf{c}) = \begin{vmatrix} 1 & -1 & 1 \\ 2 & 3 & 4 \\ 3 & -2 & 1 \end{vmatrix} = 1\begin{vmatrix} 3 & 4 \\ -2 & 1 \end{vmatrix} - (-1)\begin{vmatrix} 2 & 4 \\ 3 & 1 \end{vmatrix} + 1\begin{vmatrix} 2 & 3 \\ 3 & -2 \end{vmatrix} = 11 - 10 - 13 = -12$$

$$\mathbf{a} \cdot (\mathbf{b} \times \mathbf{d}) = \begin{vmatrix} 1 & -1 & 1 \\ 2 & 3 & 4 \\ -2 & 1 & 3 \end{vmatrix} = 1\begin{vmatrix} 3 & 4 \\ 1 & 3 \end{vmatrix} - (-1)\begin{vmatrix} 2 & 4 \\ -2 & 3 \end{vmatrix} + 1\begin{vmatrix} 2 & 3 \\ -2 & 1 \end{vmatrix} = 5 + 14 + 8 = 27$$

Hence $\mathbf{a} \cdot (\mathbf{b} \times [\mathbf{c} + \mathbf{d}]) = 15 = -12 + 27 = \mathbf{a} \cdot (\mathbf{b} \times \mathbf{c}) + \mathbf{a} \cdot (\mathbf{b} \times \mathbf{d})$.

Exercise 15.4

1 By evaluating both expressions, verify that $\mathbf{a} \cdot (\mathbf{b} \times \mathbf{c}) = (\mathbf{a} \times \mathbf{b}) \cdot \mathbf{c}$, given $\mathbf{a} = 2\mathbf{i} + \mathbf{j} + 3\mathbf{k}$, $\mathbf{b} = 5\mathbf{i} + 3\mathbf{j} - 2\mathbf{k}$ and $\mathbf{c} = -\mathbf{i} + 2\mathbf{j} + 4\mathbf{k}$.

2 a Evaluate $\mathbf{p} \cdot (\mathbf{q} \times \mathbf{r})$ where $\mathbf{p} = -\mathbf{i} + 2\mathbf{j} - 2\mathbf{k}$, $\mathbf{q} = 3\mathbf{i} + 5\mathbf{j} - 2\mathbf{k}$, $\mathbf{r} = 2\mathbf{i} - 4\mathbf{j} + 4\mathbf{k}$.

b Why is this value obtained?

c Evaluate i $\mathbf{q} \times \mathbf{r}$ ii $\mathbf{p} \times (\mathbf{q} \times \mathbf{r})$

3 Given $\mathbf{r} = \begin{pmatrix} 2 \\ 1 \\ 3 \end{pmatrix}$, $\mathbf{s} = \begin{pmatrix} -3 \\ 4 \\ -1 \end{pmatrix}$, $\mathbf{t} = \begin{pmatrix} -1 \\ 3 \\ -2 \end{pmatrix}$, $\mathbf{u} = \begin{pmatrix} 5 \\ -2 \\ 1 \end{pmatrix}$

and that $[\mathbf{r}, \mathbf{s}, \mathbf{t}]$ means $\mathbf{r} \cdot (\mathbf{s} \times \mathbf{t})$

evaluate a $[\mathbf{r}, \mathbf{s}, \mathbf{t}]$ b $[\mathbf{s}, \mathbf{t}, \mathbf{u}]$ c $[\mathbf{u}, \mathbf{s}, \mathbf{r}]$

4 Calculate the volume of the parallelepiped shown.

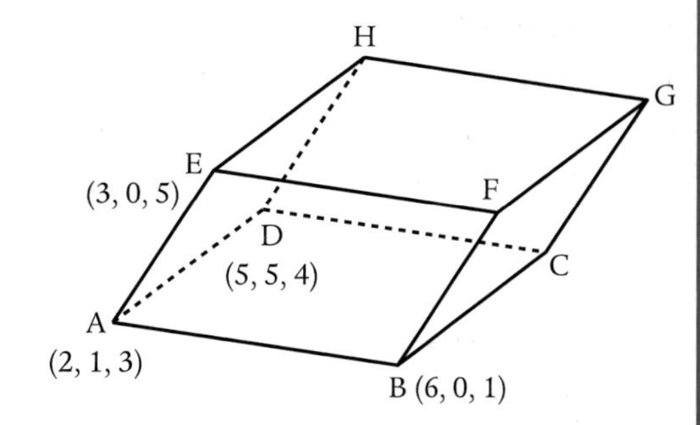

5 Calculate the volume of the parallelepiped shown, in terms of **a**.

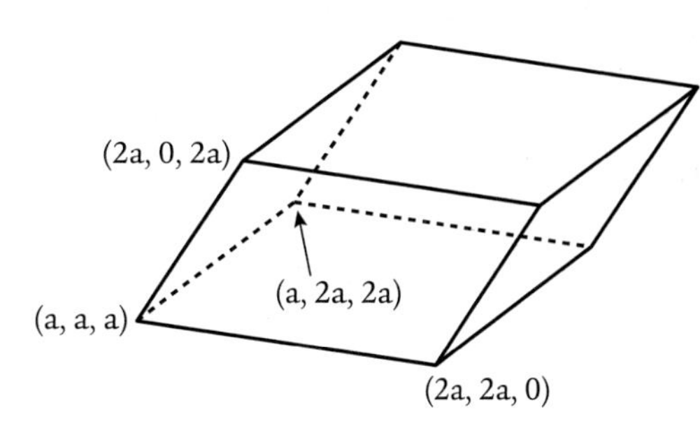

6 Given $\mathbf{a} = 2\mathbf{i} - \mathbf{j} + 3\mathbf{k}$, $\mathbf{b} = \mathbf{i} + 4\mathbf{j} - 2\mathbf{k}$ and $\mathbf{c} = -\mathbf{i} + 2\mathbf{j} + t\mathbf{k}$, for what value of t is $\mathbf{a} \cdot \mathbf{b} \times \mathbf{c} = 33$?

7 Given $\mathbf{p} = 3\mathbf{i} + m\mathbf{j} + 2\mathbf{k}$, $\mathbf{q} = \mathbf{i} + 3\mathbf{j} + 2\mathbf{k}$, $\mathbf{r} = 4\mathbf{i} - \mathbf{j} + \mathbf{k}$, $\mathbf{u} = 2\mathbf{i} + 2\mathbf{j} + \mathbf{k}$, $\mathbf{v} = 4\mathbf{i} + 2m\mathbf{j}$ and $\mathbf{w} = -\mathbf{i} + 2\mathbf{j} + 3\mathbf{k}$, find the value of m for which $\mathbf{u} \cdot \mathbf{v} \times \mathbf{w} = 4(\mathbf{p} \cdot \mathbf{q} \times \mathbf{r})$.

8 a Evaluate $\mathbf{i} \cdot (\mathbf{j} \times \mathbf{k})$.

b Write two other scalar triple products involving **i**, **j** and **k** only which have this same value.

c Write three other scalar triple products involving **i**, **j** and **k** only which have the *negative* of this value.

15.5 The equation of a plane

A plane in space can be uniquely identified if

- three points on the plane are known, or
- two lines on the plane are known, or
- one point on the plane and a normal to the plane are known.

Reminder:
The normal at a point on a plane is at right-angles to *every line* on the plane which passes through that point.

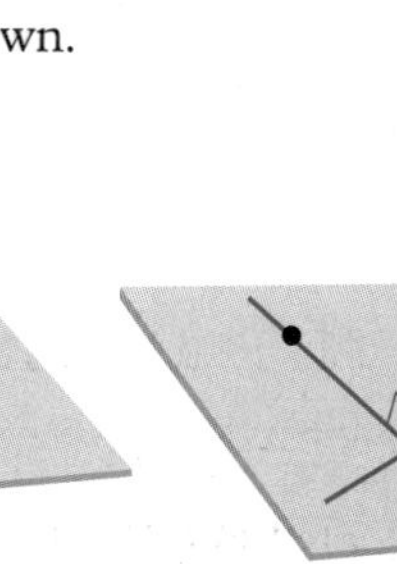

Suppose that relative to a right-handed set of axes, we have a plane called π.

Let $P(x, y, z)$ be a typical point on the plane, and let $\mathbf{a} = \begin{pmatrix} a \\ b \\ c \end{pmatrix}$ be a normal to the plane passing through the plane at Q.

Since $\overrightarrow{QP}$ is perpendicular to **a**,

$$\mathbf{a} \cdot \overrightarrow{QP} = 0$$
$$\Rightarrow \mathbf{a} \cdot (\mathbf{p} - \mathbf{q}) = 0$$
$$\Rightarrow \mathbf{a} \cdot \mathbf{p} - \mathbf{a} \cdot \mathbf{q} = 0$$
$$\Rightarrow \mathbf{a} \cdot \mathbf{p} = \mathbf{a} \cdot \mathbf{q}$$

Both **a** and Q are fixed. So $\mathbf{a} \cdot \mathbf{q}$ is a constant for the plane. Let $\mathbf{a} \cdot \mathbf{q} = k$

$$\Rightarrow \mathbf{a} \cdot \mathbf{p} = k$$
$$\Rightarrow \begin{pmatrix} a \\ b \\ c \end{pmatrix} \begin{pmatrix} x \\ y \\ z \end{pmatrix} = k$$
$$\Rightarrow ax + by + cz = k$$

If we know the normal, and any point on the plane, k can be easily computed.

- $ax + by + cz = k$ is the equation of the plane π.

It is referred to as the Cartesian equation of the plane.

To find the equation of a plane we must be able to reduce given data to **i** the components of a suitable normal **ii** a point on the plane.

- If three points are known, we can use them to find two vectors on the plane.
- If two vectors on the plane are known, we can use them to find a normal to the plane.

Example 4

P, Q, R and S are the points (1, 2, 3), (2, 1, −4), (1, 1, 1) and (7, −6, 5) respectively.

a Find the equation of the plane perpendicular to PQ which contains the point P.

b Which of the other points lies on the plane?

---

a $\overrightarrow{PQ}$ is a normal to the desired plane: $\overrightarrow{PQ} = \mathbf{q} - \mathbf{p} = \begin{pmatrix} 2 \\ 1 \\ -4 \end{pmatrix} - \begin{pmatrix} 1 \\ 2 \\ 3 \end{pmatrix} = \begin{pmatrix} 1 \\ -1 \\ -7 \end{pmatrix}$.

P is a point on the plane

$$\mathbf{p} = \begin{pmatrix} 1 \\ 2 \\ 3 \end{pmatrix} \Rightarrow k = \mathbf{a} \cdot \mathbf{p} = \begin{pmatrix} 1 \\ -1 \\ -7 \end{pmatrix} \cdot \begin{pmatrix} 1 \\ 2 \\ 3 \end{pmatrix} = 1 - 2 - 21 = -22$$

Equation of plane: $\mathbf{a} \cdot \mathbf{p} = \begin{pmatrix} 1 \\ -1 \\ -7 \end{pmatrix} \cdot \begin{pmatrix} x \\ y \\ z \end{pmatrix} = k$

That is $x - y - 7z = -22$

All points on the plane satisfy this equation.

All points not on the plane do not satisfy this equation.

b Substitute R(1, 1, 1) into the equation $1 - 1 - 7 \cdot 1 = -7 \neq -22$.

This does not satisfy the equation. So R does not lie on the plane.

Substitute S(7, −6, 5) into the equation $7 + 6 - 7 \cdot 5 = -22$.

This does satisfy the equation. So S does lie on the plane.

Example 5

Find the equation of the plane which passes through the points A(−2, 1, 2), B(0, 2, 5) and C(2, −1, 3).

Strategy: find two vectors which lie on the plane, for example $\overrightarrow{AB}$ and $\overrightarrow{AC}$; then $\overrightarrow{AB} \times \overrightarrow{AC}$ is a vector normal to the plane.

$$\overrightarrow{AB} = \begin{pmatrix} 2 \\ 1 \\ 3 \end{pmatrix}, \overrightarrow{AC} = \begin{pmatrix} 4 \\ -2 \\ 1 \end{pmatrix} \Rightarrow \overrightarrow{AB} \times \overrightarrow{AC} = \begin{vmatrix} \mathbf{i} & \mathbf{j} & \mathbf{k} \\ 2 & 1 & 3 \\ 4 & -2 & 1 \end{vmatrix}$$

$$= \mathbf{i}(1 + 6) - \mathbf{j}(2 - 12) + \mathbf{k}(-4 - 4) = 7\mathbf{i} + 10\mathbf{j} - 8\mathbf{k}$$

Using A(−2, 1, 2) as the point on the plane

$$k = \begin{pmatrix} 7 \\ 10 \\ -8 \end{pmatrix} \cdot \begin{pmatrix} -2 \\ 1 \\ 2 \end{pmatrix} = -14 + 10 - 16 = -20$$

Thus the required equation is $7x + 10y - 8z = -20$.

Exercise 15.5

1 Find the equation of the plane perpendicular to the given vector and containing the given point.

a $2\mathbf{i} + 3\mathbf{j} + \mathbf{k}$; A(0, 2, 6) b $5\mathbf{i} + 4\mathbf{j} - 3\mathbf{k}$; B(2, 1, −1)

c $2\mathbf{i} - 3\mathbf{j} + \mathbf{k}$; C(5, 3, −2) d $-4\mathbf{i} + 6\mathbf{j} + 7\mathbf{k}$; D(−4, 6, 7)

2 Find, in each case, the equation of the plane passing through P and perpendicular to PQ.

a P(0, 1, 4), Q(0, 1, 7) b P(3, −2, 1), Q (5, −7, 3)

c P(5, −1, 0), Q(2, 2, −5) d P(−7, 3, 3), Q (1, 1, 4)

3 a A plane is parallel to both the vectors $3\mathbf{i} + 2\mathbf{j} - \mathbf{k}$ and $4\mathbf{i} - 2\mathbf{k}$.

i By considering the cross product of these vectors, find a vector normal to the plane.

ii The plane contains the point (1, 1, 0). What is the equation of the plane?

b In a similar fashion find the equations of the planes that are

i parallel to $4\mathbf{i} - \mathbf{k}$ and $6\mathbf{i} - 2\mathbf{j} + 3\mathbf{k}$, containing (3, 4, −7)

ii parallel to $\mathbf{i} + \mathbf{j} + \mathbf{k}$ and $-2\mathbf{i} - 3\mathbf{j} + 4\mathbf{k}$, passing through the origin

iii parallel to $\mathbf{i} - \mathbf{k}$ and $6\mathbf{j} + 5\mathbf{k}$, passing through the point (−2, 3, 7).

4 Find the equation of the plane passing through the three points

a O(0, 0, 0), B(1, 2, 1) and C(−2, 1, 2) b D(2, 1, 2), E(0, 3, −1) and F(3, 0, 4)

c G(−1, 1, 0), H(3, 3, 3) and I(2, −1, 2) d K(a, 0, 0), L(0, a, 0) and M(0, 0, a)

5 Find the equation of the plane passing through the first three points and say whether the fourth point is on the plane.

a A(3, 1, −4), B(2, −1, 2), C(−3, 2, 1) and D(1, 2, 3) b M(1, 0, 1), N(1, 1, 1), S(2, 1, −1) and T(1, 5, 1)

c P(2, 1, 4), Q(−1, 1, 0), R(3, 0, 4) and V(1, 2, 4)

6 Prove that the points in each set are coplanar.

[Hint: show the fourth point lies on the plane defined by the first three.]

a S(5, 7, −1), T(2, −3, 6), U(1, −4, 7) and V(6, 1, 2)

b V(2, −1, 0), W(5, 7, 6), H(−3, 3, −3) and A(−1, −9, −6)

c X(4, 2, 11), Y(6, −9, 5), Z(−3, 2, 8) and B(15, −20, 2)

7 This spreadsheet has been made to find the equation of a plane given three points. (The data used is from Question **6a**.) Can you identify the various formulae used?

	A	B	C	D	E	F	G
1	5	7	–1	S			
2	2	–3	6	T			
3	1	–4	7	U			
4	–3	–10	7	ST			
5	–1	–1	1	TU			
6	–3	–4	–7	Normal			
7			–36	k			
8	Equation						
9	–3 x + –4 y + –7 z = –36						

8 Find the equation of the plane which

a contains the x- and y-axes

b contains the x- and z-axes

c contains the y- and z-axes

d contains the z-axis and the line $x = y$ in the (x, y)-plane.

9 Show that the planes with equations $2x + 3y - 2z = 1$ and $4x - 2y + z = 1$ are perpendicular to each other. [Hint: show the normal to one lies on the other.]

10 Find a unit vector which is normal to the plane which

a is parallel to $4\mathbf{i} - 2\mathbf{j} + \mathbf{k}$ and $\mathbf{i} + 3\mathbf{j} + 3\mathbf{k}$

b passes through the points O(0, 0, 0), P(1, -1, 2) and Q(3, 2, -1).

11 Find the equation of the plane π which passes through the points A(1, 1, 1) and B(3, 2, 2) and which is also perpendicular to another plane π_1 which is parallel to $-\mathbf{i} + \mathbf{j} + \mathbf{k}$ and $2\mathbf{i} - \mathbf{j} - \mathbf{k}$.

12 Show that the line $2x + y = 4$ in the (x, y)-plane lies on the plane $2x + y - z = 4$.

[Hint: find the 3D coordinates of the typical point on the line – in terms of x.]

15.6 The angle between two planes

The angle between two planes can be constructed by picking any point, B, on the *line of intersection* of the planes and drawing perpendiculars to the line, BA and BC, on both planes.

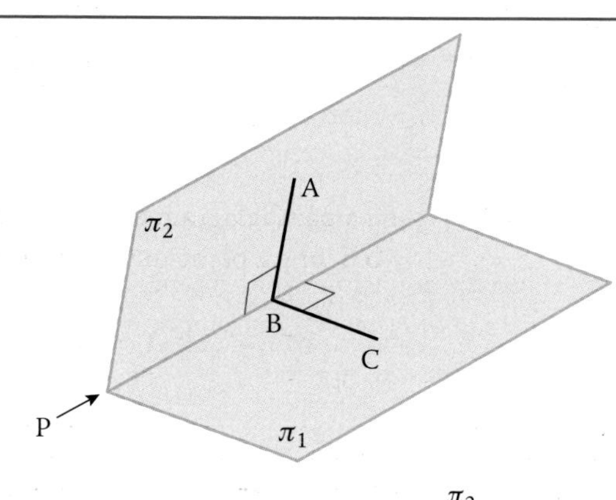

The angle $\angle ABC$ is the required angle.

Viewing from P, along the line of intersection of the planes, we can see that the angle $\angle ABC$ is the same as the angle between the normals.

A rotation of 90° makes $\angle ABC$ coincide with the angle between the normals.

Example 6

Find the angle between the planes with equations $x + 2y + z = 5$ and $x + y = 0$.

By inspection the normals to the planes are $\mathbf{a} = \begin{pmatrix}1\\2\\1\end{pmatrix}$ and $\mathbf{b} = \begin{pmatrix}1\\1\\0\end{pmatrix}$.

We can find the angle between them by employing the scalar product.

$\cos\theta = \dfrac{\mathbf{a}\cdot\mathbf{b}}{|\mathbf{a}|\,|\mathbf{b}|} = \dfrac{1+2+0}{\sqrt{6}\sqrt{2}} = \dfrac{\sqrt{3}}{2}$

Thus the angle between the normals is 30°.

Thus the angle between the planes is 30°.

Exercise 15.6

Work to 2 decimal places as appropriate.

1 Find the exact value of the *cosine* of the angle between the planes with equations $2x - 2y + 6z = 11$ and $5x + 9y + 13z = 5$.

2 The plane π_1 contains the vectors $2\mathbf{i} + \mathbf{j}$ and $3\mathbf{i} + 2\mathbf{k}$.

The plane π_2 contains the vectors $\mathbf{i} + 3\mathbf{j} - \mathbf{k}$ and $\mathbf{i} + \mathbf{j} - \mathbf{k}$.

Find the angle between the planes π_1 and π_2.

3 Find the acute angle between the plane passing through the points O(0, 0, 0), P(1, 0, 1) and Q(0, 1, 1) and the plane passing through the points A(1, −1, 1), B(3, 1, −2) and C(0, 2, −1).

4 A is the point (1, 2, 3), B is (2, 3, 1) and C is (3, 0, −1). Find the acute angle between the planes ABC and OBC.

15.7 Coplanar vectors

If $\mathbf{a} = \overrightarrow{OA}$ and $\mathbf{b} = \overrightarrow{OB}$ are non-zero, non-parallel vectors then they define the plane AOB. If another vector, $\mathbf{c}$, can be represented by a line segment on this plane then $\mathbf{a}$, $\mathbf{b}$ and $\mathbf{c}$ are said to be **coplanar**.

Given three vectors $\mathbf{a}$, $\mathbf{b}$ and $\mathbf{c}$, if there exist two real numbers t, u such that $\mathbf{c} = t\mathbf{a} + u\mathbf{b}$ then the three vectors are coplanar.

Proof

If $\mathbf{c} = t\mathbf{a} + u\mathbf{b}$ then a parallelogram can be drawn as shown.
Note that $t\mathbf{a}$ and $u\mathbf{b}$ define a plane in which $\mathbf{c}$ lies.
So $t\mathbf{a}$, $u\mathbf{b}$ and $\mathbf{c}$ are coplanar.
But the plane defined by $t\mathbf{a}$ and $u\mathbf{b}$ is the same as that defined by $\mathbf{a}$ and $\mathbf{b}$ and so $\mathbf{a}$, $\mathbf{b}$ and $\mathbf{c}$ are coplanar.

The converse is also true, namely that if three non-zero, non-parallel vectors $\mathbf{a}$, $\mathbf{b}$ and $\mathbf{c}$ are coplanar then there exist two real numbers t, u such that $\mathbf{c} = t\mathbf{a} + u\mathbf{b}$.

Proof

If $\mathbf{a}$, $\mathbf{b}$ and $\mathbf{c}$ are non-zero and non-parallel then representatives can be found that intersect at O. If the three are coplanar then two vectors, one parallel to $\mathbf{a}$ and the other parallel to $\mathbf{b}$, can always be found to form a parallelogram with $\mathbf{c}$ as a diagonal.

The Vector Equation of a Plane

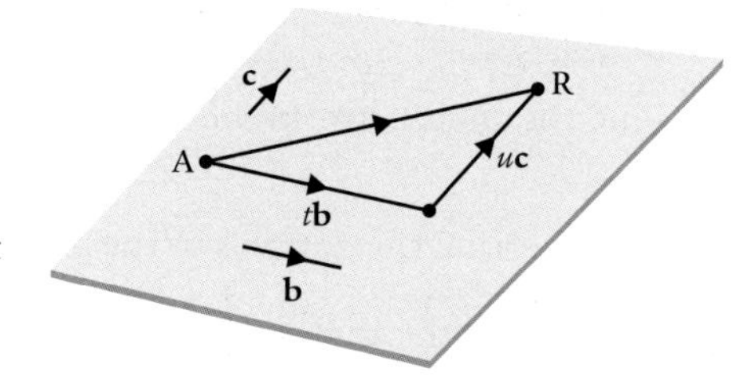

Let A be a known point on a plane.
Let **b** and **c** be two non-parallel vectors in the plane.
Let R be *any* point on the plane.
Since $\overrightarrow{AR}$, **b** and **c** are coplanar, there exist real numbers t and u such that

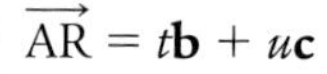

$\overrightarrow{AR} = t\mathbf{b} + u\mathbf{c}$
$\Rightarrow \mathbf{r} - \mathbf{a} = t\mathbf{b} + u\mathbf{c}$
$\Rightarrow \mathbf{r} = \mathbf{a} + t\mathbf{b} + u\mathbf{c}$

If, for some vector **r**, we can find values for t and u to satisfy the equation then **r** is the position vector of a point R on the plane.

This equation $\mathbf{r} = \mathbf{a} + t\mathbf{b} + u\mathbf{c}$ is known as the **vector equation** of the plane.
We refer to t and u as the parameters of the plane.

The form of the equation depends on the initial choice of vectors.
So different equations can represent the same plane.

The Parametric Equation of a Plane

If $\mathbf{r} = \begin{pmatrix} x \\ y \\ z \end{pmatrix}$, $\mathbf{a} = \begin{pmatrix} a_1 \\ a_2 \\ a_3 \end{pmatrix}$, $\mathbf{b} = \begin{pmatrix} b_1 \\ b_2 \\ b_3 \end{pmatrix}$ and $\mathbf{c} = \begin{pmatrix} c_1 \\ c_2 \\ c_3 \end{pmatrix}$,

then $\mathbf{r} = \begin{pmatrix} x \\ y \\ z \end{pmatrix} = \begin{pmatrix} a_1 + tb_1 + uc_1 \\ a_2 + tb_2 + uc_2 \\ a_3 + tb_3 + uc_3 \end{pmatrix}$ is the position vector of a point on the plane.

It is sometimes written as a list of distinct components, that is

$$\begin{cases} x_R = a_1 + tb_1 + uc_1 \\ y_R = a_2 + tb_2 + uc_2 \\ z_R = a_3 + tb_3 + uc_3 \end{cases}$$

We might also write $\mathbf{r} = (a_1 + tb_1 + uc_1)\mathbf{i} + (a_2 + tb_2 + uc_2)\mathbf{j} + (a_3 + tb_3 + uc_3)\mathbf{k}$.

This is the position vector of a point on the plane determined by the values of the parameters t and u. For this reason the list is often referred to as the **parametric equation** of a plane.

As we run through all possible combinations of t and u we will always find the position vector of a point on the plane.

Example 7

a Find the equation of the plane, in vector form, which contains the points D(1, 2, −1), E(−2, 3, 2) and F(4, 5, 6).

b Express this equation in parametric form.

c Find the point on the plane corresponding to the parameter values $t = 2$, $u = 3$.

---

a $\mathbf{d} = \begin{pmatrix} 1 \\ 2 \\ -1 \end{pmatrix}$, $\mathbf{e} = \begin{pmatrix} -2 \\ 3 \\ 2 \end{pmatrix}$, $\mathbf{f} = \begin{pmatrix} 4 \\ 5 \\ 6 \end{pmatrix}$

$$\overrightarrow{DE} = \mathbf{e} - \mathbf{d} = \begin{pmatrix} -2 \\ 3 \\ 2 \end{pmatrix} - \begin{pmatrix} 1 \\ 2 \\ -1 \end{pmatrix} = \begin{pmatrix} -3 \\ 1 \\ 3 \end{pmatrix}$$

and

$$\overrightarrow{DF} = \mathbf{f} - \mathbf{d} = \begin{pmatrix} 4 \\ 5 \\ 6 \end{pmatrix} - \begin{pmatrix} 1 \\ 2 \\ -1 \end{pmatrix} = \begin{pmatrix} 3 \\ 3 \\ 7 \end{pmatrix}$$

are two vectors on the plane.

The vector equation of the plane has the form $\mathbf{r} = \mathbf{a} + t\mathbf{b} + u\mathbf{c}$

$$\Rightarrow \mathbf{r} = \begin{pmatrix} 1 \\ 2 \\ -1 \end{pmatrix} + t\begin{pmatrix} -3 \\ 1 \\ 3 \end{pmatrix} + u\begin{pmatrix} 3 \\ 3 \\ 7 \end{pmatrix}$$

b Tidying up gives **r** in parametric form

$$\mathbf{r} = \begin{pmatrix} 1-3t+3u \\ 2+t+3u \\ -1+3t+3u \end{pmatrix} \text{ or } \begin{cases} x_R = 1-3t+3u \\ y_R = 2+t+3u \\ z_R = -1+3t+3u \end{cases}$$

c $t = 2, u = 3 \Rightarrow \mathbf{r} = \begin{pmatrix} 1-6+9 \\ 2+2+9 \\ -1+6+9 \end{pmatrix} = \begin{pmatrix} 4 \\ 13 \\ 14 \end{pmatrix}$

So the required point is R(4, 13, 14).

Example 8

What conditions must be met so that P(−8, 9, 14) lies on the plane with equation $\mathbf{r} = (1-3t+3u)\mathbf{i} + (2+t+3u)\mathbf{j} + (-1+3t+3u)\mathbf{k}$?

For P to lie on this plane then there must be a *consistent* set of solutions to

$1 - 3t + 3u = -8$ (1)

$2 + t + 3u = 9$ (2)

$-1 + 3t + 3u = 14$ (3)

thus $4t = 16 \Rightarrow t = 4$ (1) – (2)

$\Rightarrow u = 1$ Substituting into (1)

Check for consistency by substituting into (3)

$-1 + 3\cdot 4 + 3\cdot 1 = 14 \Rightarrow$ consistency

For P to be a point on the plane we must have $t = 4$ and $u = 1$.

Example 9

Find the Cartesian equation of the plane whose parametric equation is $\mathbf{r} = (2+t+3u)\mathbf{i} + (1+t-3u)\mathbf{j} + (3-t-7u)\mathbf{k}$.

Rearranging, we get $\mathbf{r} = 2\mathbf{i} + t\mathbf{i} + 3u\mathbf{i} + 1\mathbf{j} + t\mathbf{j} - 3u\mathbf{j} + 3\mathbf{k} - t\mathbf{k} - 7u\mathbf{k}$

$= 2\mathbf{i} + \mathbf{j} + 3\mathbf{k} + t(\mathbf{i} + \mathbf{j} - \mathbf{k}) + u(3\mathbf{i} - 3\mathbf{j} - 7\mathbf{k})$

This is a vector equation, as it is of the form $\mathbf{r} = \mathbf{a} + t\mathbf{p} + u\mathbf{q}$.

By inspection we see that $\mathbf{a} = 2\mathbf{i} + \mathbf{j} + 3\mathbf{k}$ is the position vector of a point on the plane and $\mathbf{p} = \mathbf{i} + \mathbf{j} - \mathbf{k}$ and $\mathbf{q} = 3\mathbf{i} - 3\mathbf{j} - 7\mathbf{k}$ are two vectors lying on the plane.

So a vector normal to the plane is

$$\mathbf{n} = \mathbf{p} \times \mathbf{q} = \begin{pmatrix} 1 \\ 1 \\ -1 \end{pmatrix} \times \begin{pmatrix} 3 \\ -3 \\ -7 \end{pmatrix} = \begin{vmatrix} \mathbf{i} & \mathbf{j} & \mathbf{k} \\ 1 & 1 & -1 \\ 3 & -3 & -7 \end{vmatrix} = \begin{pmatrix} -10 \\ 4 \\ -6 \end{pmatrix}$$

The position vector of a point on the plane, A, is $\begin{pmatrix} 2 \\ 1 \\ 3 \end{pmatrix}$

$\Rightarrow$ The Cartesian equation of the plane is

$$-10x + 4y - 6z = \begin{pmatrix} -10 \\ 4 \\ -6 \end{pmatrix} \cdot \begin{pmatrix} 2 \\ 1 \\ 3 \end{pmatrix} = -34$$

that is $5x - 2y + 3z = 17$

Exercise 15.7

1 Find a vector equation for the plane ABC, given

a A(2, 1, 2), B(0, 3, −1), C(3, 0, 4) [Hint: first find $\overrightarrow{AB}$ and $\overrightarrow{AC}$.]

b A(−3, 2, 1), B(2, −1, 2), C(3, 1, −4)

c A(4, 2, 1), B(3, 1, −2), C(5, 2, 4)

2 A plane passes through the point A(1, 1, 1) and is parallel to $2\mathbf{i} + \mathbf{j}$ and $\mathbf{i} - \mathbf{j} + 2\mathbf{k}$. Find a vector equation for the plane.

3 Find a vector equation for the plane passing through the point

a A(1, 1, 1) with normal vector $\mathbf{u} = 2\mathbf{i} - \mathbf{j} + 2\mathbf{k}$

b B(3, −1, 4) with normal vector $\mathbf{v} = \mathbf{i} - \mathbf{j} + \mathbf{k}$

c C(1, 3, −4) with normal vector $\mathbf{w} = 3\mathbf{i} + \mathbf{j} + \mathbf{k}$.

4 Find the Cartesian equation of the plane whose parametric equations are

a $\begin{cases} x_R = 3 + t + 3u \\ y_R = 4 + 2t + 2u \\ z_R = 2 + 2t + 3u \end{cases}$ b $\begin{cases} x_R = 1 + t - u \\ y_R = 1 - t + u \\ z_R = 1 - t + u \end{cases}$

c $\mathbf{r} = (4 + t - 4u)\mathbf{i} + (-2 + t + 3u)\mathbf{j} + (1 + t - u)\mathbf{k}$

5 Find a vector equation for the plane with Cartesian equation

a $4x + 2y + 3z = 7$ b $5x - 2y + 6z = 9$ c $2x + 5y - 3z = 11$

6 a Show that the point P(−4, 15, 2) lies on the plane with parametric equation

$\mathbf{r} = (2 - t + 3u)\mathbf{i} + (1 + 4t - 2u)\mathbf{j} + (2t + u - 3)\mathbf{k}$

b Show also that the point Q(−5, 13, 5) does not lie on this plane.

7 a Show that the point K(11, −5, 0) lies on the plane with vector equation

$$\mathbf{r} = \begin{pmatrix} 3 \\ 1 \\ -3 \end{pmatrix} + \begin{pmatrix} -1 \\ 4 \\ 2 \end{pmatrix} t + \begin{pmatrix} 3 \\ -2 \\ 1 \end{pmatrix} u$$

b Show also that the point L(−5, 11, 19) does not lie on this plane.

8 a Prove that the four points

W(2, −1, 3), X(7, −3, −3), Y(−7, 7, 20) and Z(18, −3, −10) are coplanar.

b Find a vector equation for the plane containing W, X, Y, Z.

c Find also its Cartesian equation.

9 Prove that the four points E(1, −1, −2), F(3, 3, 2), G(−2, 1, −2) and H(2, 1, 3) are not coplanar.

10 Show that the angle between the planes with parametric equations

$\mathbf{r} = (4 + 2t + 3u)\mathbf{i} + (5 + t + 2u)\mathbf{j} + (9 + 2t + 4u)\mathbf{k}$ and

$\mathbf{r} = (3 + t + 4u)\mathbf{i} + (7 + 2t + 3u)\mathbf{j} + (10 + t + 2u)\mathbf{k}$ is equal to $\cos^{-1}\left(-\frac{3\sqrt{6}}{10}\right)$

11 Show that the planes with equations

$\mathbf{r} = (2 + 5t + 3u)\mathbf{i} + (6 - 2t - 9u)\mathbf{j} + (1 + 4t + 5u)\mathbf{k}$ and

$\mathbf{r} = (3 + 2t + 5u)\mathbf{i} + (7 + t + u)\mathbf{j} + (5 + t + 3u)\mathbf{k}$ are parallel.

12 Consider the plane with equation

$\mathbf{r} = (3 + t + 3u)\mathbf{i} + (2 + 3t + 2u)\mathbf{j} + (7 + 4t - u)\mathbf{k}$

Describe the subset of points in the plane for which the values of the parameters t and u are the same.

15.8 The equations of a line

A line in space is completely determined when we know the direction in which it runs and we know a point which lies on the line.

Its direction is unambiguously described by stating a vector parallel to the line. Such a vector is known as a **direction** vector.

Consider the line L which passes through the point $A(x_1, y_1, z_1)$ with direction vector $u = a\mathbf{i} + b\mathbf{j} + c\mathbf{k}$.

Let $P(x, y, z)$ be any point on the line L.

Then $\overrightarrow{AP} = t\mathbf{u}$ for some scalar t so $\mathbf{p} - \mathbf{a} = t\mathbf{u}$

$$\mathbf{p} = \mathbf{a} + t\mathbf{u} \qquad (1)$$

In component form this becomes $\begin{pmatrix} x \\ y \\ z \end{pmatrix} = \begin{pmatrix} x_1 \\ y_1 \\ z_1 \end{pmatrix} + t\begin{pmatrix} a \\ b \\ c \end{pmatrix} = \begin{pmatrix} x_1 + at \\ y_1 + bt \\ z_1 + ct \end{pmatrix}$

giving $\quad x = x_1 + at, y = y_1 + bt, z = z_1 + ct \qquad (2)$

also $\quad \dfrac{x - x_1}{a} = \dfrac{y - y_1}{b} = \dfrac{z - z_1}{c} = t \qquad (3)$

We have three forms of the equation of a line in space.
Equation (1) is known as the vector equation.
Equation (2) is the parametric form (t being the parameter).
Equation (3) is the symmetric form (also referred to as the standard or canonical form).

Symmetric form equations of a line

In the symmetric form

- '$= t$' is often omitted in the symmetric form but will have to be inserted to convert to other forms.
- If any of the components of the direction vector is zero then some parts of the symmetric form will be undefined in which case the parametric form is better.
- Each point on L is uniquely associated with a value of the parameter t.
- The equations of a particular line are not unique. For example $\dfrac{x-1}{2} = \dfrac{y+2}{4} = \dfrac{z+4}{6}$ and $\dfrac{x-2}{1} = \dfrac{y}{2} = \dfrac{z+1}{3}$ both represent the line which passes through the point (3, 2, 2) and parallel to $\mathbf{i} + 2\mathbf{j} + 3\mathbf{k}$.

Example 10

a Write the symmetric form of the equation of the line which passes through $(1, -2, 8)$ and is parallel to $3\mathbf{i} + 5\mathbf{j} + 11\mathbf{k}$.

b Does the point $(-2, -7, -3)$ lie on the line?

a Direct substitution produces $\dfrac{x-1}{3} = \dfrac{y+2}{5} = \dfrac{z-8}{11} = t$.

b Substituting $(-2, -7, -3)$ we get $\dfrac{-2-1}{3} = -1, \dfrac{-7+2}{5} = -1, \dfrac{-3-8}{11} = -1$.

Since the results are consistently the same answer (-1), the point lies on the line.

Example 11

Find the symmetric form equations of the line passing through A(2, 1, 3) and B(3, 4, 5).

Obviously the line is parallel to $\overrightarrow{AB}$

$$\overrightarrow{AB} = \mathbf{b} - \mathbf{a} = \begin{pmatrix} 3 \\ 4 \\ 5 \end{pmatrix} - \begin{pmatrix} 2 \\ 1 \\ 3 \end{pmatrix} = \begin{pmatrix} 1 \\ 3 \\ 2 \end{pmatrix}$$

and since it passes through A we get

$$\frac{x-2}{1} = \frac{y-1}{3} = \frac{z-3}{2} = t$$

Exercise 15.8

1 Write the system of equations which represents the line which passes through the point

a $(1, -2, 3)$ with direction vector $2\mathbf{i} + \mathbf{j} - \mathbf{k}$

b $(-1, 2, -2)$ with direction vector $\mathbf{i} - \mathbf{j} + \mathbf{k}$

c $(4, 2, -1)$ with direction vector $3\mathbf{i} + \mathbf{j} + 3\mathbf{k}$.

2 Write the equations of the line which passes through the point

a $(5, -3, -1)$ and is parallel to $2\mathbf{i} + \mathbf{k}$

b $(0, 0, 0)$ and is parallel to $\mathbf{i} - \mathbf{j} + 2\mathbf{k}$

c $(0, 0, 0)$ and is parallel to $\mathbf{k}$.

3 Write the equations of the line which passes through the points

a $(0, 1, 3)$ and $(-1, 2, -4)$

b $(5, -1, 0)$ and $(6, 2, -7)$

c $(3, 11, -2)$ and $(6, -1, 0)$

d $(2, 1, 0)$ and $(3, 7, 10)$

e $(0, 0, 0)$ and $(1, 2, 3)$

f $(a, 0, 0)$ and $(0, a, 0)$

4 Show that the point $A(2, 3, -4)$ lies on both the lines with equations

$\frac{x+2}{2} = \frac{y-1}{1} = \frac{z-2}{-3}$ and $\frac{x+4}{2} = \frac{y+3}{2} = \frac{z+7}{1}$, and show that the angle between these lines is $\cos^{-1}\left(\frac{1}{\sqrt{14}}\right)$.

5 Show that the lines with equations

$\frac{x+5}{2} = \frac{y+7}{-1} = \frac{z-1}{4}$ and $\frac{x-3}{3} = \frac{y+6}{-2} = \frac{z+7}{-2}$ are perpendicular.

6 ΔABC has vertices $A(2, -1, 3)$, $B(4, 3, 5)$ and $C(-3, 2, 1)$. Find systems of equations to represent each of the three sides of this triangle.

15.9 The vector equation of a straight line

Example 12

Triangle ABC has a median AD cutting BC at D.

Find in terms of $\mathbf{a}$, $\mathbf{b}$ and $\mathbf{c}$ the vector equation of the median AD of ΔABC.

The vector equation of a line is $\mathbf{r} = \mathbf{a} + t\mathbf{u}$.

Note: it is traditional to use $\mathbf{r}$ instead of $\mathbf{p}$.

Using $\overrightarrow{AD}$ for $\mathbf{u}$

$$\begin{aligned}\mathbf{r} &= \mathbf{a} + t\overrightarrow{AD} \\ &= \mathbf{a} + t(\mathbf{d} - \mathbf{a}) \\ &= (1-t)\mathbf{a} + t\mathbf{d} \\ &= (1-t)\mathbf{a} + t\left(\frac{\mathbf{b}+\mathbf{c}}{2}\right) \\ &= (1-t)\mathbf{a} + \tfrac{1}{2}t\mathbf{b} + \tfrac{1}{2}t\mathbf{c}\end{aligned}$$

Note:

$$\overrightarrow{CD} = \overrightarrow{DB}$$
$$\mathbf{d} - \mathbf{c} = \mathbf{b} - \mathbf{d}$$
$$\Rightarrow \mathbf{d} = \frac{\mathbf{b}+\mathbf{c}}{2}$$

If we wish, we can get rid of the fractions by letting $t = 2k$: k is a more convenient parameter. The equation becomes $\mathbf{r} = (1 - 2k)\mathbf{a} + k\mathbf{b} + k\mathbf{c}$.

Exercise 15.9

1 The points A, B, C have position vectors $\mathbf{a}$, $\mathbf{b}$, $\mathbf{c}$. Find a vector equation for each of these lines.

a AB

b BC

c AM, where M is the mid-point of BC

d the line through A parallel to BC.

2 Find a vector equation for AB where

a $\mathbf{a} = \mathbf{i} + \mathbf{j} - \mathbf{k}$ and $\mathbf{b} = 2\mathbf{i} - \mathbf{j} - \mathbf{k}$

b A is the point $(-1, 2, 0)$ and B is $(2, 3, -1)$

c $\mathbf{a} = 2\mathbf{i} + 2\mathbf{j} + \mathbf{k}$ and the line AB is parallel to $3\mathbf{i} - \mathbf{j} - \mathbf{k}$

d B is the point $(2, 1, -1)$ and AB is parallel to the join of $(1, 0, -1)$ and $(3, 1, 2)$.

3 Find a vector equation for PQ where $\mathbf{p}$ and $\mathbf{q}$ respectively are given by

a $\mathbf{0}, 2\mathbf{a}$ b $\mathbf{a}, 2\mathbf{b}$ c $\mathbf{a} + \mathbf{b}, \mathbf{a} - \mathbf{b}$ d $\mathbf{a} + 2\mathbf{b}, 2\mathbf{a} + \mathbf{b}$

4 Points P, Q, R and S are determined by $\mathbf{p} = 2\mathbf{i} + 3\mathbf{j}$, $\mathbf{q} = 3\mathbf{i} + 2\mathbf{j}$, $\mathbf{r} = 4\mathbf{i} + 6\mathbf{j}$ and $\mathbf{s} = 9\mathbf{i} + 6\mathbf{j}$.

Determine the position vector of the point of intersection of PQ and RS.

5 In ΔOBC, M and N are the mid-points of BC and CO respectively.

Find the position vector of the point of intersection of BN and the line through C parallel to MO, in terms of the position vectors of B and C.

6 OBCD is a parallelogram. Find a vector equation in terms of $\mathbf{b}$ and $\mathbf{c}$ for

a OD

b CD

c the line joining the mid-points of BC and OD

d the line from D to the mid-point of OC

e the line through C parallel to DB.

15.10 When a line intersects a plane

The Angle between the Line and the Plane

The acute angle $\theta°$ between the line and the plane is the complement of the angle between the line and the normal to the plane.

If the line has direction vector $\mathbf{u}$ and the plane has normal $\mathbf{a}$,

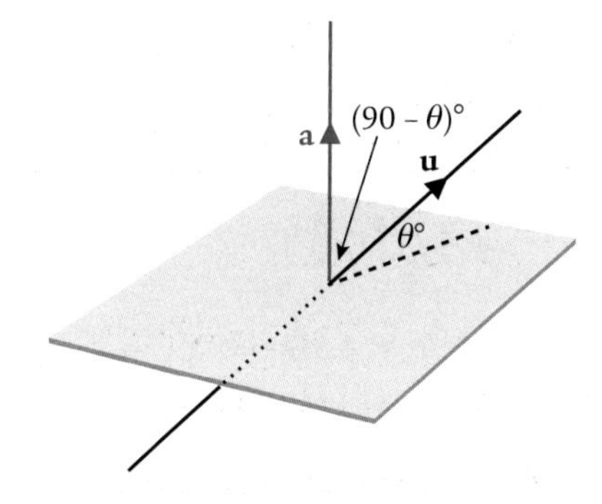

then $|\cos(90 - \theta)°| = \sin\theta° = \left|\dfrac{\mathbf{a}\cdot\mathbf{u}}{|\mathbf{a}||\mathbf{u}|}\right|$

(use the modulus since $\theta \leq 90$).

The Point of Intersection of the Line and the Plane

Strategy:

1 Find the parametric form of the equation of the line.

2 Substitute the parametric expressions for x, y and z into the equation of the plane.

3 Solve the resultant equation for, the value of the parameter and hence the coordinates of the point. of intersection.

Example 13

Given the line $\dfrac{x-7}{3} = \dfrac{y-11}{4} = \dfrac{z-24}{13}$ and the plane $6x + 4y - 5z = 28$

find

a the point of intersection

b the angle the line makes with the plane.

---

a Introduce the parameter into the equation of the line $\dfrac{x-7}{3} = \dfrac{y-11}{4} = \dfrac{z-24}{13} = t$.
This gives $x = 3t + 7, y = 4t + 11, z = 13t + 24$

So $(3t + 7, 4t + 11, 13t + 24)$ is a typical point on the line.

Substituting into the equation of the plane, $6(3t + 7) + 4(4t + 11) - 5(13t + 24) = 28$

$\Rightarrow 18t + 42 + 16t + 44 - 65t - 120 - 28 = 0$

$\Rightarrow -31t - 62 = 0 \Rightarrow t = -2$

Thus the point of intersection is $(3 \cdot (-2) + 7, 4 \cdot (-2) + 11, 13 \cdot (-2) + 24) = (1, 3, -2)$

b $\sin \theta° = \cos(90 - \theta)° = \left|\dfrac{\mathbf{a} \cdot \mathbf{u}}{|\mathbf{a}||\mathbf{u}|}\right| = \dfrac{(6\mathbf{i} + 4\mathbf{j} - 5\mathbf{k}) \cdot (3\mathbf{i} + 4\mathbf{j} + 13\mathbf{k})}{\sqrt{(36 + 16 + 25)(9 + 16 + 169)}}$

$\Rightarrow \sin \theta° = \dfrac{31}{\sqrt{77 \times 194}} \; (0 \leqslant \theta \leqslant 90)$

$\Rightarrow \theta = 14.7$ (3 sf)

Exercise 15.10

1 For each of these plane and line pairs find

i the coordinates of the point of intersection

ii the angle between the line and the plane.

a $\dfrac{x - 12}{5} = \dfrac{y + 7}{-4} = \dfrac{z - 5}{3}$; $5x + 3y - z = 14$

b $x - 3 = 2t, y + 3 = 0, z - 2 = -t$; $3x - 4y + 2z = 33$

c $\dfrac{2x + 7}{1} = \dfrac{y + 5}{2} = \dfrac{3z + 9}{2}$; $7x - y + 3z + 4 = 0$

d $x = 5 - y = 7 - z$; $4x - 3y + z = 10$

e $\dfrac{x + 9}{2} = \dfrac{y + 13}{5} = \dfrac{z - 3}{-1}$; $8x + 5y - 2z + 14 = 0$

f $\dfrac{x + 7}{3} = \dfrac{y - 6}{-1} = \dfrac{z - 17}{-5}$; $7x - 2y + z + 8 = 0$

g $-x = -(y + 4) = \dfrac{z - 15}{3}$; $5x - 7y + 2z = 26$

h $x - 1 = 2(2 - y) = 2z - 6$; $4x + 3y - 2z + 5 = 0$

2 Show that in each case the given line is parallel to the given plane.

a $\dfrac{x - 2}{5} = \dfrac{y + 7}{-4} = \dfrac{z - 5}{3}$ and $3x + 3y - z = 11$

b $\dfrac{x - 6}{2} = \dfrac{y + 5}{4} = \dfrac{z + 8}{13}$ and $5x + 4y - 2z = 21$

c $\dfrac{x - 9}{3} = \dfrac{y - 4}{2} = \dfrac{z + 3}{-1}$ and $3x - 4y + z = 9$

3 Relative to a certain set of axes, an aircraft flies along a course with equation $\dfrac{x + 2}{4} = \dfrac{y - 27}{-3} = \dfrac{z - 4}{5}$

The ground over which it flies is a plane with equation $x + 3y + z = 13$.

Show that the aircraft is flying parallel to the ground.

4 Show that in each case the given line lies within the given plane.

a $\dfrac{x - 3}{12} = \dfrac{y + 4}{-4} = \dfrac{z - 1}{3}$ and $2x + 3y - 4z + 10 = 0$

b $\dfrac{x - 2}{3} = \dfrac{y - 3}{-5} = \dfrac{z - 4}{2}$ and $3x + y - 2z = 1$

c $x + 1 = y + 2 = z + 5$ and $3x - 4y + z = 0$

d $x = 6t - 2, y = 1 - 2t, z = 7$ and $x + 3y + 2z = 15$

5 During a laser-light show, two beams of light must intersect at a point on the surface of a roof. Relative to a suitable set of axes these beams have equations

$$\frac{x-5}{1}=\frac{y+10}{-3}=\frac{z-17}{4} \text{ and } \frac{x-8}{3}=\frac{y-3}{2}=\frac{z-3}{-1}$$

The roof surface has the equation $3x - 2y + z = 13$.

Show that the beams do intersect on the roof.

6 A microscope is set up so that, relative to a certain set of axes, the slide lies on the (x, y)-plane.

The line of sight down the microscope is represented by $\frac{x-10}{3}=\frac{y+5}{-4}=\frac{z-4}{2}$.

The beam of light meant to illuminate the slide has equation $\frac{x-7}{1}=\frac{y-9}{2}=\frac{z+3}{-1}$.

Show that the system is set up correctly and that the two lines do indeed intersect on the slide.

15.11 The intersection of two lines

Two lines in space can either

a be parallel
b intersect at a point
c be skew [not parallel but will never intersect]

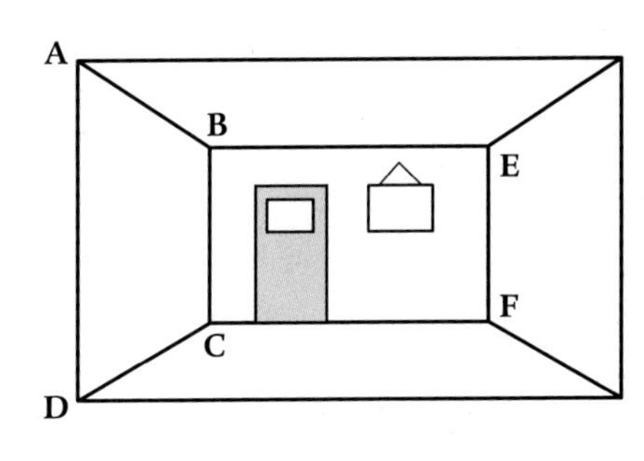

For example, looking into the room we should find AB and DC are parallel, AB and BC intersect at B and AB and EF are skew.

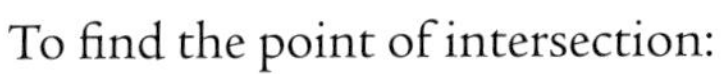

To find the point of intersection:

1 Express the equations of the lines in parametric form using parameters t_1 and t_2.
2 Equate corresponding expressions for x, y and z, producing three equations in two unknowns.
3 Use two of the equations to find values for the parameters t_1 and t_2.
4 Substitute the new-found values for parameters t_1 and t_2 in the third equation. If they satisfy the equation then the point of intersection has been found; if they do not then the lines do not intersect.

Example 14

Show that the lines with equations $x - 5 = -(y + 2) = z$ and $\frac{x-12}{5}=\frac{y+3}{-2}=\frac{z-5}{4}$ intersect and find the point of intersection.

Using the parameters t_1 and t_2 we get $x = t_1 + 5, y = -t_1 - 2, z = t_1$ and $x = 5t_2 + 12, y = -2t_2 - 3, z = 4t_2 + 5$.

Equating corresponding coordinates

$t_1 + 5 = 5t_2 + 12 \quad \Rightarrow \quad t_1 = 5t_2 + 7 \quad (1)$

$-t_1 - 2 = -2t_2 - 3 \quad \Rightarrow \quad t_1 = 2t_2 + 1 \quad (2)$

$t_1 = 4t_2 + 5 \quad \Rightarrow \quad t_1 = 4t_2 + 5 \quad (3)$

Subtracting (2) from (1) we find $3t_2 + 6 = 0 \Rightarrow t_2 = -2; \Rightarrow t_1 = -3$

By inspection we see that these values satisfy (3): $-3 = 4(-2) + 5$

Thus the lines *do* intersect at a point $x = t_1 + 5, y = -t_1 - 2, z = t_1$ with $t_1 = -3$

The point of intersection is $(2, 1, -3)$.

[The answer can be checked using the fact that the point is also $x = 5t_2 + 12, y = -2t_2 - 3, z = 4t_2 + 5$ with $t_2 = -2$.]

Example 15

Find the acute angle between the lines with equations $\frac{x-2}{1} = \frac{y+1}{-2} = \frac{z-11}{-1}$

and $x = -t + 3, y = t - 4, z = -8$.

By inspection we get direction vectors for both lines: $\begin{pmatrix} 1 \\ -2 \\ -1 \end{pmatrix}$ and $\begin{pmatrix} -1 \\ 1 \\ 0 \end{pmatrix}$.

The angle between two lines, $\theta°$, is the angle between their direction vectors.

$\cos\theta° = \frac{-1-2-0}{\sqrt{6} \times 2} = \frac{-\sqrt{3}}{2}$

$\Rightarrow \quad \theta = 150$

Thus the acute angle is 30°.

Exercise 15.11

1 For each of these pairs of lines

i prove that the lines intersect

ii find the point of intersection

iii find the acute angle between the lines (to 3 sf)

iv find the equation of the plane defined by the pair of lines.

a $\frac{x+13}{4} = \frac{y-7}{-3} = \frac{z+1}{2}$ and $\frac{x+13}{-3} = \frac{y-6}{2} = \frac{z-21}{4}$

b $\frac{x-19}{4} = \frac{y+6}{-3} = \frac{z-13}{5}$ and $x - 8 = 2 - y = \frac{z}{2}$

2 While studying a group of quartz crystals relative to a certain set of axes, one edge was found to have equation $\frac{x+10}{1} = \frac{y+20}{3} = \frac{z-15}{-2}$ and another edge, $\frac{x-18}{5} = \frac{y+12}{-4} = \frac{z-11}{3}$.

a Show that these edges intersect.

b **i** State the point of intersection.

ii Calculate the acute angle between the edges.

c Find the equation of the face of the crystal defined by these two edges.

3 A conduit running through the wall of a house can be represented by a line with equation $\frac{x-17}{6} = \frac{y+9}{-3} = \frac{z-10}{5}$. Within the wall, it then bends to run along the line $\frac{x-17}{4} = \frac{y+9}{-2} = \frac{z-9}{3}$.

a Find the coordinates of the point representing the bend.

b Find the angle of the bend, given that it is obtuse.

c Find the equation of the plane representing the wall.

15.12 The intersection of two planes

Two planes must be either parallel or intersect in a line.

To determine the equations of the line of intersection we need to know its *direction vector* and a point on the line.

To find a point on the line:

- The line must either cross the (x, y)-plane (which has equation $z = 0$) or be parallel to it.
- If it crosses it, set $z = 0$ in the equations of both planes to obtain a pair of simultaneous equations in x and y. Solving these will provide the required point on the line $(x_1, y_1, 0)$.
- If the line is parallel to the (x, y)-plane then a similar point can be found on the (x, z)-plane by a similar strategy.

To find a direction vector:

- The line of intersection lies in both planes.
- Its direction vector is therefore perpendicular to the normal vector of each plane.
- Thus for the direction vector we could use the vector product of these normal vectors or a vector parallel to it.

Example 16

Find the equations of the line of intersection of the planes with equations

$$x - 2y + 3z = 1 \text{ and } 2x + y + z = -3$$

Let $z = 0$ then $x - 2y = 1$ and $2x + y = -3$

$\Rightarrow \quad 2(1 + 2y) + y = -3$

$\Rightarrow \quad 5y = -5 \quad \Rightarrow y = -1 \quad \Rightarrow x = -1$

$\Rightarrow \quad (-1, -1, 0)$ lies on the line of intersection

Normal vectors are $\mathbf{u} = \mathbf{i} - 2\mathbf{j} + 3\mathbf{k}$ and $\mathbf{v} = 2\mathbf{i} + \mathbf{j} + \mathbf{k}$.

$$\mathbf{u} \times \mathbf{v} = \begin{vmatrix} i & j & k \\ 1 & -2 & 3 \\ 2 & 1 & 1 \end{vmatrix} = \begin{pmatrix} -5 \\ 5 \\ 5 \end{pmatrix} = -5\begin{pmatrix} 1 \\ -1 \\ -1 \end{pmatrix}$$

Hence the equation of the line of intersection is $\dfrac{x+1}{1} = \dfrac{y+1}{-1} = \dfrac{z}{-1}$.

Exercise 15.12

1 Find the equations of the line of intersection of each of these pairs of planes.

a $x - y - 3z + 7 = 0$ and $2x + 3y - z + 4 = 0$

b $x - 2y - 2z + 8 = 0$ and $2x - y - 2z = 1$

2 Relative to a suitable set of axes the sides of a factory roof have equations $2x - y - z = 11$ and $2x - 2y + z = 9$.

a Find a point on the line representing the roof ridge.

b Find the direction vector of the roof ridge by considering the vector product of the normal vectors of the planes representing the two parts of the roof.

c Find the equation of the roof ridge.

3 A geological fault runs through a bed of rock.
Geologists perceive this fault as a straight line where the fault plane meets the surface of the Earth.
The plane of the fault can be represented by the equation $4x - 7y - 10z = 35$.
Locally the surface can be represented by the plane $2x + 3y - 5z = 24$.

a Find the equation of this fault line.

b Calculate the angle the fault line makes with

i the (x, y)-plane

ii the (y, z)-plane.

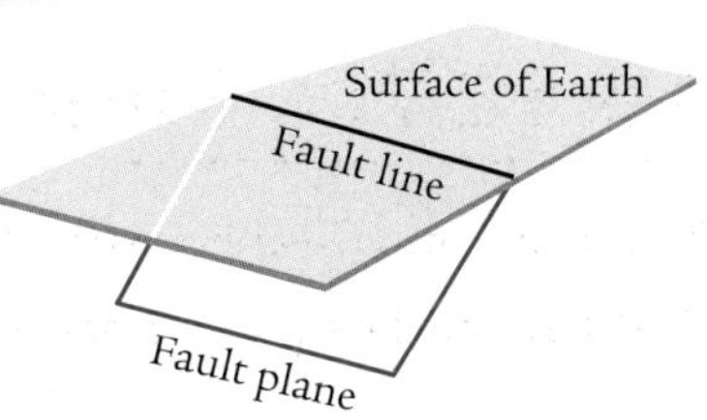

15.13 The intersection of three planes

When examining the intersection of three planes we must consider six cases. The intersection could be

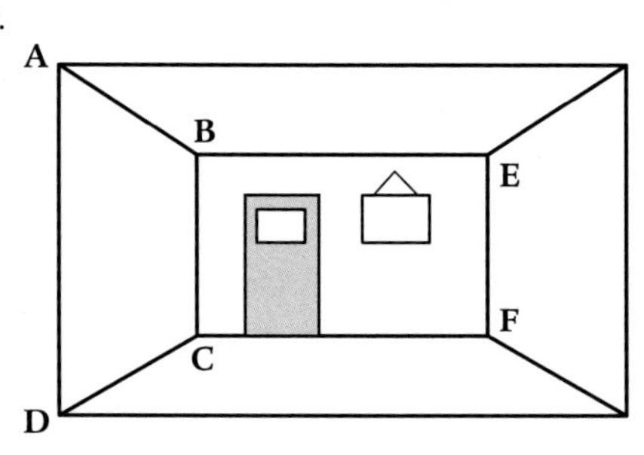

- A single point
- A line
- Two lines
- Three lines
- A plane
- Undefined

Various examples of each type can be found by considering the structure of a room, including the diagonal planes.

Since each plane has an equation of the form $ax + by + cz = d$, the intersection is the solution of a 3×3 system of equations. We can use the planar equations to form an augmented matrix and solve for x, y and z using Gaussian elimination.

The six cases are best described through example.

A point of intersection

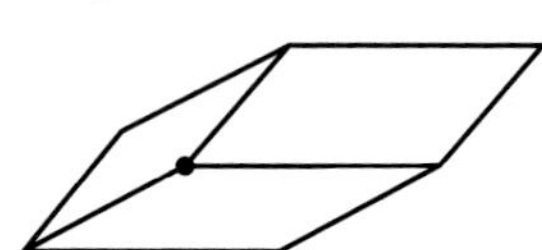

$$x - 2y + z = 8$$
$$3x + y - z = 1$$
$$2x - 2y + 3z = 18$$

The augmented matrix $\left(\begin{array}{ccc|c} 1 & -2 & 1 & 8 \\ 3 & 1 & -1 & 1 \\ 2 & -2 & 3 & 18 \end{array}\right)$ by EROs becomes $\left(\begin{array}{ccc|c} 1 & 0 & 0 & 2 \\ 0 & 1 & 0 & -1 \\ 0 & 0 & 1 & 4 \end{array}\right)$.

The unique solution indicates that the three planes all intersect at the point $(2, -1, 4)$.

A line of intersection

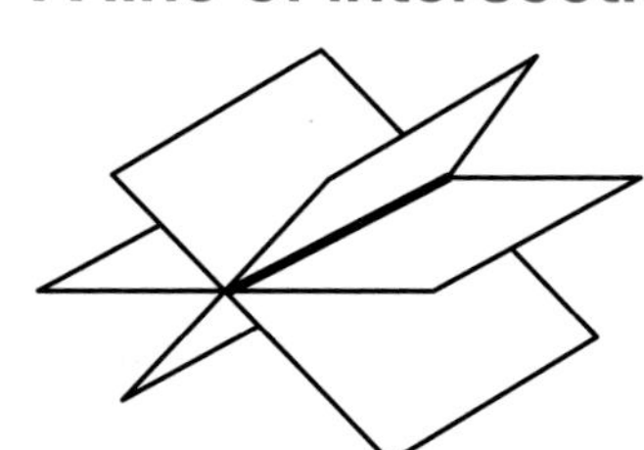

$$x + 2y - 2z = -7$$
$$x - 2y + z = 6$$
$$3x + 2y - 3z = -8$$

The augmented matrix $\left(\begin{array}{ccc|c} 1 & 2 & -2 & -7 \\ 1 & -2 & 1 & 6 \\ 3 & 2 & -3 & -8 \end{array}\right)$ by EROs gives $\left(\begin{array}{ccc|c} 1 & 2 & -2 & -7 \\ 0 & -4 & 3 & 13 \\ 0 & 0 & 0 & 0 \end{array}\right)$.

The third row, all zeros, means the third equation is redundant. So we have two equations in three unknowns, which will yield an infinite number of solutions. These we represent by a set of parametric equations.

Let $z = t$

From the second row we have $\quad -4y + 3z = 13 \Rightarrow y = \dfrac{3z - 13}{4} \Rightarrow y = \dfrac{3t - 13}{4}$

From the first row $\quad x + 2y - 2z = -7 \Rightarrow x = -7 - 2y + 2z = -7 - \dfrac{3t - 13}{2} + 2t = \dfrac{t - 1}{2}$

So the intersection is the line with parametric equations $x = \dfrac{t-1}{2}, y = \dfrac{3t - 13}{4}, z = t$

or, in symmetric form, $\dfrac{2x + 1}{1} = \dfrac{4y + 13}{3} = \dfrac{z}{1} = t$

Of course it needs to be expressed as $\dfrac{x + \frac{1}{2}}{\frac{1}{2}} = \dfrac{y + \frac{13}{4}}{\frac{3}{4}} = \dfrac{z}{1} = t$ to get the direction vector.

Two lines of intersection

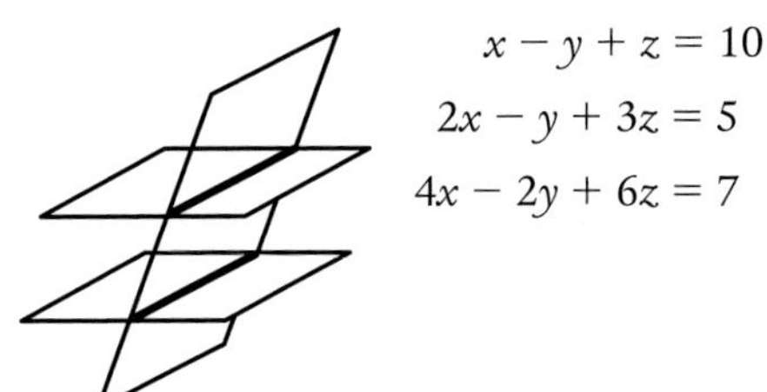

$$x - y + z = 10$$
$$2x - y + 3z = 5$$
$$4x - 2y + 6z = 7$$

The augmented matrix $\left(\begin{array}{ccc|c} 1 & -1 & 1 & 10 \\ 2 & -1 & 3 & 5 \\ 4 & -2 & 6 & 7 \end{array}\right)$ by EROs gives $\left(\begin{array}{ccc|c} 1 & -1 & 1 & 10 \\ 0 & 1 & 1 & -15 \\ 0 & 0 & 0 & -3 \end{array}\right)$.

The third row gives $0 = -3 \Rightarrow$ no solutions, the system being inconsistent.
Let $z = t$ and examine the planes in pairs.

Planes 1 and 2

$x - y = 10 - t$ (1)
$2x - y = 5 - 3t$ (2)

Subtracting (1) from (2) gives $x = -5 - 2t$

Substituting into (1) gives $-5 - 2t - y = 10 - t \Rightarrow y = -15 - t$

Thus in symmetric form planes 1 and 2 intersect at the line $\dfrac{x+5}{-2} = \dfrac{y+15}{-1} = z = t$.

Planes 1 and 3

$x - y = 10 - t$ (1)
$4x - 2y = 7 - 6t$ (2)

Subtracting $2 \times$ (1) from (2) gives $2x = -13 - 4t \Rightarrow x = -6.5 - 2t$
Substituting into (1) gives $-6.5 - 2t - y = 10 - t \Rightarrow y = -16.5 - t$

Thus in symmetric form planes 1 and 3 intersect at the line $\dfrac{x+6.5}{-2} = \dfrac{y+16.5}{-1} = z = t$.

Planes 2 and 3

$2x - y = 5 - 3t$ (1)
$4x - 2y = 7 - 6t$ (2)

Subtracting $2 \times$ (1) from (2) gives $0 = -3 \Rightarrow$ inconsistency $\Rightarrow$ no intersection.

Note

- These two lines of section are parallel.
- The second and third planes are parallel, having the same normal vector.

Three lines of intersection

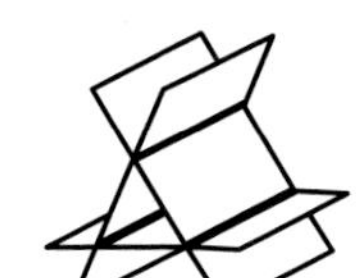

$$x + 2y - 2z = -7$$
$$3x + 2y - 3z = -15$$
$$5x + 2y - 4z = -9$$

The augmented matrix $\left(\begin{array}{ccc|c} 1 & 2 & -2 & -7 \\ 3 & 2 & -3 & -15 \\ 5 & 2 & -4 & -9 \end{array}\right)$ by EROs gives $\left(\begin{array}{ccc|c} 1 & 2 & -2 & -7 \\ 0 & -4 & 3 & 6 \\ 0 & 0 & 0 & 14 \end{array}\right)$.

The third row gives $0 = 14 \Rightarrow$ the system is inconsistent and so has no solutions.

Let $z = t$ and examine the planes in pairs.

Planes 1 and 2

$x + 2y = -7 + 2t$ (1)
$3x + 2y = -15 + 3t$ (2)

Subtracting (1) from (2) $2x = -8 + t \Rightarrow x = \frac{t-8}{2}$

Substituting in (1) $2y = -7 + 2t - \frac{t-8}{2} = \frac{3t-6}{2} \Rightarrow y = \frac{3t-6}{4}$

These planes intersect at $2x + 8 = \frac{4y+6}{3} = z$ giving $\frac{x+4}{\frac{1}{2}} = \frac{y+\frac{3}{2}}{\frac{3}{4}} = z.$

Planes 1 and 3

$x + 2y = -7 + 2t$ (1)
$5x + 2y = -9 + 4t$ (2)

Subtracting (1) from (2) $4x = -2 + 2t \Rightarrow x = \frac{t-1}{2}$

Substituting in (1) $2y = -7 + 2t - \frac{t-1}{2} = \frac{3t-13}{2} \Rightarrow y = \frac{3t-13}{4}$

These planes intersect at $2x + 1 = \frac{4y+13}{3} = z$ giving $\frac{x+\frac{1}{2}}{\frac{1}{2}} = \frac{y+\frac{13}{4}}{\frac{3}{4}} = z.$

Planes 2 and 3

$3x + 2y = -15 + 3t$ (1)
$5x + 2y = -9 + 4t$ (2)

Subtracting (1) from (2) $2x = 6 + t \Rightarrow x = \frac{t+6}{2}$

Substituting in (1) $2y = -15 + 3t - \frac{3t+18}{2} = \frac{3t-48}{2} \Rightarrow y = \frac{3t-48}{4}$

These planes intersect at $2x - 6 = \frac{4y+48}{3} = z$ giving $\frac{x-3}{\frac{1}{2}} = \frac{y+12}{\frac{3}{4}} = z.$

Observe that the three lines of section are parallel, with direction vector $\begin{pmatrix} \frac{1}{2} \\ \frac{3}{4} \\ 1 \end{pmatrix}$.

A plane of intersection

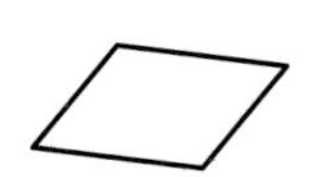

$$2x - y + 3z = 4$$
$$6x - 3y + 9z = 12$$
$$8x - 4y + 12z = 16$$

The augmented matrix $\left(\begin{array}{ccc|c} 2 & -1 & 3 & 4 \\ 6 & -3 & 9 & 12 \\ 8 & -4 & 12 & 16 \end{array}\right)$ by EROs gives $\left(\begin{array}{ccc|c} 2 & -1 & 3 & 4 \\ 0 & 0 & 0 & 0 \\ 0 & 0 & 0 & 0 \end{array}\right)$.

There are two redundant equations. The three planes coincide.

Thus the intersection is the plane $2x - y + 3z = 4$.

No intersection

$$4x - 8y + 12z = 12$$
$$2x - 4y + 6z = 2$$
$$3x - 6y + 9z = 6$$

The augmented matrix $\left(\begin{array}{ccc|c} 4 & -8 & 12 & 12 \\ 2 & -4 & 6 & 2 \\ 3 & -6 & 9 & 6 \end{array}\right)$ by EROs gives $\left(\begin{array}{ccc|c} 1 & -2 & 3 & 3 \\ 0 & 0 & 0 & -4 \\ 0 & 0 & 0 & -3 \end{array}\right)$.

This is a completely inconsistent set of equations, thus there are no solutions. Even a cursory glance at these equations reveals a set of three parallel planes.

Exercise 15.13

1 Determine how each of these sets of three planes intersect. Give the coordinates of the point of intersection or the equations of any lines of intersection.

a $x + 2y + 3z = 3$
$2x - y + 4z = 5$
$x - 3y + 2z = 2$

b $x + 2y + 3z = 3$
$2x - y + 4z = 5$
$x - 3y + z = 2$

c $2x + y + 3z = 5$
$3x - y + 2z = 1$
$x - 2y - z = -3$

d $2x + 3y + 4z = 1$
$5x + 6y + 7z = 2$
$8x + 9y + 10z = 4$

2 Comment on the intersection of these sets of planes.

a $x + 4y + 5z = 6$
$2x + 8y + 10z = 12$
$8x + 32y + 40z = 48$

b $2x - 4y + 4z = 8$
$x - 2y + 2z = 7$
$3x - 6y + 6z = -2$

c $3x + 2y + z = 0$
$x - y + z = 1$
$5x \quad + 2z = 2$

d $x + y = 1$
$x + z = 1$
$y + z = 1$

Review 15

1 A is the point (8, 6, 0) and B is (3, 4, 0). Find the exact value of sin AOB.
[Hint: use the compound angle formula.]
Hence express $\overrightarrow{OA} \times \overrightarrow{OB}$ as a multiple of **k**, the unit vector in the z-direction.

2 P is the point (1, −1, 0), Q is (3, 0, 3) and R is (5, −2, 2). Evaluate $\overrightarrow{PQ} \times \overrightarrow{PR}$.

3 Evaluate $\mathbf{a} \cdot (\mathbf{b} \times \mathbf{c})$ where $\mathbf{a} = -2\mathbf{i} + 3\mathbf{j} + \mathbf{k}$, $\mathbf{b} = 4\mathbf{i} + 5\mathbf{j} - 2\mathbf{k}$ and $\mathbf{c} = -2\mathbf{i} + 3\mathbf{j} - 4\mathbf{k}$.

4 Find the equation of the plane which passes through the point (2, 1, 4) and is perpendicular to the line joining the points (1, 3, 2) and (3, 1, 5).

5 Calculate the angle between the planes which have equations $3x + 5y - 2z = 11$ and $4x - 2y - 3z = 15$.

6 Find a vector equation for the plane which passes through the points K(2, 1, −4), L(3, −2, 5) and M(−4, 1, 2).

7 Find the equations of the line which passes through the point P(2, 1, 1) and

a the point Q(4, 5, 6)

b is parallel to both the planes $2x + 3y - 5z = 0$ and $3x - y + 2z = 0$.

8 Obtain a parametric equation for the line passing through the points (1, −2, 1) and (0, 3, 2).

9 Find

a the coordinates of the point where the line with equations $\frac{x-14}{4} = \frac{y+14}{-5} = \frac{z-6}{3}$ meets the plane with equation $3x + y - 2z = 13$.

b the angle between this line and this plane.

10 a Prove that the lines with equations $\frac{x+4}{3} = \frac{y+7}{5} = \frac{z+12}{8}$ and $\frac{x+3}{1} = \frac{y}{-1} = \frac{z+10}{3}$ intersect and state their point of intersection.

b Find also the equation of the plane within which they lie.

11 a Find the equations of the line of intersection of the planes with equations
$3x - 2y + 3z = 32$ and $2x + y - 2z + 8 = 0$.

b Calculate the angle between these two planes.

12 Investigate the intersection(s) of the planes with equations $x + y - z = 1$, $2x + 3y - 4z = 5$ and $4x + 6y - 8z = 3$, stating the coordinates of any point of intersection or the equations of any lines of intersection.

Summary 15

1 a The **vector product** is $\mathbf{a} \times \mathbf{b} = \mathbf{n}|\mathbf{a}|\,|\mathbf{b}| \sin\theta$ where $\mathbf{n}$ is a unit vector such that $\mathbf{a}$, $\mathbf{b}$ and $\mathbf{n}$ form a right-handed system and θ is the angle between $\mathbf{a}$ and $\mathbf{b}$.

b $|\mathbf{a} \times \mathbf{b}|$ = the area of the parallelogram contained by $\mathbf{a}$ and $\mathbf{b}$

c $\mathbf{a} \times \mathbf{b} = -(\mathbf{b} \times \mathbf{a})$

d $\mathbf{a} \times \mathbf{a} = 0$

f $\mathbf{a} \times \mathbf{b} = 0 \Rightarrow \mathbf{a}$ and $\mathbf{b}$ are parallel

g $\mathbf{i} \times \mathbf{j} = \mathbf{k}; \mathbf{j} \times \mathbf{k} = \mathbf{i}; \mathbf{k} \times \mathbf{i} = \mathbf{j}$

h The distributive law $\mathbf{a} \times (\mathbf{b} + \mathbf{c}) = \mathbf{a} \times \mathbf{b} + \mathbf{a} \times \mathbf{c}$

2 In **component form** the vector product is

$$\mathbf{a} \times \mathbf{b} = \begin{vmatrix} \mathbf{i} & \mathbf{j} & \mathbf{k} \\ a_1 & a_2 & a_3 \\ b_1 & b_2 & b_3 \end{vmatrix} = (a_2b_3 - a_3b_2)\mathbf{i} - (a_1b_3 - a_3b_1)\mathbf{j} + (a_1b_2 - a_2b_1)\mathbf{k}$$

3 The **scalar triple product** is $\mathbf{a} \cdot (\mathbf{b} \times \mathbf{c}) = \begin{vmatrix} a_1 & a_2 & a_3 \\ b_1 & b_2 & b_3 \\ c_1 & c_2 & c_3 \end{vmatrix}$

which can be interpreted geometrically as the volume of the parallelepiped defined by $\mathbf{a}$, $\mathbf{b}$ and $\mathbf{c}$.

$V = \mathbf{a} \cdot (\mathbf{b} \times \mathbf{c}) = \mathbf{b} \cdot (\mathbf{c} \times \mathbf{a}) = \mathbf{c} \cdot (\mathbf{a} \times \mathbf{b}) = -\mathbf{a} \cdot (\mathbf{c} \times \mathbf{b}) = -\mathbf{b} \cdot (\mathbf{a} \times \mathbf{c}) = -\mathbf{c} \cdot (\mathbf{b} \times \mathbf{a})$

4 a The equation of a plane is $\mathbf{a} \cdot \mathbf{x} = k$ (k = constant) or $ax + by + cz = k$.

b $\mathbf{a} = \begin{pmatrix} a \\ b \\ c \end{pmatrix}$ is the **normal vector** to the plane.

c $\mathbf{r} = \mathbf{a} + t\mathbf{b} + u\mathbf{c}$ is the vector form, where $\mathbf{a}$ lies on the plane and $\mathbf{b}$ and $\mathbf{c}$ are vectors parallel to plane.

d If $\mathbf{r} = \begin{pmatrix} x \\ y \\ z \end{pmatrix}$, $\mathbf{a} = \begin{pmatrix} a_1 \\ a_2 \\ a_3 \end{pmatrix}$, $\mathbf{b} = \begin{pmatrix} b_1 \\ b_2 \\ b_3 \end{pmatrix}$ and $\mathbf{c} = \begin{pmatrix} c_1 \\ c_2 \\ c_3 \end{pmatrix}$

then $\mathbf{r} = \begin{pmatrix} x \\ y \\ z \end{pmatrix} = \begin{pmatrix} a_1 + tb_1 + uc_1 \\ a_2 + tb_2 + uc_2 \\ a_3 + tb_3 + uc_3 \end{pmatrix}$ is the position vector of a point on the plane.

It is sometimes written as a list of distinct components, that is

$$\begin{cases} x = a_1 + tb_1 + uc_1 \\ y = a_2 + tb_2 + uc_2 \\ z = a_3 + tb_3 + uc_3 \end{cases}$$

We might also write $\mathbf{r} = (a_1 + tb_1 + uc_1)\mathbf{i} + (a_2 + tb_2 + uc_2)\mathbf{j} + (a_3 + tb_3 + uc_3)\mathbf{k}$.

This is the parametric equation of the plane.

5 The equations of a line.

If $A(x_1, y_1, z_1)$ lies on the line which has direction vector $\mathbf{u} = a\mathbf{i} + b\mathbf{j} + c\mathbf{k}$ the equations of the line are

$\dfrac{x - x_1}{a} = \dfrac{y - y_1}{b} = \dfrac{z - z_1}{c} = t$ ... **symmetric form**

$x = x_1 + at; \quad y = y_1 + bt; \quad z = z_1 + ct$ ... **parametric form**

$\mathbf{r} = \mathbf{a} + t\mathbf{u}$ ... **vector form**

6 You should be able to find these.

a The *angle between*

- two planes ...defined as the angle between their normal vectors
- two lines ...defined as the angle between their direction vectors
- a line and a plane ...defined as the complement of the angle between the direction vector of the line and the normal vector to the plane.

b The *intersection* of

- a line and a plane is a point
- two lines is a point
- two planes is a line
- three planes is variable.

16 Number theory

Historical note

Euclid was a mathematician working in Alexandria around 300 BC. The most famous work attributed to him is that entitled 'Elements'. This work consisted of 13 books. The geometric content is the most well-known and publicised but the later books concerned themselves with the behaviour of positive integers.

This chapter will examine some of the content of book VII and book IX. In these books he explores problems associated with aspects of divisibility.

16.1 Divisibility

Reminders

- Unless otherwise stated, all variables represent integers.
- b divides a means $\exists\, c \in Z$ such that $a = bc$.
- If b divides a then we call b a **factor** of a.
  It is also referred to as a **divisor** of a.
- If b divides a and b divides c then b is a **common divisor** of a and c.
  It is important to be able to find the **greatest common divisor** (GCD).
- If a number greater than 1 has only two factors, namely itself and 1, then we call that number **prime**.
- If a number greater than 1 has more than two factors then we call that number **composite**.
  It will be the product of at least two primes.
- Multiplying the set of natural numbers by a will generate the multiples of a, namely, $a, 2a, 3a, 4a, \ldots$
- If $n_1a = n_2b$ where $n_1, n_2 \in N$ then n_1a and n_2b are common multiples of a and b.
  Generally speaking we are most interested in the lowest common multiple (LCM).

Notation

b divides a is written as $b \mid a$. If b does not divide a we write $b \nmid a$.

1 $a \mid b$ and $b \mid c \Rightarrow a \mid c$

Proof

$a \mid b \Rightarrow b = an, n \in N$ and $b \mid c \Rightarrow c = bm, m \in N$

So, $c = (an)m = anm$

Since $nm \in N$ then $a \mid c$

2 $a \mid b$ and $a \mid c \Rightarrow a \mid (b + c)$

Proof

$a \mid b \Rightarrow b = an, n \in N$ and $a \mid c \Rightarrow c = am, m \in N$

So, $b + c = an + am = a(n + m)$

Since $(n + m) \in N$ then $a \mid (b + c)$

3 $a \mid b \Rightarrow a \mid bc, \forall\, c \in Z$

By extension, $a \mid b \Rightarrow a \mid bc_1 c_2 c_3 c_4 \dots c_n, \forall\, c_n \in Z$

4 If $b + c = d$ then $a \mid b$ and $a \mid c \Rightarrow a \mid d$ also $a \mid c$ and $a \mid d \Rightarrow a \mid b$

Example 1

Consider the equation $x^2 + 2xy + y^2 = 0$.

a Explain why $\exists\, a \in Z$ such that $y^2 = ax$.

b Explain why $\exists\, b \in Z$ such that $x^2 = by$.

c Explore the solutions to $x^2 + 2xy + y^2 = 0$.

---

a There are four terms in the equation.

Since $x \mid 0$ and $x \mid x^2$ and $x \mid 2xy$ then, by result 4 above, $x \mid y^2$.

$x \mid y^2 \Rightarrow \exists\, a \in Z$ such that $y^2 = ax$

b Similarly, since $y \mid 0$ and $y \mid y^2$ and $y \mid 2xy$ then, by result 4 above, $y \mid x^2$.

$y \mid x^2 \Rightarrow \exists\, b \in Z$ such that $x^2 = by$

c Treating $x^2 + 2xy + y^2 = 0$ as a quadratic equation in x, we get

$$x = \frac{-2y \pm \sqrt{4y^2 - 4 \cdot 1 \cdot y^2}}{2} = -y$$

Solutions are $(x, -x), \forall\, x \in Z$.

Exercise 16.1

1 A number, n, is even if $2 \mid n, n \in Z$.

A number, n, is odd if $2 \mid (n + 1), n \in Z$.

a x and y are both integers.
Prove xy is odd if and only if both x and y are odd.

b Prove that $x^2 + x + k$ is even if and only if k is even.

2 Prove **a** result 3 above, namely, $a \mid b \Rightarrow a \mid bc\ \forall\, c \in Z$

b result 4, namely

if $b + c = d$ then $a \mid b$ and $a \mid c \Rightarrow a \mid d$

also $a \mid c$ and $a \mid d \Rightarrow a \mid b$

3 Consider the equation $4x^2 + 12xy + 9y^2 = 0, x, y \in Z$.

a Explain why we know x^2 is divisible by 3.

b Explain why we know y^2 is divisible by 4.

c Explore the solutions to $4x^2 + 12xy + 9y^2 = 0, x, y \in Z$, and give the first three solutions for $x > 0$.

4 A whole number greater than 10, n, can be expressed as $n = 10a + b$ where $a, b \in Z$ and b is the units digit.

a Show that if b is even then the original number is even.

b Show that if $a - 2b$ is divisible by 3 then $3 \mid n$.

c Show that if $a - 5b$ is divisible by 3 then $3 \mid n$.

d Show that if $a - 2b$ is divisible by 7 then $7 \mid n$.

e Show that if $a - 5b$ is divisible by 17 then $17 \mid n$.

f Show that if $5 \mid b$ then $5 \mid n$.

g Show that there is no test of the form 'if $a - kb$ is divisible by 5 then $5 \mid n$'.

5 A well-known rule for divisibility is that a number is only divisible by 9 if the sum of its digits is divisible by 9.
Consider 4-digit numbers of the form '*abcd*' which thus equal $1000a + 100b + 10c + d$.
Show that '*abcd*' will be divisible by 9 if and only if $a + b + c + d$ is divisible by 9.

6 A test for divisibility by 11 is to see if the digits taken in order and alternately added and subtracted produce a number which is divisible by 11.
Consider 5-digit numbers of the form '*abcde*'.
Show that '*abcde*' will be divisible by 11 if and only if $a - b + c - d + e$ is divisible by 11.

7 a For $n \in \mathrm{N}$ prove that $2^n - 1$ is never a square number.
[Hint: Let $2^n - 1 = k^2$ and consider the two cases i k even and ii k odd separately.]

b Prove that $2^n - 1$ is never a cube or any higher power.

8 a Prove, by factorising, that $x^3 - x$ is divisible by i 2 ii 3 iii $6 \ \forall x \in Z$

b Prove that $x^3 - x + 12$ is divisible by i 2 ii 3 iii $6 \ \forall x \in Z$

16.2 Prime numbers

An IT Aside

This listing for an Excel spreadsheet will help you explore the prime numbers.

```
Function prime(n)
If Int(n / 2) = n / 2 Then n = n - 1
flag = 1
Do While flag = 1
   n = n + 2
   flag = 0
   For x = 3 To Int(Sqr(n)) Step 2
       If Int(n / x) = n / x Then flag = 1
   Next x
   If flag = 0 Then prime = n
Loop
End Function
```

Open a fresh spreadsheet in Excel. Follow the menu trail

- Tools > Macro > Visual Basic Editor
- Insert > Module
- Now type the above listing into the Form that appears.
- Follow the trail Excel > Close and return to Microsoft Excel.
- Save the blank sheet as an .xls or .xlsm file.

You now have a spreadsheet that can generate prime numbers using a user-defined function, '= Prime(n)'.
This will return the first prime number bigger than n, where n is a positive integer greater than 1.

For example, type '= prime(4)' into a cell and 5 appears.
If we type '2' into A1 and then '= prime(A1)' into A2, '3' will appear in A2.
If we fill A2 down column A, you will generate the primes.

The function can also be used to test if a number is prime:
Put the test number in A1.
In A2 type, '= Prime(A1−1)'.
If A2 = A1 then the original number was prime.
This check can be programmed into the sheet.
In A3 type '= IF(A1 = A2, "Prime", "not Prime")'.

Prime factorisation

Every integer greater than 1 is either prime or composite and, hence, the product of primes. When a composite number is expressed as such a product, we call the product the **prime factorisation** of the number, or the **prime representation** or the **prime decomposition**.

We can find the prime factorisation of a number by systematically dividing the number by the primes in order. [namely 2, 3, 5, 7, 11, 13, ...]

Example 2

Find the prime factorisation of 2772.

Reducing the number by repeated division by the lowest prime that is a factor produces the result that $2772 = 2^2 3^2 5^0 7^1 11^1$.

This is generally written as $2772 = 2^2 \cdot 3^2 \cdot 7 \cdot 11$.

These prime factorisations can be used to assist in a systematic listing of all the factors of a number.

Working

2	2772
2	1386
3	693
3	231
7	77
11	11
	1

Example 3

List all the factors of 150.

First find the prime factorisation: $150 = 2^1 \cdot 3^1 \cdot 5^2$.
When constructing factors we may use $2^0, 2^1, 3^0, 3^1, 5^0, 5^1, 5^2$.

	3^0	3^1
2^0	1	3
2^1	2	6

possible factors considering 2 and 3 only

	1	2	3	6
5^0	1	2	3	6
5^1	5	10	15	30
5^2	25	50	75	150

then considering 5^2

The factors of 150 are {1, 2, 3, 5, 6, 10, 15, 25, 30, 50, 75, 150}.

Note: the powers in the prime factorisation, 1, 1, 2, gave rise to the number of factors: $(1 + 1) \times (1 + 1) \times (2 + 1) = 2 \times 2 \times 3 = 12$ factors.

Example 4

Find the lowest number with 60 factors.

Working the logic of Example 2 backwards: $60 = 2 \times 2 \times 3 \times 5$.
So we want the powers in the prime factorisation of the target number to be 1, 1, 2, 4.
Associate the smallest prime with the largest power: $2^4 \cdot 3^2 \cdot 5^1 \cdot 7^1 = 5040$.
Note: using any four distinct primes will produce a number with 60 factors.

Unique prime factorisation

Some findings are useful:

1 Every integer greater than 1 is prime or can be written as the product of primes.

2 Every integer greater than 1 is divisible by a prime.
The number is either prime, in which case the statement is proved, or the number is composite and the product of at least two primes.

3 There are infinitely many primes.

Proof

Euclid proved this in his 'Elements'.
He used proof by contradiction.
Suppose there is a finite list of primes $p_1, p_2, p_3, p_4, p_5, \dots p_n$. with p_n the largest.
Let $N = p_1 \cdot p_2 \cdot p_3 \cdot p_4 \cdot p_5 \cdot \dots p_n + 1$.
With p_n the largest prime, N is composite. So it has a prime divisor, p_q.
However, this divisor cannot be any one of $p_1, p_2, p_3, p_4, p_5, \dots p_n$ since $N \div p_i$ leaves a remainder of 1 for all i, $1 \leqslant i \leqslant n$.
But $p_1, p_2, p_3, p_4, p_5, \dots p_n$ represents all the primes, and p_q is a prime not on the list.
So we have a contradiction.
So there is not a finite list of primes, nor a highest prime.[1]

4 It follows that if the prime p divides $p_1 \cdot p_2 \cdot p_3 \cdot p_4 \cdot p_5 \cdot \dots p_n$, all prime, then $p = p_k$ for $1 \leqslant k \leqslant n$.

5 Any positive integer can be prime factorised in one and only one way.

This is known as the **unique factorisation theorem** or the **fundamental theorem of arithmetic**.

Proof

Suppose that $N = p_1 \cdot p_2 \cdot p_3 \cdot p_4 \cdot p_5 \cdot \dots p_n$ where each p_i is prime.
Suppose that N can also be expressed as $N = q_1 \cdot q_2 \cdot q_3 \cdot q_4 \cdot q_5 \cdot \dots q_r$ where each q_i is prime.
Thus $p_1 \cdot p_2 \cdot p_3 \cdot p_4 \cdot p_5 \cdot \dots p_n = q_1 \cdot q_2 \cdot q_3 \cdot q_4 \cdot q_5 \cdot \dots q_r$.
Since p_1 divides the left-hand side it must also divide the right.
Since p_1 divides $q_1 \cdot q_2 \cdot q_3 \cdot q_4 \cdot q_5 \cdot \dots q_r$ then by 4 $p = q_k$ for $1 \leqslant k \leqslant r$.
We can divide the equation by this common factor and it becomes
$p_2 \cdot p_3 \cdot p_4 \cdot p_5 \cdot \dots p_n = q_1 \cdot q_2 \cdot q_3 \cdot q_4 \cdot q_5 \cdot \dots q_{k-1}, q_{k+1} \dots q_r$.
We can repeat this argument cancelling out a p and q at each step.
The number of p and q must be the same or we would arrive at either $p_a \cdot p_b \cdot \dots p_i = 1$ or $1 = q_a \cdot q_b \cdot \dots q_i$ which is impossible. So $n = r$ and $p_1 \cdot p_2 \cdot p_3 \cdot p_4 \cdot p_5 \cdot \dots p_n = q_1 \cdot q_2 \cdot q_3 \cdot q_4 \cdot q_5 \cdot \dots q_n$; the left-hand side is just a rearrangement of the right-hand side.
Thus the prime factorisation of a number is unique.

Example 5

a Prove that if $n > 1$, $n \in Z$, then n^2 has an even number of factors in its prime factorisation.

b Use the prime factorisation theorem to prove that $\sqrt{2}$ is irrational.

---

a Let the prime factorisation of $n = n_1 n_2 n_3 \dots n_k$, where all n_i are prime, not necessarily distinct.
Then the prime factorisation of $n^2 = {n_1}^2 {n_2}^2 {n_3}^2 \dots {n_k}^2$.
Where n has k prime factors, n^2 has $2k$ factors.
Hence $n > 1$, $n \in Z$, n^2 has an even number of factors in its prime factorisation.

[1] [Note: there is a highest *known* prime. A project called the Great Internet Mersennes Prime Search (GIMPS) uses the idle time of people's home computers to hunt for primes. An internet query will give you the 'state of play'; Google 'GIMPS'.]

b Assume that $\sqrt{2}$ is rational

$\Rightarrow \sqrt{2} = \frac{m}{n}, m, n \in Z, m, n \neq 1$

$\Rightarrow 2n^2 = m^2$

Consider the prime factorisation of the left-hand side:
there is an even number of prime factors from n^2 plus the 2 giving an odd number of factors.
Consider the prime factorisation of the right-hand side:
there is an even number of prime factors from m^2.
The number of factors in the prime factorisation of $2n^2$ and m^2 should be the same since they are equal. So we have a contradiction.
So $\sqrt{2}$ is not rational.

Example 6

a Show that if $13x + 4, x \in W$, is a perfect square then $\exists\ a \in W$ such that $13x = (a - 2)(a + 2)$.

b Use the fundamental theorem of arithmetic to deduce that there is at least one prime number p for which $13p + 4$ is a perfect square.

---

a If $13x + 4$ is a perfect square then $\exists\ a \in W$ such that $13x + 4 = a^2$.
So $13x = a^2 - 4 = (a - 2)(a + 2)$.

b If there is a prime, p, for which $13p + 4$ is a perfect square then $\exists\ a \in W$ such that $13p = (a - 2)(a + 2)$.
The left-hand side has only two prime factors, namely 13 and p.
By the unique factorisation theorem, this must also be the case for the right-hand side.
So one of $(a - 2)$ or $(a + 2)$ must be 13.
So a must be 15 or 11.
When $a = 15$, the factors are 13 and 17.
When $a = 11$, the factors are 9 and 13.
So $a = 15$ gives the required solution: the prime $p = 17$.

Exercise 16.2

1 **a** Find the prime factorisation of

i 1400 **ii** 5445 **iii** 23 660 **iv** 7056

b State how many factors, prime and composite, each number has.

2 List all the factors of

a 108 **b** 3528 **c** 10 241

3 **a** Find the lowest number with

i six factors **ii** 36 factors **iii** 40 factors

b Find the two smallest numbers which have 15 factors.

4 Show that for all positive integers, n, there exists a sequence of n consecutive positive integers which are all composite.

For example three consecutive non-primes: 8, 9, 10
five consecutive non-primes: 24, 25, 26, 27, 28
17 consecutive non-primes: 524, 525, 526, 527, ... , 539, 540

Hint: consider the sequence that starts $n! + 2, n! + 3, n! + 4$.

a How do we know **i** the first term **ii** the second term is composite?

b Up to what 'value' of k are we guaranteed that $n! + k$ is composite?

c How many composite numbers will we generate?

5 Use the unique factorisation theorem to prove

a $\sqrt{7}$ is irrational b $\sqrt{p}$ is irrational where p is a prime.

6 a By considering the unique factorisation theorem find a prime number, p, such that $19p + 81$ is a perfect square.

b Find two non-prime whole numbers, x, which make $19x + 81$ a perfect square.

7 Find a prime number p so that $7p - 3$ is the product of two whole numbers which differ by 4.

8 a Identify a prime number p such that $7p + 1$ is a perfect cube.

b Find two non-prime integers x for which $7x + 1$ is a perfect cube.

9 Prove that there are no integers x and y such that $6^x = 21^y$.

10 Prove $\log_{10} 5$ is irrational by

a assuming it is rational

b using the laws of logs to show some power of 10 is equal to a power of 5

c using the unique factorisation theorem

16.3 Division

Consider the division $203 \div 8 = 25$ remainder 3.

It may also be written as $\frac{203}{8} = 25 + \frac{3}{8}$.

In the context of division, 203 is called the **dividend**, 8 the **divisor**, 25 the **quotient** and 3 the **remainder**.

The relation between these four quantities can also be expressed as $203 = 8 \times 25 + 3$.

The division algorithm

Given any positive integers a and b ($b \neq 0$) there exist *unique* integers q and r, where $0 \leq r < b$, such that

$$a = bq + r$$

This is referred to as the **division algorithm** or the **division identity**.

If we divide by b ($b \neq 0$) we get $\frac{a}{b} = q + \frac{r}{b}$ which makes the theorem almost self-evident:

when a is divided by b we get a quotient q and a remainder r, $0 \leq r < b$ ... and it cannot be done in more than one way (q and r are unique).

Proof

Either a is a multiple of b in which case $\exists\, q \in Z: a = bq$ and $r = 0$
or a lies between two consecutive multiples of b *and* $r = a - bq$,
in which case $\exists\, q \in Z: bq < a < b(q + 1)$

$$\Rightarrow \quad 0 < a - bq < bq + b - bq$$

$$\Rightarrow \quad 0 < a - bq < b$$

$$\Rightarrow \quad 0 < r < b$$

Thus $0 \leq r < b$.

Proof of uniqueness

Suppose another such pair of integers exist so that $a = bq_1 + r_1, 0 \leq r_1 < b$.
We now have a system of equations $a = bq + r$ and $a = bq_1 + r_1$.

Subtracting gives $0 = b(q - q_1) + (r - r_1)$.
Since b divides 0 and b divides $b(q - q_1)$ then b divides $(r - r_1)$.
Since $0 \le r < b$ and $0 \le r_1 < b$ we have $-b < r - r_1 < b$ (see subtraction table).

	$-$	r_1: 0	r_1: b
r	0	0	$-b$
r	b	b	0

But the only number between b and $-b$ which b divides is zero.
Thus $r = r_1$,

and so $q = \frac{a - r}{b} = \frac{a - r_1}{b} = q_1$

proving that q and r are unique.

The greatest common divisor

The **greatest common divisor** (GCD) of a and b can be denoted by (a, b) when the context is unambiguous.

A theorem

If $a = bq + r$, then $(a, b) = (b, r)$.

Proof

Let $d = (a, b)$ ... by definition $d \mid a$ and $d \mid b$.
Since $a = bq + r$ it follows that $d \mid r$.
So d is a common divisor of a, b and r.

Let $e = (b, r)$. By definition $e \mid r$ and $e \mid b$ so it follows that $e \mid a$.
Thus e is a common divisor of a, b and r.
But by the definition of d (GCD) $e \le d$.
Thus d is the greatest common divisor of b and r.
Thus $(a, b) = (b, r)$.

Thus finding the GCD of two numbers can be made simpler by finding the GCD of the smaller number and the remainder when the larger is divided by the smaller.

The Euclidean algorithm

The repeated application of the above theorem until the greatest common divisor is identified is known as the **Euclidean algorithm**.

Suppose we have two integers a and b $(b \ne 0)$. Then by the division algorithm

$a = bq_1 + r_1 \; (0 \le r_1 < b)$ and by the theorem $(a, b) = (b, r_1)$
then $b = r_1q_2 + r_2 \; (0 \le r_2 < r_1)$ and by the theorem $(a, b) = (b, r_1) = (r_1, r_2)$
then $r_1 = r_2q_3 + r_3 \; (0 \le r_3 < r_2)$ and by the theorem $(a, b) = (b, r_1) = (r_1, r_2) = (r_2, r_3)$

Given that each r_n is an integer less than the previous r, such that $0 \le r_{n+1} < r_n$, then eventually for some $n = k$ we get $r_k = 0$ giving $r_{k-2} = r_{k-1}q_k + 0$ $(r_k = 0)$ and by the theorem $(a, b) = (b, r_1) = (r_1, r_2) = (r_2, r_3) = \ldots = (r_{k-2}, r_{k-1}) = (r_{k-1}, 0) = r_{k-1}$.
Thus $(a, b) = r_{k-1}$.

Example 7

Find the greatest common divisor of 203 and 8 using the Euclidean algorithm.

[$203 \div 8 = 25$ r 3] $\quad 203 = 8 \times 25 + 3 \Rightarrow (203, 8) = (8, 3)$
[$8 \div 3 = 2$ r 2] $\quad 8 = 3 \times 2 + 2 \Rightarrow (8, 3) = (3, 2)$
[$3 \div 2 = 1$ r 1] $\quad 3 = 2 \times 1 + 1 \Rightarrow (3, 2) = (2, 1)$
[$2 \div 1 = 2$ r 0] $\quad 2 = 1 \times 2 + 0 \Rightarrow (2, 1) = (1, 0) = 1$

The greatest common divisor of 203 and 8 is 1.

Note that when the GCD of two numbers is 1 then the numbers are said to be **co-prime** or **relatively prime**.

Example 8

Find the greatest common divisor of 132 and 424 using the Euclidean algorithm.

$$\begin{aligned} 424 &= 132 \times 3 + 28 \Rightarrow (424, 132) = (132, 28) \\ 132 &= 28 \times 4 + 20 \Rightarrow (132, 28) = (28, 20) \\ 28 &= 20 \times 1 + 8 \Rightarrow (28, 20) = (20, 8) \\ 20 &= 8 \times 2 + 4 \Rightarrow (20, 8) = (8, 4) \\ 8 &= 4 \times 2 + 0 \Rightarrow (8, 4) = (4, 0) = 4 \end{aligned}$$

The greatest common divisor of 132 and 424 is 4.

A second IT aside

The method is completely automatic and it can easily be programmed into a spreadsheet.
It can be quite constructive to see how these formulae work.
Note that = MOD(12, 5) gives the remainder when 12 is divided by 5.

	A	B	C
1	424	132	
2	132	28	
3	28	20	
4	20	8	
5	8	4	
6	4	0	4
7			
8			
9			

Cell A1 holds the higher number. Cell B1 holds the lower number.
A2 holds = IF(B1=0, “”, B1)
B2 holds = IF(OR(B1=0,B1="(66 not 99)”), “”, MOD(A1,B1))
C2 holds = IF(B2=0, B1, “”)
These three cells are then filled down for about 10 lines.
(The comma separators on some spreadsheets are semicolons.)

Exercise 16.3

1 Find the GCD of each of these pairs of numbers using the Euclidean algorithm.

a 111 and 481 b 451 and 168 c 679 and 388
d 756 and 714 e 1470 and 1330 f 1498 and 535
g 738 and 205 h 1356 and 432 i 2446 and 2040
j 2172 and 1267 k 1692 and 684 l 34 034 and 51 051

2 You wish to find the GCD of three numbers, 264, 156 and 378.

a Find the GCD of the two smaller numbers, that is 156 and 264.

b Find the GCD of (264, 156) and 378.

3 In a similar fashion find the GCD of these number triples.

a 185, 222 and 259 b 420, 336 and 924

4 The lowest common multiple (LCM) of a and b is the lowest number which both a and b divide.
If $G = (a, b)$ then there exist m and $n \in Z$ such that $a = mG$ and $b = nG$.
$(m, n) = 1$ or else G would not be the GCF of a and b.
Thus if the LCM of a and b is L, we have $L = mnG$.

a Starting from this point, prove that LCM $= \dfrac{ab}{(a, b)}$.

b Use the Euclidean algorithm and the above fact to find the LCM of each pair of numbers.

i 6539 and 1547 ii 252 and 322 iii 8892 and 11 115
iv 9554 and 9537 v 325 and 5200 vi 174 and 319

5 A old-fashioned bicycle has two wheels, one of circumference 540 cm and the other of 420 cm.
The point of contact with the ground is marked on both wheels.
How far will the bicycle travel before the marks are next on the ground together?

6 The Moon goes round the Earth in 28 days.
The Earth goes round the Sun in 365 days.
How long will it be before the Earth, Moon and Sun are in the same relative positions as they are today?

16.4 A consequence of the Euclidean algorithm

If $d = (a, b)$ then there exist integers s and t such that $d = as + bt$.

Examining the start of the Euclidean algorithm

$$a = bq_1 + r_1 \Rightarrow r_1 = a - bq_1 \qquad (a, b) \Rightarrow (b, r_1)$$
$$b = r_1q_2 + r_2 \Rightarrow r_2 = b - r_1q_2 \qquad (b, r_1) \Rightarrow (r_1, r_2)$$
$$r_1 = r_2q_3 + r_3 \Rightarrow r_3 = r_1 - r_2q_3 \qquad (r_1, r_2) \Rightarrow (r_2, r_3)$$

From line 1 we have $\quad r_1 = a - bq_1$

Substitute this into line 2 $\quad b - r_1q_2 = b - (a - bq_1)q_2 = b(1 + q_1q_2) - aq_2$

and both into line 3 $\quad r_3 = r_1 - r_2q_3 \Rightarrow r_3 = (a - bq_1) - [b(1 + q_1q_2) - aq_2]q_3$

$$= a - bq_1 - b(1 + q_1q_2)q_3 + aq_2q_3 = a(1 + q_2q_3) - b(q_1 + q_3 + q_1q_2q_3)$$

We can continue in this manner till we reach the last non-zero remainder, d, which will then be expressed in the required form, namely $d = as + bt$, $s, t \in \mathbb{Z}$.

In practice, with actual values, the steps are best performed in reverse.
For the sake of clarity a product such as 66×5 can be written as $66 \cdot 5$ without ambiguity since, in this context, we are exclusively working with integers.

Example 9

Express the greatest common divisor of 132 and 424 in the form $132s + 424t$ where $s, t \in \mathbb{Z}$.

Each line is rearranged to give *expressions* for the remainders:

$424 = 132 \cdot 3 + 28$	$\Rightarrow$	$28 = 424 - 3 \cdot 132$	(4)
$132 = 28 \cdot 4 + 20$	$\Rightarrow$	$20 = 132 - 4 \cdot 28$	(3)
$28 = 20 \cdot 1 + 8$	$\Rightarrow$	$8 = 28 - 1 \cdot 20$	(2)
$20 = 8 \cdot 2 + 4$	$\Rightarrow$	$4 = 20 - 2 \cdot 8$	(1)
$8 = 4 \cdot 2 + 0$	$\Rightarrow$	$0 = 8 - 4 \cdot 2$	

The GCD is identified at line (1) as 4, the last non-zero remainder.
The labeling of lines as (1) – (4) will only occur once the GCD is identified.

(1) gives an expression for 4 $\quad 4 = 20 - 2 \cdot \mathbf{8}$

(2) gives a substitute for 8 $\quad 4 = 20 - 2 \cdot (\mathbf{28} - \mathbf{1} \cdot \mathbf{20})$

$\Rightarrow \quad 4 = 20 - 2 \cdot 28 + 2 \cdot 20 = 3 \cdot 20 - 2 \cdot 28$

$\Rightarrow \quad 4 = 3 \cdot \mathbf{20} - 2 \cdot 28$

(3) gives a substitute for 20 $\quad 4 = 3 \cdot (\mathbf{132} - \mathbf{4} \cdot \mathbf{28}) - 2 \cdot 28$

$\Rightarrow \quad 4 = 3 \cdot 132 - 12 \cdot 28 - 2 \cdot 28 = 3 \cdot 132 - 14 \cdot 28$

$\Rightarrow \quad 4 = 3 \cdot 132 - 14 \cdot \mathbf{28}$

(4) gives a substitute for 28 $\quad 4 = 3 \cdot 132 - 14 \cdot (\mathbf{424} - \mathbf{3} \cdot \mathbf{132})$

$\Rightarrow \quad 4 = 3 \cdot 132 - 14 \cdot 424 + 42 \cdot 132$

$\Rightarrow \quad 4 = 45 \cdot 132 - 14 \cdot 424$

Thus $4 = 45 \cdot \mathbf{132} - 14 \cdot \mathbf{424}$, the required form.

The remainders and substitution have been emboldened in this first example to highlight their role in the process.
At each stage we merely substitute for the remainders in order (1) – (4).

Example 10

a Show that 280 and 117 are relatively prime, that is $(280, 117) = 1$.

b Find $a, b \in Z$ such that $280a + 117b = 1$.

---

a The Euclidean algorithm shows GCD = 1

$$280 = 117 \cdot 2 + 46$$
$$117 = 46 \cdot 2 + 25$$
$$46 = 25 \cdot 1 + 21$$
$$25 = 21 \cdot 1 + 4$$
$$21 = 4 \cdot 5 + 1$$
$$4 = 1 \cdot 4 + 0$$

The GCD is the last non-zero remainder, namely 1.

Make the remainder the subject in each line.

$280 = 117 \cdot 2 + 46$	$\Rightarrow$	$46 = 280 - 2 \cdot 117$	(5)
$117 = 46 \cdot 2 + 25$	$\Rightarrow$	$25 = 117 - 2 \cdot 46$	(4)
$46 = 25 \cdot 1 + 21$	$\Rightarrow$	$21 = 46 - 1 \cdot 25$	(3)
$25 = 21 \cdot 1 + 4$	$\Rightarrow$	$4 = 25 - 1 \cdot 21$	(2)
$21 = 4 \cdot 5 + 1$	$\Rightarrow$	$1 = 21 - 5 \cdot 4$	(1)

b Line (1) gives $1 = 21 - 5 \cdot 4$

Use (2) to substitute for 4 $1 = 21 - 5 \cdot (25 - 1 \cdot 21) = 6 \cdot 21 - 5 \cdot 25$

Use (3) to substitute for 21 $1 = 6 \cdot (46 - 1 \cdot 25) - 5 \cdot 25 = 6 \cdot 46 - 11 \cdot 25$

Use (4) to substitute for 25 $1 = 6 \cdot 46 - 11 \cdot (117 - 2 \cdot 46) = 28 \cdot 46 - 11 \cdot 117$

Use (5) to substitute for 46 $1 = 28 \cdot (280 - 2 \cdot 117) - 11 \cdot 117 = 28 \cdot 280 - 67 \cdot 117$

Thus we have the required form $1 = 28 \cdot 280 - 67 \cdot 117$
giving $a = 28$ and $b = -67$.

Exercise 16.4

1 Find the greatest common divisor of 345 and 285 and express it in the form $345s + 285t$, where $s, t \in Z$.

2 Calculate $(583, 318)$ and express it in the form $583s + 318t$, where $s, t \in Z$.

3 a Evaluate $d = (1292, 1558)$.

b Hence, express d in the form $1292s + 1558t$ where $s, t \in Z$.

4 a Show that 763 and 662 are relatively prime.

b Use this fact to express 1 as the sum of multiples of 763 and 662.

c Repeat this for the numbers 1479 and 1178.

5 Find a and $b \in Z$ such that $248a + 261b = 1$.

6 $5612x + 540y = 4$. Assuming x and y are integers, find their values.

7 a Find integers s, t, u, v such that $1485s + 952t = 690u + 539v$.

b 211, 307, 401, 503 are four primes. Find integers a, b, c, d such that
$211a + 307b + 401c + 503d = 0$

c Find integers a, b, c such that
$211a + 307b + 401c = 0$

8 The first four primes are 2, 3, 5 and 7.

a Find integers a, b, c, d such that $2a + 3b + 5c + 7d = 2$.

b Hence find integers a, b, c, d such that $2a + 3b + 5c + 7d = 14$.

c Find integers a, b, c such that $2a + 3b + 5c = 2$. Explain why this means that every even integer can be expressed as the sum of multiples of 2, 3 and 5.

9 A 20p coin weighs 5 g. A £2 coin weighs 12 g.
One pan of a beam balance holds an object whose weight is a number of whole grams.

a Prove you can find out its weight by placing just 20p and £2 coins on either or both pans. For example if putting ten 20p coins on the empty pan and four £2 coins on the pan with the object makes it balance then the object weighs 2 g. [50 − 48 = 2]

b A penny weighs 356 centigrams; a 5p piece weighs 325 centigrams. Show that a similar strategy will allow you to weigh objects to the nearest centigram using only 1p and 5p coins.

16.5 The division algorithm and number bases

We take it for granted that a number can be expressed as a sum of multiples of powers of 10, for example $2314 = 2 \cdot 10^3 + 3 \cdot 10^2 + 1 \cdot 10^1 + 4 \cdot 10^0$.
Perhaps the fact that we have 10 fingers is the reason our number system developed like this.
There is evidence from cuneiform tablets that the Babylonians used a different base: 60.
Computers work using a logic which calculates using 2 as a base.
Computer programmers use bases 8 and 16 frequently.
Any positive integer greater than 1 is suitable for use as a base.
For example $48 = 1 \cdot 5^2 + 4 \cdot 5^1 + 3 \cdot 5^0$ which is recorded as 143_{five} or 143_5.

In this notation the subscript gives the base, for example
$4152_6 = 4 \cdot 6^3 + 1 \cdot 6^2 + 5 \cdot 6^1 + 2 \cdot 6^0 = 932_{10}$.
We do not really need the subscript for base 10.
In base 16 we have to invent new digits A = 10, B = 11, C = 12, ... , F = 15.
For example $13C_{16} = 1 \cdot 16^2 + 3 \cdot 16^1 + 12 \cdot 16^0 = 316_{10}$.

Every number A can be written *uniquely* in any base n, where $n \geqslant 2, n \in N$.

Proof

This can be proved using the division algorithm.
Dividing A by n, the division algorithm gives $A = nq_1 + r_0, 0 < r_0 < n$.
Dividing q_1 by n $\quad q_1 = nq_2 + r_1, 0 < r_1 < n$
Dividing q_2 by n $\quad q_2 = nq_3 + r_2, 0 < r_2 < n$
Dividing q_3 by n $\quad q_3 = nq_4 + r_3, 0 < r_3 < n$

Now $q_k < q_{k-1}$ at each step.
Given that q is a non-negative integer means that for some k, $q_k = 0$, giving a final line $q_k = n \cdot 0 + r_k, 0 < r_k < n$.

So, $A = nq_1 + r_0 = n(nq_2 + r_1) + r_0 = n^2q_2 + n^1r_1 + n^0r_0$
$\Rightarrow A = n^2(nq_3 + r_2) + n^1r_1 + n^0r_0 = n^3q_3 + n^2r_2 + n^1r_1 + n^0r_0$
$\Rightarrow A = n^3(nq_4 + r_3) + n^2r_2 + n^1r_1 + n^0r_0 = n^4q_4 + n^3r_3 + n^2r_2 + n^1r_1 + n^0r_0$

Continuing in this way, we arrive at
$\Rightarrow A = n^k r_k + \ldots + n^3 r_3 + n^2 r_2 + n^1 r_1 + n^0 r_0$
Thus in base n A takes the form $(r^k \ldots r^3 r^2 r^1 r^0)_n$.

The uniqueness can be proved by assuming another representation exists and then showing that it must be the same.

The division algorithm shows that to represent a base 10 number in another base, n, all we need do is perform repeated division by n and record the remainders as they are generated.

Example 11

Express 1136_{10} as a base 6 number.

$1136 \div 6 = 189$ remainder 2
$189 \div 6 = 31$ remainder 3
$31 \div 6 = 5$ remainder 1
$5 \div 6 = 0$ remainder 5

giving $1136_{10} = 5132_6$.

Example 12

Express 2213_4 as a number in base 5.

Convert first of all to a base 10 number
$2213_4 = 2 \cdot 4^3 + 2 \cdot 4^2 + 1 \cdot 4^1 + 3 \cdot 4^0 = 128 + 32 + 4 + 3 = 167_{10}$
Now use repeated division by 5
$167 \div 5 = 33$ remainder 2
$33 \div 5 = 6$ remainder 3
$6 \div 5 = 1$ remainder 1
$1 \div 5 = 0$ remainder 1

giving $2213_4 = 1132_5$.

We can add, subtract, multiply and divide numbers expressed in different bases by converting each number to base 10, then converting back after performing the required operation.
However, if you are comfortable with the algorithms of arithmetic operations, you can perform the operation in the given base.

Example 13

Calculate $3220_3 + 222_3$

3220	➡	32 20	➡	32 20	➡	32 20
+ 222		$+\ 2_1 22$		$+\ {}_1 2_1 22$		$+\ {}_1 2_1 22$
2		12		2 12		11 2 12
$0 + 2 = 2$		$2+2 = 4 = 11_3$		$2 + 2 + 1 = 5 = 12_3$		$1 + 3 = 4 = 11_3$

Exercise 16.5

1 Express these numbers in base 10.

a 1234_7 **b** 777_8 **c** 110110_2

d $t81e_{12}$ where t and e are digits representing 10 and 11 respectively.

2 Change these numbers to the base indicated.

a 63_{10} to base 2   b 333_{10} to base 4   c 1727_{10} to base 12

d 626_7 to base 5   e 401_6 to base 7   f $tt5_{12}$ to base 6

3 In computer programming it is very common to convert from binary (base 2) to hexadecimal (base 16). Use A = 10, B = 11, C = 12, D = 13, E = 14, F = 15 and convert these binary numbers to hexadecimal.

a i 1101_2 ii 1001_2 iii $1101\ 1001_2$

b i 1111_2 ii 1000_2 iii $1111\ 1000_2$

c i 1100_2 ii 1011_2 iii $1100\ 1011_2$

d i 100_2 ii 11_2 iii $0100\ 0011_2$

e Compare your answers to parts **i** and **ii** with part **iii** and comment on a method of converting from base 2 to base 16.

4 A puzzle often included in conjuring tricks comprises five cards containing these arrays.

Card 1	Card 2	Card 3	Card 4	Card 5
1 3 5 7	2 3 6 7	4 5 6 7	8 9 10 11	16 17 18 19
9 11 13 15	10 11 14 15	12 13 14 15	12 13 14 15	20 21 22 23
17 19 21 23	18 19 22 23	20 21 22 23	24 25 26 27	24 25 26 27
25 27 29 31	26 27 30 31	28 29 30 31	28 29 30 31	28 29 30 31
33 35 37 39	34 35 38 39	36 37 38 39	40 41 42 43	48 49 50 51
41 43 45 47	42 43 46 47	44 45 46 47	44 45 46 47	52 53 54 55
49 51 53 55	50 51 54 55	52 53 54 55	56 57 58 59	56 57 58 59
57 59 61 63	58 59 62 63	60 61 62 63	60 61 62 63	60 61 62 63

The 'victim' is invited to think of a number between 1 and 32 and indicate on which cards his chosen number appears.

The performer can almost instantly identify the selected number by using a simple addition.

a What number is he thinking about if he indicates cards

i 1, 3, 4, 5   ii 1, 4   iii 2, 3, 5

b Using base 2, the answers to part **a** are

i 11101_2 ii 01001_2 iii 10110_2. Explain.

c Adding another card would extend the range of the puzzle so that the target number was between 1 and 64. Reconstruct this card.

d Can you adapt the trick to exploit base 3?

5 A chemist uses a beam balance to weigh objects.

He only has four different-sized weights.

However, using these he can weigh objects to the nearest gram for every weight between 1 g and 40 g.

a What are the four weights?

b What is the relevance of the question to this topic?

6 A company in 1971 ran an advert which read 'If you can solve this problem you could be a computer programmer. Continue this sequence. 110, 20, 12, 11, … … …'

Can you solve the problem?

7 Perform each calculation, expressing your answer in the base given.

a i $213_4 + 312_4$ ii $763_8 + 651_8$ iii $10111_2 + 1011_2$

b i $745_9 - 217_9$ ii $1100_2 - 111_2$ iii $4243_5 - 424_5$

c i $212_3 \times 2_3$ ii $316_7 \times 3_7$ iii $111_2 \times 11_2$

d i $122_4 \div 2_4$ ii $45_7 \div 3_7$ iii $1110_2 \div 10_2$

Review 16

1 Prove that $2 \mid n^4 \Leftrightarrow 2 \mid n^2$.

2 Prove by induction that, $\forall n \in N$, $3^{2n} + 7$ is divisible by 8.

3 Every integer greater than 10 can be expressed in the form $10a + b$ where a and b are integers and $0 \le b < 10$.
It has been suggested, as a test of divisibility of 13, that if $a - 9b$ is divisible by 13 then the original number is divisible by 13.
Prove that the test is true.

4 Use the unique factorisation theorem to prove that $\sqrt{5}$ is irrational.

5 Find (726, 240).

6 If $d = (653, 251)$, show that $d = 1$ and express d in the form $653s + 251t$ where $s, t \in Z$.

7 What is the value of $1101\ 0011_2$ in base 10.

8 Express 825_9 as a base 4 number.

Summary 16

1 Divisibility and notation
b divides a is written as $b \mid a$. If b does not divide a we write $b \nmid a$.

a $a \mid b$ and $b \mid c \Rightarrow a \mid c$

b $a \mid b$ and $a \mid c \Rightarrow a \mid (b + c)$

c $a \mid b \Rightarrow a \mid bc \ \forall c \in Z$
By extension, $a \mid b \Rightarrow a \mid bc_1 c_2 c_3 c_4 \dots c_n \ \forall c_n \in Z$

d If $b + c = d$ then $a \mid b$ and $a \mid c \Rightarrow a \mid d$
also $a \mid c$ and $a \mid d \Rightarrow a \mid b$

2 **Prime factorisation**

a Every integer greater than 1 is prime or can be written as the product of primes.

b Every integer greater than 1 is divisible by a prime.

c There are infinitely many primes.

d If the prime p divides $p_1 \cdot p_2 \cdot p_3 \cdot p_4 \cdot p_5 \cdot \dots p_n$, all prime, then $p = p_k$ for some $1 \leqslant k \leqslant n$.

e Any positive integer can be prime factorised in one and only one way.
This is known as the **unique factorisation theorem**.

3 **The Division algorithm**
Given any positive integers a and b ($b \neq 0$) there exist *unique* integers q and r, where $0 \leqslant r < b$, such that $a = bq + r$.

4 **The Euclidean algorithm**
If $a = bq + r$, then $(a, b) = (b, r)$.
Repeated application of this until the GCD is obtained is called the Euclidean algorithm.

5 If $d = (a, b)$ then there exist integers s and t such that $d = as + bt$.

6 Every number A can be written *uniquely* in any base n, where $n \geqslant 2, n \in N$.

Answers

Chapter 1

Exercise 1.1

1 a i $3x + 5x \neq 7x$ ii T $(x \neq 0)$
b i $3 + 6 \leq 7$ ii F
c i $4^3 < 3^4$ ii T
d i $\sin x < -1$ or $\sin x > 1$ ii F
e i $\frac{d}{dx} \sin x \neq \cos x$ ii F
f i $2x + 1$ is even given $x \in W$ ii F

2 a There exists a whole number $2x + 1 \leqslant 5$.
b There exists an x, for which $\frac{1}{x}$ does not exists.
c $\exists x, x^2 \leq 0$ d $\exists n, 2^n + 1$ is not prime.

3 a All numbers of the form $2x + 1$ are not even. True
b For All x, $2^x \leq 3^x$. False
c All natural numbers are greater than or equal to 1. True
d All primes are odd. False (2)
e $\forall x, \ln x \leq \ln(x + 1)$. True
f $\forall x, \sqrt{x} \in R$. False $(x < 0)$

4 a *If* a shape is an isosceles triangle *then* it will have two equal sides.
i *If* a shape is not an isosceles triangle *then* it will not have 2 equal sides.
ii *If* a shape has two equal sides *then* it is an isosceles triangle.
iii *If* a shape has not 2 equal sides *then* it is not an isosceles triangle.
b *If* a whole number can be divided by 2 without remainder *then* it is even.
i *If* a whole number cannot be divided by 2 without remainder *then* it is not even.
ii *If* it is even *then* a whole number can be divided by 2 without remainder.
iii *If* it is not even *then* a whole number cannot be divided by 2 without remainder.
c *If* $2x + 4 > 12$ *then* $x > 4$
i *If* $2x + 4 \leqslant 12$ *then* $x \leq 4$
ii *If* $x > 4$ *then* $2x + 4 > 12$
iii *If* $x \leq 4$ *then* $2x + 4 \leq 12$
d $\sqrt{x} > 1 \Rightarrow x > 1$
i $\sqrt{x} \leq 1 \Rightarrow x \leq 1$
ii $x > 1 \Rightarrow \sqrt{x} > 1$
iii $x \leq 1 \Rightarrow \sqrt{x} \leq 1$

5 a ii True, True iii Two-way
b ii True, True iii Two-way
c ii True, False iii One-way
d ii True, True iii Two-way
e ii True, False iii One-way
f ii True, True iii Two-way
g ii True, False iii One-way
h ii True, True iii Two-way
i ii True, False iii One-way

6 a i $a = 6 \Rightarrow a^2 = 36$;
$a = 6 \Leftarrow a^2 = 36$
ii Counter: $a = -6$.
b i Shape square $\Rightarrow$ 4 equal sides;
Shape square $\Leftarrow$ 4 equal sides
ii Counter: rhombus
c i Football team $\Rightarrow$ 11 players at start;
Football team $\Leftarrow$ 11 players at start
ii counter: cricket
d i $t = 30 \Rightarrow \sin t° = 0{\cdot}5$;
$t = 30 \Leftarrow \sin t° = 0{\cdot}5$
ii Counter: $t = 150$
e i For integers $a|b$ and $b|c \Rightarrow a|c$;
For integers $a|b$ and $b|c \Leftarrow a|c$
ii Counter: $a = 1, b = 2, c = 3$
f i For integers a and b, $a^2|b^3 \Rightarrow a|b$;
For integers a and b, $a^2|b^3 \Leftarrow a|b$
ii Counter: $a = 8, b = 12$

7 a (Only if shape is rectilinear)
d (Only if $a, b, > 0$) g, h, i.

8 a $x = 0$ b $x = 1$ c $x = 0$
d $x = -1$ e $x = \pi$ f $a = 1, b = -1$
g $x = 0$

9 a $x = 0$ b $x = 1$ c $a = b = 0$
d $a = b = 0$ e $x = 0$ f $a = b = 0$
g $x = 2$

Exercise 1.2

Hints and guidelines only are given.

1 a 3rd to 4th line: division by zero occurs.
b 3rd to 4th line: division by a negative occurs $[\ln\left(\frac{1}{2}\right) = -\ln 2]$. Reverse inequality.

2 a Line 2 to 3: $x^2 = 16 \Rightarrow x = \pm 4$
b Line 1: diagonals of parallelogram are not equal.
c Line 4: triangle is right-angled at P.
d Line 2 should be $-9x < -20$
e Line 3 to 4: x = irrational $\div$ irrational does not imply x is irrational, for example, $\sqrt{2} \div \sqrt{2} = 1$

3 a Lines 2, 3, 4, 5 b Lines 2, 3, 4, 5
c Lines 4, 5, 6 d Lines 2, 3, 4, 5, 6

4 a $x^2 = 49 \Leftrightarrow x = 7, x \in N$
b Counter: $x = -7$
c A, B and C could form triangle.
d $a = b = 0{\cdot}5$
e $a = 0{\cdot}5, b = 2$ gives $ab = 1 \in Z$ but $a \notin Z$
f Both statements false.

5 a $u_4 = 13$
b Could be a rectangle.
c Could be Wednesday.
d $p = 3, a = 1, b = 11, c = 4$
e $n = -1$
f $S(6) = 1 + 2 + 3 = 6$

6 $2^{11} - 1 = 2047 = 23 \times 89$ [not prime]

Exercise 1.3

Hints and guidelines only are given.

1 a $2S = n(2n + 2) \Rightarrow S = n(n + 1)$
b $2S = n(2n) \Rightarrow S = n(n) = n^2$

2 a $2S = 3^{n+1} - 3 = 3(3^n - 1)$
b $2S = 4 . 3^n - 4 . 3 = 4(3^n - 1)$

3 a $2k$ or $2k - 1$ where $k \in N$
b The number has two factors which are consecutive numbers. So one of them must be even.
c There are only 3 possibilities: $n = 3k, n = 3k - 1, n = 3k + 1$. Substitute each expression into $n^3 - 7n$ and factorise to get $3k(9k^2 - 7), 3(3k + 1)(3k^2 + 2k - 2), 3(3k - 1)(3k^2 - 2k - 2)$, each of which has a factor of 3.
d given 3 consecutive numbers: at least 1 must have a factor of 2, and one must have a factor of 3. So the product must have a factor of 6.

4 n must be of the form $4k$ or $4k + 1$ or $4k + 2$ or $4k + 3$. Substitute each into the expression and factorise to get: $4 . 2k(4k + 3), 4 . 2 . (4k + 1)(k + 1), 4 . (2k + 1)(4k + 5), 4 . (4k + 3)(2k + 3)$. Each has a factor of 4.

5 Let the 3 edges which meet at the right angles be a, b, c. The three sides of the base are
$A = \sqrt{a^2 + b^2}, B = \sqrt{a^2 + c^2}, C = \sqrt{c^2 + b^2}$. Without loss of generalization, let C be the largest side.
$A^2 + B^2 = 2a^2 + b^2 + c^2$; $C^2 = b^2 + c^2$. So $A^2 + B^2 \neq C^2$. By converse of Pythagoras, base triangle is not right angled.

6 Two 2p stamps give a value of 4p; one 5p gives a value of 5p. Adding 2ps to the 4p gives the sequence 4p, 6p, 8p, etc. Adding 2ps to the 5p gives the sequence 5p, 7p, 9p, etc. So each value greater than 4p can be achieved.

7 $n \in W$ is odd implies there exists $k \in W$ such that $n = 2k + 1$
$n^2 + 1 = (2k + 1)^2 + 1 = 4k^2 + 4k + 2 = 2(2k^2 + 2k + 1)$ which is even.

8 Follow the stated steps.

9 Multiplying any number whose unit digit is 6 will produce a product whose unit digit is 6 ... since $(10k + 6) . 6 = 60k + 36 = 60k + 30 + 6$.
So 6^n takes the form $10k + 6$. So $6^n + 4$ takes the form $10k + 10$, which is divisible by 10.

10 a Two consecutive even numbers take the form $2n$ and $2n + 2, n \in Z$ so $2n(2n + 2) = 4n(n + 1)$. Now n and $n + 1$ are consecutive numbers so one must have a factor of 2. Thus $4n(n + 1)$ has a factor of 8.
b $3^{2n} - 1 = (3^n - 1)(3^n + 1)$, Now 3^n is odd so $3^n - 1$ and $3^n + 1$ are consecutive even numbers and so, by **a**, have 8 as a factor.
c $3^{2n} + 7 = 3^{2n} - 1 + 8$.
Since, by **b**, $3^{2n} - 1$ has a factor of 8 then so does $3^{2n} - 1 + 8$.

11 a $9 \times 1089 = (10 - 1)(10 + 1)99 = (100 - 1)99 = 9900 - 99 = 9801$
b $9 \times 1099\,999\,989 = (10 - 1)(10 + 1) . 99\,999\,999 = (100 - 1)(100\,000\,000 - 1)$

12 The sum of 3 consecutive squares takes the form $3n^2 + 2$. n must take the form $10k + u$ where u is its units digit. So $3n^2 + 2 = 300k^2 + 60uk + 3u^2 + 2$. So the units digit of the the sum is the units digit of $3u^2 + 2$. Trying all 10 possible values for u, viz 0, 1, 2, 3, 4, …., 9 gives the unit digits 2, 5, 4, 9, 0, 7, 0, 9, 4, 5.

13 n odd implies there exists an integer k so that $n = 2k - 1$. So $n^2 - 1 = (2k - 1)^2 - 1 = 4k^2 - 4k = 4k(k - 1)$. Since k and $k - 1$ are consecutive numbers, one has a factor of 2. Thus the expression has a factor of 8.

14 Product of three consecutives + middle one $= (x - 1)x(x + 1) + x = x^3$.

15 $(a - b)^2 \geq 0 \Rightarrow a^2 + b^2 - 2ab \geq 0 \Rightarrow a^2 + b^2 \geq 2ab \Rightarrow a^2 + b^2 + 2ab \geq 4ab$
$$\Rightarrow (a + b)^2 \geq 4ab \Rightarrow \frac{(a + b)^2}{4} \geq ab \Rightarrow \frac{a + b}{2} \geq \sqrt{ab}$$

16 a w.r.t. division by 6, $k = 6n + r$ where $r = 0, 1, 2, 3, 4, 5$.
$k(k^2 + 5) = (6n + r)(36n^2 + 12nr + r^2 + 5)$
letting $r = 0, 1, 2, 3, 4, 5$ you find the expression has a factor of 6 in each case.
b If $n = 2k, n(n^2 + 20) = 2k(4k^2 + 20) = 8k(k^2 + 5)$.
Since $k(k^2 + 5)$ has a factor of 6 then $8k(k^2 + 5)$ has a factor of 48.

Exercise 1.4

Hints and guidelines only are given.

1 Assume $\sqrt{3} \in Q \Rightarrow \sqrt{3} = \frac{m}{n}$ where m, n integers with no common factor.
$\Rightarrow 3n^2 = m^2 \Rightarrow 3 \mid m^2 \Rightarrow 3 \mid m \Rightarrow m = 3k \Rightarrow 3n^2 = 9k^2$
$\Rightarrow 3 \mid n^2 \Rightarrow 3 \mid n$
and contradiction over 'no common factor'.

2 Assume $\sqrt{7} \in Q \Rightarrow \sqrt{7} = \frac{m}{n}$ where m, n integers with no common factor.
$\Rightarrow 7n^2 = m^2 \Rightarrow 7 \mid m^2 \Rightarrow 7 \mid m \Rightarrow m = 7k \Rightarrow 7n^2 = 49k^2$
$\Rightarrow 7 \mid n^2 \Rightarrow 7 \mid n$
and contradiction over 'no common factor'.

3 Use contradiction to prove $\sqrt{3} \notin Q$. Thereafter:

$6\sqrt{3} \notin Q$ else if $6\sqrt{3} \in Q \Rightarrow 6\sqrt{3} = \frac{m}{n} \Rightarrow \sqrt{3} = \frac{m}{6n} \Rightarrow \sqrt{3} \in Q$

$6\sqrt{3} - 1 \notin Q$ else if $6\sqrt{3} - 1 \in Q \Rightarrow 6\sqrt{3} - 1 = \frac{m}{n} \Rightarrow$

$6\sqrt{3} = \frac{m+n}{n} \Rightarrow 6\sqrt{3} \in Q$

$\frac{1}{2}(6\sqrt{3} - 1) \notin Q$ else if $\frac{1}{2}(6\sqrt{3} - 1) \in Q \Rightarrow \frac{1}{2}(6\sqrt{3} - 1)$

$= \frac{m}{n} \Rightarrow 6\sqrt{3} - 1 = \frac{2m}{n} \Rightarrow 6\sqrt{3} - 1 \in Q$

4 LHS has a factor of two; RHS doesn't. So they can't be equal if $m, n \in Z$

5 LHS has a factor of seven; RHS doesn't. So they can't be equal if $m, n \in Z$.

6 a **i** Suppose if n is odd, then $n^2 + 1$ is not even.

n odd $\Rightarrow n^2 + 1$ odd $\Rightarrow \exists\, k$ s.t. $n^2 + 1 = 2k + 1$

$\Rightarrow n^2 = 2k \Rightarrow n^2$ even $\Rightarrow n$ even

ii n odd $\Rightarrow \exists\, k$ s.t. $n = 2k + 1 \Rightarrow n^2 = (2k + 1)^2 =$ $4k^2 + 4k + 1 \Rightarrow n^2$ odd $\Rightarrow n^2 + 1$ even

b **i** Must prove "n is even implies $n^2 + 1$ is odd."

n even $\Rightarrow n^2$ *even* $\Rightarrow \exists\, k$ s.t $n^2 = 2k$

$\Rightarrow n^2 + 1 = 2k + 1 \Rightarrow n^2 + 1$ odd.

ii and **iii** are more awkward.

7 Must prove "if x is even then $6x + 1$ is odd."

n even $\Rightarrow 6n + 1 = 2 \,.\, 3n + 1 \Rightarrow 6n + 1$ odd.

8 a Must prove "if x is odd then x^2 is odd ."

$\Rightarrow x$ odd $\Rightarrow \exists\, k$ s.t. $x = 2k + 1$

$\Rightarrow x^2 = (2k + 1)^2 = 4k^2 + 4k + 1 \Rightarrow x^2$ odd.

b Must prove "if x is even then $x^2 + 5x - 3$ is odd ."

$\Rightarrow x$ even $\Rightarrow \exists\, k$ s.t. $x = 2k \Rightarrow x^2 + 5x - 3 =$ $(2k)^2 + 5(2k) - 3 = 2[2k^2 + 5k - 1] - 1$

$\Rightarrow x^2 + 5x - 3$ odd

9 Suppose $n^2 + n$ odd; $\Rightarrow n(n + 1)$ odd $\Rightarrow n$ is odd (else $n^2 + n$ even)

$\Rightarrow (n + 1)$ even. But $(n + 1)$ is a factor of $n^2 + n$

$\Rightarrow n^2 + n$ even. Contradiction.

10 Suppose $a + b\sqrt{2} = 3 + 4\sqrt{2}$ implies ($a \neq 3$ or $b \neq 4$)

$a + b\sqrt{2} = 3 + 4\sqrt{2} \Rightarrow a - 3 = (4 - b)\sqrt{2} \Rightarrow \sqrt{2} = \frac{a-3}{4-b},$

$b \neq 4$. However, this would make $\sqrt{2}$ rational.

11 Must show "If both numbers are rational then their sum is rational".

$a \in Q \Rightarrow \exists\, m, n \in Z$ s.t. $a = \frac{m}{n}$ and $b \in Q$

$\Rightarrow \exists\, p, q \in Z$ s.t. $b = \frac{p}{q}$

$\Rightarrow a + b = \frac{m}{n} + \frac{p}{q} = \frac{mq + pn}{nq} \in Q$

12 a **i** Product even then a factor of 2 must come from a or b.

ii If ab is even then both a and b odd.

Product takes form $(2k + 1)(2m + 1)$ which is odd.

iii Show a and b odd implies product odd.

b/c Note **c** is basically same problem.

13 a Original conjecture: $x = 4k + 2$ or $x = 4k + 3, k \in Z$ implies $\sqrt{x} \notin N$

Contrapositive: $\sqrt{x} \in N$ implies $x \neq 4k + 2$ and $x \neq 4k + 3, k \in Z$

b $\sqrt{x} \in N \Rightarrow x = a^2, a \in Z \Rightarrow x = 4k + r, k \in Z$

$\Rightarrow a^2 = 4k + r \Rightarrow k = \dfrac{a^2 - r}{4} \in Z$:

$r = 0$, then any even $a = 2m$ fits.

$r = 1$, then any odd $a = 2m + 1$ fits.

$r = 2, 3$ then neither odd nor even numbers fit.

14 Contrapositive: $a, b \in Q \Rightarrow ab \in Q$

$a \in Q \Rightarrow \exists\, m, n \in Z$ *s.t.* $a = \frac{m}{n}$ and $b \in Q$

$\Rightarrow \exists\, p, q \in Z$ *s.t.* $b = \frac{p}{q}$

$\Rightarrow ab = \frac{m}{n}\frac{p}{q} = \frac{mp}{nq} \in Q$

Exercise 1.5

Hints and guidelines only are given.

Q1, 2, 3 Proofs as per examples.

Q4 a $\displaystyle\sum_{r=1}^{n} (2r - 1) = n^2$ [Sum of first n odd numbers is n^2]

b Proof as per examples

Q5 a $u_{n+1} = u_n + 3(n - 1) + 1 = u_n + 3n - 2, u_1 = 1$

b/c Student proof.

Q6 a $2^k > k \Rightarrow 2^{k+1} = 2^k \,.\, 2 > 2k > k + 1$

b $3^k > 2^k \Rightarrow 3^{k+1} = 3^k \,.\, 3 > 2^k \,.\, 3 > 2^k \,.\, 2 \Rightarrow 3^{k+1} > 2^{k+1}$

c $k = 5 \Rightarrow k^2 > 2k + 1$ also $2^5 > 5^2$:

$2^k > k^2 \Rightarrow 2^{k+1} = 2^k \,.\, 2 > 2k^2$;

$2k^2 = k^2 + k^2 > k^2 + 2k + 1 = (k + 1)^2$

7 a Standard proof : must make sure proved for $n = 3$.

b $S = 5 + 7 + 9 + ... + (2n - 1)$: $S = (2n - 1) + ... + 9 + 7 + 5$

Adding the two lists: $2S = (2n - 4)(n - 2)$ etc.

8 True for $n = k$: $2^{3k} - 1 = 7m \Rightarrow 2^{3k} = 7m + 1$

$2^{3(k+1)} - 1 = 2^{3k}2^3 - 1 = (7m + 1)2^3 - 1$

$= 7 \,.\, 2^3m + 2^3 - 1 = 7(2^3m + 1)$

9 a True for $n = k$: $3^{2k} - 5 = 4m \Rightarrow 3^{2k} = 4m + 5$

$3^{2(k+1)} - 5 = 3^{2k}3^2 - 5 = (4m + 5)3^2 - 5$

$= 4 \,.\, 3^2m + 40 = 4(3^2m + 10)$

b $9^n = (8 + 1)9^{n-1} = 8 \,.\, 9^{n-1} + 9^{n-1}$ [theorem]

Thus, repeatedly using this theorem:

$9^n = 8 \,.\, 9^{n-1} + 9^{n-1} = 8 \,.\, 9^{n-1} + 8 \,.\, 9^{n-2} + ... 8 \,.\, 9^2 + 8 \,.\, 9^1 + 9^0$

Hence result.

c **i** $3^{2n} - 5 = 9^n - 5 = 8m + 1 - 5 = 8m - 4$

$= 4\,(2m - 1)$

10 a Induction $\displaystyle\sum_{r=1}^{k} F_n = F_{k+2} - 1 \Rightarrow \sum_{r=1}^{k+1} F_n =$

$\displaystyle\sum_{r=1}^{k} F_n + F_{k+1} = F_{k+2} - 1 + F_{k+1} = F_{k+3} - 1$

b Induction $\displaystyle\sum_{r=1}^{k} F_{2n} = F_{2k+1} - 1 \Rightarrow \sum_{r=1}^{k+1} F_{2(k+1)} =$

$\displaystyle\sum_{r=1}^{k} F_{2n} + F_{2(k+1)} = F_{2k+1} - 1 + F_{2k+2} = F_{2k+3} - 1$

c Similar induction.

d Induction: $\displaystyle\sum_{r=1}^{k} F_r^{\,2} = F_kF_{k+1} \Rightarrow \sum_{r=1}^{k+1} F_r^{\,2} = \sum_{r=1}^{k} F_r^{\,2} +$

$F_{k+1}^{\;2} = F_kF_{k+1} + F_{k+1}^{\;2} = F_{k+1}(F_k + F_{k+1}) = F_{k+1}F_{k+2}$

11 i True for $n = 1$: $\frac{d}{dx}(x^k) = kx^{k-1} \Rightarrow \frac{d}{dx}(x^{k+1}) = \frac{d}{dx}(x^k . x) = kx^{k-1} . x + 1 . x^k = (k+1)x^k$

ii Technique requires **i** a starting value and **ii** a whole number increment.

12 For $n = 1, 2, 3$ $n! < 2^n$. For $n = 4$, $n! > 2^n$.
$k! > 2^k : (k+1)! = k!(k+1) > 2^k(k+1) > 2^k . 2$
[When $k \geq 4$, $k + 1 \geq 5 > 2$].

13 RTP: $4p + 7q = n, \forall n \geq 18; p, q \in W: p = 1, q = 2$ gives $n = 18$; $p = 3, q = 1$ gives $n = 19$; $p = 5, q = 0$ gives $n = 20$; $p = 0, q = 3$ gives $n = 21$;
$\exists p, q \in W$ s.t. $4p_1 + 7q_1 = k$, $4p_2 + 7q_2 = k + 1$, $4p_3 + 7q_3 = k + 2$, $4p_4 + 7q_4 = k + 3$ adding 4 to each p we get $4p_n + 7q_n = n \Rightarrow 4p_n + 7q_n + 4 = n + 4 \Rightarrow 4(p_n + 1) + 7q_n = n + 4$ since p, q exists to generate $k, k+1, k+2, k+3$ then they exist to generate $k+4, k+5, k+6, k+7$ and by induction there exists p, q to generate all whole numbers 18 or bigger.

14 Each natural greater than 1 up to $n = k$ is prime or the product of primes.
Consider $n = k + 1$: It is either prime or composite. If it is prime then the theorem is proved. If it is composite then it is the product of two natural greater than 1 and less than k. These must be either prime or the product of primes. Thus $k + 1$ is prime or product of primes. Since true for $n = 2$ then true for all $n \geq 2$.

Exercise 1.6

Hints and guidelines only are given.

1 a $16^n = 16.16^{n-1} = 15.16^{n-1} + 16^{n-1}$
$= 15.16^{n-1} + 15.16^{n-2} + ... + 15.16^1 + 16^0$
$= 15.k + 1$

b Suppose $4^{2n} + 5 = 15m$
$\Rightarrow 16^n + 5 = 15m = 15k + 6 = 15m$
$\Rightarrow 6 = 15(m - k)$, that is 6 is a multiple of 15.
Contradiction.

2 abcd Student follows steps.

3 Use $a = \frac{a}{2} + \frac{a}{2}$

4 Consider $x^2 = S$. x takes form $5x$, $5x \pm 1$, $5x \pm 2$.
Square each case:
$(5x)^2 = 5(5x^2) = 5n$;
$(5x \pm 1)^2 = 25x^2 \pm 10x + 1 = 5(5x^2 \pm 2x) + 1 = 5n + 1$
$(5x \pm 2)^2 = 25x^2 \pm 20x + 4 = 5(5x^2 \pm 4x + 1) - 1 = 5n - 1$

Review 1

1 $S = 2 + 4 + 6 + ... + (2n - 2) + 2n$.
Reverse sum $S = 2n + (2n - 2) + ... + 2$.
Add corresponding terms:
$2S = (2n + 2) + (2n - 2 + 4) + ... + (2n + 2)$
$2S = n(2n + 2)$. So $S = n(n + 1)$

2 $(a + b)^2 - (a - b)^2 > 0$
$\Rightarrow a^2 + 2ab + b^2 - a^2 + 2ab - b^2 > 0 \Rightarrow 4ab > 0$
If also $a > 0 \Rightarrow 4b > 0 \Rightarrow b > 0$

3 The diagonals of a kite intersect at right angles and it is not a rhombus.

4 Assume $\sqrt{11} \in Q \Rightarrow \exists\, m, n \in Z$ [GCD $(m, n) = 1$] s.t. $\sqrt{11} = \frac{m}{n}$
$\Rightarrow 11n^2 = m^2 \Rightarrow 11 \mid m^2 \Rightarrow 11 \mid m$
$\Rightarrow m = 11k$ where $k \in W$
$\Rightarrow 11n^2 = 121k^2 \Rightarrow n^2 = 11k^2 \Rightarrow 11 \mid n^2 \Rightarrow 11 \mid n$
Contradicts [GCD $(m, n) = 1$].

5 Contrapositive: if x is odd $x^2 + 4x - 1$ is even.
$x = 2m - 1 \Rightarrow x^2 + 4x - 1 = (2m - 1)^2 + 4(2m - 1) - 1$
$= 4m^2 - 4m + 1 + 8m - 4 - 1 = 4m^2 + 4m - 4$
$= 2(2m^2 + 2m - 2)$ which is even.

6 True for $n = 1$; True for $n = k \Rightarrow S_k = \frac{1}{2}k(3k + 1)$
$\Rightarrow S_{k+1} = S_k + (3(k + 1) - 1)$
$= \frac{1}{2}k(3k + 1) + (3k + 2) = \frac{1}{2}(3k^2 + 7k + 4)$
$= \frac{1}{2}(k + 1)(3k + 4)$
$= \frac{1}{2}(k + 1)(3(k + 1) + 1)$

7 a $k(k^2 - 1)(3k + 2) = 24p, p \in Z$:
$(k + 1)((k + 1)^2 - 1)(3(k + 1) + 2) =$
$k(k^2 - 1)(3k + 2) + 12k(k + 1)^2$
$= 24p + 12 . 2q = 24(p + q)$ [either k or $k + 1$ is even.]

b i Given 2 consecutive numbers one must be divisible by 2

ii Given 3 consecutive numbers one must be divisible by 2 and one by 3.

iii $A = n(n^2 - 1)(3n + 2)$: $n(n^2 - 1)$ being 3 consecutive numbers has a factor of 3. When n odd: $n = 2k - 1$, $n(n^2 - 1) = 4k(k + 1)(2k + 1)$ has distinct factors of 3, 4, and 2 (since either k or $k + 1$ is even). Hence the factor of 24

When n even: $n = 2k$, $A = 2k(2k - 1)(2k + 1)(6k + 2)$. If k even, $2k$ has factor of 4, there is a factor of 3, $6k + 2$ has a factor of 2. Hence factor of 24.

If k odd, $2k$ has factor of 2, there is a factor of 3, $6k + 2$ has a factor of 4. Hence factor of 24.

Chapter 2

Exercise 2.1

1 $x + 1 + \frac{3}{x + 2}$

2 $x - 5 + \frac{19}{x + 3}$

3 $x + 5 + \frac{5}{x - 2}$

4 $3x + 7 + \frac{29}{x - 4}$

5 $3 + \frac{-7x + 2}{x^2 + x + 1}$

6 $1 + \frac{-2x + 3}{x^2 + x - 2}$

7 $1 + \frac{x - 2}{x^2 - x + 2}$

8 $x + 3 + \frac{3x - 8}{x^2 + 1}$

9 $x + \frac{4x + 1}{x^2 - 4}$

10 $3x + 10 + \frac{44}{x - 4}$

11 $1+\dfrac{7}{x^2-4}$

12 $x^2+x+\dfrac{-3}{x^2+2x}$

13 $x^2+1+\dfrac{-x^2+x}{x^3-x+1}$

14 $3x+\dfrac{-2x-1}{x^2+3}$

Exercise 2.2

1 $\dfrac{1}{x-1}+\dfrac{1}{x+1}$

2 $\dfrac{4}{x-2}+\dfrac{6}{x+3}$

3 $\dfrac{-1}{x+1}+\dfrac{5}{x+5}$

4 $\dfrac{4}{x-3}+\dfrac{-4}{x+2}$

5 $\dfrac{1}{x-1}+\dfrac{-1}{x+2}$

6 $\dfrac{5}{x+2}+\dfrac{-5}{x+3}$

7 $\dfrac{4}{x-2}+\dfrac{1}{x-3}$

8 $\dfrac{2}{x+2}+\dfrac{1}{x-2}$

9 $\dfrac{4}{2x-1}+\dfrac{-3}{x+3}$

10 $\dfrac{3}{x-1}+\dfrac{4}{x+3}$

11 $\dfrac{-2{\cdot}5}{x-3}+\dfrac{1{\cdot}5}{x+1}$

12 $\dfrac{-5}{x}+\dfrac{11}{x+3}$

13 $\dfrac{2}{x}+\dfrac{1}{x+2}$

14 $\dfrac{-2}{x}+\dfrac{-1}{x+6}$

15 $\dfrac{1}{x}+\dfrac{-7}{x+4}$

16 $\dfrac{4}{5-x}-\dfrac{3}{x+1}$

17 $\dfrac{1}{3x+1}+\dfrac{3}{2x+3}$

18 $\dfrac{2}{2x-3}+\dfrac{-3}{4x-1}$

19 $\dfrac{2}{x-5}+\dfrac{3}{x+6}$

20 $\dfrac{13}{x+3}+\dfrac{-8}{x+1}$

21 $\dfrac{3}{x+2}+\dfrac{1}{x+1}$

22 $\dfrac{10}{3x}+\dfrac{2}{3(x-3)}$

23 $\dfrac{1}{2x-1}+\dfrac{2}{2x+1}$

24 $\dfrac{-2}{2x+1}+\dfrac{3}{x+1}$

25 $\dfrac{1}{x+1}+\dfrac{2}{x+2}-\dfrac{1}{x-1}$

26 $\dfrac{1}{x}+\dfrac{3}{x-2}+\dfrac{2}{x-1}$

Exercise 2.3

1 $\dfrac{-5}{x-2}+\dfrac{8}{x-1}+\dfrac{3}{(x-1)^2}$

2 $\dfrac{2}{x-3}+\dfrac{4}{x+2}+\dfrac{-3}{(x+2)^2}$

3 $\dfrac{3}{x+1}+\dfrac{1}{x-2}+\dfrac{5}{(x-2)^2}$

4 $\dfrac{-1}{x-1}+\dfrac{2}{x}+\dfrac{1}{x^2}$

5 $\dfrac{-3}{x}+\dfrac{4}{x-1}+\dfrac{4}{(x-1)^2}$

6 $\dfrac{4}{x-1}+\dfrac{3}{(x+2)^2}$

7 $\dfrac{7}{9(1-x)}+\dfrac{7}{9(x+2)}+\dfrac{1}{3(x+2)^2}$

8 $\dfrac{2}{2-x}+\dfrac{4}{2x+1}+\dfrac{20}{(2x+1)^2}$

9 $\dfrac{1}{x}-\dfrac{2}{2x+1}+\dfrac{3}{(2x+1)^2}$

10 $\dfrac{3}{2-3x}+\dfrac{1}{x}+\dfrac{1}{x^2}$

11 $\dfrac{9}{1-3x}+\dfrac{3}{x}+\dfrac{1}{x^2}$

12 $\dfrac{1}{x+1}-\dfrac{1}{x-3}+\dfrac{4}{(x-3)^2}$

13 $\dfrac{1}{x-2}-\dfrac{2}{x}+\dfrac{3}{x^2}$

14 $\dfrac{3}{2x+1}+\dfrac{2}{(x-5)^2}$

15 $\dfrac{4}{x+5}-\dfrac{1}{x-1}-\dfrac{2}{(x-1)^2}$

16 $\dfrac{8}{x-1}-\dfrac{1}{x}-\dfrac{1}{x^2}$

17 $\dfrac{2}{x+1}-\dfrac{1}{x-1}-\dfrac{5}{(x-1)^2}$

18 $\dfrac{3}{x}-\dfrac{1}{x+1}+\dfrac{2}{(x+1)^2}$

Exercise 2.4

1 $\dfrac{1}{x+1}+\dfrac{2-x}{x^2-x+1}$

2 $\dfrac{1}{1-x}+\dfrac{x+3}{x^2+2x+5}$

3 $\dfrac{9}{x-3}+\dfrac{3-2x}{2x^2-x+1}$

4 $\dfrac{2}{x-1}+\dfrac{1}{x^2+x+1}$

5 $\dfrac{1}{x-3}+\dfrac{x+4}{x^2-x+1}$

6 $\dfrac{x+3}{x^2+2}-\dfrac{1}{x}$

7 $\dfrac{3}{x-1}-\dfrac{2x}{x^2+3}$

8 $\dfrac{4}{x+1}+\dfrac{1}{x^2+x+3}$

9 $\dfrac{3}{x-2}+\dfrac{x+1}{x^2-x+1}$

10 $\dfrac{1}{2x+1}+\dfrac{1}{x^2+x+2}$

11 $\dfrac{2}{x-1}+\dfrac{2-x}{x^2-x+1}$

12 $\dfrac{6}{x+2}+\dfrac{2x-3}{x^2-x+2}$

13 $\dfrac{1}{3(x-1)}+\dfrac{2x-5}{3(x^2+x+1)}$

14 $\dfrac{3x}{x^2+2x+4}-\dfrac{2}{x-2}$

15 $\dfrac{1}{x-1}+\dfrac{3x-1}{x^2+x+1}$

16 $\dfrac{1}{3(1-x)}-\dfrac{2}{3(2-x)}$

17 $\dfrac{4}{7(2x+1)}+\dfrac{5}{7(x-3)}$

18 $\dfrac{2}{x-1}+\dfrac{1}{x+1}$

19 $\dfrac{1}{2(x+1)}-\dfrac{1}{2(x-1)}+\dfrac{1}{(x-1)^2}$

20 $\dfrac{7x}{x^2+1}-\dfrac{4}{x}$

21 $\dfrac{3}{4x}-\dfrac{3}{4(x-2)}+\dfrac{3}{2(x-2)^2}$

22 $\dfrac{1}{4x}-\dfrac{x}{4(x^2+4)}$

23 $\dfrac{7}{x+1}-\dfrac{7}{x}+\dfrac{7}{x^2}-\dfrac{3}{x^3}$

24 $\dfrac{12}{5(x-3)^2}+\dfrac{13}{25(x-3)}-\dfrac{13}{25(x+2)}$

25 $\dfrac{8}{7(x+2)}+\dfrac{13x-12}{7(x^2+3)}$

26 $\dfrac{1}{1-x}+\dfrac{x+2}{1+x+x^2}$

27 $\dfrac{1}{x-1}-\dfrac{1}{x}+\dfrac{1}{x+1}$

28 $\dfrac{1}{5(x-2)}+\dfrac{1}{2(x+1)}-\dfrac{7}{10(x+3)}$

29 $\dfrac{7}{16(x-2)}+\dfrac{9}{16(x+2)}-\dfrac{1}{x}+\dfrac{1}{4x^2}$

30 $\dfrac{\sqrt{2}}{4(x-\sqrt{2})}-\dfrac{\sqrt{2}}{4(x+\sqrt{2})}$

31 $\dfrac{1}{x-3}+\dfrac{6}{(x-3)^2}+\dfrac{9}{(x-3)^3}$

32 $\dfrac{1}{x+5}+\dfrac{32}{(x-3)^2}$

33 $\dfrac{1}{x+1}-\dfrac{x}{x^2-x+1}$

34 $\dfrac{1}{16(x-2)}+\dfrac{1}{16(x+2)}-\dfrac{x}{8(x^2+4)}$

35 $\dfrac{11}{64(x-3)}+\dfrac{5}{8(x-3)^2}-\dfrac{11}{64(x+5)}$

36 $\frac{3(\sqrt{3}-1)}{4(\sqrt{3}-x)}+\frac{3(\sqrt{3}+1)}{4(\sqrt{3}+x)}-\frac{3}{2(x+1)}$

37 $\frac{1}{2(x-1)}+\frac{7}{6(x+1)}-\frac{1}{6(x-2)}-\frac{3}{2(x+2)}$

38 $\frac{8}{1-2x}+\frac{4}{x}+\frac{2}{x^2}+\frac{1}{x^3}$

39 $\frac{4}{5(x-1)}-\frac{1}{(x-1)^2}+\frac{1-4x}{5(x^2+4)}$

40 $\frac{1}{x}-\frac{1}{2(x-1)}+\frac{1}{4(x-1)^2}-\frac{1}{2(x+1)}-\frac{1}{4(x+1)^2}$

41 $\frac{1}{16x}-\frac{x}{16(x^2+4)}-\frac{x}{4(x^2+4)^2}$

Exercise 2.5

1 a $1-\frac{4}{x+2}+\frac{2}{x-1}$

b $x+1-\frac{1}{x-3}+\frac{1}{x+1}$

c $x+\frac{3}{x-3}+\frac{2}{x-2}$

d $2+\frac{1}{4(x-2)}-\frac{1}{4(x+2)}$

e $x+1-\frac{2}{3(x+1)}+\frac{2}{3(x-2)}$

f $1+\frac{2}{x-1}+\frac{1}{(x-1)^2}$

g $1-\frac{2}{3x}+\frac{2-3\sqrt{3}}{6(x+\sqrt{3})}+\frac{2+3\sqrt{3}}{6(x-\sqrt{3})}$

h $x+\frac{1}{2x}-\frac{5x}{2(x^2+2)}$

i $3x+1-\frac{1}{x^2}+\frac{3}{x}+\frac{2}{x+1}$

j $1+\frac{3}{2(x+1)}-\frac{3}{2(x-1)}$

k $1+\frac{3}{x+2}-\frac{4}{x+1}$

l $x+6+\frac{4}{x-1}+\frac{12}{x-3}$

2 $\frac{x^2}{(x+a)(x+b)}=A+\frac{B}{x+a}+\frac{C}{x+b}=$

$\frac{Ax^2+x(Aa+Ab+B+C)+(Aab+Bb+Ca)}{(x+a)(x+b)}$

Equating coefficients in the numerator gives: $A=1$,

$B=\frac{-a^2}{a-b}$, $C=\frac{b^2}{a-b}$

Review 2

1 a $\frac{3}{x-4}-\frac{2}{x+2}$ b $-\frac{1}{x-2}-\frac{2}{x+1}+\frac{1}{(x+1)^2}$

c $\frac{3}{x-1}+\frac{2x+2}{x^2+2x+3}$

2 a $-\frac{3}{x}+\frac{2}{x-1}+\frac{1}{x+1}$ b $\frac{3}{x^2}-\frac{1}{x-1}$

c $\frac{1}{x}-\frac{2x+3}{x^2+x+1}$

3 a $1+\frac{1}{x-1}-\frac{2}{x+2}$ b $x+\frac{1}{x}-\frac{2}{x^2+1}$

Chapter 3

Exercise 3.1

1 a

Summary of the eight outcomes				
Number of Heads	0	1	2	3
Frequency	1	3	3	1

Summary of the sixteen outcomes					
Number of Heads	0	1	2	3	4
Frequency	1	4	6	4	1

2 a i $x^4+4x^3y+6x^2y^2+4xy^3+y^4$

ii $x^5+5x^4y+10x^3y^2+10x^2y^3+5xy^4+y^5$

iii $x^6+6x^5y+15x^4y^2+20x^3y^3+15x^2y^4+6xy^5+y^6$

3 a i $u_n=\frac{1}{2}n(n-1)$ ii $u_n=\frac{n}{6}(n-1)(n-2)$

b i $x^8+8x^7y+28x^6y^2+56x^5y^3+70x^4y^4+56x^3y^5+28x^2y^6+8xy^7+y^8$

ii $x^9+9x^8y+36x^7y^2+84x^6y^3+126x^5y^4+126x^4y^5+84x^3y^6+36x^2y^7+9xy^8+y^9$

iii $x^{10}+10x^9y+45x^8y^2+120x^7y^3+210x^6y^4+252x^5y^5+210x^4y^6+120x^3y^7+45x^2y^8+10xy^9+y^{10}$

c i 1, 5, 10, 10, 5, 1; $(n, r)=(n, n-r)$ ii No

d i $u_{n+1}+u_n=\frac{1}{2}(n+1).n+\frac{1}{2}n(n-1)=n^2$

ii Student's own findings.

e Student's own findings.

Exercise 3.2

1 a i 24 ii 720 iii 1

b i −24 ii Error report iii −24 on some machines

2 a 24 b 5040 c $8{\cdot}07\times10^{67}$

3 a i 840 ii 5040 iii 12

b If $a>b$ then $b!$ is a factor of $a!$.

c i 840 ii 5040 iii 12

4 a 10626 b $10^4=10\,000$

c i 5 ii 5 iii same − 1 in boot = 4 on road.

5 a i 35 ii 210 iii 12 iv 35 v 210

b The product of n consecutive numbers must have distinct factors of 1, 2, 3, ..., n. e.g 3 consecutive numbers must have factors of 1, 2, 3 (See Proof chapter). Thus n consecutive numbers are divisible by $n!$

${}^nC_r=\frac{n!}{r!(n-r)!}$. We know $r!$ is a factor of $n!$. Cancelling out leaves $n\times(n-1)\times(n-2)\times\ldots\times(n-r-1)\ldots$ a product of $(n-r)$ consecutive numbers.

So it can be divided by $(n-r)!$ Hence result.

c i ${}^7C_4$ ii ${}^{10}C_6$ iii ${}^{12}C_{11}$ iv ${}^7C_3$ v ${}^{10}C_4$

d $^nC_r = \frac{n!}{r!(n-r)!} = \frac{n!}{(n-r)!r!}$
$= \frac{n!}{(n-r)!(n-(n-r))!} = {}^nC_{n-r}$

6 a i $^{52}C_3 = \frac{52!}{3!49!} = 22100$
ii $^{52}C_{13} = \frac{52!}{13!39!} = 6.35 \times 10^{11}$
iii $^{52}C_{52} = \frac{52!}{52!0!} = 1$
b 13 983 816
c $^{12}C_2 = \frac{12!}{2!10!} = 66 \Rightarrow P(\text{correct pair}) = \frac{1}{66}$

7 57

Exercise 3.3

1 a 210 b 45 c 120
2 a 55 b 55 c $^{11}C_2 = {}^{11}C_9$
3 a i 10 ii 5 iii 5
b There are $^nC_2$ ways of pairing n points. Of these n will be the n sides of the ngon. So the rest, $^nC_2 - n$, are diagonals.
c $\binom{n}{2} = 15 = \frac{n!}{(n-2)!2!} \Rightarrow \frac{n(n-1)}{2} = 15 \Rightarrow$
$(n-6)(n+5) = 0 \Rightarrow n = 6$. Hexagon.
4 a 4 b 10 c 8 d 16
e 3 f 5 g 6 h 12
5 a 4 b 5 c 7 d 10
6 a 6 b 11 c 9
7 a 7 b 10 c 1 or 4 d 9

Exercise 3.4

1 a $a^5 + 5a^4b + 10a^3b^2 + 10a^2b^3 + 5ab^4 + b^5$
b $1^3 + 3.1^2.(2x) + 3.1.(2x)^2 + (2x)^3 = 1 + 6x + 12x^2 + 8x^3$
c $16 + 96b + 216b^2 + 216b^3 + 81b^4$
d $27a^3 + 54a^2b + 36ab^2 + 8b^3$
e $a^4 - 4a^3b + 6a^2b^2 - 4ab^3 + b^4$
f $1 - 3p + 3p^2 - p^3$
g $81 - 108x + 54x^2 - 12x^3 + x^4$
h $8a^3 - 36a^2b + 54ab^2 - 27b^3$

2 a $x^3 + 3x^2\left(\frac{1}{x}\right) + 3x\left(\frac{1}{x}\right)^2 + \left(\frac{1}{x}\right)^3 = x^3 + 3x + \frac{3}{x} + \frac{1}{x^3}$
ii $x^4 + 4x^3\left(\frac{1}{x}\right) + 6x^2\left(\frac{1}{x}\right)^2 + 4x\left(\frac{1}{x}\right)^3 + \left(\frac{1}{x}\right)^4 =$
$x^4 + 4x^2 + 6 + \frac{4}{x^2} + \frac{1}{x^4}$
iii $x^5 - 5x^3 + 10x - \frac{10}{x} + \frac{5}{x^3} - \frac{1}{x^5}$
iv $x^6 - 6x^4 + 15x^2 - 20 + \frac{15}{x^2} - \frac{6}{x^4} + \frac{1}{x^6}$
b n even, $\left(x - \frac{1}{x}\right)^n$

3 a $\binom{12}{2} x^{12-2}y^2 = 66x^{10}y^2$
b $\binom{8}{3} 3^{8-3}a^3 = 13608a^3$
c $\binom{9}{6}(2x)^{9-6}(3y)^6 = 489\,888x^3y^6$
d $\binom{7}{1}(2x)^{7-1}5^1 = 2240x^6$
e $\binom{6}{6}x^{6-6}(-y)^6 = y^6$
f $\binom{5}{4}(3x)^{5-4}(-4y)^4 = 3840xy^4$

4 a $70x^4y^4$ b $720a^3$ c $64x^0$
d $490x^3$ e $1215a^4$ f 70

5 a $[(1+x)+y]^3 = (1+x)^3 + 3(1+x)^2y + 3(1+x)y^2 + y^3 = 1 + 3x + 3x^2 + x^3 + 3y + 6xy + 3x^2y + 3y^2 + 3xy^2 + y^3$
b i $8 + 12a + 6a^2 + a^3 + 24b + 24ab + 6a^2b + 24b^2 + 12ab^2 + 8b^3$
ii $1 - 5x + 10x^2 - 10x^3 + 5x^4 - x^5 + 5y - 20xy + 30x^2y - 20x^3y + 5x^4y + 10y^2 - 30xy^2 + 30x^2y^2 - 20x^3y + 10y^3 - 20xy^3 + 10x^2y^3 + 5y^4 - 5xy^4 + y^5$
iii $1 + 4x - 4y + 6x^2 - 12xy + 6y^2 + 4x^3 - 12x^2y + 12xy^2 - 4y^3 + x^4 + 4x^3 - 4x^3y + 6x^2y^2 + y^4$

6 $(1+x)^n = \sum_{r=0}^{n}\binom{n}{r}1^{n-r}.x^r = \sum_{r=0}^{n}\binom{n}{r}x^r = {}^nC_0x^0 + {}^nC_1x^1 + {}^nC_2x^2 + \ldots + {}^nC_nx^n$
Letting $x = 1$ gives $(1+1)^n = 2^n = {}^nC_0 + {}^nC_1 + {}^nC_2 + \ldots + {}^nC_n$

7 $(x+a)^3 = x^3 + 3ax^2 + 3a^2x + a^3 \Rightarrow x^3 + 3ax^2 = (x+a)^3 - 3a^2x - a^3$. So we use this to combine the terms in x^3 and x^2. Note that $a = \frac{1}{3}$ of the coefficient of x^2.
In the question given, $x^3 + 6x^2 + 10x + 4$, $a = 2$. So $x^3 + 6x^2 = (x+2)^3 - 3.2^2x - 2^3$ and the expression becomes $(x+2)^3 - 12x - 8 + 10x + 4 = (x+2)^3 - 2x - 4$

8 a i $P(2) = 0.384$ ii $P(3) = 0.512$
b $P(2 \text{ in } 4) = 0.1536$

9 a 0.261 (3 sf) b 0.028 (3 sf)

Exercise 3.5

1 a 28 b −3 c 1024
2 $30x^3$; $51x^5$
3 $4x^3$; $4x^{10}$
4 a $1 + 5x + 13x^2 + 22x^3 + 26x^4 + 22x^5 + 13x^6 + 5x^7 + x^8$
b $1 - 5x - 3x^2 + 31x^3 + 19x^4 - 63x^5 - 81x^6 - 27x^7$
c $9 - 24x + 46x^2 - 40x^3 + 19x^4 + 20x^5 - 26x^6 + 20x^7 + x^8 - 4x^9 + 4x^{10}$
d $1 - 2x - 24x^3 + 48x^4 + 192x^6 - 384x^7 - 512x^9 + 1024x^{10}$
5 a $x^5 - x^3 - 2x + \frac{2}{x} + \frac{1}{x^3} - \frac{1}{x^5}$
b $x^6 - 2x^4 - x^2 + 4 - \frac{1}{x^2} - \frac{2}{x^4} + \frac{1}{x^6}$
c When powers are both odd or both even.
d 40
6 $702a^5$, $7290a^6$

7 $\frac{7}{18}$

8 a $\binom{19}{r}3^r2^{19-r}$ and $\binom{19}{r+1}3^{r+1}2^{18-r}$

Note for Q9 etc: In the binomial expansion each term takes the form $\binom{n}{r}x^{n-r}y^r$.

The first term occurs when $r = 0$. i.e. $u_1 = \binom{n}{0}x^{n-0}y^0 = x^n$

9 $\frac{u_8}{u_7} = \frac{9}{14}$

10 a $u_9 = 43758 \, . \, 1^{10} \, . \, \left(\frac{3}{4}\right)^8$

b $u_3 = 66 \, . \, 1^{10} \, . \, \left(\frac{1}{4}\right)^2$

c $u_4 = 56 \, . \, 4^5 \, . \, 3^3$

d $u_3 = u_4 : u_3 = 91 \, . \, 2^{12} \, . \, \left(\frac{1}{2}\right)^2; u_4 = 364 \, . \, 2^{11} \, . \, \left(\frac{1}{2}\right)^3$

11 a $u_4 = 220 \, . \, 2^9 \, . \, \left(-\frac{2}{3}\right)^3$ b $u_5 = 1820 \, . \, 3^{12} \, . \, 1^4$

12 a $u_6 = 252x^5$

b $u_4 = 42\,240x^4$ and $u_5 = 42\,240x^3$:

c x^n and n^{n+1}

13 Terms 4 and 5 : value 0·0486111...

Exercise 3.6

1 a 1·05 b 1·27

c 0·648 d 250 000

e 2980 f 3020

g 0·0156 h 1 570 000 000

2 a $2x\delta x$ b $3x^2\delta x$

3 a $1 + 6a + 15a^2$ b $-1 + 14a - 84a^2$

c $256 + 1024a^2$

4 Expand both brackets to the term in x^2 then multiply.

5 $f'(x) \approx nx^{n-1}$

6 a $v_n \approx 10\,000(1 - 0{\cdot}1n)$ b $v_n \approx 5\,000(1 + 0{\cdot}05n)$

Review 3

1

1

1 1

1 2 1

1 3 3 1

1 4 6 4 1

1 5 10 10 5 1

1 6 15 20 15 6 1

2 a $p = 20; q = 5; r = 15$ b $s = 14; t = 6$

c i 38 760 ii 167 960

3 a $n = 5$ b $p = 8; q = 4$

4 a $x^5 - 20x^4 + 160x^3 - 640x^2 + 1280x - 1024$

b $8y^3 - 36y^2 + 54y - 27$

5 a $120x^7$ b $525y^3$

6 $\binom{10}{5}x^5\left(\frac{-2}{x}\right)^5 = -8064$

7 a $2^{11} = 2048$ b i 1024 ii 1024

8 Use theorem: $\binom{n}{r} + \binom{n}{r+1} = \binom{n+1}{r+1}$ three times.

$$\binom{n}{r} + 2\binom{n}{r+1} + \binom{n}{r+2} = \left[\binom{n}{r} + \binom{n}{r+1}\right] + \left[\binom{n}{r+1} + \binom{n}{r+2}\right] = \binom{n+1}{r+1} + \binom{n+1}{r+2} = \binom{n+2}{r+2}$$

Chapter 4

Exercise 4.1

Indicative workings are shown for a representative set of answers.

1 $\lim_{h\to0}\left(\frac{3(x+h) - 3x}{h}\right) = \lim_{h\to0}\left(\frac{3h}{h}\right) = \lim_{h\to0}(3) = 3$

2 4

3 $\lim_{h\to0}\left(\frac{5(x+h)^2 - 5x^2}{h}\right) = \lim_{h\to0}\left(\frac{h(10x + 5h)}{h}\right)$

$= \lim_{h\to0}(10x + 5h) = 10x$

4 $4x$

5 $\lim_{h\to0}\left(\frac{(x+h)^3 - x^3}{h}\right) = \lim_{h\to0}\left(\frac{h(3x^2 + 3xh + h^2)}{h}\right)$

$= \lim_{h\to0}(3x^2 + 3xh + h^2) = 3x^2$

6 $12x^2 + 5$

7 $\lim_{h\to0}\left(\frac{\frac{1}{x+h} - \frac{1}{x}}{h}\right) = \lim_{h\to0}\left(\frac{\frac{-h}{x(x+h)}}{h}\right) = \lim_{h\to0}\left(\frac{-1}{x(x+h)}\right) = -\frac{1}{x^2}$

8 $-\frac{6}{x^3}$

9 $2\cos 2x$

10 $\lim_{h\to0}\left(\frac{\cos(x+h) - \cos x}{h}\right)$

$= \lim_{h\to0}\left(\frac{\cos x\cos h - \sin x\sin h - \cos x}{h}\right)$

$= \lim_{h\to0}\left(\frac{\cos x(\cos h - 1)}{h} - \frac{\sin x\sin h}{h}\right)$

$= \cos x \times 0 - \sin x \times 1 = -\sin x$

11 $-3\sin 3x$

12 $-2(3 - x)$

13 $-\frac{1}{(x+2)^2}$

14 $3\cos(3x + 1)$

15 $-\frac{2}{(x+1)^3}$

Exercise 4.2

1 a $4x^3 - \cos x$ b $2\cos 2x - 2\sin 2x$ c $1 - \frac{1}{x^2}$

2 a $2x - \frac{2}{x^3}$ b $-\frac{3}{x^4} + 6x$

c $-\frac{6}{x^4} + x$ d $6\cos 3x + 6\sin 2x$

3 a $1 + \frac{2}{x^2}$ b $-\frac{4}{x^3} - \frac{15}{x^4}$

4 a $4x$ b $4x + 4$

5 a $-\frac{1}{x^4} + 16x^3\Big|_1 = -1 + 16 = 15$

b $-\frac{1}{2}\sin\frac{x}{2} + \frac{4}{x^3}\Big|_1 = -\frac{1}{2}\sin\frac{1}{2} + 4 \approx 3.76$

Exercise 4.3

1 a $18(3x+4)^5$ b $24(2x-5)^3$

c $5(6x+2)(3x^2+2x-1)^4$ d $3x^2\cos(x^3)$

e $3\cos x\sin^2 x$

2 a $-7\sin 7x$

b $4(6x^2+8x)(2x^3+4x^2-1)^3$

c $(4x-5)\cos(2x^2-5x)$

3 a $-\dfrac{3}{(3x+1)^2}$ b $-\dfrac{6}{(3x+1)^3}$ c $-\dfrac{27}{(3x+2)^4}$

d $-\dfrac{\cos x}{\sin^2 x}$ e $\dfrac{\sin x}{\cos^2 x}$

4 a $\frac{\pi}{180}\cos x°$ b $-\frac{\pi}{180}\sin x°$

c $\frac{\pi}{90}\cos(2x+30)°$

5 a $-\sin x\cos(\cos x)$ b $\sin x\sin(\cos x)$

c $\cos x\cos(\sin x)$ d $-\cos x\sin(\sin x)$

6 a $y=x\Rightarrow\dfrac{dy}{dx}=1\Rightarrow\dfrac{d\sin(\sin^{-1}x)}{dx}=1$

$\Rightarrow\cos(\sin^{-1}x)\dfrac{d(\sin^{-1}x)}{dx}=1$

$\Rightarrow\dfrac{d(\sin^{-1}x)}{dx}=\dfrac{1}{\cos(\sin^{-1}x)}$

b $\cos(\sin^{-1}x)=\sqrt{1-(\sin(\sin^{-1}x))^2}=\sqrt{1-x^2}$

c $\dfrac{d(\sin^{-1}x)}{dx}=\dfrac{1}{\sqrt{1-x^2}}$ d $\dfrac{d(\cos^{-1}x)}{dx}=\dfrac{-1}{\sqrt{1-x^2}}$

Exercise 4.4

1 a $6\sin 3x\cos 3x$

b $-2\cos(\sin x).\sin(\sin x).\cos x$

c $2(x+\sin 3x)(1+3\cos 3x)$

d $-2\sin(\sin^2 x)\sin x\cos x$

2 a $-6\cos^2(2x+4)\sin(2x+4)$

b $-\dfrac{6\cos(3x+1)}{\sin^3(3x+1)}$

c $\sin\left(\dfrac{1}{x^2+2x+1}\right)\dfrac{2x+2}{(x^2+2x+1)^2}$

3 a $\dfrac{(2x+1)\sin(x^2+x)}{\cos^2(x^2+x)}$ b $\dfrac{\sin x\cos(\cos x)}{\sin^2(\cos x)}$

c $-\dfrac{3\cos(3x+2)}{2(\sin(3x+2))^{\frac{3}{2}}}$

4 a $\sin x+\dfrac{1}{\sin^2 x}-1$ b $\cos x-\dfrac{2\cos x}{\sin^3 x}$

Exercise 4.5

1 a $3x^2\sin x+x^3\cos x$

b $2(x+1)\cos x-(x+1)^2\sin x$

c $4(2x+3)\cos 3x-3(2x+3)^2\sin 3x$

d $4(x+1)^3(x-1)^3+3(x+1)^4(x-1)^2$

e $-4(3-x)^3(x+2)^2+2(3-x)^4(x+2)$

f $-2x^{-3}(x+4)^3+3x^{-2}(x+4)^2$

g $-2(x+1)^{-3}(x-1)^2+2(x+1)^{-2}(x-1)$

h $-(x+2)^{-2}(x-1)^{-1}-(x+2)^{-1}(x-1)^{-2}$

2 a 16 b $\pi-2$

3 a $4(2x+1)\cos x-(2x+1)^2\sin x$

b $2\cos 2x\cos 3x-3\sin 2x\sin 3x$

c $4x^3\sin 3x+3x^4\cos 3x$

d $4(2x+1)(3x-1)^4+12(2x+1)^2(3x-1)^3$

e $(2x+1)\sin 2x+2(x^2+x)\cos 2x$

f $2x(x^3-1)+3(x^2-1)x^2$

g $2\cos 2x\sin 3x+3\sin 2x\cos 3x$

h $(x^2+3x)^3+3x(2x+3)(x^2+3x)^2$

i $4x^3(x^2+3x)+x^4(2x+3)$

j $\cos^2 x-\sin^2 x=\cos 2x$

k $2\cos(2x+1)\sin(3x+2)+3\sin(2x+1)\cos(3x+2)$

l $2\sin x\cos^3 x-2\sin^3 x\cos x$

4 a $-15(1-5x)^2(1+5x)^2+10(1-5x)^3(1+5x)$

b $3\cos 3x\cos 5x-5\sin 3x\sin 5x$

c $(x+1)^2(4x+1)\sin 2x+2x(x+1)^3\cos 2x$

d $-2(2x+1)^2(x+1)^{-3}+4(2x+1)(x+1)^{-2}$

5 a $\dfrac{1}{2}-\dfrac{\pi}{4}$

b $\cos\left(\dfrac{\pi^2}{16}\right)-\dfrac{\pi^2}{8}\sin\dfrac{\pi^2}{16}\approx 0.093$

6 a $-\dfrac{\sqrt{3}}{4}$ b $-\dfrac{\sqrt{3}}{8}$

7 15

8 a $-\dfrac{2}{(x-1)^2}$

b i $-\dfrac{5}{(2x-1)^2}$ ii $-\dfrac{11}{(x+4)^2}$

iii $1+\tan^2 x=\sec^2 x$

9 a $x^2y=4(2-y)\Rightarrow(x^2+4)y=8$

b $-\dfrac{1}{2}$

Exercise 4.6

1 a $\dfrac{4x^3+3x^2}{(2x+1)^2}$ b $-\dfrac{1}{\sin^2 x}$

c $\dfrac{x^2-2x-1}{(1+x^2)^2}$ d $\dfrac{x\cos x-\sin x}{x^2}$

2 a $\dfrac{2x\sin x-x^2\cos x}{\sin^2 x}$ b $\dfrac{x+10}{(x+5)^{\frac{3}{2}}}$

c $\dfrac{2\sin x-(x+2)\cos x}{2(\sin x)^{\frac{3}{2}}}$ d $\dfrac{-x-2}{4x^2\sqrt{x+1}}$

e $\dfrac{-3x^{\frac{1}{2}}(x+4)}{x^3}$

3 a $-\dfrac{\cos x}{\sin^2 x}$ b $\dfrac{\sin x}{\cos^2 x}$

c $\dfrac{1+\sin^2 x}{\cos^3 x}$ d $\dfrac{\cos 2x\cos x+2\sin x\sin 2x}{\cos^2 2x}$

4 a $\dfrac{1}{2}$ b 2

5 $x = 0, 4$

6 a $-\dfrac{8(x-1)}{(x-3)^2(x+1)^2}$

b i $\dfrac{1}{x-3} - \dfrac{1}{x+1}$ ii $-\dfrac{1}{(x-3)^2} + \dfrac{1}{(x+1)^2}$

c The partial fractions method involves more working but simpler derivatives.

7 a $\dfrac{\sin x - \cos x}{(\sin x + \cos x)^2}$

b $\dfrac{\sin x - \cos x}{\sin^2 + \cos^2 x + 2\sin x \cos x} = \dfrac{\sin x - \cos x}{1 + \sin 2x}$

c i -1 ii 1

Exercise 4.7

1 a $\dfrac{3 - 2x - x^2}{(x^2+3)^2}$ b $-\dfrac{2\cos 2x}{\sin^2 2x}$

c $6\sin 3x \cos 3x = 3\sin 6x$

d $3(x+1)^2(x^3+1) + 3x^2(x+1)^3$

2 $\cos x \cos(\sin x)$

3 $2(x+1)\cos 2x - 2(x+1)^2 \sin 2x$

4 $\dfrac{-(\cos x + \sin x)\sin x - \cos x(-\sin x + \cos x)}{(\cos x + \sin x)^2}$

$= \dfrac{-\cos x \sin x - \sin^2 x + \cos x \sin x - \cos^2 x}{\cos^2 x + \sin^2 x + 2\sin x \cos x}$

$\left.\dfrac{dy}{dx}\right|_{x=\frac{\pi}{4}} = -\dfrac{1}{2}$

5 $\dfrac{6(x^2+3x-1)(2x+3)^2 - (2x+3)^4}{(x^2+3x-1)^2}$

6 a $y = \dfrac{ax}{x^2+a^2}$

b $\dfrac{(x^2+a^2)a - ax\,2x}{(x^2+a^2)^2} = \dfrac{a(x^2+a^2-{}^2x^2)}{(x^2+a^2)^2}$ hence result.

c 1

d $m_1 = \dfrac{12}{25a}$; $m_2 = 0$; $m_3 = -\dfrac{3}{25a}$ hence result.

Exercise 4.8

1 a $-\cos x \operatorname{cosec}^2 x$ b $-\operatorname{cosec}^2 x$

2 a $2\sin 2x \sec^2 2x$ b $2\sec^2 2x$

c $-2\cos 2x \operatorname{cosec}^2 2x$

d $-2\cos(2x+3)\operatorname{cosec}^2(2x+3)$

e $-6x\sin(4-3x^2)\sec^2(4-3x^2)$

f $-5\operatorname{cosec}^2 5x$

g $-2x\operatorname{cosec}^2(x^2)$

h $-17\sec^2(1-17x)$

3 a $\sec x \tan^2 x + \sec^3 x$

b $-\operatorname{cosec}^2(\tan x)\sec^2 x$

c $-\operatorname{cosec}(\sin x)\cot(\sin x)\cos x$

d $-6\operatorname{cosec}^2 3x \cot 3x$

e $2\sec^2 x \tan x$

f $8\tan 4x \sec^2 4x$

g $\frac{1}{2}\sqrt{\sec x}\,.\tan x$

h $\frac{1}{2}(1+\operatorname{cosec} x)^{-\frac{3}{2}}\operatorname{cosec} x \cot x$

4 a $\dfrac{(1+\cot x)(2x+1) + (x^2+x)\operatorname{cosec}^2 x}{(1+\cot x)^2}$

b $\dfrac{2\sec x(1+\operatorname{cosec}^2 x)}{(\cot x - \sec x)^2}$

c $\dfrac{(x+1)(\sec x \tan x - \operatorname{cosec}^2 x) - 2(\sec x + \cot x)}{(x+1)^3}$

5 $f'(x) = 2\sin x \cos x \tan x + \sin^2 x \sec^2 x$, hence result.

6 a $f'(x) = \cos x \sec x + \sin x \sec x \tan x$
$= 1 + \sin x \sec x \tan x$ hence result.

b $\sin x \sec x = \tan x$

Exercise 4.9

1 a $4e^{4x}$ b $4e^{4x+1}$

c $2xe^{x^2}$ d $-2xe^{1-x^2}$

e $-\sin x\, e^{\cos x}$ f $6e^{3x+4}$

g $e^{\frac{x}{3}}$ h $4(3x^2-2)e^{x^3-2x}$

i $5\cos x\, e^{\sin x}$ j $2\sin x\, e^{2\cos x}$

k $\dfrac{1}{x+3}$ l $\dfrac{3}{3x-1}$

m $-\dfrac{6}{1-2x}$ n $\dfrac{6x^2}{2x^3+5}$

o $\dfrac{\cos x}{\sin x} = \cot x$ p $\dfrac{2(x+3)}{(x+3)^2} = \dfrac{2}{x+3}$

q $-\dfrac{1}{x}$ r $\dfrac{\cos(\ln x)}{x}$

s $\dfrac{3(\ln x)^2}{x}$ t $-\dfrac{1}{x(\ln x)^2}$

2 a $-\dfrac{1}{2x^2}e^{\frac{1}{2x}}$ b $2\sin x \cos x\, e^{\sin^2 x}$

c $-\dfrac{2}{(x-1)^2}e^{\frac{x+1}{x-1}}$

d $(\cos^2 x - \sin^2 x)e^{\sin x \cos x}$

e $\sec x \tan x\, e^{\sec x}$ f $-\dfrac{2}{x^3}x^2 = -\dfrac{2}{x}$

g $\dfrac{2\sin x \cos x}{\sin^2 x} = 2\cot x$ h $e^x \ln x + \dfrac{e^x}{x}$

i $\dfrac{2\ln(x+2)}{x} + \dfrac{\ln x^2}{x+2}$ j $\dfrac{\sec x \tan x}{\sec x} = \tan x$

3 a $-3\tan 3x$ b $\dfrac{1}{x\ln x}$

c $2e^{2x+1}\ln(2x+1) + \dfrac{2e^{2x+1}}{2x+1}$

d $3\sec x \tan x\, e^{\sec x}$ e $e^x \cdot e^{e^x} = e^{e^x+x}$

4 a $3e^{3x}(2+3x)$

b $-\sin x\, e^{\cos x}(1+\cos x)$

c $e^{1-3x}(-3\tan 2x + 2\sec^2 2x)$

d $-\dfrac{e^{1-\ln x}}{x} = -\dfrac{e^1}{xe^{\ln x}} = -\dfrac{e}{x^2}$

e $4e^x(\cot x - \operatorname{cosec}^2 x)$

5 a $\dfrac{2-2x}{3e^x}$ b $\dfrac{2e^x(x-1)}{(x-e^x)^2}$

c $\dfrac{-4}{(e^x - e^{-x})^2}$ d $\dfrac{2 - x\ln(2x^2)}{xe^{x-1}}$

e $\dfrac{3+x-x^2}{e^{x-1}}$

f $\dfrac{(e^x + \ln x)\dfrac{1}{(x+1)} - \ln(x+1)\left(e^x + \frac{1}{x}\right)}{(e^x + \ln x)^2}$

g $\dfrac{\sqrt{\ln x}\, e^x - \dfrac{e^x}{2x\sqrt{\ln x}}}{\ln x} = \dfrac{e^x(2x\ln x - 1)}{2x(\ln x)^{\frac{3}{2}}}$

h $\dfrac{2x+2}{(x^2+2x-1)e^{\frac{x}{2}}} - \dfrac{\ln(x^2+2x-1)}{2e^{\frac{x}{2}}}$

i $-\sin\left(\dfrac{\ln x}{e^x}\right)\left(\dfrac{1 - x\ln x\, e}{x\, e^x}\right)$

6 a $\ln 3 \times 3^x$ b $\ln 4 \times 4^x$ c $\ln 5 \times 5^x$

d $2\ln a \times a^x$ e $3\ln 5 \times 5^{3x}$ f $2\ln 6 \times 6^{2x+3}$

7 $\dfrac{d}{dx}x^x = \dfrac{d}{dx}e^{\ln x^x} = \dfrac{d}{dx}e^{x\ln x} = e^{x\ln x}\left(1 . \ln x + x . \frac{1}{x}\right)$

$= x^x(\ln x + 1)$

8 a $\dfrac{1}{x\ln 3}$ b $\dfrac{1}{x\ln 10}$

c $\dfrac{2}{(2x-1)\ln 8}$ d $-\dfrac{1}{x\ln 2}$

Exercise 4.10

1 a i 1 ii 2 iii 3 iv 4 v 5

b $c_n = n!$

2 a i $6(2x+1)^2$ ii $24(2x+1)$ iii 48

b 4

3 Multiplications not performed to emphasise pattern.

$4 . 2 . (2x+3)^3, 4 . 3 . 2 . 2 . (2x+3)^2, 4 . 3 . 2 . 2 . 2 . 2 . (2x+3), 4 . 3 . 2 . 1 . 2 . 2 . 2 . 2$

4 a i $-\sin x, -\cos x, \sin x$

ii $\dfrac{d^n y}{dx^n} = \sin\left(x + \dfrac{(n-1)\pi}{2}\right)$

iii Proofs using Example **21** as a model.

b i $2\cos 2x, -2^2\sin 2x, -2^3\cos 2x$

ii $2^n \sin\left(2x + \dfrac{n\pi}{2}\right)$

c i $-1 . x^{-2}, 1 . 2 . x^{-3}, -1 . 2 . 3 . x^{-4}$

ii $(-1)^n n!\, x^{-(n+1)}$

d i $x^{-1}, -1 . x^{-2}, 1 . 2 . x^{-3}$

ii $(-1)^{n-1}(n-1)!x^{-n}$

e i $3e^{3x}, 3^2e^{3x}, 3^3e^{3x}$ ii $3^n e^{3x}$

f i $\dfrac{1}{2}x^{-\frac{1}{2}}, -\dfrac{1}{2}\cdot\dfrac{1}{2}x^{-\frac{3}{2}}, \dfrac{1}{2}\cdot\dfrac{1}{2}\cdot\dfrac{3}{2}x^{-\frac{5}{2}}$

ii $(-1)^{n-1}\dfrac{1}{2^n}(1 . 3 . 5 .... (2n-3))x^{-\frac{(2n-1)}{2}}$

g i $e^x + xe^x, 2e^x + xe^x, 3e^x + xe^x$ ii $ne^x + xe^x$

5 a $\sec^2 x, 2\sec^2 x\tan x$ b $-\tan x, -\sec^2 x$

c $\dfrac{d^n y_1}{dx^n} = -\dfrac{d^{n+1}y_2}{dx^{n+1}}$

6 $a^n b e^{ax}$

7 a $y = \dfrac{x}{2x+1} \Rightarrow \dfrac{y}{x} = \dfrac{1}{2x+1}$ and

$\dfrac{dy}{dx} = \dfrac{(2x+1) . 1 - x . 2}{(2x+1)^2} = \dfrac{1}{(2x+1)^2} = \dfrac{y^2}{x^2}$

b $\dfrac{d^2y}{dx^2} = \dfrac{-4}{(2x+1)^3} = -4\dfrac{y^3}{x^3}$

c $\dfrac{d^3y}{dx^3} = \dfrac{24}{(2x+1)^4} = 24\dfrac{y^4}{x^4}$

8 $y = e^x\sin x \Rightarrow \dfrac{dy}{dx} = e^x\sin x + e^x\cos x$

$\Rightarrow \dfrac{d^2y}{dx^2} = e^x\sin x + e^x\cos x + e^x\cos x - e^x\sin x$

$= 2e^x\cos x$

$\Rightarrow \dfrac{d^3y}{dx^3} = 2e^x\cos x - 2e^x\sin x$

$\Rightarrow \dfrac{d^4y}{dx^4} = 2e^x\cos x - 2e^x\sin x - 2e^x\sin x - 2e^x\cos x$

$= -4e^x\sin x = -4y$

9 a $\dfrac{dy}{dx} = \frac{4}{3}(x-1)^{\frac{1}{3}};\ \dfrac{d^2y}{dx^2} = \frac{4}{9}(x-1)^{-\frac{2}{3}}$

b

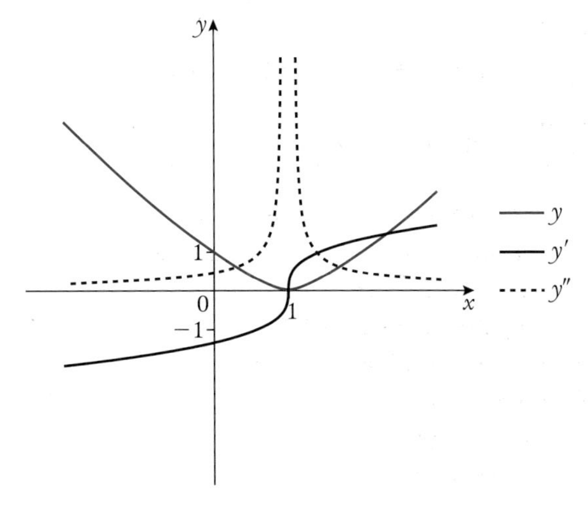

c y and y' are continuous over R; y'' is discontinuous at $x = 1$.

10 a i $f'(x) = \dfrac{e^x + e^{-x}}{2}; f''(x) = \dfrac{e^x - e^{-x}}{2}; f'''(x) = \dfrac{e^x + e^{-x}}{2}$

ii $f^{(n)}(x) = \dfrac{e^x - (-1)^n e^{-x}}{2}$

b $f'(x) = g(x)$ and $f(x) = g'(x)$

c $h'(x) = \dfrac{(e^x + e^{-x})^2 - (e^x - e^{-x})^2}{(e^x + e^{-x})^2} = \dfrac{4}{(e^x + e^{-x})^2}$

$= \dfrac{1}{(g(x))^2}$

d $\dfrac{d}{dx}\left[\dfrac{4}{(e^x + e^{-x})^2}\right] = \dfrac{-4.2.(e^x + e^{-x})(e^x - e^{-x})}{(e^x + e^{-x})^4}$

$= \dfrac{-8(e^{2x} - e^{-2x})}{(e^x + e^{-x})^4}$

$= \dfrac{-16}{(e^x + e^{-x})^4} \cdot \dfrac{(e^{2x} - e^{-2x})}{2} = -\dfrac{f(2x)}{(g(x))^4}$

Review 4

1 $\lim_{h\to 0}\left(\dfrac{[3(x+h)^2 + (x+h) + 1] - [3x^2 + x + 1]}{h}\right)$

$= \lim_{h\to 0}\left(\dfrac{6xh + 3h^2 + h}{h}\right) = \lim_{h\to 0}(6x + 3h + 1) = 6x + 1$

2 $\frac{10}{3}x - \frac{4}{3x^2}$

3 $\sqrt{3}$

4 $\dfrac{2\cos x - 3x\sin x}{3\sqrt[3]{x}}$

5 $\dfrac{(2x-5)\cos x - 4\sin x}{(2x-5)^3}$

6 $\dfrac{4\sin 4x}{\cos^2 4x}$

7 $-\dfrac{(1+\cos^2 x)}{\sin^3 x}$

8 $\dfrac{dy}{dx} = -\dfrac{3\cos x}{\sin^4 x} \Rightarrow$

$\dfrac{dy}{dx} + 3y\cot x = -\dfrac{3\cos x}{\sin^4 x} + 3\dfrac{1}{\sin^3 x}\dfrac{\cos x}{\sin x} = 0$

9 $\dfrac{dy}{dx} = 2x\ln x + x^2\dfrac{1}{x} = x(2\ln x + 1) = x(\ln x^2 + \ln e)$

$= x\ln(ex^2)$

10 a i $\dfrac{dy}{dx} = \dfrac{\cos x - \sin x}{e^x}$ ii $\dfrac{d^2y}{dx^2} = -\dfrac{2\cos x}{e^x}$

iii $\dfrac{d^3y}{dx^3} = \dfrac{2(\sin x + \cos x)}{e^x}$ iv $\dfrac{d^4y}{dx^4} = -\dfrac{4\sin x}{e^x}$

b $\dfrac{d^4y}{dx^4} = -4y$

11 $y = e^{x^2} \Rightarrow \dfrac{dy}{dx} = 2xe^{x^2} \Rightarrow \dfrac{d^2y}{dx^2} = 2e^{x^2} + 4x^2e^{x^2}$

$\Rightarrow \dfrac{d^2y}{dx^2} - 2x\dfrac{dy}{dx} - 2y = 2e^{x^2} + 4x^2e^{x^2} - 2x.2xe^{x^2} - 2e^{x^2} = 0$

Chapter 5

Exercise 5.1

1 a i $x \in R$ ii $f(x) \in [-1, 1]$

b i $x \geqslant 2$ ii $f(x) \geqslant 0$

c i $x \in W$ ii $f(x) \in W$

d i $x \in R - \left\{\dfrac{2k-1}{2}\right\}\pi$ ii $f(x) \in R$

e i $x \in R$ ii $f(x) \geqslant 0$

f i $x \in R$ ii $f(x) \in [0, 2]$

g i $x \in R$ ii $f(x) \geqslant 0$

h i $x \in R - \{\pi k\}$ ii $f(x) \geq 1$ or $f(x) \leq -1$

2 a i ± 3 ii None

b for each value of y in the range $-5 < y < 5$ there are two values of x.

c $-5 \leqslant x \leqslant 5$; $0 \leqslant y \leqslant 5$

3 a yes b yes c no

d no e yes f no

Exercise 5.2

In each example the solid line is $f(x)$ and the broken line $|f(x)|$

1

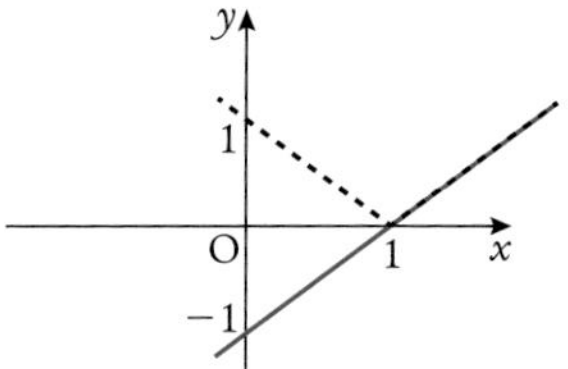

2

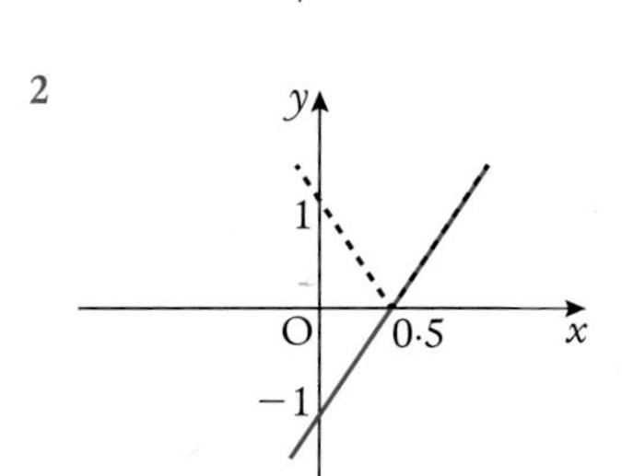

3

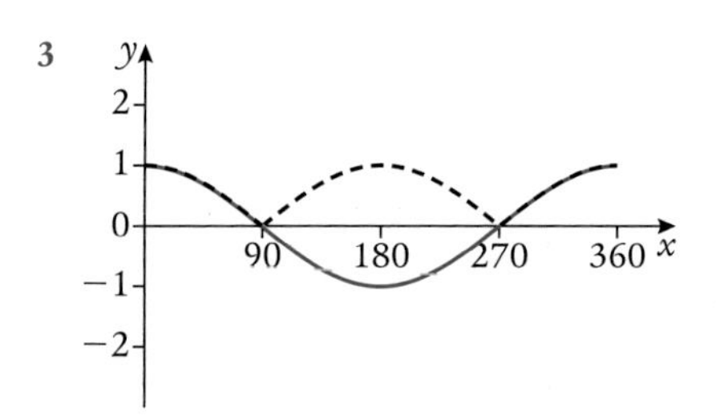

4

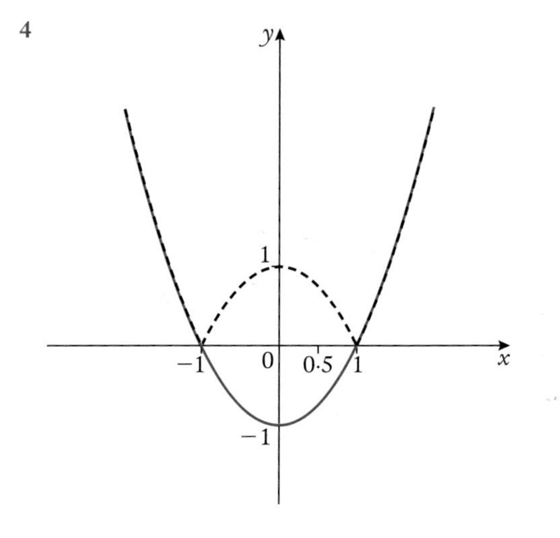

5

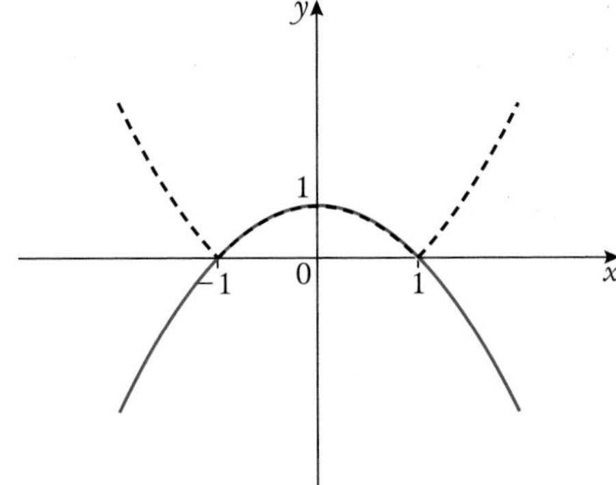

6

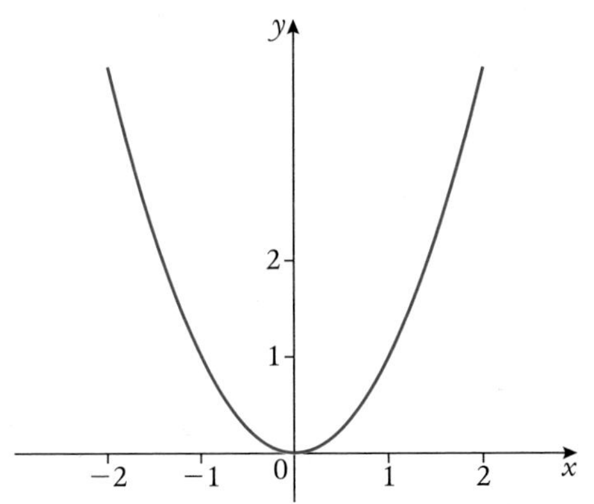

7

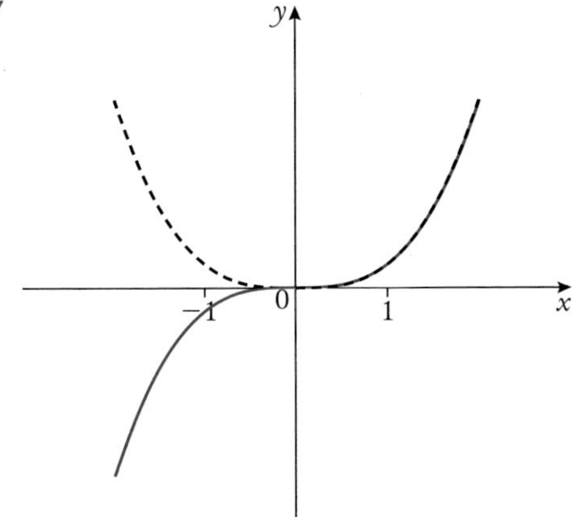

8

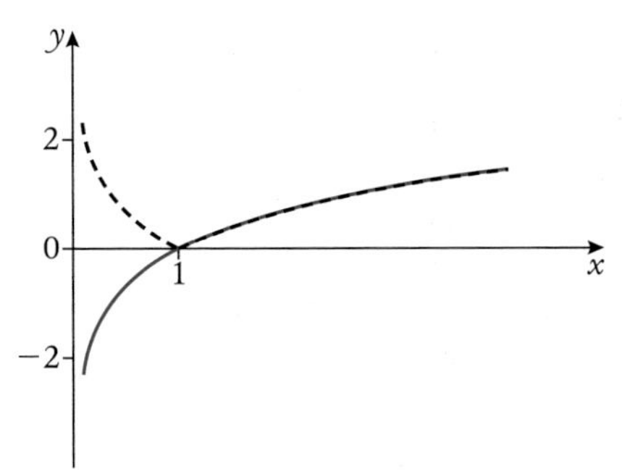

9

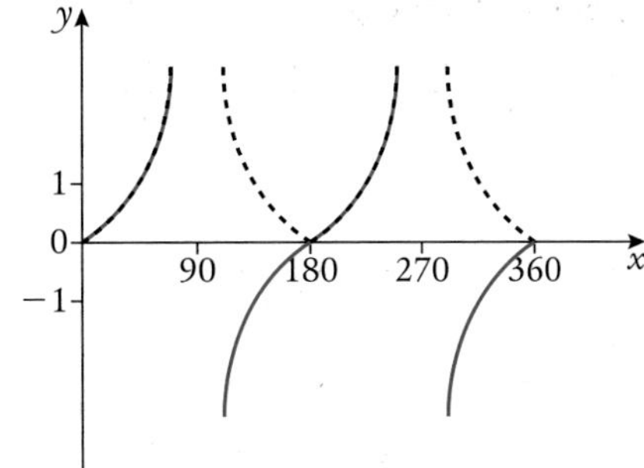

Exercise 5.3

1 **a** $\dfrac{x-4}{3}$ **b** $\dfrac{x+1}{5}$ **c** $3-x$

d $\dfrac{4-x}{2}$ **e** $\dfrac{\sqrt[3]{x}}{2}$ **f** $\sqrt[5]{1-x}$

g $\dfrac{1-x}{x}$ **h** $\dfrac{x}{x-1}$ **i** x^3+1

2 **a** $\sqrt{x}$; Domain $x \geqslant 0$; Range $y \geqslant 0$

b $\sqrt{x+4}$; Domain $x \geqslant 0$; Range $y \geqslant -4$

c $\sqrt{x}-1$; Domain $x \geqslant -1$; Range $y \geqslant 0$

d $\frac{1}{2}\left(\sqrt{x+1}+1\right)$; Domain $x \geqslant \frac{1}{2}$; Range $y \geqslant -1$

e $\sqrt{x+10}-3$; Domain $x \geqslant -3$; Range $y \geqslant -1$

f $\sqrt{\dfrac{1-x}{x}}$; Domain $x \geqslant 0$; Range $1 \geqslant y > 0$

g $\frac{1}{2}(1+x^2)$; Domain $x \geqslant \frac{1}{2}$; Range $y \geqslant 0$

3 **a**

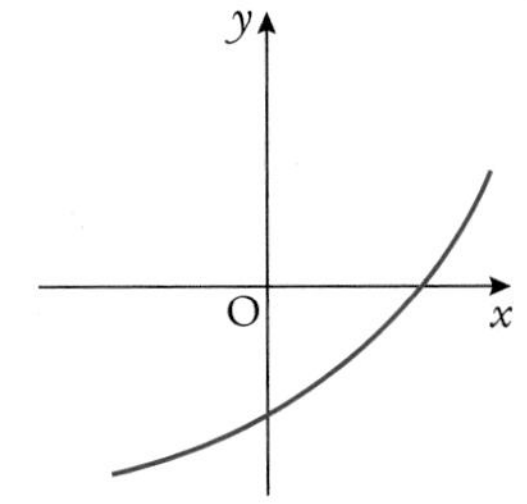

b

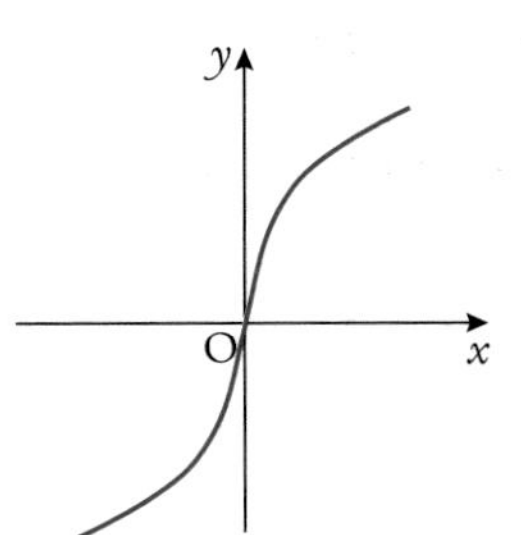

c

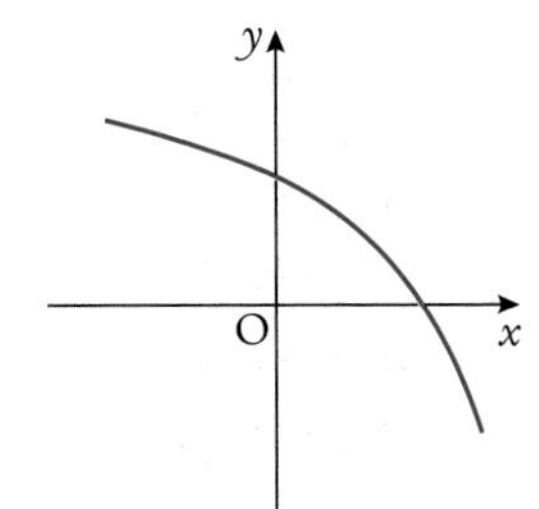

d

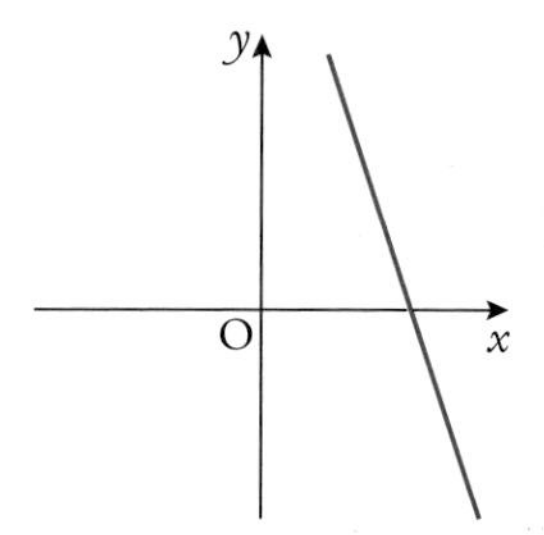

e

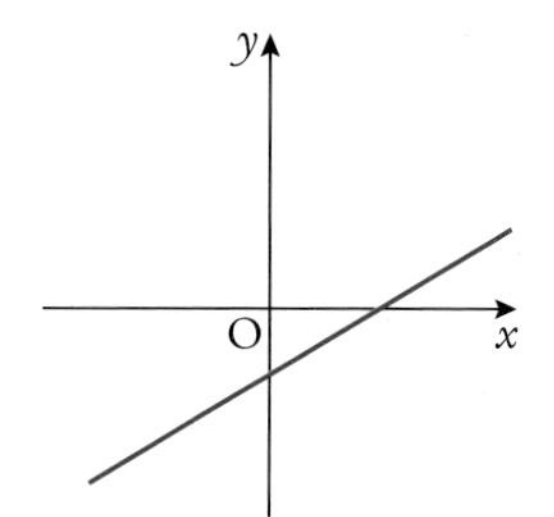

f

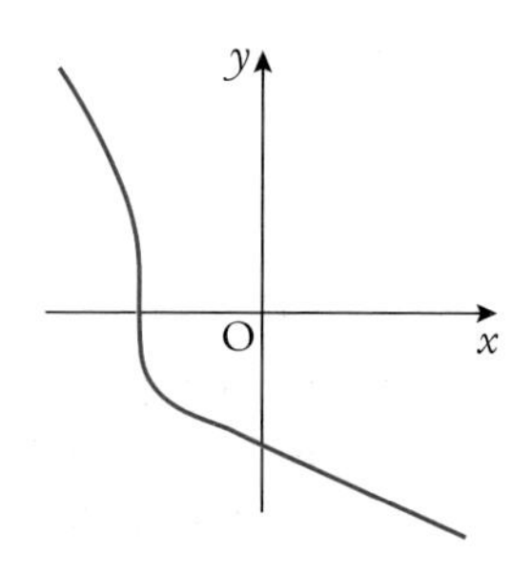

Exercise 5.4

1 a

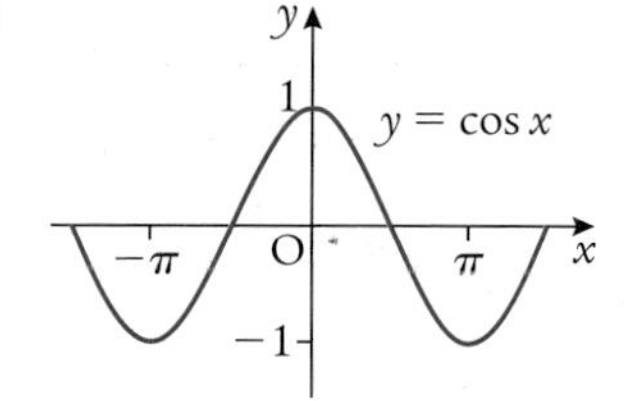

b

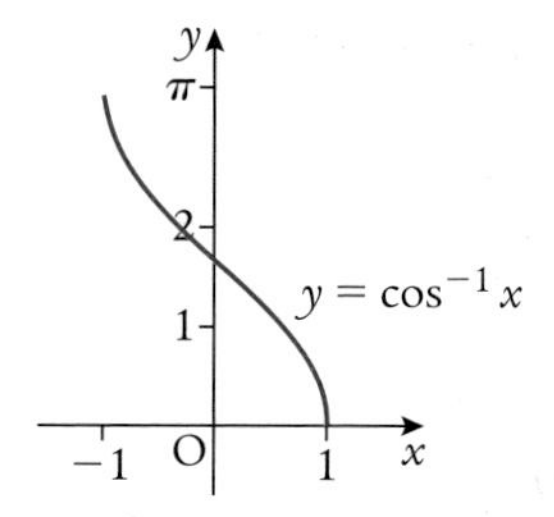

2 a

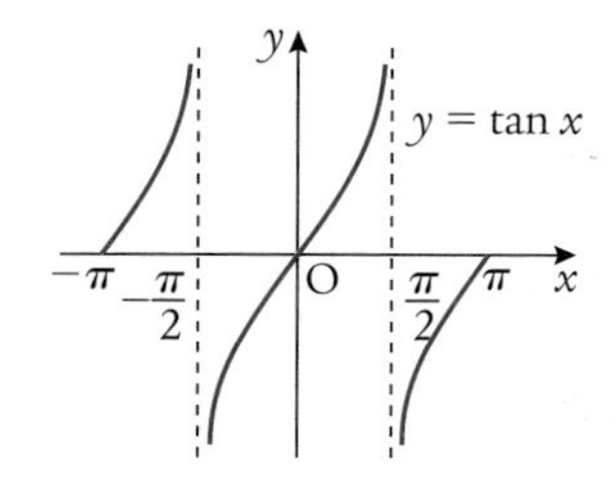

b

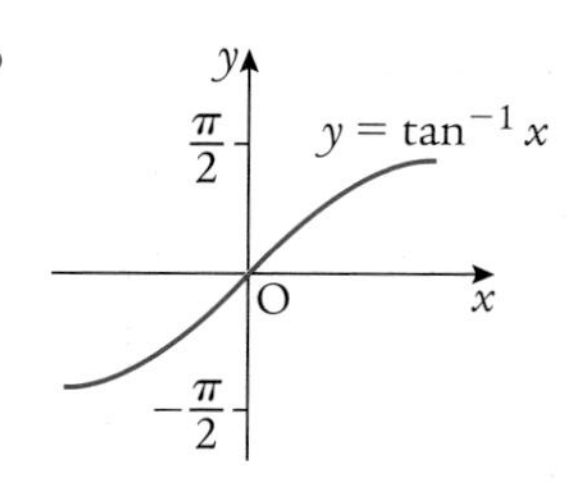

3 a Domain $0 \leqslant x \leqslant \pi/2$; Range $y \geq 1$

b Domain $x \geq 1$; Range $0 \leqslant y \leqslant \pi/2$

c Domain $0 \leqslant x \leqslant \pi/2$; Range $y \geq 1$

d Domain $x \geq 1$; Range $0 \leqslant y \leqslant \pi/2$

e Domain $0 \leqslant x \leqslant \pi$; Range R

f Domain R; Range $0 \leqslant y \leqslant \pi$

4 a iii $\pi/6 \leqslant x \leqslant \pi/6$; $-1 \leqslant y \leqslant 1$

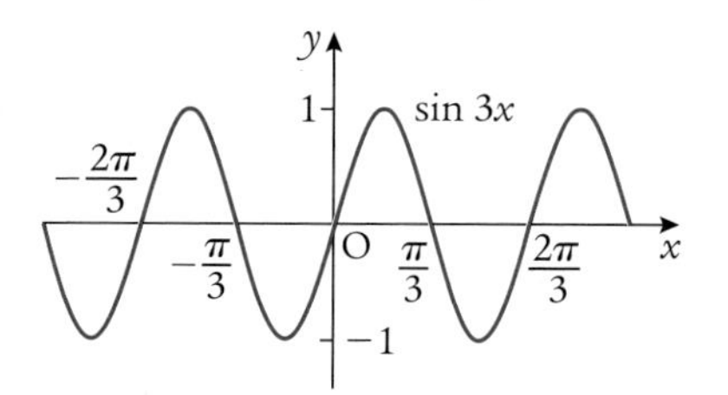

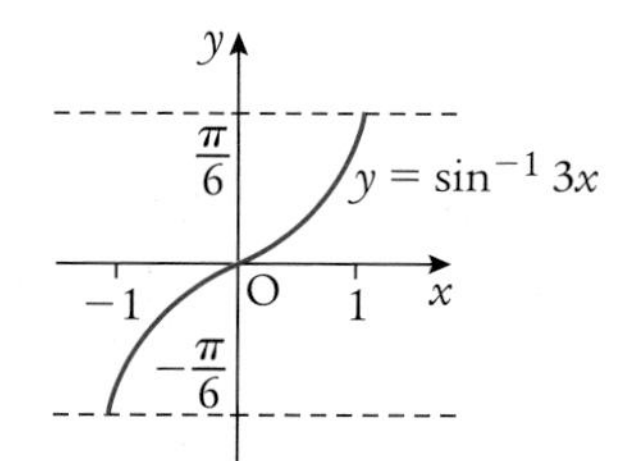

b iii $-\pi/2 \leqslant x \leqslant \pi/2$; $-3 \leqslant y \leqslant 3$

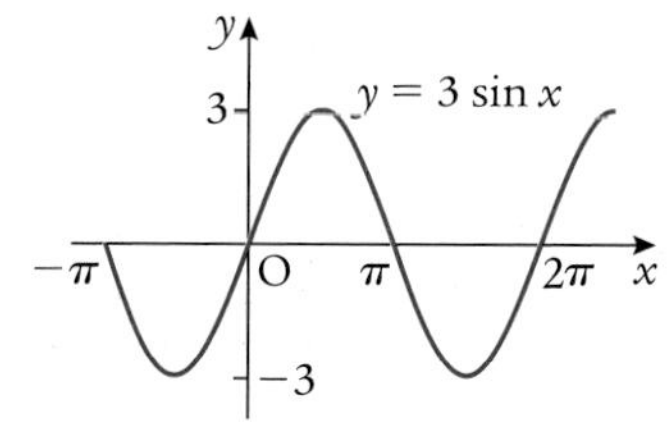

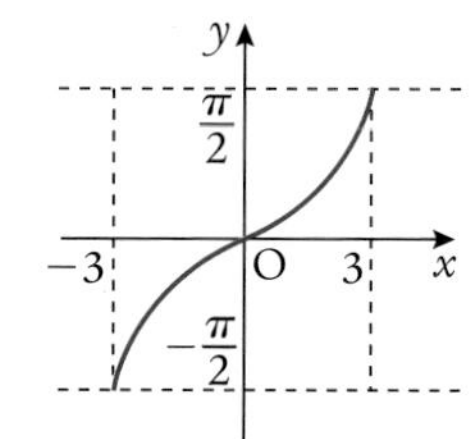

c $-\pi/2 \leqslant x \leqslant \pi/2$; $2 \leqslant y \leqslant 4$

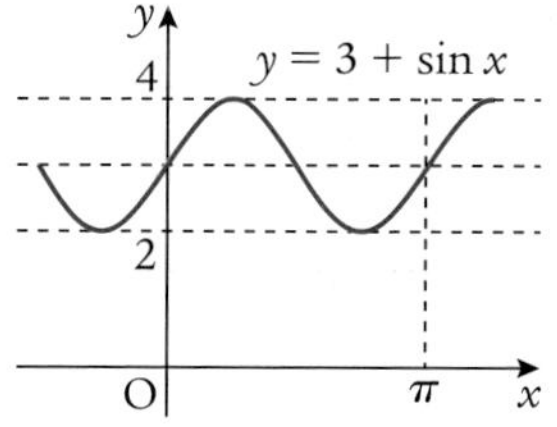

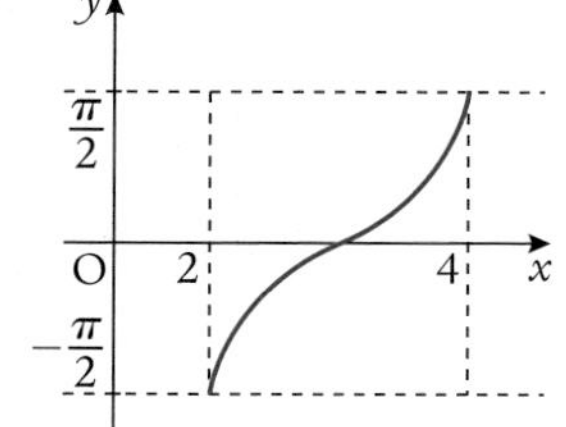

d iii $0 \leqslant x \leqslant \pi/2; -1 \leqslant y \leqslant 1$

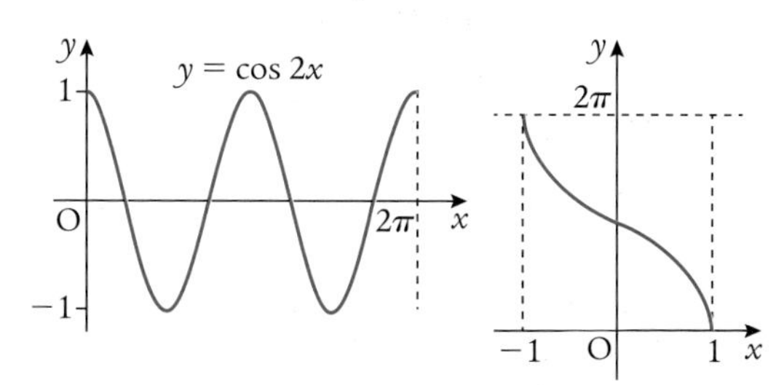

e iii $0 \leqslant x \leqslant \pi; -2 \leqslant y \leqslant 2$

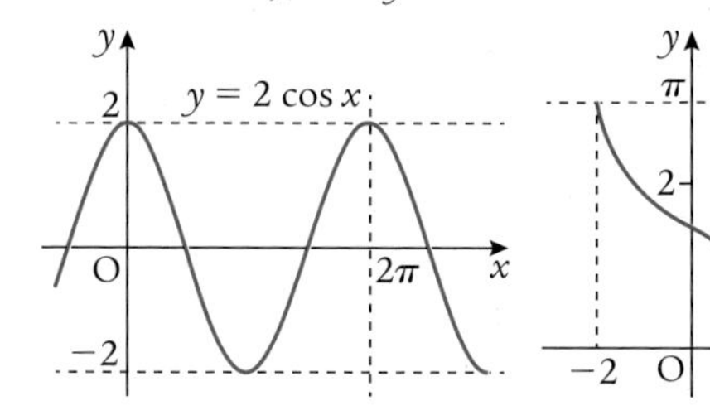

f iii $0 \leqslant x \leqslant \pi; 1 \leqslant y \leqslant 3$

g iii $-\pi/4 \leqslant x \leqslant \pi/4; -1/2 \leqslant y \leqslant ½$

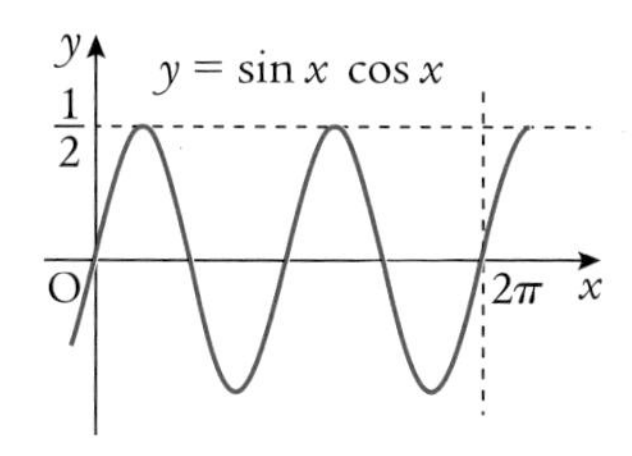

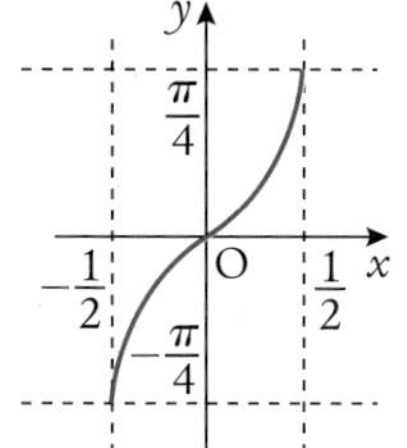

h iii $0 \leqslant x \leqslant \pi/2; 0 \leqslant y \leqslant 1$

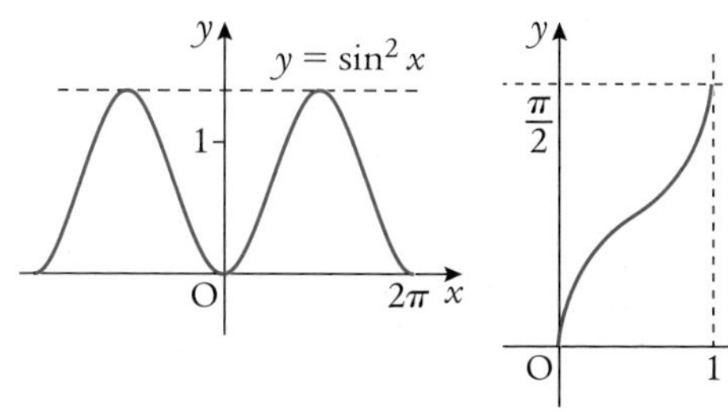

i iii $x = 1; y = 1$

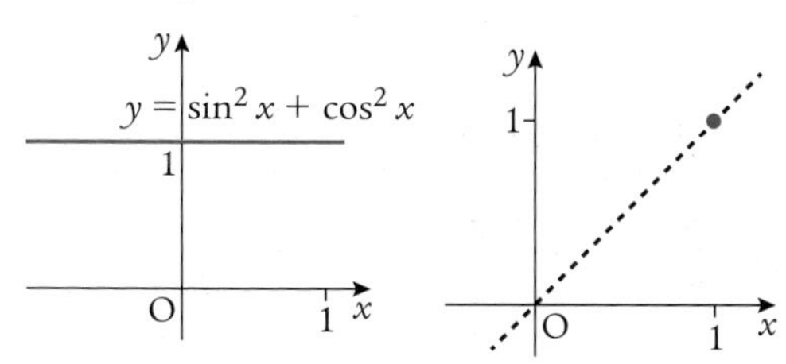

5 a i

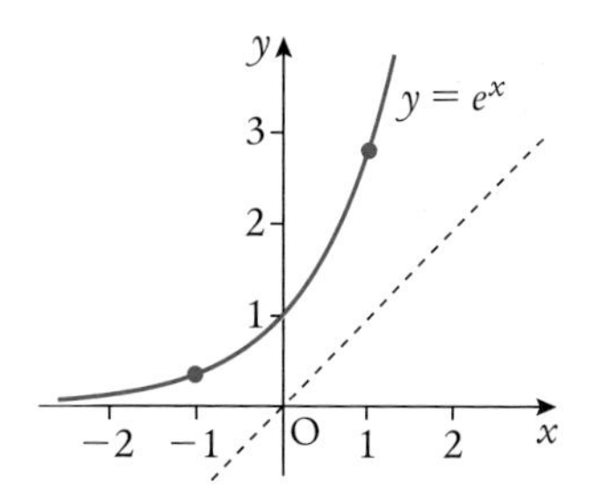

b $x \in R; y > 0$

c i

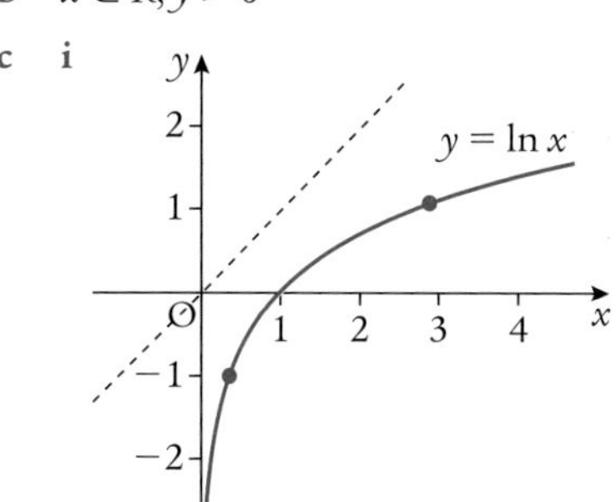

ii $\ln x$

iii $x > 0; y \in \mathrm{R}$

6 a iii $x \in R; y > 0$

b iii $x \in R; y > 0$

c iii $x \in R; y > -1$

d iii $x > 0; y \in R$

e iii $x > 0; y \in R$

f iii $x > 0; y \in R$

7 a $x \in R; y \geq 2$

b $x \in R; y \in R$

c $x > 0; y \leqslant \frac{10}{e}$

Exercise 5.5

1 a Min $(3, -15)$

b Min $(3, -14)$

c Min $(1, -1)$

d Min$(1, -6)$, Max $(-2, 21)$

e Min $(1, -7)$, Max $(2, -5)$

f Max $(0, 16)$, Min $(2, 0)$, Min $(-2, 0)$

2 a

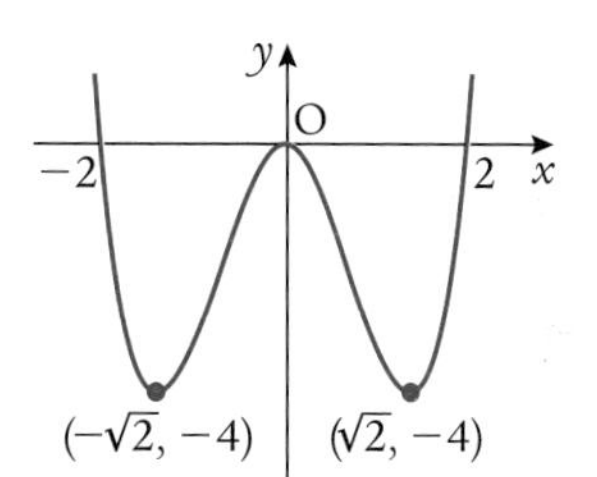

b

y
O
9
x
$(6, -108)$

c

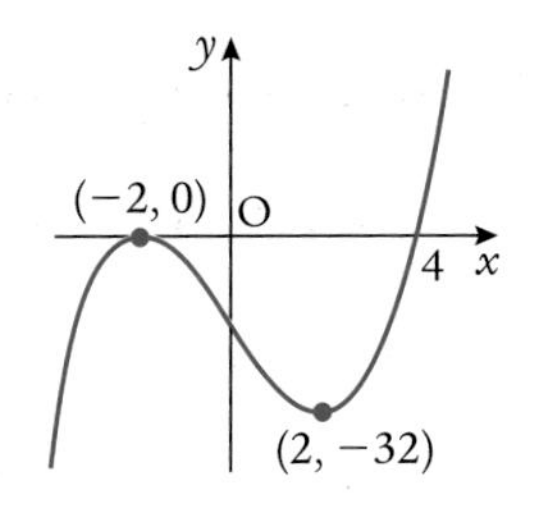

d

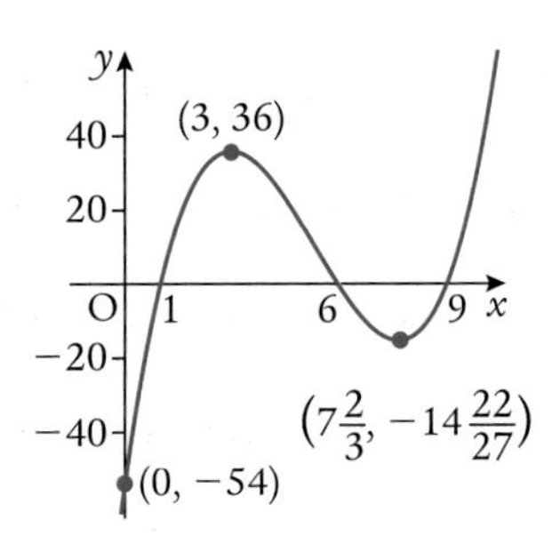

e

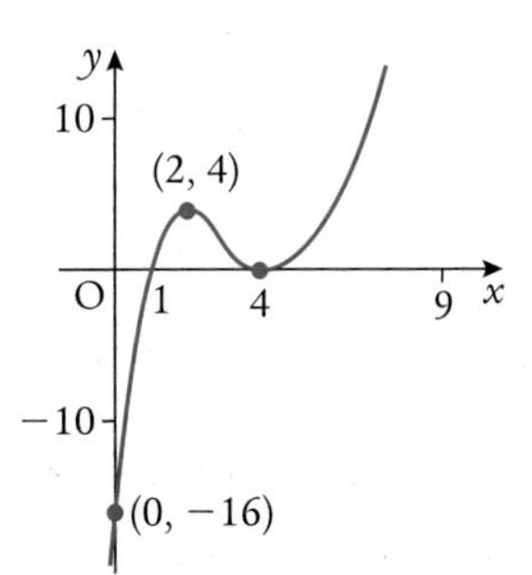

Exercise 5.6

1 a $(-1, 1)$ end point max; $(2, 4)$ end point max.

b $(-1, 3)$ end point min; $(1, 3)$ end point min.

c $(-3, -30)$ end point min; $(0, 0)$ end point max.

d $(0, 6)$ 0 not in domain; $(2, -2)$ end point min.

e $(-2, 4)$ end point max; $(3, 6)$ 3 not in domain.

2 a $(-1, 0)$ local min; $(3, 16)$ end point max; $(-2, 1)$ end point max.

b $(-1, 0)$ end point min; $(3, 2)$ end point max.

c $(0, 3)$ local min; $(-4, 5)$ end point max.

d $-\frac{2}{3}, \frac{4}{27}$ local max; $(0, 0)$ local min; $(2, 12)$ end point max.

e $(1, 2)$ local min; $\left(3, 3\frac{1}{3}\right)$ end point max.

3 a i ii $(-2, 7)$ end pt max; $(2, -9)$ local min; $(4, -5)$ end pt max.

iii $(2, -9)$ global min; $(-2, 7)$ global max.

b i ii $\left(\frac{\pi}{4}, \frac{1}{\sqrt{2}}\right)$ end pt max; $\left(\frac{\pi}{2}, 0\right)$ local min; $\left(\frac{2\pi}{3}, \frac{1}{2}\right)$ end pt max.

i ii $\left(\frac{\pi}{2}, 0\right)$ global min; $\left(\frac{\pi}{4}, \frac{1}{\sqrt{2}}\right)$ global max.

c i ii $(1, 0)$ local min; $(e, 1)$ local max

iii $(1, 0)$ global min; no global max.

d i ii $(-1, -11)$ end pt min; $(2, 16)$ local max; $(3, -27)$ end pt min; $(0, 0)$ point of inflexion.

i ii $(3, -27)$ global min; $(2, 16)$ global max.

e i ii $\left(-2, -\frac{2}{5}\right)$ end point max; $\left(-1, -\frac{1}{2}\right)$ local min

iii $\left(-1, -\frac{1}{2}\right)$ global min; no global max.

Exercise 5.7

1 a $f''(x) = 2 > 0$

b $f''(x) = -\frac{1}{x^2} < 0$

2 a Down   b Up

c Down when $x < 0$; up when $x > 0$; inflexion at $(0, 0)$

d Down when $x < 0$; up when $x > 0$; inflexion at $(0, 6)$

e i Up   ii Down

3 a/b $(0, 0)$ positive, $(\pi, 0)$ negative, $(2\pi, 0)$ positive

c

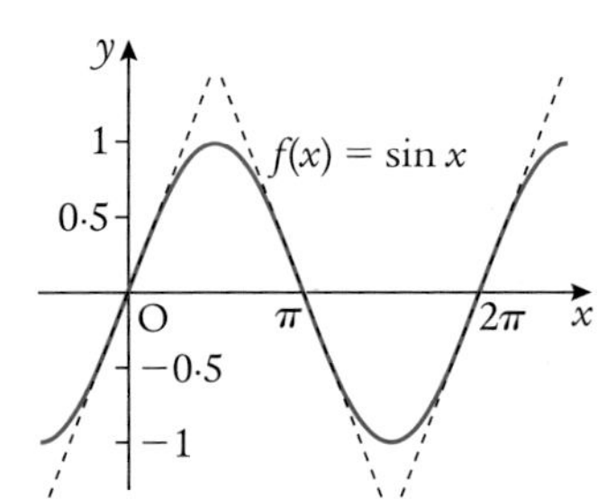

4 a Up

b Up

5 a $(0, 0)$ zero

b $(1, -5)$ negative; $(-1, -5)$ positive

c $(-3, 567)$ negative; $(0, 0)$ zero; $(3, -567)$ negative

d $\left(\frac{\pi}{2}, 0\right)$ negative

6 $a = \frac{1}{3}(x_1 + x_2 + x_3)$

Exercise 5.8

1 a $f(x) = 2x^2 + 5 \Rightarrow$
$f(-x) = 2(-x)^2 + 5 = 2x^2 + 5 = f(x)$

b $f(x) = 3x^5 + 7x^3 - 4x \Rightarrow f(-x)$
$= 3(-x)^5 + 7(-x)^3 - 4(-x)$
$= -(3x^5 + 7x^3 - 4x) = -f(x)$

2 a Even

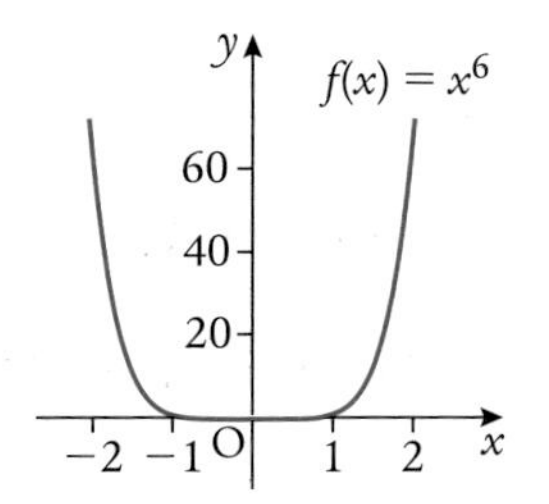

b Odd

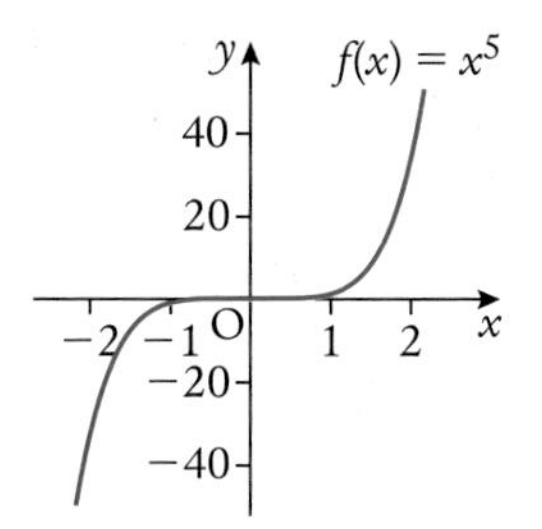

c Odd

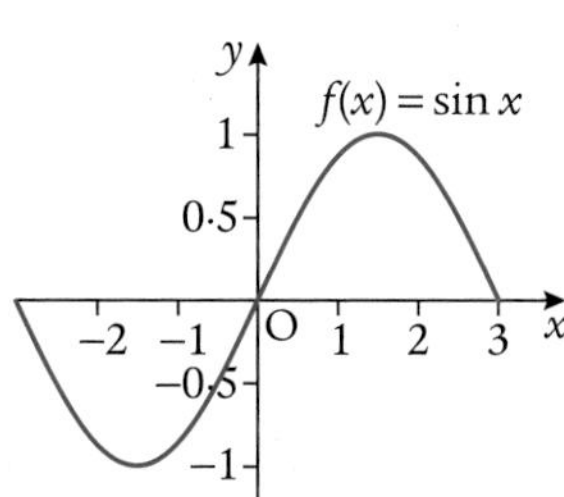

d Even

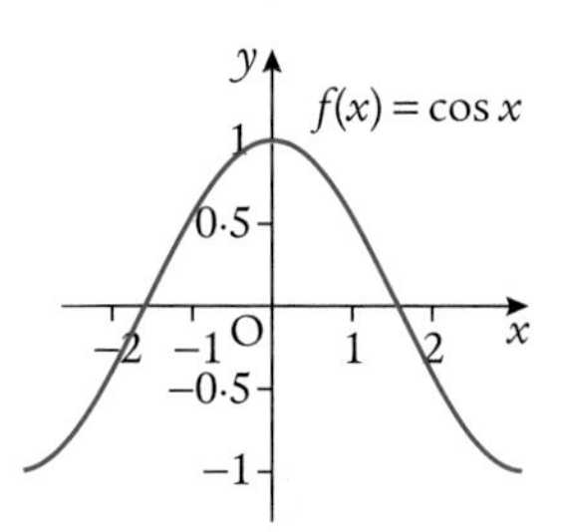

e Even

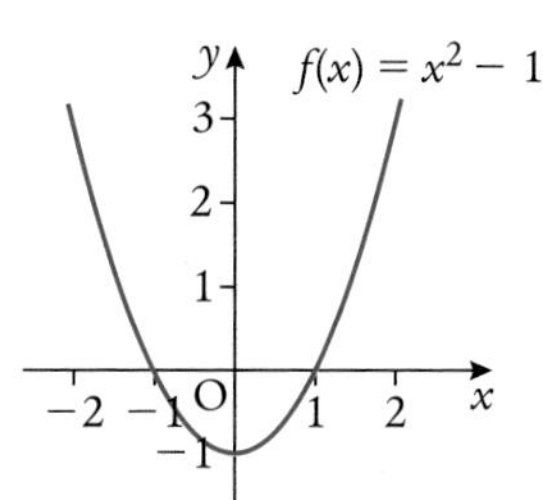

f Odd

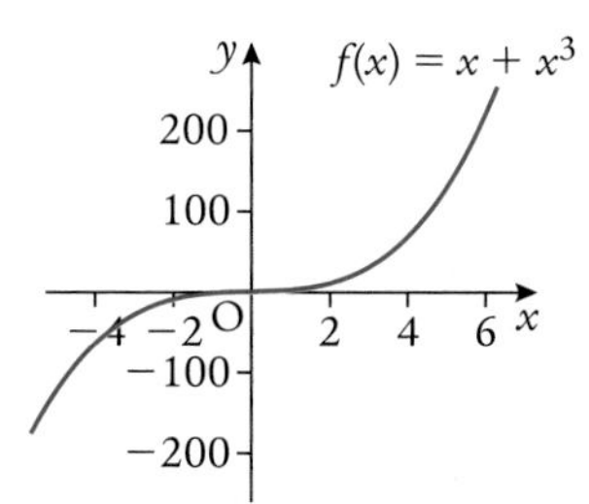

3 a Odd b Neither c Even
d Odd e Neither f Odd
g Neither h Neither i Even
j Even k Odd l Neither

Exercise 5.9

1 a i $x = -1$
ii From left $f(x) \to +\infty$; from right $f(x) \to -\infty$

b i $x = -1$
ii From left $f(x) \to -\infty$; from right $f(x) \to +\infty$

c i $x = 1$
ii From left $f(x) \to -\infty$; from right $f(x) \to +\infty$
i $x = -2$
ii From left $f(x) \to +\infty$; from right $f(x) \to -\infty$

d i $x = 0$
ii From left $f(x) \to -\infty$; from right $f(x) \to +\infty$
i $x = -1/2$
ii From left $f(x) \to +\infty$; from right $f(x) \to -\infty$

e i $x = 5$
ii From left $f(x) \to -\infty$; from right $f(x) \to +\infty$
i $x = -1$
ii From left $f(x) \to -\infty$; from right $f(x) \to +\infty$

f i $x = -1$
ii From left $f(x) \to -\infty$; from right $f(x) \to +\infty$
i $x = 2$
ii From left $f(x) \to -\infty$; from right $f(x) \to +\infty$

g i $x = 1$
ii From left $f(x) \to -\infty$; from right $f(x) \to +\infty$
i $x = -1$
ii From left $f(x) \to +\infty$; from right $f(x) \to -\infty$

h i $x = 2$
ii From left $f(x) \to -\infty$; from right $f(x) \to +\infty$
i $x = 3$
ii From left $f(x) \to +\infty$; from right $f(x) \to -\infty$

i i $x = -1$
ii From left $f(x) \to -\infty$; from right $f(x) \to +\infty$

2 a Asymptotes $x = (2k-1)\frac{\pi}{2}$; from left $f(x) \to +\infty$; from right $f(x) \to -\infty$ for all k

b Asymptotes $x = (2k-1)\frac{\pi}{2}$; from left $f(x) \to +\infty$; from right $f(x) \to -\infty$ for odd k
from left $f(x) \to -\infty$; from right $f(x) \to +\infty$ for even k

c $x = 0$; from left $f(x) \to -\infty$; from right $f(x) \to +\infty$

d $x = 0$; from left $f(x) \to +\infty$; from right $f(x) \to +\infty$

e $x = 1$; from left $f(x) \to -\infty$; from right $f(x) \to +\infty$

f $x = 0$; from left $f(x) \to -\infty$; from right $f(x) \to +\infty$

3 $f(x) = \begin{cases} -1 \text{ where } x < 0 \\ \text{undefined at } x = 0 \\ 1 \text{ where } x > 0 \end{cases}$

Exercise 5.10

1 a i $x = 0$ ii – iii $y = 0$
iv From above as $x \to +\infty$; from below as $x \to -\infty$.

b i $x = 0$ ii $f(x) = 1 + \frac{1}{x}$ iii $y = 1$
iv From above as $x \to +\infty$; from below as $x \to -\infty$.

c i $x = 0$ ii $f(x) = x + \frac{2}{x}$ iii $y = x$
iv From above as $x \to +\infty$; from below as $x \to -\infty$.

d **i** $x = -1$ **ii** $f(x) = 1 - \dfrac{2}{x+1}$

iii $y = 1$

iv From below as $x \to +\infty$; from above as $x \to -\infty$.

e **i** $x = -1$ **ii** $f(x) = -1 + \dfrac{2}{x+1}$

iii $y = -1$

iv From above as $x \to +\infty$; from below as $x \to -\infty$.

f **i** $x = -1$ **ii** $f(x) = x - 1 + \dfrac{2}{x+1}$

iii $y = x - 1$

iv From above as $x \to +\infty$; from below as $x \to -\infty$.

g **i** $x = 1, x = -1$ **ii** $f(x) = 1 + \dfrac{2}{x^2 - 1}$

iii $y = 1$

iv From above as $x \to +\infty$; from below as $x \to -\infty$.

h **i** None **ii** –

iii $y = 0$

iv From above as $x \to +\infty$; from below as $x \to -\infty$.

i **i** $x = -1, x = 2$ **ii** –

iii $y = 0$

iv From above as $x \to +\infty$; from below as $x \to -\infty$.

j **i** $x = 1$ **ii** $f(x) = x + 1 + \dfrac{4}{x-1}$

iii $y = x + 1$

iv From above as $x \to +\infty$; from below as $x \to -\infty$.

k **i** $x = -2$ **ii** $f(x) = 2x - 2 + \dfrac{1}{x+2}$

iii $y = 2x - 2$

iv From above as $x \to +\infty$; from below as $x \to -\infty$.

l **i** None **ii** $f(x) = x - \dfrac{4x}{x^2 + 1}$

iii $y = x$

iv From below as $x \to +\infty$; from above as $x \to -\infty$.

2 **a** $(0, 0)$ **b** $(-1, -1)$

3 **a** $\dfrac{x^3 - x^2 + 1}{x - 1} = x^2 + \dfrac{1}{x-1} \to x^2$ as $x \to \infty$

b Behaves like $y = x^2 + 1$

Exercise 5.11

1 **a**

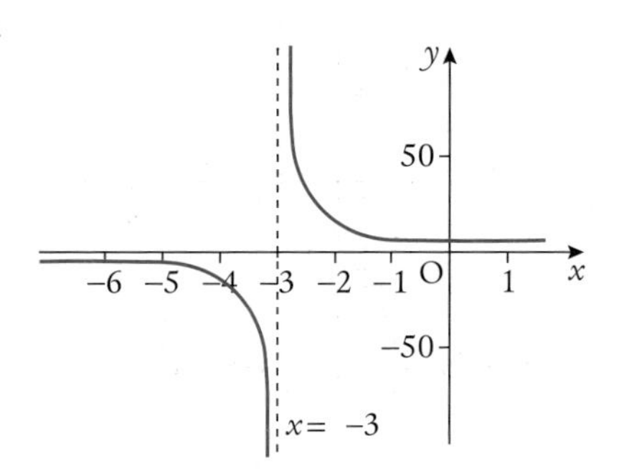

b

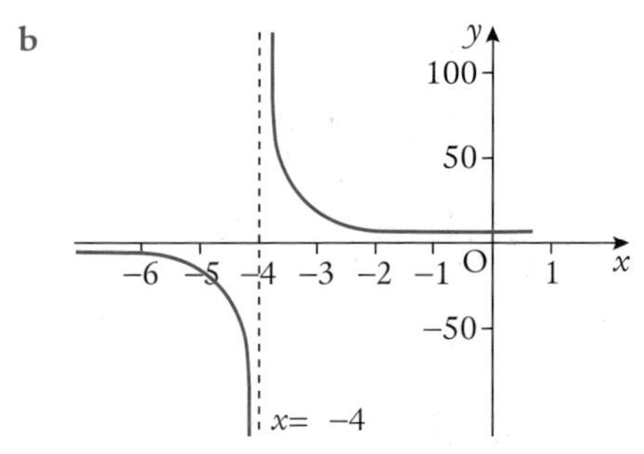

c

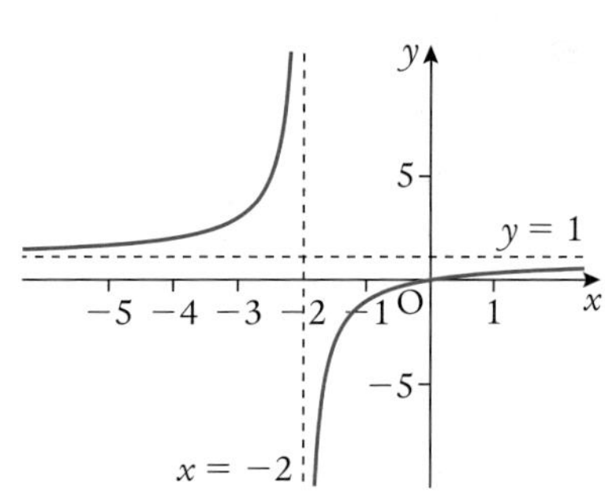

d

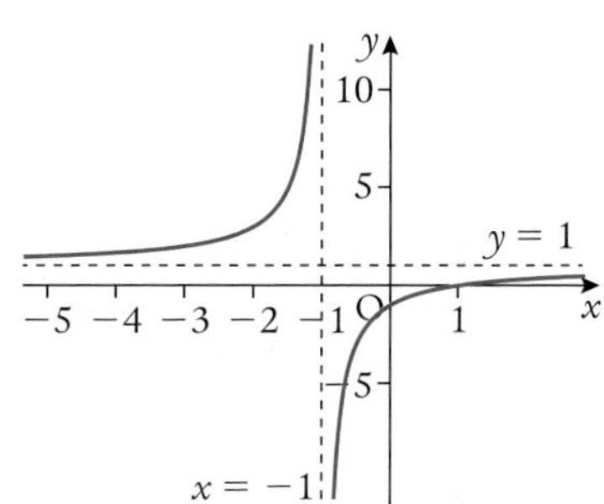

e

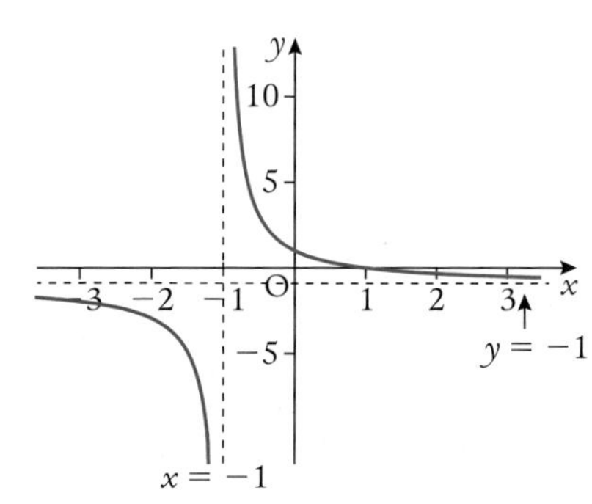

f

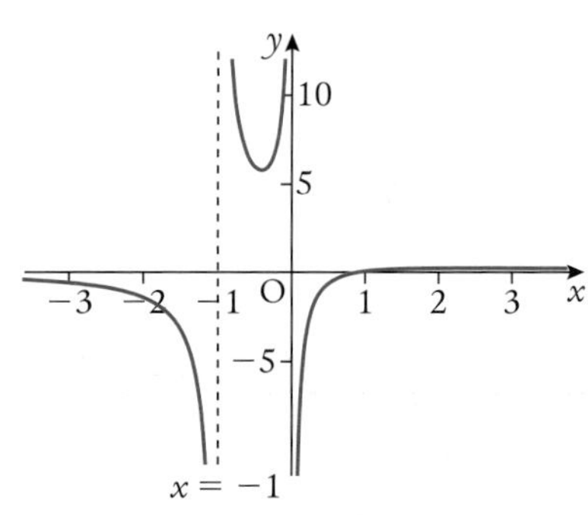

g

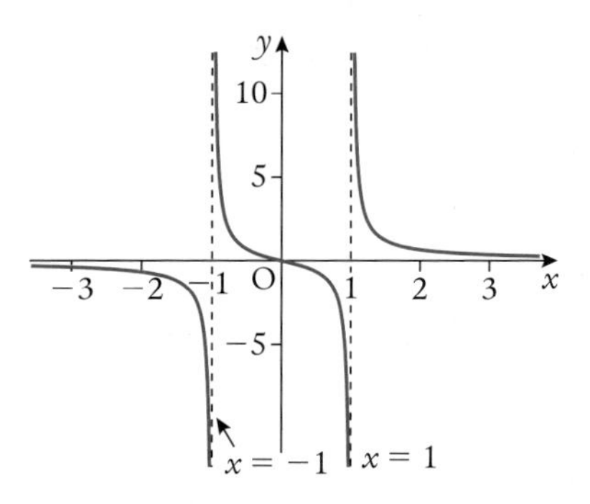

h

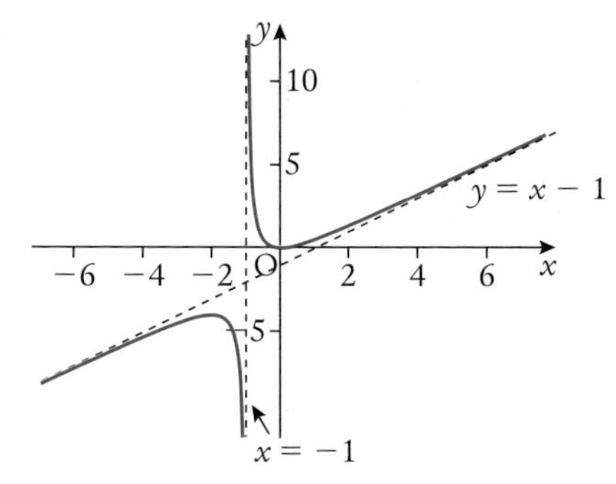

i

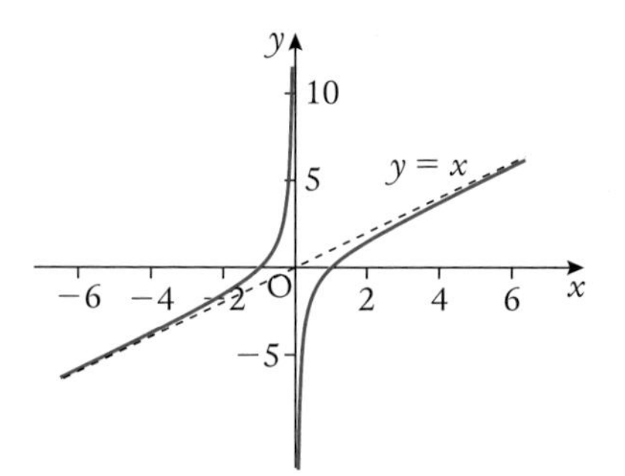

j

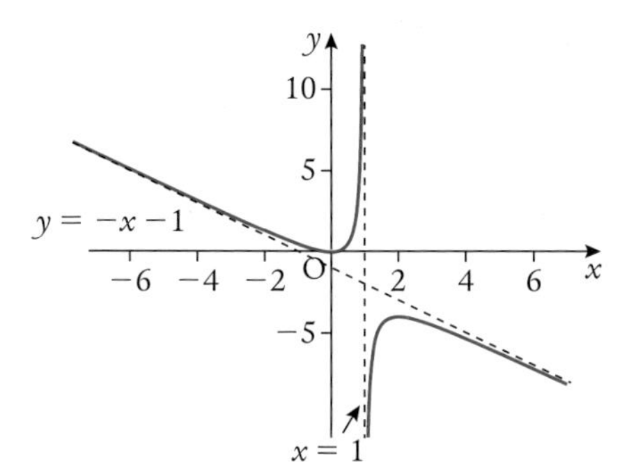

k

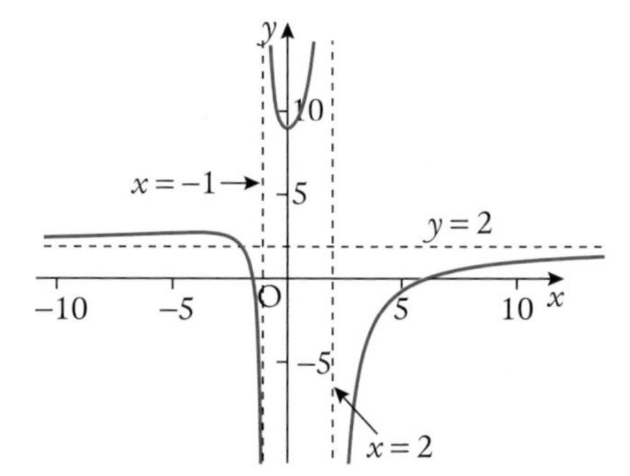

l

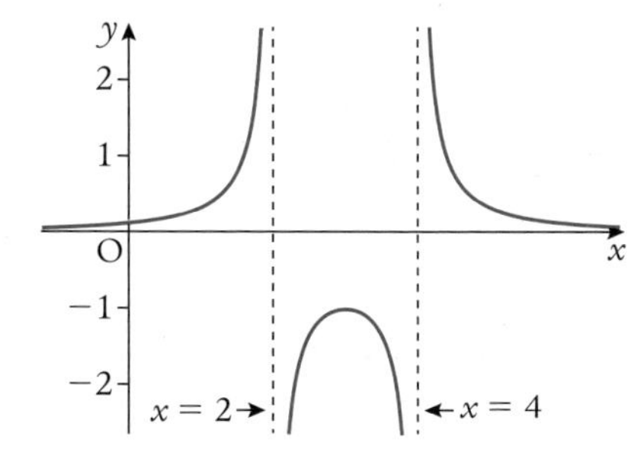

m

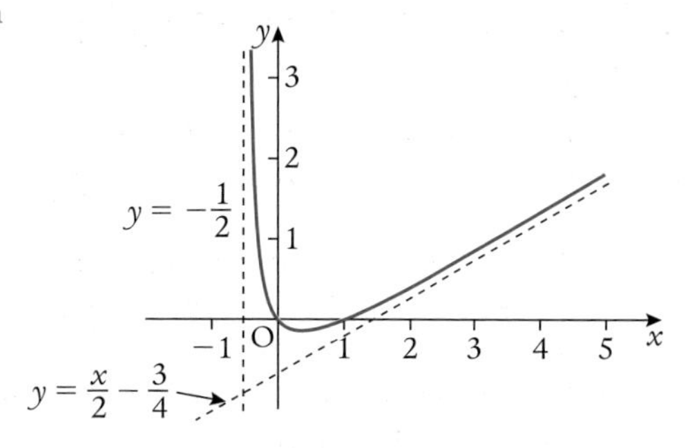

n

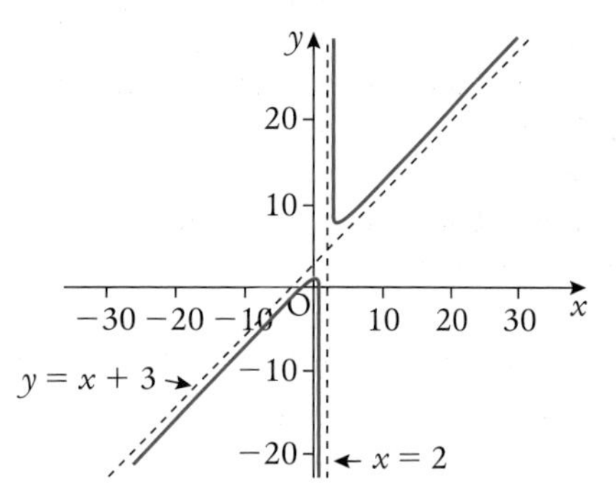

o

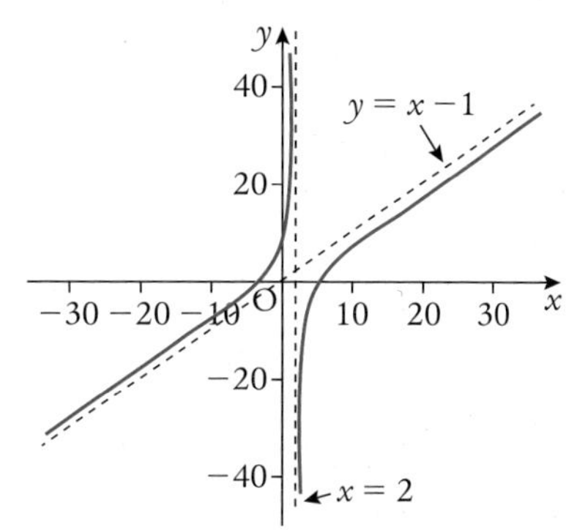

2 a

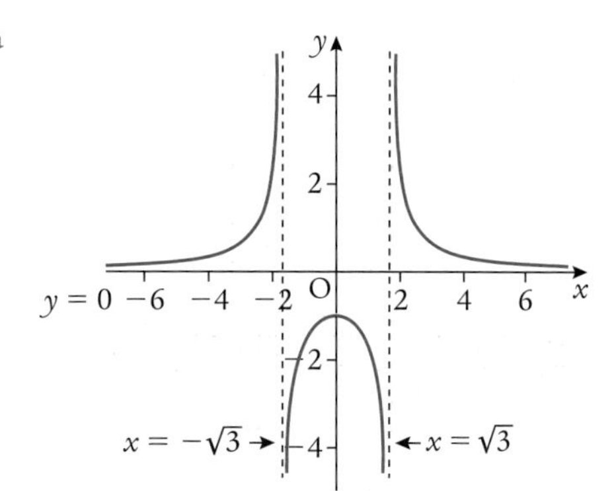

b

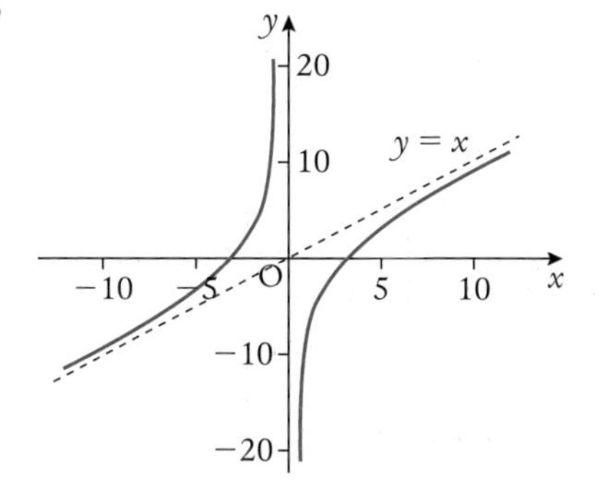

c

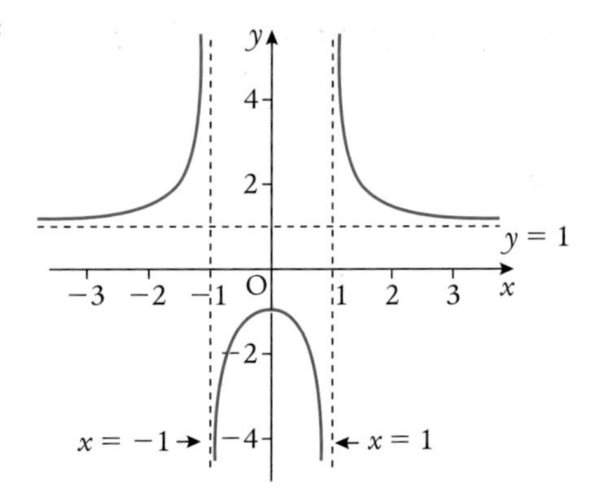

3 a Global max $\left(1, \frac{1}{2}\right)$, global min $-\left(1, -\frac{1}{2}\right)$

b i Odd ii $f(x) = \dfrac{x}{x^2 + 1}$

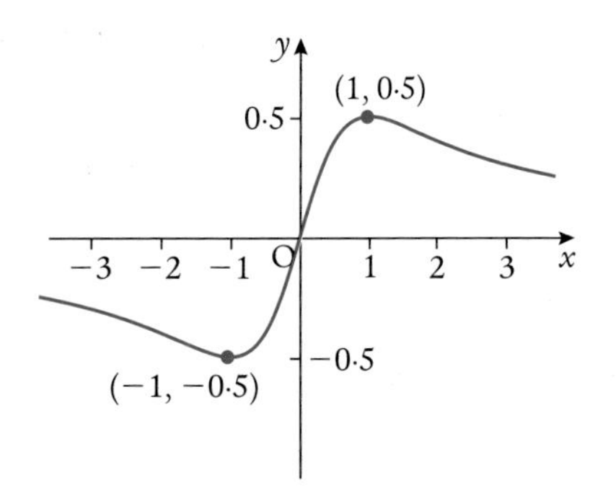

4 a $2x^2 - x + 2 = 2\left[\left(x - \frac{1}{4}\right)^2 + \frac{15}{16}\right] > 0$

b $a = \frac{3}{5}, b = \frac{5}{3}$

c

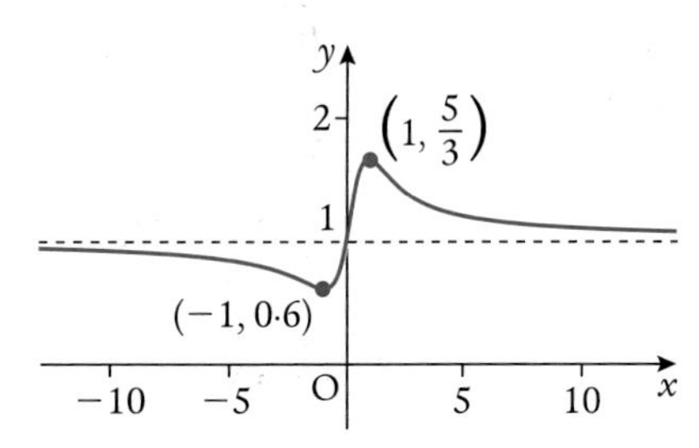

5 a A vertical asymptote at $x = \frac{5}{3}$ which gives a change of sign.

b

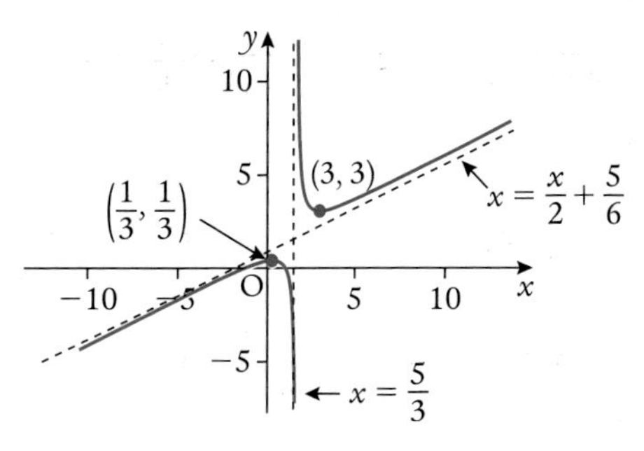

6 a, b

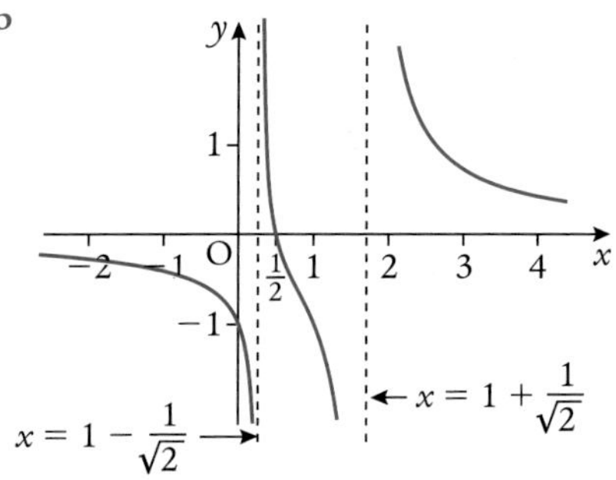

Review 5

1 Domain: $x \in W$; Range: subset of the natural numbers defined by the recurrence relation $\{u_n : u_n = nu_{n-1}; u_0 = 1, n \in W\}$

2 a $(1·5, -1·5), (2, -1)$ b/c $(1·5, -1·5)$ global min, $(2, -1)$ end pt max, no local or global max.

3 $x \geq -3$ concave up; $x \leq -3$ concave down; $(-3, 1)$ inflexion.

4 a

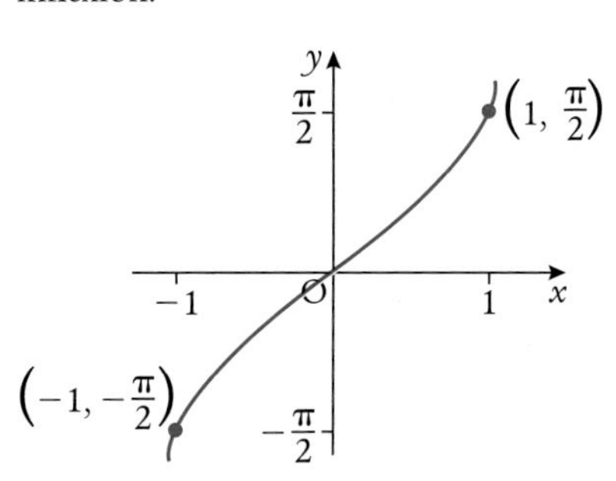

b Domain: $-1 \leq x \leq 1$; range $-\pi/2 \leq y \leq \pi/2$

5 a

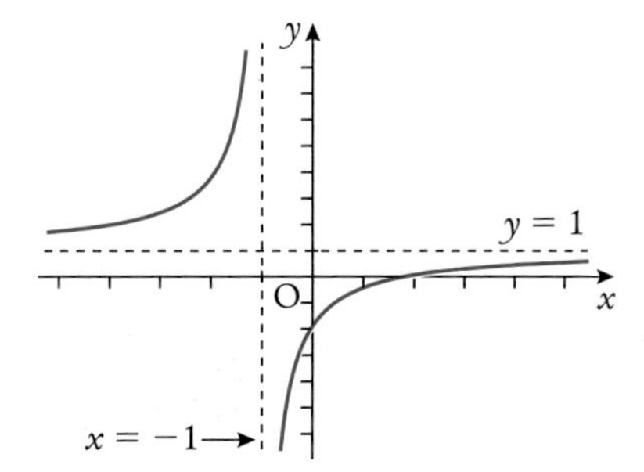

b

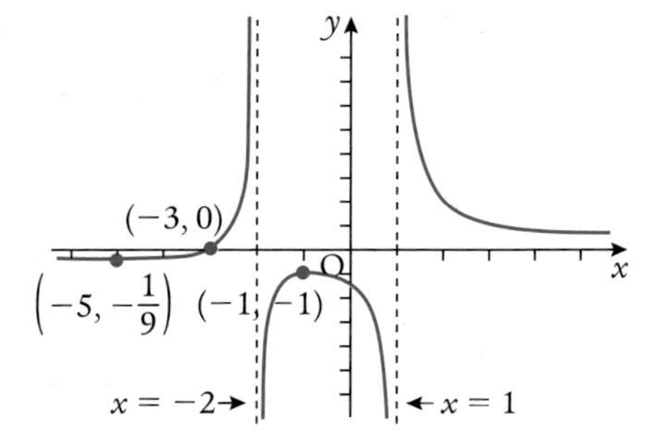

c

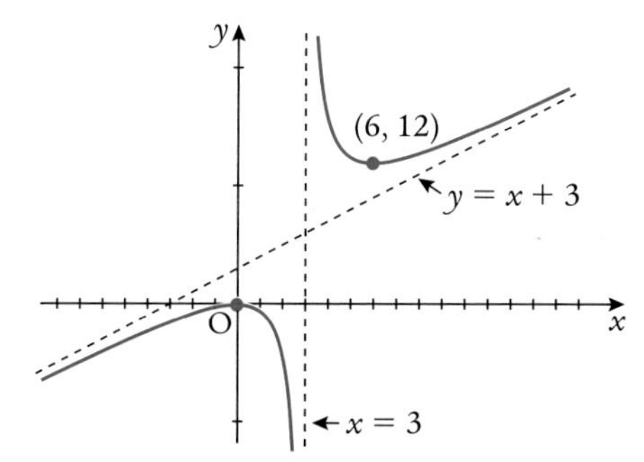

d

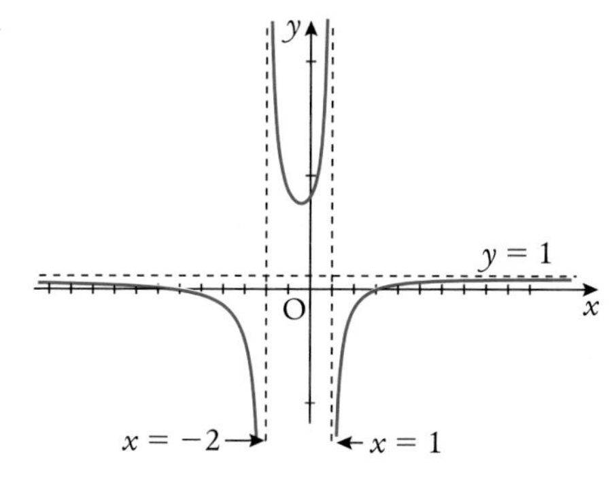

e

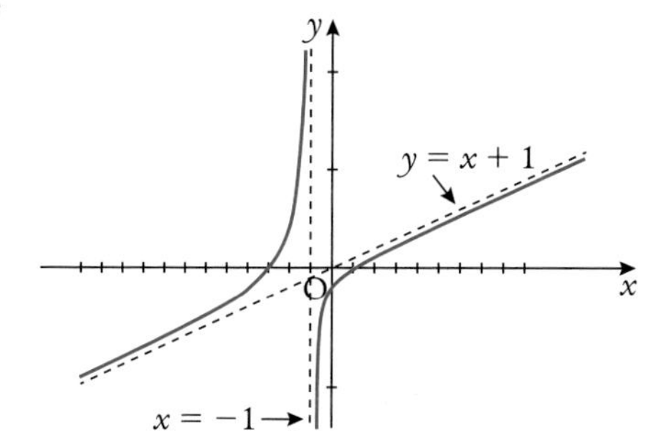

Chapter 6

Exercise 6.1

1 a $\frac{1}{5}x^{-\frac{4}{5}}$ b $\frac{4}{3}x^{\frac{1}{3}}$

c $-\frac{1}{x\sqrt{2x}}$ d $\frac{1}{2\sqrt{x-1}}$

2 a i $(x+2)^2+1$ ii $\sqrt{x-1}-2$

iii $2x+4, \frac{1}{2\sqrt{x-1}}$

b i $(x+3)^2-10$ ii $\sqrt{x+10}-3$

iii $2x+6, \frac{1}{2\sqrt{x+10}}$

c i $2\left(x-\frac{1}{2}\right)^2+\frac{1}{2}$ ii $\frac{1}{2}+\frac{1}{2}\sqrt{2x-1}$

iii $4x-2, \frac{1}{2\sqrt{2x-1}}$

d i $3\left(x+\frac{1}{3}\right)^2-\frac{1}{3}$ ii $\frac{1}{3}\sqrt{3x+1}-\frac{1}{3}$

iii $6x+2, \frac{1}{2\sqrt{3x+1}}$

3 a $y=\ln x \Rightarrow x=e^y: \frac{d\ln x}{dx}=\frac{1}{\frac{de^y}{dy}}=\frac{1}{e^y}=\frac{1}{x}$

b $\frac{1}{2x}$

4 $-\frac{1}{\sqrt{1-x^2}}$

5 a $\frac{1}{1+(x+1)^2}=\frac{1}{x^2+2x+2}$

b $\frac{3}{\sqrt{1-(3x+1)^2}}$

6 a i $(x+3)^2-8$ ii $x=\sqrt{y+8}-3$

iii $\frac{1}{2\sqrt{y+8}}$ iv $2x+6$

b i $(x+1)^2-6$ ii $x+\sqrt{y+6}-1$

iii $\frac{1}{2\sqrt{y+6}}$ iv $2x+2$

c i $3\left(x-\frac{2}{3}\right)^2-\frac{13}{3}$ ii $x=\frac{2}{3}+\frac{1}{3}\sqrt{3y+13}$

iii $\frac{1}{2\sqrt{3y+13}}$ iv $6x-4$

d i $2(x+1)^2-2$ ii $x=\sqrt{\frac{y+2}{2}}-1$

iii $\frac{\sqrt{2}}{4\sqrt{y+2}}$ iv $4x+4$

7 Student's own investigation.

Exercise 6.2

1 a $\frac{2x}{\sqrt{1-x^4}}$ b $\frac{1}{x^2+4x+5}$

c $\frac{-1}{x\sqrt{x^2-1}}$ d $\frac{-1}{2(x+1)\sqrt{x}}$

e $\frac{1}{x\sqrt{x^2-1}}$ f $\frac{-a}{\sqrt{1-a^2x^2}}$

2 a $\frac{e^x}{\sqrt{1-e^{2x}}}$ b $\frac{-2(x+2)}{\sqrt{1-(x+2)^4}}$

c $\frac{-1}{\sqrt{1-x^2}}$ d $\frac{1}{\cos x\sqrt{\cos 2x}}$

e $\frac{1}{\sqrt{a^2-x^2}}$

3 a $\frac{-2e^{2x}}{\sqrt{1-e^{4x}}}$ b -1

c $\frac{1}{x^2+2x+2}$ d $\frac{-1}{x\sqrt{1-(\ln 3x)^2}}$

e $\frac{1}{x\sqrt{9x^2-1}}$

4 a $\frac{1}{2(1+x)\sqrt{x}\tan^{-1}\sqrt{x}}$ b $\frac{1}{2x\sqrt{x-1}\sin^{-1}\left(\frac{1}{\sqrt{x}}\right)}$

c $\frac{e^x}{\sin^{-1}(e^x)\sqrt{1-e^{2x}}}$ d $\frac{e^{\sin^{-1}x}}{\sqrt{1-x^2}}$

5 a $-\frac{e^{\frac{\pi}{4}}}{2}$ b $-\frac{2}{\pi}$

c $\frac{64}{125}$ d $\frac{1}{8}$

6 a $\frac{8\sqrt{3}}{\pi}$ b $\frac{9(4+\pi)^2}{32}$

c $\frac{2\sqrt{3}}{\pi}$ d $e^{\frac{\pi}{4}}$

7 a $x > 0$

b $y = \ln\frac{2}{\tan^{-1}x} \Rightarrow \frac{dy}{dx} = -\frac{1}{(1+x^2)\tan^{-1}x} \Rightarrow$
$\frac{dy}{dx} < 0, \forall x > 0$

8 $\frac{dy}{dx} = \frac{12(\sin^{-1}3x)^3}{\sqrt{1-9x^2}}$: SP when $12(\sin^{-1}3x)^3 = 0 : x = 0$
is a solution. $y_{x=0} = 0$
A table of signs confirms that it is a minimum TP.

9 a $-\frac{1}{2} \le x \le \frac{1}{2}$

b $\frac{dy}{dx} = \frac{-1}{\sqrt{1+\cos^{-1}2x}\sqrt{1-4x^2}}$: Throughout
domain this is negative

Exercise 6.3

1 a $\frac{x^2}{\sqrt{1-x^2}} + 2x\sin^{-1}x$ b $\frac{2x^2}{\sqrt{1-x^4}} + \sin^{-1}x^2$

c $\frac{1}{2\sqrt{x}}\cos^{-1}x - \sqrt{\frac{x}{1-x^2}}$ d $\frac{1}{2\sqrt{1-x}} + \frac{\sin^{-1}\sqrt{x}}{2\sqrt{x}}$

2 a $1 + 2x\tan^{-1}x$ b $e^x\left[\sin^{-1}x + \frac{1}{\sqrt{1-x^2}}\right]$

c $e^{2x}\left[2\cos^{-1}\left(\frac{x}{2}\right) - \frac{1}{\sqrt{4-x^2}}\right]$

d $\frac{\ln x}{x^2+1} + \frac{\tan^{-1}x}{x}$

3 a $\frac{x-(1+x^2)\tan^{-1}x}{x^2(1+x^2)}$

b $\frac{2x - \sqrt{1-x^2}\sin^{-1}x}{2x\sqrt{x}(1-x^2)}$

c $\frac{4x + 3\sqrt{1-4x^2}\cos^{-1}2x}{-2x^{\frac{5}{2}}\sqrt{1-4x^2}}$

d $\frac{x - 2(x^2+2x+2)\tan^{-1}(x+1)}{x^3(x^2+2x+2)}$

4 a $\frac{\sqrt{1-x^2}\sin^{-1}x - x}{\sqrt{1-x^2}(\sin^{-1}x)^2}$

b $\frac{2x\sqrt{2x-x^2}\cos^{-1}(x-1) + x^2}{\sqrt{2x-x^2}(\cos^{-1}(x-1))^2}$

c $\frac{e^x\sqrt{1-4x^2}\sin^{-1}2x - 2e^x}{\sqrt{1-4x^2}(\sin^{-1}2x)^2}$ d $\frac{(1+x^2)\tan^{-1}x - x\ln x}{x(1+x^2)(\tan^{-1}x)^2}$

5 a $-\frac{4}{5}$ b $\frac{6-8\sqrt{3}}{13}$

6 a $(1, \tan^{-1}e)$ b $\left(e, \cos^{-1}\left(\frac{1}{e}\right)\right)$

7 $\frac{dy}{dx} = \frac{-1}{(1+x)\sqrt{x}} \ne 0$

8 $\frac{6(1+\cos x)}{5+4\cos x}$

9 a $f'(x) = g'(x) = \frac{2}{1+x^2}$

b Let $a = \cos^{-1}\left(\frac{1-x^2}{1+x^2}\right)$ and $2b = 2\tan^{-1}x \Rightarrow$
$\cos a = \frac{1-x^2}{1+x^2}$ and $\tan b = x$
$\cos a = \frac{1-x^2}{1+x^2} = \frac{1-\tan^2 b}{1+\tan^2 b} = \frac{\cos^2 b - \sin^2 b}{\cos^2 b + \sin^2 b}$
$= \frac{\cos 2b}{1} = \cos 2b \Rightarrow a = 2b \Rightarrow f(x) = g(x)$

10 $\frac{3\sqrt{x}}{(x^3+1)}$; 0

11 Note: $\frac{dy}{dx}$ is given for each rather than full proof.

a $\frac{1-x}{x\sqrt{2x-1}} + \cos^{-1}\left(\frac{x-1}{x}\right)$

b $\frac{1}{\sqrt{2x+1}} + \sin^{-1}\left(\frac{x}{x+1}\right)$

c $\frac{x^2}{x^2+1} + 2x\tan^{-1}\left(\frac{x-1}{x+1}\right)$

d $e^x\cos^{-1}\left(\frac{x-1}{x+1}\right) - \frac{e^x}{|x+1|\sqrt{x}}$

e $\frac{-2(x\sin x + \cos x)}{\sqrt{x^2-\cos^2 x}}\frac{|x|}{x} + 2\sin^{-1}\left(\frac{\cos x}{x}\right)$

f $\frac{x(x-1)e^x}{x^2+e^{2x}} + \tan^{-1}\left(\frac{e^x}{x}\right)$

Exercise 6.4

1 a $-\frac{x+2y}{2x+y}$ b $2xy$

c $\frac{5-4x}{4(y+1)}$ d e^{-y}

e $\frac{y-2x}{6y-x}$ f $\frac{e^x - \tan y}{x\sec^2 y}$

g $-\left(\frac{y}{x}\right)^{\frac{3}{5}}$ h $\frac{x+y-x^2-1}{x^2+1}$

i $\frac{5x-2y}{2x-3y}$ j $\sqrt{\frac{1-y^2}{1-x^2}} - 6x^2\sqrt{1-y^2}$

2 a i $\frac{1}{\cos y}$ ii $\frac{1}{\sqrt{1-x^2}}$

b i $-\frac{1}{\sin y} = -\frac{1}{\sqrt{1-x^2}}$ ii $\frac{1}{\sec^2 y} = \frac{1}{1+x^2}$

3 $\frac{2x^3+y}{x(1-2xy)}$

4 Differentiation gives $e^x + e^y\frac{dy}{dx} = \frac{y - \frac{dy}{dx}x}{y^2}$; $x = 0, y = 1$
$\Rightarrow \frac{dy}{dx} = 0$

5 $10x + 11y = 32$

6 Differentiation gives $1 + \frac{dy}{dx} = \frac{1 - \frac{dy}{dx}}{x-y}$; $\frac{dy}{dx} = 1 \Rightarrow 2 = 0$

7 At $x = 0$, $\cos y = -1$ and $\sin y = 0$; differentiating:
$\frac{x}{y}\frac{dy}{dx} + \ln y = -\sin x - \sin y\frac{dy}{dx}$
At $x = 0$, $\ln y = -\sin y\frac{dy}{dx} \Rightarrow \frac{dy}{dx} = \frac{\ln y}{-\sin y} = \frac{\ln y}{0}$
(undefined)

8 $x^2 = y^2 \ln y \Rightarrow \ln y = \frac{x^2}{y^2} \Rightarrow \frac{1}{y}\frac{dy}{dx} = \frac{y^2 . 2x - x^2 . 2y\frac{dy}{dx}}{y^4}$

$\Rightarrow \frac{dy}{dx} = \frac{2xy}{y^2 + 2x^2}$.

9 $8x + 21y = 21$

10 $-\frac{2}{3}$

11 The point lies on both curve and line.
The gradient at the point for line and curve is 1.

12 a $(2, 2), (2, -2)$ b $-\frac{1}{2}, -1; 71{\cdot}6°$

13 Substitution into equations gives first part; substitution into derivatives to end.

14 a $(20, 6), (20, -6), (-20, 6), (-20, -6)$

b Differentiate and show that at these four points the product of the derivatives is -1.

15 $\ln (x - y)$

16 $x + y = \frac{x}{y} \Rightarrow x = \frac{y^2}{1 - y} \Rightarrow \frac{dx}{dy} = \frac{y(2 - y)}{(1 - y)^2} \Rightarrow$

$\frac{dy}{dx} = \frac{(1 - y)^2}{y(2 - y)}$; also

$x = \frac{y^2}{1 - y} \Rightarrow \frac{y^3}{x^2(2 - y)} = \frac{y^3}{\left(\frac{y^2}{1 + y}\right)(2 - y)} = \frac{(1 - y)^2}{y(2 - y)}$

Exercise 6.5

1 a $\frac{2x + y}{x}, \frac{2(x + y)}{x^2}$ b $-\frac{3x^2}{2y}, \frac{-3x(4y^2 + 3x^3)}{4y^3}$

c $-\frac{1}{6\sqrt{x}y^2}, \frac{3y^3 - 2\sqrt{x}}{36x\sqrt{x}y^5}$ d $\frac{y}{2y - x}, \frac{2y(y - x)}{(2y - x)^3}$

e $\frac{e^x - y + 1}{x + 1}, \frac{2(y - 1) + e^x(x - 1)}{(x + 1)^2}$

f $\frac{y^2}{1 - 2xy}, \frac{2y^3(2 - 3xy)}{(1 - 2xy)^3}$

g $\frac{x + y - 1}{x + y + 1}, \frac{4(x + y)}{(x + y + 1)^3}$

h $\frac{2x}{1 + \ln y}, \frac{2y(1 + \ln y)^2 - 4x^2}{y(1 + \ln y)^3}$

i $\frac{2(x + y)}{e^y - 2(x + y)}, \frac{2e^y(e^y - 2(x + y)^2)}{(e^y - 2(x + y))^3}$

j $\frac{x \cos x + \sin x + y}{1 - x}$,

$\frac{2y + 2\sin x + 2\cos x - x\sin x - x^2 \sin x}{(1 - x)^2}$

k $\frac{\cos (x + y)}{1 - \cos (x + y)}, \frac{\sin (x + y)}{(\cos (x + y) - 1)^3}$,

$\frac{(e^x - \sin^{-1} y)\sqrt{1 - y^2}}{x}$,

$\frac{e^x\sqrt{1 - y^2}}{x}$

$-\frac{(e^x - \sin^{-1} y)(2\sqrt{1 - y^2} + y(e^x - \sin^{-1} y))}{x^2}$

2 $-e(e + 1)$, concave up

3 -1, concave up

4 $e^y = x^2 \Rightarrow e^y \frac{dy}{dx} = 2x \Rightarrow \frac{dy}{dx} = \frac{2x}{e^y} = \frac{2}{x} \Rightarrow \frac{d^2y}{dx^2} = -\frac{2}{x^2}$;
substitution gives result.

5 $y = xe^y \Rightarrow \frac{dy}{dx} = xe^y \frac{dy}{dx} + e^y \Rightarrow \frac{dy}{dx} = \frac{e^y}{1 - xe^y} = \frac{e^y}{1 - y}$

$\Rightarrow \frac{d^2y}{dx^2} = \frac{\frac{dy}{dx} e^y(2 - y)}{(1 - y)^2} \Rightarrow \frac{d^2y}{dx^2} = \frac{\frac{e^y}{1 - y} e^y(2 - y)}{(1 - y)^2} = \frac{e^{2y}(2 - y)}{(1 - y)^3}$;
substitution gives result.

6 $-2, 18$

7 $2e^{\frac{\pi}{3}}(1 + \sqrt{3}), 4e^{\frac{\pi}{3}}(4 + \sqrt{3})$

8 $(1, 2), (-1, -2); (2, 1), (-2, -1)$

9 $(1, 4)$ maximum TP; $(-1, -4)$ minimum TP.

Exercise 6.6

1 a $(2 \ln 5)5^{2x}$

b $(x + 1)^{x - 1}\left(\left(\frac{x - 1}{x + 1}\right) + \ln(x + 1)\right)$

c $\sin 2x\, e^{\sin^2 x}$ d $\ln 3\, e^x 3^{e^x}$

e $(\ln \cos x - x \tan x)(\cos x)^x$

2 a $(x + 2x \ln x)x^{x^2}$ b $3x^2 \ln \pi . \pi^{x^3}$

c $\frac{e^x((x - 1)\sin x + x \cos x)}{x^2}$

d $(\cos x - x \sin x - x \cos x)e^{-x}$

e $(1 - x^3)^{\sin x}\left(\cos x \ln (1 - x^3) - \frac{3x^2 \sin x}{1 - x^3}\right)$

3 $\frac{dy}{dx} = e^{\cos 2x \cos^2 x} . -2\cos x(\cos 2x \sin x + \sin 2x \cos x)$

Hence result.

4 $\frac{dy}{dx} = -2\cos x \sin x . e^{\cos^2 x} = -\sin 2x\, e^{\cos^2 x}$

$\Rightarrow \frac{d^2y}{dx^2} = -\sin 2x . e^{\cos^2 x} . -2\cos x \sin x$
$+ e^{\cos^2 x} . -2\cos 2x = (\sin^2 2x - 2\cos 2x)\, e^{\cos^2 x}$

5 $\ln y = x \ln(\sin x) \Rightarrow \frac{1}{y}\frac{dy}{dx} = x\frac{\cos x}{\sin x} + \ln(\sin x) \Rightarrow$

$\frac{dy}{dx} = x \cos x (\sin x)^{x - 1} + (\sin x)^x \ln(\sin x) = 0$ when $x = \frac{\pi}{2}$

6 $\ln y = \sin x \ln x \Rightarrow \frac{1}{y}\frac{dy}{dx} = \cos x \ln x$

$+ \frac{1}{x}\sin x \Rightarrow \frac{dy}{dx} = x^{\sin x} \cos x \ln x + x^{\sin x - 1} \sin x$

When $x = \frac{\pi}{2}, \frac{dy}{dx} = 1$, hence result.

7 $y = 9x - 9$

8 $-\frac{11}{288}$

9 $\frac{9}{10}$

10 a $\frac{7x^2 + 18x - 1}{12(x + 1)^{\frac{1}{2}}(x - 1)^{\frac{2}{3}}(x + 2)^{\frac{5}{4}}}$

b $\frac{(5x^2 - 24x + 9)(2x + 3)^{\frac{3}{2}}}{3x^2(x - 1)^{\frac{5}{3}}}$

Exercise 6.7

1 a $2x + y = 3$ b $xy = 9$

c $y^2 = 20x$ d $\frac{x^2}{16} + \frac{y^2}{9} = 1$

e $\frac{x^2}{25} - \frac{y^2}{144} = 1$ f $\frac{(x-3)^2}{4} + \frac{(y-2)^2}{9} = 1$

g $x^2 + y^2 = 2$ h $16x + 15y = 17$

2 a A straight line

b Hyperbola approaching axes asymptotically

c Parabola with horizontal axis of symmetry on x-axis.

d Ellipse with major axis 8 units on x-axis and minor axis 6 units on y-axis, centre (0, 0)

e Hyperbola with asymptotes intersecting at (0, 0) and branches symmetrically placed on either side of y-axis. centre (0, 0)

f Ellipse centre (3, 2) ; horiz. axis of 4 units; vert. axis of 6 units

g Circle centre (0, 0) radius $\sqrt{2}$

h Straight line.

3 a

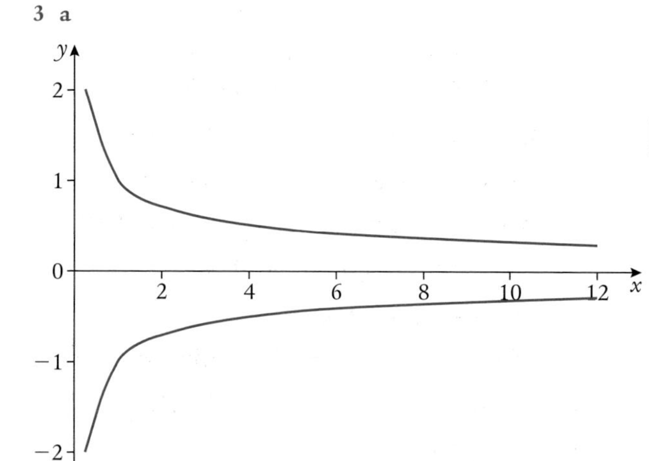

b

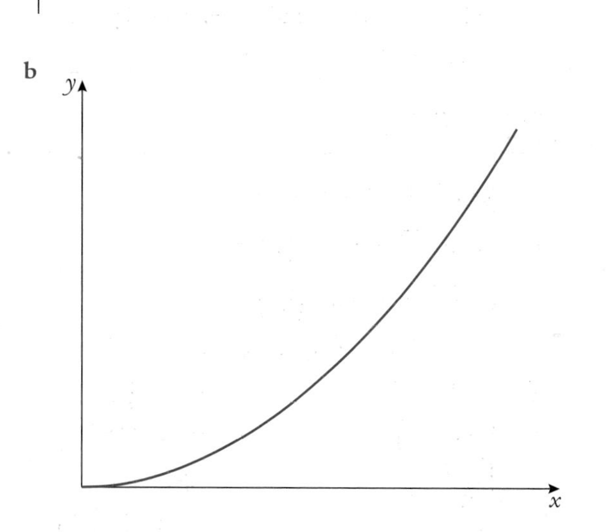

c

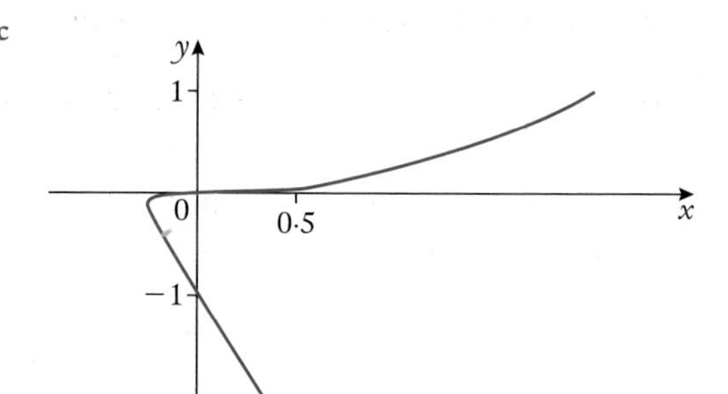

d

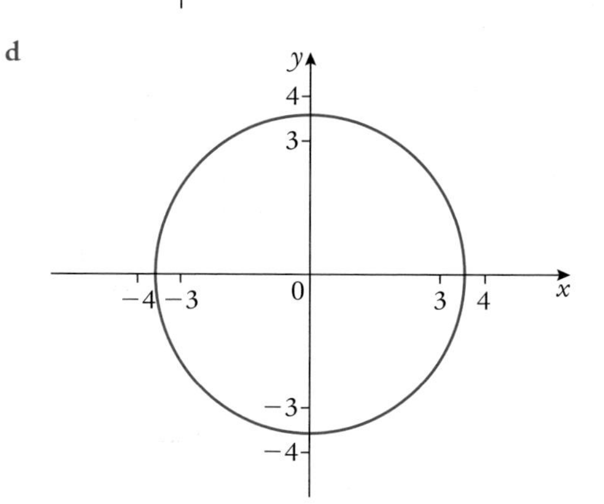

4 Student's own findings.

Exercise 6.8

1 a $-\frac{1}{t^2}, \frac{2}{t^3}$ b $\frac{1}{2t^2}, -\frac{1}{2t^4}$

c $\frac{1 + \sin t}{1 + \cos t}, \frac{(\cos t + \sin t + 1)}{(1 + \cos t)^3}$

d $\frac{8t}{9t^2 - 1}, \frac{-8 - 72t^2}{(9t^2 - 1)^3}$

e $\frac{\sin \theta}{\cos \theta - 1}, \frac{1}{(1 - \cos \theta)^2}$

2 a $(-1, 3)$ b Minimum TP

3 a $\frac{t^4 - 1}{t^4 + 1}, \frac{4t^6}{(t^4 + 1)^3}$ b $(0, 2)$ minimum TP

4 a $\frac{dx}{dt} = \frac{2 + 2t^2}{(1 - t^2)^2}; \frac{dy}{dt} = \frac{4t}{(1 - t^2)^2}; \frac{dy}{dx} = \frac{2t}{1 + t^2} = \frac{x}{y}$

b $\frac{dy}{dx} = \frac{x}{y} \Rightarrow \frac{d^2y}{dx^2} = \frac{y^2 - x^2}{y^3}; y^2 - x^2 = \left(\frac{1 + t^2}{1 - t^2}\right)^2 - \left(\frac{2t}{1 - t^2}\right)^2 = 1$. Hence result.

5 Max at $\left(\frac{e^{\frac{\pi}{4}}}{\sqrt{2}}, \frac{e^{\frac{\pi}{4}}}{\sqrt{2}}\right)$; min at $\left(-\frac{e^{\frac{5\pi}{4}}}{\sqrt{2}}, -\frac{e^{\frac{5\pi}{4}}}{\sqrt{2}}\right)$

6 a $\frac{dy}{dx} = -\frac{\sin \theta + \cos 2\theta}{\cos \theta - \sin 2\theta} = 0 \Rightarrow \sin \theta = 1$ or $-\frac{1}{2} \Rightarrow \theta$

$= \frac{7\pi}{6}, \frac{11\pi}{6}, \ldots$ Derivative undefined at $\frac{\pi}{2}$

At $\theta = \frac{7\pi}{6}, \frac{11\pi}{6} \Rightarrow \frac{d^2y}{dx^2} = \frac{\sqrt{3}}{4}$

b $(1, 0), (-3, 0), \left(\frac{3}{2}, \frac{\sqrt{3}}{2}\right), \left(\frac{3}{2}, -\frac{\sqrt{3}}{2}\right)$

7 a $(0, \sqrt{2})$, end point minimum. b $x = \sqrt{2}$

8 $\dfrac{dy}{dx} = -\dfrac{1}{\cos^4\theta}$. When $\tan\theta = 2$, $\cos\theta = \frac{1}{\sqrt{5}}$, $\sin\theta = \frac{2}{\sqrt{5}}$

9 a Similar strategy to Q8 b $\left(0, \pm\frac{1}{\sqrt{2}}\right), \left(\pm\frac{1}{\sqrt{2}}, 0\right)$

10 a $2\cos\theta$; $-2\tan\theta$ b,c Proof

11 a $(0,0)$ min, $\left(2^{\frac{1}{3}}, 2^{\frac{2}{3}}\right)$ max b $\dfrac{d^2y}{dx^2} = \dfrac{2(1+t^3)^2}{(1-2t^3)^2} \neq 0$

Review 6

1 a $\dfrac{3x^2}{2}, \sqrt[3]{2x+5}$ b $\dfrac{2}{3(2x+5)^{\frac{2}{3}}}$

2 $\dfrac{4-x}{\sqrt{1-x^2}}$ 3 $\dfrac{5}{\sqrt{1-25x^2}}$

4 $\dfrac{9}{4\pi}$ 5 $\frac{1}{2}e^{\frac{x}{2}}\left(\cos^{-1}2x - \dfrac{4}{\sqrt{1-4x^2}}\right)$

6 $-\dfrac{1}{2}$ 7 $-\dfrac{y^2}{x^2}; \dfrac{2y^3+2xy}{x^4}$

8 $\ln 2 + \frac{1}{4}$ 9 $y = -\dfrac{x^2-4x+5}{x^2-4x+3}$

10 a i $y = x + 4$, $3y = 2x - 1$ ii $(-13, -9)$

b $\dfrac{d^2y}{dx^2} = 0 \Rightarrow t = 0 \Rightarrow x, y \to \infty$

Chapter 7

Exercise 7.1

1 a $\frac{1}{2}x^6 + x^4 + c$ b $\frac{2}{5}x^5 - \cos x + c$

c $\frac{1}{9}(3x+1)^3 + c$ d $\dfrac{x^5}{5} + \dfrac{2x^3}{3} + x + c$

e $x^2 - x^{-1} + c$ f $\frac{2}{3}x^{\frac{3}{2}} + 2x^{\frac{1}{2}} + c$

g $\frac{1}{2}\tan(2x+3) + c$ h $-2\cos 2x + x + c$

i $-\frac{1}{2}\sin(1-2x) + c$

2 a $-\frac{1}{2}(2x+5)^{-1} + c$ b $\frac{1}{3}(4-3x)^{-1} + c$

c $-\frac{1}{5}\cos(5x-1) + \frac{1}{5}\sin(1-5x) + c$

d $\frac{1}{5}x^5 + \frac{1}{4}x^4 + x^3 + x^2 + x + c$

e $\ln|x| - 2x - \dfrac{x^2}{2} + c$ f $-\tan(1-x) + c$

g $\frac{1}{3}\cos(2-3x) + c$

h $\sin 2x + 3\cos(1-x) + c$

i $-\frac{2}{3}\sin(1-3x) + \frac{1}{9}x^3 + c$

3 a $\frac{1}{2}\ln|x| + c = \ln|A\sqrt{x}|$ or $\frac{1}{2}\ln|2x| + c = \ln|A\sqrt{2x}|$

Note: Answers really only differ in the form and the value of the constant.

b $\frac{3}{2}\ln|2x+1| + c$ c $\frac{1}{4}\ln|4x+5| + c$

d $\frac{1}{3}e^{3x} + c$ e $\frac{3}{4}e^{4x-1} + c$

f $-3e^{1-x} + c$ g $-e^{-x} + c$

h $\frac{1}{2}\ln|2x+1| + \frac{1}{3}\ln|3x-1|$

i $-\dfrac{1}{e^{x+1}} + \ln|3x-1| + c$ j $\frac{1}{2}\ln|2x+3| + c$

k $\dfrac{4^x}{\ln 4}$ l $\dfrac{4^{3x-1}}{3\ln 4}$

4 a $\ln 2$ b $\frac{1}{2} - \frac{1}{2e}$ c $\frac{1}{4}\ln 45$

d $\frac{1}{2} + \sqrt{3}$ e $\frac{1}{2}(e^2+1)$ f 0

5 a $2 + \frac{\pi}{2}$ b $4 - \frac{\pi}{2}$ c $\frac{1}{\sqrt{3}}$

d $\ln 2$ e $\ln\sqrt{3}$ f 0

Exercise 7.2

1 a $\frac{1}{5}(x^3+3)^5 + c$ b $\frac{1}{12}(x^2+1)^6 + c$

c $\frac{1}{7}(x^2+x+1)^7 + c$ d $\frac{3}{10}(x^2+14x)^{\frac{5}{3}} + c$

e $\ln|x^2+1| + c$ f $4\sqrt{x+1} + c$

g $\frac{9}{8}(x^2+1)^{\frac{4}{3}} + c$ h $\frac{1}{2}(\ln x)^2 + c$

i $\ln|\ln|x|| + c$

(**hint:** let $\ln x = u \Rightarrow e^u = x$ and $e^u\,du = dx$)

j $-e^{\cos x} + c$ k $\frac{1}{2}e^{x^2+4x} + c$

l $-\cos(\ln|x|) + c$ m $-\frac{1}{5}\cos^5 x + c$

n $\frac{1}{4}\tan^4 x + c$ o $2\sqrt{\tan x} + c$

p $\frac{1}{3}(3x^2+2x+1)^{\frac{3}{2}} + c$ q $\frac{3}{4}(e^x+1)^4 + c$

r $\frac{2}{3}\ln|3e^{2x}-2| + c$ s $\ln|\sin x| + c$

t $\ln|x^2+5x-1| + c$ u $\frac{1}{2}(x-3)^2(x+2)^2 + c$

v $\ln|(x+4)(2x+1)| + c$ w $\ln|e^x + e^{-x}| + c$

x $\frac{1}{3}(\ln x)^3 + (\ln x)^2 + \ln x + c$

2 a $-\tan x$ b $-\frac{1}{2}(\ln|\cos x|)^2 + c$

3 a $-\operatorname{cosec}^2 x$ b $-\frac{1}{4}\cot^4 x + c$

c $\dfrac{1}{2\cot^2 x} + c$

4 a Multiply numerator and denominator by e^{-x}.

b i $-\ln|1+e^{-x}| + c$ ii $-\ln|e^{-x}-1| + c$

Exercise 7.3

1 a $\frac{1}{2}x\sqrt{1-x^2} + \frac{1}{2}\sin^{-1}x + c$

b $\frac{1}{2}x\sqrt{9-x^2} + \frac{9}{2}\sin^{-1}\left(\frac{x}{3}\right) + c$

c $\frac{1}{2}x\sqrt{5-x^2} + \frac{5}{2}\sin^{-1}\left(\frac{x}{\sqrt{5}}\right) + c$

d $\frac{1}{2}x\sqrt{1-2x^2} + \frac{\sqrt{2}}{4}\sin^{-1}(x\sqrt{2}) + c$

2 a $\sin^{-1}x + c$ b $\sin^{-1}\left(\frac{x}{2}\right) + c$

c $3\sin^{-1}\left(\frac{x}{5}\right) + c$ d $\frac{1}{\sqrt{2}}\sin^{-1}(x\sqrt{2}) + c$

3 a $\displaystyle\int \frac{du}{\sqrt{1-u^2}}$ b $\sin^{-1}(x^2) + c$

4 a $\tan^{-1}x + c$ b $\frac{1}{3}\tan^{-1}\left(\frac{x}{3}\right) + c$

c $\frac{3}{4}\tan^{-1}\left(\frac{x}{4}\right) + c$ d $\frac{1}{2}\tan^{-1}(2x) + c$

5 a, b $\frac{1}{4}\tan^{-1}(x^4) + c$ **c** $-\tan^{-1}(\cos x) + c$

6 a $-\frac{1}{3}(1 - x^2)^{\frac{3}{2}} + c$ **b** $-\frac{2}{3}(4 - x^2)^{\frac{3}{2}} + c$

c $-\frac{1}{6}(16 - x^2)^{\frac{3}{2}} + c$ **d** $-\frac{1}{9}(1 - 3x^2)^{\frac{3}{2}} + c$

7 a $-\frac{1}{3}\cos^3 x + c$

b $-\frac{1}{3}\cos^3 x + \frac{2}{5}\cos^5 x - \frac{1}{7}\cos^7 x + c$

c $\frac{1}{4}\sin^4 x - \frac{1}{3}\sin^6 x + \frac{1}{8}\sin^8 x + c$

d $\frac{1}{2}\sin^2 x + c$

e $\sin x - \frac{1}{3}\sin^3 x + c$

f $-\cos x + \frac{2}{3}\cos^3 x - \frac{1}{5}\cos^5 x + c$

8 a $u = 1 - \sqrt{x} \Rightarrow \sqrt{x} = 1 - u \Rightarrow du = -\frac{1}{2\sqrt{x}}dx$

$\Rightarrow -2\sqrt{x}\,du = dx$, hence result.

b $4(1 - \sqrt{x}) - 4\ln|1 - \sqrt{x}| + c$

c $4(1 + \sqrt{x}) - 4\ln|1 + \sqrt{x}| + c$

9 a/b $\int \frac{dx}{x^2\sqrt{1 + x^2}} = \int \frac{\cos u\,du}{\sin^2 u} = \int \frac{dv}{v^2} = -\frac{1}{v} = -\frac{1}{\sin u}$

$= -\frac{1}{\sin(\tan^{-1} x)} + c$

10 a/b/c $\int \operatorname{cosec} x\,dx = \int \frac{dx}{2\sin\frac{x}{2}\cos\frac{x}{2}} = \int \frac{\sec^2\frac{x}{2}\,dx}{2\tan\frac{x}{2}}$

$= \int \frac{du}{2u} = \frac{1}{2}\ln|u| = \frac{1}{2}\ln|\tan\frac{x}{2}|$

d $\frac{d}{dx}\ln|\sec x + \tan x| = \frac{\sin x\sec^2 x + \sec^2 x}{\sec x + \tan x}$

$= \frac{\sec^2 x(\sin x + 1)}{\sec x(1 + \sin x)} = \sec x$. Hence result.

11 a $(\ln|x|)^2$ **b** $\frac{1}{4}(\ln|x|)^2$

c $\frac{\ln 3}{4}\ln|x| + \frac{1}{8}(\ln|x|)^2$ **d** $\frac{x^2}{2} + (\ln|x|)^2$

Exercise 7.4

1 a $-100\frac{2}{3}$ **b** 4 **c** $\frac{1}{3}$

d $\frac{32}{3}\sqrt{2}$ **e** $\ln\sqrt{2}$ **f** 28

g $\frac{1}{2}$ **h** $\frac{14}{3}$ **i** $\frac{1}{3}\ln 2$

j 0 **k** $\frac{2}{15}$ **l** $\frac{\pi}{4}$

m $\frac{289}{4480}$ **n** $\frac{43}{60\sqrt{2}}$ **o** $\frac{14}{9}$

2 a $\frac{175}{4}$ **b** 2

c $\frac{1}{6}(3 + 2x)^{\frac{3}{2}} - \frac{3}{2}(3 + 2x)^{\frac{1}{2}} + c$

d $-\frac{3}{5(5\ln x + 4)} + c$ **e** $4 - 12\ln\left(\frac{6}{5}\right)$

f $\frac{1}{9}(2 - 3\cos x)^6 + c$

g $3\sin^{-1}\left(\frac{x}{3}\right) + c$ **h** $5 - \ln 6$

i $-e^{\frac{1}{x}} + c$ **j** $\frac{1}{2}$

Exercise 7.5

1 a $\frac{3}{12}(3x - 4)^{\frac{4}{3}} + c$ **b** $\frac{1}{7}\cos(3 - 7x) + c$

c $\frac{1}{2}\tan(2x - 5) + c$ **d** $-\frac{1}{6}e^{1-6x} + c$

e $\frac{1}{8}\ln|8x + 1| + c$

f $-\frac{1}{2}\cos(2x + 1) - \sin(1 - x) + c$

g $-e^{-x} - \ln|3 - x| + c$

2 a $\frac{1}{2}(-\cot(2x - 1) - (2x - 1)) + c$

b $-\frac{1}{3}\ln|\operatorname{cosec}(4 - 3x) - \cot(4 - 3x)| + c$

3 a $\frac{1}{2}(x^2 + 3x + 4)^2 + c$ **b** $\frac{1}{2}(\sin x)^2 + c$

c $\frac{1}{2}(\ln x)^2 + c$ **d** $\frac{1}{2}(e^x + 1)^2 + c$

e $\frac{1}{2}(\tan x)^2 + c$ **f** $\frac{1}{2}(\cos x + \sin x)^2 + c$

g $\frac{1}{2}(e^x + e^{-x})^2 + c$ **h** $\frac{1}{2}(x^2 + \tan x)^2 + c$

4 a $-\frac{1}{2}\cos 2x + c_1$ **b** $\sin^2 x + c_2$

c $-\frac{1}{2}\cos 2x + c_1 = -\frac{1}{2}(1 - 2\sin^2 x) + c_1 = \sin^2 x + c_1$

$-\frac{1}{2} = \sin^2 x + c_2$

5 a $\ln|x^3 + 2x^2 - 4x + 1| + c$ **b** $\ln|\sin 2x| + c$

c $3\ln|x + 1| + \ln|2x - 1| + c$

d $\ln|x + e^x| + c$ **e** $\ln|\tan x| + c$

f $\ln|\ln x| + c$ **g** $\ln|3 + 3^x| + c$

h $\frac{1}{2}\ln|x^2 - 1| + \frac{1}{3}\ln|x^3 - 1| + \frac{1}{4}\ln|x^4 - 1| + c$

Exercise 7.6

1 a $\sin^{-1}\left(\frac{x}{4}\right) + c$ **b** $\sin^{-1}\left(\frac{x}{\sqrt{3}}\right) + c$

c $\frac{1}{\sqrt{2}}\sin^{-1}\left(\frac{x}{4}\right) + c$ **d** $\frac{1}{\sqrt{3}}\sin^{-1}\left(\frac{x}{\sqrt{\frac{5}{3}}}\right) + c$

2 a $\frac{1}{7}\tan^{-1}\left(\frac{x}{7}\right) + c$ **b** $\frac{1}{\sqrt{6}}\tan^{-1}\left(\frac{x}{\sqrt{6}}\right) + c$

c $\frac{1}{15}\tan^{-1}\left(\frac{x}{5}\right) + c$ **d** $\frac{1}{\sqrt{10}}\tan^{-1}\left(\frac{x\sqrt{2}}{\sqrt{5}}\right) + c$

3 a $\frac{\pi}{6}$ **b** $\sin^{-1}\left(\frac{1}{\sqrt{3}}\right)$

c $\frac{\pi}{3\sqrt{3}}$ **d** $\frac{1}{\sqrt{2}}\sin^{-1}\left(\sqrt{\frac{2}{3}}\right)$

4 a 0·072 **b** 0·326

c 0·016 **d** 0·288

5 a $\frac{1}{2}\ln|25 + x^2| - \tan^{-1}\left(\frac{x}{5}\right) + c$

b $\frac{7}{4}\tan^{-1}\left(\frac{x}{4}\right) - \frac{1}{2}\ln|16 + x^2| + c$

c $\frac{1}{2}\ln|x^2 + 2| - \sqrt{2}\tan^{-1}\left(\frac{x}{\sqrt{2}}\right) + c$

d $\frac{3}{2}\ln|x^2 + 49| - \frac{1}{7}\tan^{-1}\left(\frac{x}{7}\right) + c$

6 a i $(x+1)^2+4$ ii $\frac{1}{2}\tan^{-1}\left(\frac{x}{2}\right)+c$

iii $\frac{1}{2}\tan^{-1}\left(\frac{x+1}{2}\right)+c$

b i $\frac{1}{4}\tan^{-1}\left(\frac{x+3}{4}\right)+c$ ii $\frac{1}{3}\tan^{-1}\left(\frac{x+2}{3}\right)+c$

iii $\frac{1}{\sqrt{2}}\tan^{-1}\left(\frac{x+4}{\sqrt{2}}\right)+c$

7 a 0·107 **b** 0·0178 **c** 0·0765

Exercise 7.7

1 a $\ln|x+2|+2\ln|x+3|+c$

b $2\ln|x-1|+\ln|x+5|+c$

c $3\ln|x-2|-\ln|x-3|+c$

d $\frac{1}{3}\ln|3x+1|+4\ln|x-1|+c$

e $\frac{1}{3}\ln|x-1|-\frac{1}{3}\ln|x+2|+c$

f $\frac{1}{2}\ln|x-5|-\frac{1}{2}\ln|x+1|+c$

2 a $\frac{1}{3}\ln|x|-\frac{2}{3}\ln|x-\frac{1}{3}|+c$

b $\frac{9}{2}\ln|x+\frac{1}{2}|-4\ln|x+1|+c$

c $8\ln|x-2|-3\ln|x-1|+c$

d $2\ln|x-3|-\ln|x+3|+c$

3 a $\frac{1}{2}\ln|x+1|+\frac{5}{2}\ln|x-1|-\frac{1}{x-1}+c$

b $2\ln|x-1|+\frac{1}{x+3}+c$

c $2\ln|x|-\ln|x-2|+\frac{1}{x-2}+c$

d $\ln|x-1|-\ln|x-2|-\frac{1}{x-2}+c$

e $\frac{1}{4}\ln|x-1|-\frac{1}{4}\ln|x+1|-\frac{1}{2(x+1)}+c$

f $\frac{1}{18}\ln|x|-\frac{1}{18}\ln|x+3|-\frac{2}{3(x+3)}+c$

4 a $\ln|x|-\ln|x+1|+\frac{1}{(x+1)}+c$

b $\frac{1}{9}\ln|x-1|-\frac{1}{9}\ln|x+2|-\frac{2}{3(x+2)}+c$

c $\ln|x|-\ln|2x-1|-\frac{5}{2(2x-1)}+c$

5 a $\ln|x+1|+\frac{1}{2}\ln|x^2+2|-\frac{1}{\sqrt{2}}\tan^{-1}\left(\frac{x}{\sqrt{2}}\right)+c$

b $3\ln|x|+\ln|x^2+1|+c$

c $2\ln|x-1|+\frac{1}{2}\ln|x^2+3|+\frac{1}{\sqrt{3}}\tan^{-1}\left(\frac{x}{\sqrt{3}}\right)+c$

d $\frac{1}{5}\ln|x|-\frac{1}{10}\ln|x^2+5|+c$

e $\frac{2}{7}\ln|x-2|-\frac{1}{7}\ln|x^2+3|+\frac{3}{7\sqrt{3}}\tan^{-1}\left(\frac{x}{\sqrt{3}}\right)+c$

6 a $1+\frac{2x}{x^2-1}$; $x+\ln|x^2-1|+c$

b $3+\frac{5x+1}{(2x-1)(x+3)}$; $3x+\frac{1}{2}\ln|2x-1|+2\ln|x+3|+c$

c $x+1+\frac{-3x+3}{(2x-1)(x+1)}$; $\frac{1}{2}x^2+x+\frac{1}{2}\ln|2x-1|-2\ln|x+1|+c$

d $1+\frac{3x^2-3x+2}{(x+1)(x-1)^2}$; $x+2\ln|x+1|+\ln|x-1|-\frac{1}{x-1}+c$

e $x+\frac{3x^2+2x+6}{x(x^2+2)}$; $\frac{1}{2}x^2+3\ln|x|+\sqrt{2}\tan^{-1}\left(\frac{x}{\sqrt{2}}\right)+c$

f $1+\frac{x+1}{x(x^2+5)}$; $x+\frac{1}{5}\ln|x|-\frac{1}{10}\ln|x^2+5|-\frac{1}{5\sqrt{5}}\tan^{-1}\left(\frac{x}{\sqrt{5}}\right)+c$

7 a $(x+1)^2+4$ **b** $\frac{1}{2}\tan^{-1}\left(\frac{x}{2}\right)+c$

c $\frac{1}{2}\tan^{-1}\left(\frac{x+1}{2}\right)+c$

d i $\ln|x-1|+\frac{1}{2}\tan^{-1}\left(\frac{x+1}{2}\right)+c$

ii $\frac{3}{4}\ln|x-1|+\frac{1}{8}\ln|x^2+2x+5|-\frac{1}{4}\tan^{-1}\left(\frac{x+1}{2}\right)+c$

iii $\ln|x-1|+\frac{1}{2}\ln|x^2+2x+5|-\frac{1}{2}\tan^{-1}\left(\frac{x+1}{2}\right)+c$

8 a $\frac{1}{2}\ln|x^2+6x+25|-\frac{3}{4}\tan^{-1}\left(\frac{x+3}{4}\right)+c$

b $\frac{3}{2}\ln|x^2+8x+20|-4\tan^{-1}\left(\frac{x+4}{2}\right)+c$

c $\frac{5}{2}\ln|x^2+10x+26|-28\tan^{-1}(x+5)+c$

Exercise 7.8

1 a $-x\cos x+\sin x+c$ **b** xe^x-e^x+c

c $\frac{x^2}{2}\ln x+\frac{x^2}{4}+c$ **d** $3x\tan x+3\ln|\cos x|+c$

e $\frac{2}{5}(x+1)^{\frac{5}{2}}-\frac{2}{3}(x+1)^{\frac{1}{2}}+c$

f $(3x+2)\sin x+3\cos x+c$

g $\frac{1}{2}(4-x)e^{2x}+\frac{1}{4}e^{2x}+c$

h $(x^2+x)\ln x-\left(\frac{x^2}{2}+x\right)+c$

i $-xe^{-x}-e^{-x}+c$

j $-\frac{1}{4}x^{-4}\ln x-\frac{1}{16}x^{-4}+c$

k $\frac{2}{3}x^{\frac{3}{2}}\ln x-\frac{4}{9}x^{\frac{3}{2}}+c$

l $-\cos x\ln(\cos x)+\cos x+c$

2 a $\frac{1}{2}(2x+1)\tan 2x+\frac{1}{2}\ln|\cos 2x|+c$

b $(x^3+x^2-2x-2)\ln|x+1|-\frac{1}{3}x^3+2x+c$

c $(x^3-x)\ln(x-1)-\frac{1}{3}x^3-\frac{1}{2}x^2+c$

d $-\frac{1}{2}(1-4x)\cos(2x-3)-\sin(2x-3)+c$

e $\frac{1}{3}(9x+1)e^{3x-1}-e^{3x-1}+c$

f $\frac{2}{3}(x+1)^{\frac{3}{2}}\ln(x+1)-\frac{4}{9}(x+1)^{\frac{3}{2}}+c$

g $-(2x+1)e^{4-x}-2e^{4-x}+c$

h $\tan x\ln|\tan x|-\tan x+c$

3 a i $\frac{1}{2}(1-\cos 2x)$ ii $\frac{1}{2}(\cos 2x+1)$

b i $\frac{1}{4}x^2-\frac{1}{4}x\sin 2x-\frac{1}{8}\cos 2x+c$

ii $\frac{1}{4}x^2+\frac{1}{4}x\sin 2x+\frac{1}{8}\cos 2x+c$

c i $\frac{1}{2}x^2$

ii $\int x \sin^2 x\,dx + \int x \cos^2 x\,dx = \int x(\sin^2 x + \cos^2 x)\,dx = \int x\,dx$

4 a $= \frac{1}{2}x^2 \tan^{-1} x - \frac{1}{2}x + \frac{1}{2}\tan^{-1} x + c$

b $\frac{1}{4}(2x^2 - 1)\sin^{-1} x + \frac{1}{4}x\sqrt{1 - x^2} + c$

c $\frac{1}{4}(2x^2 - 1)\cos^{-1} x - \frac{1}{4}x\sqrt{1 - x^2} + c$

5 a $(2 - x^2)\cos x + 2x \sin x + c$

b $(x^3 - 6x)\sin x + (3x^2 - 6)\cos x + c$

c $e^x(x^3 - 3x^2 + 6x - 6) + c$

d $e^x(x^2 + 1) + c$

e $\frac{x^2}{2}\left((\ln x)^2 - \ln x + \frac{1}{2}\right) + c$

f $\frac{x^2}{2}\left((1 - \ln x)^2 - \ln x + \frac{3}{2}\right) + c$

g $-e^{-x}(x^2 + 1)$

h $2x^2(x + 1)^{\frac{1}{2}} - \frac{8}{3}x(x + 1)^{\frac{3}{2}} + \frac{16}{15}(x + 1)^{\frac{5}{2}} + c$

i $-\frac{1}{3}x^3(x - 1)^{-3} - \frac{1}{2}x^2(x - 1)^{-2} - x(x - 1)^{-1} + \ln|x - 1| + c$

j $\frac{2}{3}(x + 1)^2(x - 1)^{\frac{3}{2}} - \frac{8}{15}(x + 1)(x - 1)^{\frac{5}{2}} + \frac{16}{105}(x - 1)^{\frac{7}{2}} + c$

6 a π b $\frac{1}{3}e^{3e+1} - \frac{1}{9}e^{3e} + \frac{1}{9}$

c $-\frac{29}{e} + 13$ d $\frac{\pi^2}{8} - \frac{1}{2}$

e 267 (3 sf) f $2(\ln 2)^2 - 2\ln 2 + \frac{3}{4} = 0{\cdot}325$ (3 sf)

Exercise 7.9

1 a $x \ln 3x - x + c$ b $x \ln ax - x + c$

c **Note:** $k = \log_{10} x \Rightarrow x = 10^k \Rightarrow \ln x = k \ln 10 \Rightarrow k = \frac{\ln x}{\ln 10} \Rightarrow \log_{10} x = \frac{\ln x}{\ln 10}$

$\int \log_{10} x\,dx - \int \frac{\ln x}{\ln 10}\,dx = \frac{1}{\ln 10}\int \ln x\,dx$

$= \frac{x}{\ln 10}(\ln x - 1)$

d $x \sin^{-1} x + \sqrt{1 - x^2} + c$

e $x \tan^{-1} x - \frac{1}{2}\ln(1 + x^2) + c$

f $x \ln(1 + x^2) - 2x + 2\tan^{-1} x + c$

g $x(\ln x)^2 - 2x \ln x + 2x + c$

h $x \ln(1 - x^2) - 2x - \ln|1 - x| + \ln|1 + x| + c$

2 a $\frac{e^x}{2}(\sin x - \cos x) + c$

b $\frac{e^{2x}}{5}(2\sin x - \cos x) + c$

c $\frac{e^x}{10}(\sin 3x - 3\cos 3x) + c$

d $\frac{e^{2x}}{15}(2\sin 3x - 3\cos 3x) + c$

e $-\frac{1}{3}(2\cos x \cos 2x + \sin x \sin 2x) + c$

f $\frac{1}{15}(4\cos x \sin 4x - \sin x \cos 4x) + c$

g $\frac{1}{35}(\cos x \sin 6x - 6\sin x \cos 6x) + c$

h $\frac{9}{15}\sin 2x \sin 3x + \frac{2}{5}\cos 2x \cos 3x + c$

i $-\frac{e^{-x}}{2}(\sin x + \cos x) + c$

j $\frac{e^{-x}}{5}(2\sin 2x - \cos 2x) + c$

k $-\frac{e^{-2x}}{13}(2\sin 3x + 3\cos 3x) + c$

3 a $p'(x) = q(x)$ and $q'(x) = p(x) \Rightarrow \int q(x)\,dx = p(x)$

$\Rightarrow \int p(x)q(x)\,dx = [p(x)]^2 - \int p(x)\,p'(x)\,dx$

$\Rightarrow \int p(x)q(x)\,dx = [p(x)]^2 - \frac{1}{2}[p(x)]^2 + c = \frac{1}{2}[p(x)]^2 + c$

b Verification

c $\int \left(\frac{e^x + e^{-x}}{2}\right)\left(\frac{e^x - e^{-x}}{2}\right)dx = \frac{1}{4}\left(\frac{e^{2x} + e^{-2x}}{2}\right) + c$ and $\frac{1}{2}\left[\frac{e^x + e^{-x}}{2}\right]^2 = \frac{1}{4}\left(\frac{e^{2x} + e^{-2x}}{2}\right) + \frac{1}{2}$. Hence result.

4 a $\frac{d}{dx}\left(\ln|x + \sqrt{x^2 - 1}|\right) = \frac{1 + \frac{x}{\sqrt{x^2 - 1}}}{x + \sqrt{x^2 - 1}}$

$= \frac{1}{\sqrt{x^2 - 1}} \cdot \frac{\sqrt{x^2 - 1} + x}{x + \sqrt{x^2 - 1}} = \frac{1}{\sqrt{x^2 - 1}}$

b $\frac{1}{2}x\sqrt{x^2 - 1} - \frac{1}{2}\ln|x + \sqrt{x^2 - 1}| + c$

Exercise 7.10

1 $\frac{1}{2}\sin^{-1}\left(\frac{\pi}{4}\right) = 0.452$ (3sf)

2 a Verification b $\pi \ln\left(\frac{16}{13}\right) = 0{\cdot}652$ (3 sf)

3 $A = 2\int_0^{\frac{\pi}{2}} \cos x \sin^3 x\,dx = 2\int_0^1 u^3\,du = 2\left[\frac{u^4}{4}\right]_0^1 = \frac{1}{2}$

Substitute $u = \sin x$.

4 a Verification b $e - e^{-1} = 2.35$ (3sf)

5 a $\left(2, \frac{1}{2}\right)$

b Area $= \ln\left(\frac{1024}{675}\right) = 0.417$

6 a $y = 5, y = 10$ b $x = \sqrt{y - 1}$

c Area $= \int_5^{10} \sqrt{y - 1}\,dx = 12\frac{2}{3}$

7 Area $= \int_1^2 (2y - 1)^2\,dx = 4\frac{1}{3}$

8 a (0,1)

c Area $= \int_1^{e^{-1}} \ln y\,dx + \int_1^e \ln y\,dx$

$= 2 - \frac{2}{e} = 1.26$ (3 sf)

9 Area $= \int_{0{\cdot}5}^1 e^y - (y + 2)\,dx = e - \sqrt{e} - \frac{3}{8} = 0.695$ (3 sf)

10 a Area $= \int_0^{\pi} e^x \sin x\,dx - \int_{\pi}^{\frac{4\pi}{3}} e^x \sin x\,dx = 35{\cdot}7$;

b 0·34

11 a Volume $= \int_{-a}^{a} \pi\left(b^2 - \frac{x^2b^2}{a^2}\right)dx = \pi b^2\left[x - \frac{x^3}{3a^2}\right]_{-a}^{a}$

$= \frac{4}{3}\pi ab^2$

b $\frac{4}{3}\pi a^2 b$

c $\text{Area} = 2\int_{-a}^{a} y(x)\,dx = \frac{2b}{a}\int_{-a}^{a}\sqrt{a^2 - x^2}\,dx$

$= \frac{2b}{a}\left[\frac{x}{2}\sqrt{a^2 - x^2} + \frac{a^2}{2}\sin^{-1}\left(\frac{x}{a}\right)\right]_{-a}^{a} = ab\pi$

12 a $\text{Volume} = \int_0^b \pi y^2\,dx = \pi m^2\left[\frac{x^3}{3}\right]_0^b = \frac{1}{3}\pi m^2 b^3 = \frac{1}{3}\pi r^2 h$

b $V = \frac{1}{3}\pi r^2(h_2 - h_1)$ **c** $V = \pi r^2 h$

d **i** $\frac{4}{3}\pi r^3$ **ii** $\frac{1}{3}\pi h^2(3r - h)$ **iii** $R = \sqrt{h(2r - h)}$

13 a Part of parabola, positive gradient passing through $(0, -3)$, $(1, 0)$, $(2, 5)$

b $y = (x + 1)^2 - 4$

c $x^2 = \left(\sqrt{y + 4} - 1\right)^2$

d $\pi\int_{-3}^{5}\left(\sqrt{y + 4} - 1\right)^2 dy = 13\frac{1}{3}\pi$

14 $\pi\int_0^1 \sin^{-1} y\,dy = \pi\left[y\sin^{-1} y + \sqrt{1 - y^2}\right]_0^1 = \pi\left(\frac{\pi}{2} - 1\right)$

Review 7

1 a $\frac{1}{3}\sin(3x + 1) + c$ **b** $-\frac{3}{20}(2 - 5x)^{\frac{4}{3}} + c$

c $\frac{1}{2}\tan(2x + 3) + c$ **d** $-3e^{4-x} + c$

e $-\frac{3}{4(2x + 1)^2} + c$ **f** $\frac{2}{5}\ln|5x - 2| + c$

g $\frac{3^x}{\ln 3} + c$ **h** $\frac{3^{2x+5}}{2\ln 3} + c$

i $\frac{1}{2}x - \frac{1}{4}\sin 2x + c$

2 a $\frac{2}{3}(x^2 + x + 1)^{\frac{3}{2}} + c$ **b** $\frac{1}{14}(x^2 + 2x - 5)^7 + c$

c $\sqrt{1 + 6x - x^2} + c$ **d** $\frac{1}{3}\sin^3 x + c$

e $-\frac{1}{3}\cos^3 x + \frac{1}{5}\cos^5 x + c$ **f** $\frac{1}{3}\tan^{-1}\left(\frac{x}{3}\right) + c$

g $\sin^{-1}\left(\frac{x}{\sqrt{3}}\right) + c$ **h** $-\frac{2}{9}(3 - x^3)^{\frac{3}{2}} + c$

3 a $e^8 - 1$ **b** $\frac{2}{3}$

4 a $-\ln|\cos x| + c$ **b** $\ln|x^2 + 5x - 3| + c$

c $\ln|\ln x| + c$ **d** $\ln|\tan x| + c$

e $\ln|x - \tan x| + c$ **f** $\ln|1 - e^{-x}| + c$

5 a $\tan^{-1} x + c$ **b** $\sin^{-1} x + c$

c $\frac{1}{9}\tan^{-1}\left(\frac{x}{9}\right) + c$ **d** $\sin^{-1}\left(\frac{x}{11}\right) + c$

e $\sin^{-1}\left(\frac{x}{\sqrt{7}}\right) + c$

6 a $\ln|x - 1| + 2\ln|x + 3| + c$

b $-\frac{11}{9}\ln|x + 2| + \frac{20}{9}\ln|x - 1| - \frac{1}{3(x - 1)} + c$

c $2\ln|x + 1| + \frac{1}{2}\ln|x^2 + 3| + \frac{2}{\sqrt{3}}\tan^{-1}\left(\frac{x}{\sqrt{3}}\right) + c$

d $\frac{1}{3}x^3 + \frac{3}{2}x^2 + 7x - \ln|x - 1| + 16\ln|x - 2| + c$

7 a $-(3x + 4)\cos x + 3\sin x + c$

b $\frac{1}{2}e^{2x+1}\left(x^2 - x + \frac{1}{2}\right) + c$

c $\frac{1}{13}e^{3x}[2\sin(2x + 1) + 3\cos(2x + 1)] + c$

d $x\tan^{-1}(2x) - \frac{1}{4}\ln|4x^2 + 1| + c$

8 $\ln 3 = 1.10$ (3 sf)

9 $\frac{\pi}{4} - \ln\sqrt{2} = 0.439$ (3 sf)

10 $\frac{512\pi}{15} = 107$ (3 sf)

Chapter 8

Exercise 8.1

1 a $y = \frac{3x^2}{2} + c$ **b** $y = \ln|x| + c$

c $y = \frac{1}{2}(x - \ln x) + c$ **d** $y = \tan^{-1} x + c$

e $y = e^x x - e^x + c$ **f** $\frac{1}{3}\sin^3 x + c$

g $y = e^{x+c}$ **h** $y = \cos^{-1}\left(e^{-x+c}\right)$

i $y = \sin(x + c)$ **j** $y = \frac{e^{3x+c} + 2}{1 - e^{3x+c}}$

k $\frac{1}{2}e^y(\cos y + \sin y) = x + c$ [Implicit]

l $y(\ln y - 1) = x + c$ [Implicit]

m $y = \pm\sqrt{\frac{4}{9}x^3 + c}$ **n** $y = -\sin^{-1}(\cos x + c)$

o $y = \sin\left(\frac{1}{5}\ln x + c\right)$ **p** $y = \tan^{-1}(e^x + c)$

q $y = -\ln|c - e^x|$ **r** $y = \frac{1}{1 - e^{\frac{x^2}{2}+c}}$

2 a $y = \ln x + 4$

b $y = \frac{1}{3}\tan^{-1}\left(\frac{x}{3}\right) + 1 - \frac{1}{3}\tan^{-1}\left(\frac{\pi}{4}\right)$

c $y = e^x x - e^x + e$ **d** $y = \pm\sqrt{e^{x-1}} - 1$

e $-e^{-y} + y = x - 2$ [Implicit]

f $y\sin y + \cos y = x + \frac{\pi}{4}$ [Implicit]

g $y = \frac{1}{3}\left(x^{\frac{3}{2}}4\sqrt{2} - 1\right)$

h $\frac{1}{2}y - \frac{1}{4}\sin 2y = \tan x + \frac{\pi}{24} - \frac{9}{8}$ [Implicit]

i $y = \frac{2x}{2 + x}$

j $y = \ln\left|\frac{2}{3 - 2e^x}\right|$ **k** $y = 2\left(\frac{x - 2}{x + 1}\right)^{\frac{1}{3}} + 1$

l $y = e^{\frac{x}{2}}$ **m** $y = \frac{1}{4}\left(-\frac{x}{e^x} - \frac{1}{e^x} + 5\right)^2$

n $2\sqrt{y}e^{\sqrt{y}} - 2e^{\sqrt{y}} = x\ln x - x - 1$ [Implicit]

3 a ii, iii, iv are homogeneous.

b Verification

c **i** $\tan^{-1}\left(\frac{y}{x}\right) = \ln\left|Ax^2\sqrt{x^2 + y^2}\right|$ [Implicit]

ii $-\frac{x^2}{2y^2} = \ln y + c$ [Implicit]

iii $\ln y - \frac{x}{y} = c$ [Implicit]

Exercise 8.2

1 a $\frac{ds}{dt} = ks$ **b** $\frac{ds}{dt} = \frac{k}{t}$

c $\frac{dV}{dt} = k2\pi r$ **d** $\frac{dB}{dC} = \frac{k}{C}$

2 a $D = 2k\sqrt{h} + c$ **b** $D = 4.7\sqrt{h} + 8$

c 145 km (3 sf)

3 a $T = -\frac{1}{5}t^2 + \frac{3}{2}t + 98{\cdot}4$ b $\frac{15}{2}$ days

4 a $V = -\dfrac{k}{0{\cdot}3}e^{-0{\cdot}3t} + c$ b $c = \dfrac{k}{0{\cdot}3}$

c $V = 100(1 - e^{-0{\cdot}3t})$ d No. 95% predicted.

5 $n = 3 \times 20^{\frac{t}{2}}$

6 a $\dfrac{dV}{dt} = kV$ b $V = 20\,000 \times \left(\frac{7}{8}\right)^{\frac{t}{2}}$

c i $t = 10{\cdot}4 \Rightarrow$ 11th year ii £10 258·18

7 a $F = 400\left(1 - \left(\frac{3}{8}\right)^{\frac{t}{5}}\right)$ b $t = 8{\cdot}2 \Rightarrow$ on 9th day

8 Accurate figures used: rounded for answer. p

a Use $\displaystyle\int \frac{1}{2000}\left[\frac{1}{P} + \frac{1}{2000 - P}\right] dP = \frac{1}{2000}\ln\left(\frac{P}{2000 - P}\right)$

b $c = -0{\cdot}004$

c i $t = \frac{1}{0{\cdot}6}\left[\ln\left(\dfrac{P}{2000 - P}\right)\right] + 13$ ii $P = \dfrac{2000e^{0{\cdot}6t - 7{\cdot}6}}{1 + e^{0{\cdot}6t - 7{\cdot}6}}$

d 13 days

9 a $P = \dfrac{100 \times 2{\cdot}7^t}{99 + 2{\cdot}7^t}$ b 6 days

10 16 days.

11 19 098 million

12 a $v = v_0 - g(t - t_0)$

b $x = x_0 + v_0(t - t_0) - \frac{1}{2}g(t - t_0)^2$

13 a £53 083·89 b £7·94

14 a $V = \left(10 - \frac{t}{5}\right)^2$ b 50 hours

Exercise 8.3

1 a $y = \dfrac{e^x}{2} + \dfrac{c}{e^x}$ b $y = \dfrac{1}{2e^x} + \dfrac{c}{e^{3x}}$

c $y = \frac{1}{17}(4\sin x - \cos x) + \dfrac{c}{e^{4x}}$

d $y = e^x - \dfrac{e^x}{x} + \dfrac{c}{x}$ e $y = \dfrac{x^4}{7} + \dfrac{c}{x^3}$

f $y = e^x + \dfrac{2e^x}{x} - \dfrac{2e^x}{x^2} + \dfrac{c}{x^2}$

g $y = \dfrac{x^3 - 3x}{3(x - 1)} + \dfrac{c}{x - 1}$

h $y = \sin x + \dfrac{2x\cos x - 2\sin x + c}{x^2 + 1}$

i $y = \dfrac{\sin x}{2} + \dfrac{c}{\sin x}$

j $y = \dfrac{1}{2} + \dfrac{c}{e^{x^2}}$ k $y = 3 + ce^{\cos x}$

l $y = e^{-x^3}(x + c)$ m $y = e^x + \dfrac{c}{e^{x^3}}$

n $\dfrac{e^x}{x^x}(x\sin x + \cos x + c)$ o $y = 1 + \dfrac{c}{e^{e^x}}$

p $y = (x + 2)\left(6\ln\left(\dfrac{x + 1}{x + 2}\right) + c\right)$

q $y = (2x - 1)\left(\ln\left(\dfrac{x - 1}{2x - 1}\right) + c\right)$

r $y = x\tan^{-1}x + xc$ s $y = x\sin^{-1}\left(\dfrac{x}{2}\right) + xc$

2 a $y = \frac{3}{2}e^x + ce^{-\frac{x}{3}}$ b $y = \dfrac{\sin x}{x} + \dfrac{c}{x}$

c $y = \dfrac{x^2 - 2}{4(x + 1)^2} + \dfrac{c}{x^2(x + 1)^2}$

d $y = 1 + \dfrac{c}{e^{x^2 + 2x}}$ e $y = 1 + ce^{e^{-x}}$

f $y = \frac{2}{3}\sin x + \frac{4}{3}\sin x\cos^2 x + c\cos^3 x$

g $y = x\sin x + cx$

h $y = \frac{1}{4}(x + 1)\ln\left(\dfrac{x - 1}{x + 1}\right) + \frac{1}{2} + c(x + 1)$

i $y = (x + 1)\left(\dfrac{1}{9}\ln\left(\dfrac{(x + 1)^2}{(x^2 + 2)}\right) + \dfrac{1}{3\sqrt{2}}\tan^{-1}\left(\dfrac{x}{\sqrt{2}}\right) + c\right) - \dfrac{1}{3}$

3 a $y = \frac{2}{3}e^x + \dfrac{e - \frac{2}{3}}{e^{\frac{x}{2}}}$ b $y = \dfrac{\sin x - x\cos x + \pi}{x}$

c $y = \dfrac{4 + 2x\sin x - (x^2 - 1)\cos x}{x^2 + 1}$

d $y = (x - 3)\ln\left(\dfrac{25(x - 3)}{x + 1}\right)$

e $y = \frac{1}{2}x^x(\sin x - \cos x) + \frac{1}{2}e^{\pi - x}x^x$

f $y = -\dfrac{2}{3}(x + 1)\cos^2 x + \frac{2}{3}\tan x$

$- \frac{2}{9}\tan x\sin^2 x + \dfrac{5}{3\cos x}$

4 a $\dfrac{dy}{dx} + \dfrac{y}{x} = \sqrt{x}\ln x; y = \frac{2}{5}x^{\frac{3}{2}}\left(\ln x - \frac{2}{5}\right) + \dfrac{c}{x}$

b $\dfrac{dy}{dx} - \dfrac{y\cos x}{\sin x} = x^2\sin^2 x;$

$y = (2 - x^2)\sin x\cos x + 2x\sin^2 x + c\sin x$

5 a $y = k + cx$ b $k = 1, c = 2$

c Straight line passing through (1, 3) and (3, 7).

6 a $y = ce^{ax} - \dfrac{b}{a}$ b i $V = \frac{10}{k}(1 - e^{-kt})$

ii $t \to \infty \Rightarrow e^{-kt} \to 0 \Rightarrow V \to \frac{10}{k}$

7 a $\dfrac{dN}{dt} + kN = kL$ b $N = L + \dfrac{c}{e^{kt}}$

c $t \to \infty \Rightarrow \dfrac{c}{e^{kt}} \to 0 \Rightarrow N \to L$

d i $c = -96; k = \dfrac{1}{10}\ln\left(\dfrac{48}{25}\right) = 0{\cdot}0652$ (3 sf)

ii $N(35) = 90\%$ to nearest whole percent.

Exercise 8.4

1 a $y = Ae^{2x} + Be^{-3x}$ b $y = Ae^{5x} + Be^x$

c $y = Ae^{1{\cdot}5x} + Be^{-2x}$ d $y = Ae^{\frac{x}{3}} + Be^{-\frac{x}{2}}$

e $y = Ae^{6x} + Be^{\frac{x}{3}}$ f $y = Ae^{\frac{x}{4}} + Be^{-\frac{3x}{2}}$

g $y = Ae^{-\frac{x}{2}} + Be^{-\frac{3x}{2}}$ h $y = Ae^{-\frac{x}{3}} + Be^{-4x}$

i $y = Ae^{\frac{2x}{3}} + Be^{-\frac{5x}{2}}$ j $y = Ae^{-0{\cdot}2x} + Be^{-x}$

2 a $y = 2e^{3x} + 2e^{2x}$ b $y = -e^x + 2e^{-0{\cdot}5x}$

c $y = 3e^{4x} + 2e^{2x}$ d $y = 2e^{-\frac{x}{3}} + 2e^{-\frac{2x}{3}}$

e $y = 2e^{4x} + 1$

Exercise 8.5

1 a $y = Ae^{2x} + Bxe^{2x}$ b $y = Ae^{-4x} + Bxe^{-4x}$

c $y = Ae^{-0{\cdot}5x} + Bxe^{-0{\cdot}5x}$ d $y = Ae^{-\frac{3x}{2}} + Bxe^{-\frac{3x}{2}}$

e $y = Ae^{\frac{x}{3}} + Bxe^{\frac{x}{3}}$ f $y = Ae^{-\frac{5x}{4}} + Bxe^{-\frac{5x}{4}}$

g $y = Ae^{5x} + Bxe^{5x}$ h $y = Ax + B$

i $y = Ae^{3x} + Bxe^{3x}$

2 a $y = e^{-6x} + 2xe^{-6x}$ b $y = 2e^{4x} + 3xe^{4x}$

c $y = 2e^{\frac{2x}{3}} + xe^{\frac{2x}{3}}$ d $y = -e^{0{\cdot}2x} + 3xe^{0{\cdot}2x}$

Exercise 8.6

1 a $y = e^{2x}(A\cos x + B\sin x)$
b $y = e^{x}(A\cos 2x + B\sin 2x)$
c $y = e^{-x}(A\cos 3x + B\sin 3x)$
d $y = e^{-3x}(A\cos 2x + B\sin 2x)$
e $y = e^{0.5x}(A\cos x + B\sin x)$
f $y = e^{-0.5x}(A\cos 5x + B\sin 5x)$

2 a $y = e^{3x}(2\cos x + 3\sin x)$
b $y = e^{2x}(\cos 2x + 2\sin 2x)$
c $y = e^{5x}(3\cos x + \sin x)$
d $y = e^{\frac{x}{3}}(3\cos 3x + 5\sin 3x)$

Exercise 8.7

1 a $y = Ae^{5x} + Be^{-2x}$ b $y = Ae^{0.5x} + Bxe^{0.5x}$
c $y = e^{x}(A\cos 3x + B\sin 3x)$
d $y = Ae^{3x} + Bxe^{3x}$ e $y = Ae^{x} + Be^{-x}$
f $y = e^{2x}(A\cos 3x + B\sin 3x)$
g $y = Ae^{1.5x} + Bxe^{1.5x}$ h $y = Ae^{2.5x} + Be^{0.5x}$
i $y = Ae^{1.5x} + Be^{-x}$ j $y = Ae^{-0.5x} + Be^{-0.75x}$

Exercise 8.8

1 a $2x - 2$ b $\frac{1}{2}x^2 - \frac{3}{2}x + \frac{7}{4}$
c $\cos x - \sin x$ d $2e^{3x}$

2 a $y = e^{-1.5x}\left(A\cos\frac{\sqrt{3}}{2}x + B\sin\frac{\sqrt{3}}{2}x\right) + 3e^{x}$
b $y = Ae^{-3x} + Bxe^{-3x} + 2x - 1$
c $y = e^{x}(A\cos 3x + B\sin 3x) + \cos x - \sin x$
d $y = Ae^{-3x} + Be^{-4x} + x^2 - x + 1$

Exercise 8.9

1 a $y = Ae^{x} + Be^{-3x} - x - 1$
b $y = Ae^{2x} + Be^{x} + \frac{1}{2}x^2 + \frac{5}{2}x + \frac{15}{4}$
c $y = Ae^{0.5x} + Be^{-2x} + \frac{1}{5}xe^{0.5x}$
d $y = Ae^{-0.5x} + Be^{-3x} + \sin x - 7\cos x$
e $y = Ae^{-3x} + Bxe^{-3x} + 2e^{2x}$
f $y = Ae^{5x} + Bxe^{5x} + 2x^2e^{5x}$
g $y = Ae^{0.5x} + Bxe^{0.5x} + 5x + 17$
h $y = e^{3x}(A\cos x + B\sin x) + 3e^{4x}$
i $y = e^{2x}(A\cos 2x + B\sin 2x) + \frac{1}{8}$
j $y = (A\cos 2x + B\sin 2x) - 2x\cos 2x$

2 a $y = 6e^{3x} - 7e^{2x} + 2x + 3$
b $y = e^{2x} + (2 - e)e^{x} - xe^{x}$
c $y = 3e^{x} - 8e^{0.5x} + x^2 + 6x + 14$
d $y = -e^{x} + 2xe^{x} + 3x^2e^{x}$
e $y = 2\sin 2x + \cos 2x + 2\cos x$

3 a $x = 15e^{-t} - 5e^{-3t}; \dot{x} = -15e^{-t} + 15e^{-3t}$
b $x = 10e^{-2t} + 20te^{-2t}; \dot{x} = -40te^{-2t}$
c $x = 10e^{-2t}(\cos t + 2\sin t); \dot{x} = -50e^{-2t}\sin t$

Review 8

1 $y = Ae^{-\cos x}$

2 $y = \tan\left(x + \frac{\pi}{4}\right)$

3 $y = \dfrac{\frac{2}{3}(\sin x)^{\frac{3}{2}} + c}{x - 1}$

4 $y = \frac{1}{2}(\cos x + \sin x) + e^{-x}$

5 a $y = Ae^{-0.5x} + Be^{-2x}$ b $y = Ae^{1.5x} + Bxe^{1.5x}$
c $y = e^{2x}(A\cos 3x + B\sin 3x)$

6 $y = \frac{17}{5}e^{3x} + \frac{23}{5}e^{-2x}$

7 a $y = Ae^{-0.5x} + Be^{-2} + 2x - 1$
b $y = Ae^{1.5x} + Bxe^{1.5x} + 3e^{x}$
c $y = e^{2x}(A\cos 3x + B\sin 3x) + x^2 + x + 1$

8 a $y = 3e^{3x} + 3\frac{1}{4}e^{-2x} - \frac{1}{2}x - \frac{1}{4}$
b $y = -2e^{x} - 3xe^{x} + 5x^2e^{x}$
c $y = e^{-x}(5\cos 2x + \frac{3}{2}\sin 2x) + \frac{1}{5}$

Chapter 9

Exercise 9.1

1 a 5, 3 b 3, 1 c 0, −3
d −1, 5 e −3, −4 f 0, 7
g 3, −0.2 h $\frac{1}{15}, \frac{2}{15}$ i $\frac{1}{4}, -\frac{3}{28}$

2 a $n + 1$ b $-4n + 20$ c $-2n + 7$
d $3n - 11$ e $-4n + 18$ f $-5n + 1$
g $-0.6n + 0.1$ h $\frac{n}{20} + \frac{1}{10}$
i $-\frac{5}{36}n + \frac{1}{6}$

3 a 5 b 7 c 12

4 a 4 b −8 c 2.5, 2, 1.5, 1

5 a −2 b 17 c 60

6 a i 2, 6, 10, 14 ii 5, 3, 1, −1 iii 8, 8.2, 8.4, 8.6
b i 7, 4, 1, −2, ... $(a = 7, d = -3)$ ii −302

7 a $x = 6$ b $x = \frac{2c}{m} \in N$

8 a $d = \ln 10 - \ln 5 = \ln 20 - \ln 10 = \ln 2$
b $u_n = \ln(5 \times 2^{n-1})$ c 71

9 a 20 b 10
c 36
d i $30(1 + n)$ cm ii 60 cm

10 a i 800 ii 944
b Proof by contradiction.
Assume arithmetic sequence: $u_{10} = u_1 + (10 - 1)d$
$\Rightarrow d = \dfrac{u_{10} - u_1}{9}, d \in N$
$\dfrac{800 - 500}{9} \notin N$ Hence result.

11 a Let n be the number of turns on tube.
$u_n = 10{\cdot}6 + (n - 1)0{\cdot}6 = 10 + 0{\cdot}6n$
that is $a = 10{\cdot}6$ and $d = 0{\cdot}6$

b Sequence of circumferences are $\pi u_1, \pi u_2, \pi u_3, \pi u_4, \ldots$
An arithmetic sequence: $a = 10{\cdot}6\pi$ and $d = 0{\cdot}6\pi$

c $C = \pi \times u_{14} = \pi(10 + 0{\cdot}6 \times 14) = 18{\cdot}4\pi \approx 57{\cdot}8\,\text{mm}$

Exercise 9.2

1 a 290 b 2632
c i 1030 ii 17450 iii −750 iv 0

2 a 1365, 1544 b 179 c −780, −920; −140

3 a 799 b 9425 c −700
d −468 e 7·8 f 152·5

4 a 5 b −140

5 a 16 b $S_n = \frac{n}{2}(a + L)$
c Require $na = 66, n > 1$
$[n, a, d] = [2, 33, 297], [3, 22, 99], \left[6, 11, 19\frac{4}{5}\right],$
$\left[11, 6, 5\frac{2}{5}\right], \left[22, 3, \frac{9}{7}\right], \left[33, 2, \frac{9}{19}\right], \left[66, 1, \frac{9}{65}\right]$

6 a 12 b 0·5

7 a 108 b 67

8 10 100

9 a $x = \dfrac{14}{b - 1}$ b i 14, 21, 28, ...
ii 7, 14, 21, ... iii 2, 9, 16, iv 1, 8, 15, ...
c i 455 ii 385 iii 335 iv 325

10 a $u_7 = a + 6d \Rightarrow x^3 = x + 6d \Rightarrow$
$d = \dfrac{x^3 - x}{6} = \dfrac{(x - 1)x(x + 1)}{6}$
Since $x - 1$, x, and $x + 1$ are consecutive numbers, their product can be divided by 2 and by 3 and hence by 6. Thus d is a natural number.

b $S_4 = 4x^3 = \frac{4}{2}(2x + (4 - 1)d) \Rightarrow d = \dfrac{4(x^3 - x)}{6}$.
Since $x^3 - x$ is divisible by 6 (see part **a**) then d is divisible by 4.

11 a $10{\cdot}1\pi, 10{\cdot}2\pi, 10{\cdot}3\pi, 10{\cdot}4\pi, 10{\cdot}5\pi$
b $4010\,\pi$ cm

12 a $-2n$ b $-3n$ c $n(n + 8)$

13 The terms are $3a + 3d, 3a + 12d, 3a + 21d, \ldots$ which is an arithmetic sequence with first term $3a$ and common difference $9d$. Proof by induction.

Exercise 9.3

1 a i 1, 4 ii $u_n = ar^{n-1} = 1 \times 4^{n-1}$
b i 3, −4 ii $u_n = 3 \times (-4)^{n-1}$
c i $1536, \frac{1}{2}$ ii $u_n = 1536 \times \left(\frac{1}{2}\right)^{n-1}$
d i $3645, -\frac{1}{3}$ ii $u_n = 3645 \times \left(-\frac{1}{3}\right)^{n-1}$
e i $1, \frac{1}{10}$ ii $u_n = 1 \times \left(\frac{1}{10}\right)^{n-1}$
f i $\frac{1}{2}, \frac{3}{4}$ ii $u_n = \frac{1}{2} \times \left(\frac{3}{4}\right)^{n-1}$
g i 0·12, 0·4 ii $u_n = 0{\cdot}12 \times (0{\cdot}4)^{n-1}$
h i 18·4, 1·1 ii $u_n = 18{\cdot}4 \times 1{\cdot}1^{n-1}$

2 a 23 328 b $\frac{81}{125}$
c 3072

3 a $4 \times 5^{n-1}$ b 250 000
c $u_{n+1} - u_n = 4 \times 5^n - 4 \times 5^{n-1} = 4 \times 5^{n-1}(5 - 1)$
$= 4^2 \times 5^{n-1}$; which is a geometric sequence with $a = 16$ and $r = 5$.

4 a u_6 b $u_6 = 0.5472$ c $\dfrac{u_n}{v_n} = r^{2n-3}$

5 a 2 b 1023

6 a $u_1 \neq u_2 \neq u_3 \neq u_1$; They form an arithmetic sequence $\Rightarrow u_3 - u_2 = u_2 - u_1 \Rightarrow u_3 = 2u_2 - u_1$. Suppose they form a geometric sequence. Then
$\dfrac{u_3}{u_2} = \dfrac{u_2}{u_1} \Rightarrow u_3 = \dfrac{u_2^{\,2}}{u_1}$. So $2u_2 - u_1 = \dfrac{u_2^{\,2}}{u_1} \Rightarrow$
$u_2^{\,2} - 2u_2u_1 + u_1^{\,2} = 0 \Rightarrow (u_2 - u_1)^2 = 0$
$\Rightarrow u_1 = u_2$. Contradiction. Hence result.
b i $x = \dfrac{2a + d}{a}$ ii $r = x - 1$ c $r = \sqrt{\dfrac{2d + a}{a}}$

7 a $m = \sqrt{ab}$
b i 15 ii 8 iii $\frac{1}{5}$ iv 0·08
c 1232, 616, 308

8 a i 12 ii 31 or 32 iii 4
b i 24, 36 ii 45, 67 or 68 iii 36, 43

9 a i 4160 ii 4326 iii 4499
b $r = 1{\cdot}04$ c 11 years

10 a $A_1 = P\left(1 + \frac{r}{100}\right)$ b $A_2 = P\left(1 + \frac{r}{100}\right)^2$
c ratio $= \left(1 + \frac{r}{100}\right)$
d $A_n = P\left(1 + \frac{r}{100}\right)^n$

11 a 2·1 m b 31st bounce

12 a i ii $\dfrac{P_2}{P_1} = \dfrac{P_3}{P_2} = e^a$ b 1079 (nearest whole number)
c 8th day

Exercise 9.4

1 a 765 b 27 305 c −59 048
d 4095 e −2730 f 1023

2 a $\frac{255}{256}$ b $\frac{171}{256}$ c $\frac{1}{3}$
d $\frac{132\,860}{177\,147}$ e $\frac{511}{16}$ f 562.55

3 a 8 b 11th

4 a 12 b 4368

5 a $a = 3, r = 4$ and $a = -5, r = -4$

b Both 1 048 575

c The sum of the two S_9 s is -2.
This is true for each pair of S_n s when n is odd.

6 a $a = 24, r = 5$ b 11 625 000

7 a 4 b -1364

8 a $a = 1; r = \frac{1+\sqrt{5}}{2}$ or $\frac{1-\sqrt{5}}{2}$

b i $S_n = \frac{1-\phi^n}{1-\phi}$

ii True because $(1-\phi)^{-1} = -\phi$ Verification:
$S_6 = 27{\cdot}4; S_7 = 45{\cdot}4; S_8 = 74{\cdot}4$ (1 dp)

c Students' own research: whatever the original two terms, $\frac{u_{n+1}}{u_n} \to \frac{1+\sqrt{5}}{2}$ as $n \to \infty$

9 a 8·05 cm b 71·48 cm (2 dp)

10 a Year 1: £1.85×10^8, Year 2: £1.92×10^8,
Year 3: £2.00×10^8, Year 4: £2.08×10^8,
Year 5: £2.16×10^8

b £40 760 202

11 a 111° (nearest degree) b 16·5 sec

12 a i 2 m ii 2·9 m iii 5·1 m iv 9·1 m

b Increase of 4·1 m c The height will reach 11 m.

13 a $V_1 = 0{\cdot}987V_0; V_2 = 0{\cdot}974V_0; V_3 = 0{\cdot}961V_0; V_4 = 0{\cdot}949V_0$

b 14·6%

Exercise 9.5

1 a 4 b 125 c $10\frac{2}{3}$
d $6\frac{3}{4}$ e $416\frac{2}{3}$ f $171\frac{1}{2}$

2 a $8\frac{1}{6}$ b No limit c 36
d 1 e $\frac{2}{3}$ f No limit

3 a 20

b $a = 50; ar^2 = 2 \Rightarrow |r| = \frac{\sqrt{2}}{25} < 1; S_\infty = 53{\cdot}0$

4 a i $\frac{28}{99}$ ii $\frac{115}{333}$ iii $\frac{41}{990}$

b $0{\cdot}9 + 0{\cdot}09 + 0{\cdot}009 + \ldots$ $a = 0{\cdot}9, r = 0{\cdot}1 \Rightarrow S_\infty = 1$

c i $\frac{45}{990}$ ii $\frac{936}{990}$

d i $\frac{2}{90}$ ii $\frac{65}{90}$ iii $\frac{679}{900}$

5 a 4800 b 6393·75

6 a 8, 6·4, 5·12 b i 26·89 ii 35·71

c 40 m

7 a $-1 < x < 1$ b $-2 < x < 2$

c $-\frac{1}{4} < x < \frac{1}{4}$ d $0 < x < \frac{1}{16}$

e $x < -3$ or $x > 3$ f $x < -\frac{1}{2}$ or $x > \frac{1}{2}$

g $-3 < x < 3$ h $-1 < x < 5$

i $-8 < x < -2$ j $x < -1$ or $x > 3$

8 a i $1010\frac{10}{99}$ m

ii Achilles will cover $1010\frac{10}{99}$ m to pull level with tortoise.

b i $100 + 1 + 0{\cdot}01 + 0{\cdot}0001 + \ldots$ ii $101\frac{1}{99}$ seconds

iii Achilles won't catch the tortoise if time is not allowed to exceed $101\frac{1}{99}$ seconds.

c Student research.

9 a i 12 times faster. ii 15 minutes iii 7·5°

iv $16\frac{4}{11}$ minutes after 3 o clock

b $32\frac{8}{11}$ minutes after 6 o clock

10 Unresolved

Review 9

1 a $u_n = 9n - 4$ b 302

2 a $a = -2, d = -8$ b 32

3 -10

4 2100

5 $a = 30, d = \frac{1}{2}$

6 36

7 a $u_n = 12 \times 2^{n-1}$ b 3072

8 3

9 200

10 a 44 286 b 2·50 (3 sf)

11 892·5

12 a term 10 b $-1 < 0{\cdot}6 < 1; S_\infty = 125$

13 85

14 a $\frac{6}{11}$ b $\frac{7}{22}$

15 $-\frac{7}{2} < x < -\frac{5}{2}$

Chapter 10

Exercise 10.1

1 a 30 b 140 c 182
d 230 e 75

2 a 105 b 123 c -35
d 6·15 (2 d.p.) e $1\frac{9}{20}$

3 a $5 + 10 + 15 + \ldots + 5(n-1) + 5n$

b $2 + 3 + 4 + \ldots + n + (1+n)$

c $-3 - 1 + 1 + \ldots + (2n-5) + (2n-3)$

d $5 + 3 + 1 + \ldots + (7-2n) + (5-2n)$

e $0 + 3 + 8 + \ldots + ((2n-1)^2 - 1) + ((2n)^2 - 1)$

4 a $n(n+1)$ b $-n$

c $3n(n+1) - n$ d $4n - \frac{3}{2}n(n+1)$

e $n(2n+1) - 16n$

5 a $\sum_{r=1}^{20} 4r - 1$ b $\sum_{r=1}^{50} 5r + 2$

c $\sum_{r=1}^{10} 6r$ d $\sum_{r=1}^{10000} \sqrt{r}$

e $\sum_{r=1}^{8} \frac{1}{2r-1}$ f $\sum_{r=1}^{12} 13 - 3r$

6 a i $-1 + 1 - 1 + 1 - 1 + \ldots$
ii $1 - 1 + 1 - 1 + 1 - \ldots$
iii $-2 + 4 - 6 + 8 - 10 + \ldots$
iv $3 - 6 + 9 - 12 + 15 - \ldots$

b i $-1 - 2 + 5 - 8 + 11 - \ldots$
ii $x - 2x^2 + 3x^3 - 4x^4 + 5x^5 - \ldots$
iii $x - 2x^2 + 6x^3 - 24x^4 + 120x^5 - \ldots$

c i $\sum_{r=1}^{n} (-1)^{r-1}(5r-2)$ ii $\sum_{r=1}^{n} (-1)^{r-1}(2r+5)$
iii $\sum_{r=1}^{n} (-1)^{r}(2r+2)$

d i $\sum_{r=1}^{n} x^{r-1}$ ii $\sum_{r=1}^{n} (-1)^{r-1} x^{r-1}$
iii $\sum_{r=1}^{n} (-1)^{r-1}(3x)^{r-1}$

7 a Undefined at $r = 6$ b Undefined for $r > 4$

8 a $n = 9$ b $n = 8$

9 a $(n+1)^2 - 1$ b $\sqrt{n+1} - 1$
c $\sin(n+1) - \sin 1$ d $\frac{1}{n+1} - 1$
e $\frac{1}{n} - 1$ f $1 - \frac{1}{n}$

10 a $f(n) - f(0)$ b $f(0) - f(n)$
c $f(n+1) + f(n+2) - f(1) - f(2)$

11 a $\ln\left(\frac{n+1}{n}\right)$ b $\ln(n+1) - \ln n$ c $\ln(n+1)$
d 1 e 2

12 a Verification b $\frac{1}{n(n+1)}$
c $\frac{1}{n} - \frac{1}{n+1}$ d $\frac{n}{n+1}$
e i $\frac{n}{4(n+4)}$ ii $\frac{n-9}{10(10-n)}$ iii $\frac{n}{2n+1}$

Exercise 10.2

1 a $\frac{n}{2}(n+1)(2n+1)$
b $\frac{n}{3}(n+1)(2n+1) + 3n$
c $\frac{n}{6}(n+1)(2n+1) + \frac{3n}{2}(n+1) - n$
d $\frac{5n}{6}(n+1)(2n+1) - \frac{3n}{2}(n+1) - 2n$
e $-\frac{n}{2}(n+1)(2n+1) - n(n+1) + 4n$
f $\frac{n}{6}(n+1)(2n+1) - \frac{n}{2}(n+1) - 2n$

2 a 280 b 435 c 2030
d −353 300 e 584 f 444

3 a Consider the expansion of $(n+1)^4$
$= n^4 + 4n^3 + 6n^2 + 4n + 1$
Hence $\sum_{r=1}^{n} (n+1)^4 - \sum_{r=1}^{n} n^4$
$= 4\sum_{r=1}^{n} n^3 + 6\sum_{r=1}^{n} n^2 + 4\sum_{r=1}^{n} n + \sum_{r=1}^{n} 1$ etc.

b Use $\sum_{r=1}^{k+1} r^3 = \sum_{r=1}^{k} r^3 + (k+1)^3$

4 a $4\left[\frac{n}{2}(n+1)\right]^2$
b $\left[\frac{n}{2}(n+1)\right]^2 + \frac{3n}{2}(n+1)$
c $2\left[\frac{n}{2}(n+1)\right]^2 + 2n(n+1) - 3n$
d $\left[\frac{n}{2}(n+1)\right]^2 + \frac{n}{6}(n+1)(2n+1) + \frac{n}{2}(n+1) + n$
e $\left[\frac{n}{2}(n+1)\right]^2 - \frac{n}{6}(n+1)(2n+1)$
f $\left[\frac{n}{2}(n+1)\right]^2 - \frac{5n}{6}(n+1)(2n+1) + \frac{7n}{2}(n+1) - 3n$

5 a 1125 b 3080 c 1216
d 1 756 950 e 584 f 105 300

6 a $\frac{n}{6}(n+1)(2n+1) + 2n(n+1) + 3n$
b $\frac{n}{2}(n+1)(2n+1) + \frac{n}{2}(n+1) - 2n$
c $\frac{2n}{3}(n+1)(2n+1) + 2n(n+1) - n$
d $\frac{8n}{3}(n+1)(2n+1) - 8n(n+1) + 3n$
e $\left(\frac{n}{2}(n+1)\right)^2$
f $\left(\frac{n}{2}(n+1)\right)^2 + \frac{n}{3}(n+1)(2n+1) + \frac{n}{2}(n+1)$
g $\left(\frac{n}{2}(n+1)\right)^2 + \frac{n}{2}(n+1)(2n+1) + n(n+1)$
h $\frac{n}{6}(n+1)(2n+1) - n$
i $\frac{n}{6}(n+1)(2n+1) - 2n$
j $\left(\frac{n}{2}(n+1)\right)^2 + \frac{n}{2}(n+1)(2n+1) + n(n+1)$
k $\left(\frac{n}{2}(n+1)\right)^2 + n(n+1)(2n+1) + \frac{11n}{2}(n+1) + 6n$

7 a 29 161 b 43 316 c 1 625 625

8 a $\sum_{r=1}^{k+1} 3^r = \sum_{r=1}^{k} 3^r + 3^{k+1} = \frac{3}{2}(3^k - 1) + 3^{k+1}$
$= \frac{3}{2}(3^k - 1 + \frac{2}{3}.3^{k+1}) = \frac{3}{2}(3^{k+1} - 1)$

b $\sum_{r=1}^{k+1} 2n - 1 = \sum_{r=1}^{k} 2n - 1 + (2k+1) = k^2 + 2k + 1$
$= (k+1)^2$

c $\sum_{r=1}^{k+1} (2n-1)^2 = \sum_{r=1}^{k} (2n-1)^2 + (2k-1)^2$
$= \frac{4}{3}k(k-1)(k+1) + k + (2k-1)^2$
$= \frac{4}{3}(k+1)(k+1-1)(k+1+1) + k + 1$

d $\displaystyle\sum_{r=1}^{k+1}(2n)^3 = \sum_{r=1}^{k}(2n)^3 + (2k)^3$

$= 2k^2(k+1)^2 + 8(k+1)^3 = 2(k+1)^2(k^2+4k+4)$

e $\displaystyle\sum_{r=1}^{k+1}\frac{1}{(2n-1)(2n+1)} = \sum_{r=1}^{k}\frac{1}{(2n-1)(2n+1)}$

$\displaystyle + \frac{1}{(2k+1)(2k+3)} = \frac{k}{2k+1} + \frac{1}{(2k+1)(2k+3)}$

Exercise 10.3

1 a i $\dfrac{2(1+x)}{(1-x)^2}$ ii $-1 < x < 1$

b i $\dfrac{3+2x}{(1-x)^2}$ ii $-1 < x < 1$

c i $\dfrac{12-14x}{(1-x)^2}$ ii $-1 < x < 1$

d i $\dfrac{17-22x}{(1-x)^2}$ ii $-1 < x < 1$

e i $\dfrac{2}{1-3x}$ ii $-\frac{1}{3} < x < \frac{1}{3}$

f i $\dfrac{192}{2-x}$ ii $-2 < x < 2$

g i $\dfrac{1}{(1-3x)(1-x)}$ ii $-\frac{1}{3} < x < \frac{1}{3}$

h i $\dfrac{3-4x}{(1-2x)(1-x)}$ ii $-\frac{1}{2} < x < \frac{1}{2}$

i i $\dfrac{2}{(1-4x)(1-x)}$ ii $-\frac{1}{4} < x < \frac{1}{4}$

j i $\dfrac{4(1-2x)}{(1-5x)(1-x)}$ ii $-\frac{1}{5} < x < \frac{1}{5}$

2 a $S_\infty = \dfrac{a - ax + dx}{(1-x)^2}$; $-1 < x < 1$

b $S_\infty = \dfrac{a}{1-rx}$; $-\frac{1}{r} < x < \frac{1}{r}$

c $S_\infty = \dfrac{a - ax + cx}{(1-bx)(1-x)}$; $\max\left\{-\frac{1}{b}, 1\right\} < x < \min\left\{\frac{1}{b}, 1\right\}$

Exercise 10.4

1 a 8 terms

b i 12 terms ii 13 terms

c Student's spreadsheet.

2 a 0 b i/ii 1 c i/ii 0

d $a_3 = -\frac{1}{3!}; a_4 = 0; a_5 = \frac{1}{5!}; a_6 = 0; a_7 = -\frac{1}{7!}$

so $\sin x = x - \dfrac{x^3}{3!} + \dfrac{x^5}{5!} - \dfrac{x^7}{7!} + \dfrac{x^9}{9!} - \ldots$

3 a $\cos x = 1 - \dfrac{x^2}{2!} + \dfrac{x^4}{4!} - \dfrac{x^6}{6!} + \dfrac{x^8}{8!} - \ldots$ b Verification

Exercise 10.5

1 a $1 - x + x^2 - x^3 + x^4 - \ldots$

b $1 - \dfrac{x}{2} - \dfrac{x^2}{8} - \dfrac{x^3}{16} - \dfrac{5x^4}{128} - \dfrac{7x^5}{256} - \ldots$

c $1 - 3x + 6x^2 - 10x^3 + 15x^4 - \ldots$

d $1 + x - \dfrac{x^2}{2!} + \dfrac{x^4}{4!} - \dfrac{x^6}{6!} + \ldots$

e $1 + \dfrac{x^2}{2} + \dfrac{5x^4}{24} + \dfrac{61x^6}{720} + \dfrac{277x^8}{8064} + \ldots$

f $-\dfrac{x^2}{2} - \dfrac{x^4}{12} - \dfrac{x^6}{45} - \dfrac{17x^8}{2520} - \dfrac{62x^{10}}{28\,350} - \ldots$

2 a i $\ln(1+x) = x - \dfrac{x^2}{2} + \dfrac{x^3}{3} - \dfrac{x^4}{4} + \dfrac{x^5}{5} - \ldots$

ii $\ln(1-x) = -x - \dfrac{x^2}{2} - \dfrac{x^3}{3} - \dfrac{x^4}{4} - \dfrac{x^5}{5} - \ldots$

b $\dfrac{1}{1+x} = 1 - x + x^2 - x^3 + x^4 - \ldots$

3 a $e^x \sin x = x + x^2 + \dfrac{x^3}{3} - \dfrac{x^5}{30} - \ldots$

b $\tan x = x + \dfrac{x^3}{3} + \dfrac{2x^5}{15} + \dfrac{17x^7}{315} + \ldots$

c $x \sin x = x^2 - \dfrac{x^4}{3!} + \dfrac{x^6}{5!} - \dfrac{x^8}{7!} + \ldots$

d $\dfrac{x}{1+x} = x - x^2 + x^3 - x^4 + \ldots$

4 a $(1+x)^n = 1 + nx + \dfrac{n(n-1)}{2!}x^2 + \dfrac{n(n-1)(x-2)}{3!}x^3 +$

b $(a+b)^n = a^n + na^{n-1}b + \dfrac{n(n-1)}{2!}a^{n-2}b^2$

$+ \dfrac{n(n-1)(x-2)}{3!}a^{n-3}b^3 +$

c i $(1+x^2)^{-1} = 1 - x^2 + x^4 - x^6 + x^8 - \ldots$

ii $(1-x^2)^{-1} = 1 + x^2 + x^4 + x^6 + x^8 + \ldots$

iii $(1-x^2)^{-\frac{1}{2}} = 1 + \frac{x^2}{2} + \frac{3x^4}{8} + \frac{5x^6}{16} + \frac{35x^8}{128} + \ldots$

d $\tan^{-1} x = x - \dfrac{x^3}{3} + \dfrac{x^5}{5} - \dfrac{x^7}{7} + \dfrac{x^9}{9} - \ldots$

e $\sin^{-1} x = x + \dfrac{x^3}{6} + \dfrac{3x^5}{40} + \dfrac{5x^7}{112} + \ldots$

f $\cos^{-1} x = \dfrac{\pi}{2} - x - \dfrac{x^3}{6} - \dfrac{3x^5}{40} - \dfrac{5x^7}{112} - \ldots$

[Note constant of integration $C = \frac{\pi}{2}$]

Exercise 10.6

1 a i 0·78332585 ii Accurate to 6 dp

b i 0·07011719 ii Accurate to 2 dp

c i 8·584 ii Not at all accurate

d i 2·666666 ii Accurate to 1 dp

e i 1·14660494 ii Accurate to 1 dp

f i −0·25 ii Accurate to 1 dp

g i 3·25 ii Not accurate ... expect 4

h i 0·40104167 ii Accurate to 1 dp

2 a 0·6442 b 6 Terms c 1·837

3 a i $\ln(1+x) = x - \dfrac{x^2}{2} + \dfrac{x^3}{3} - \dfrac{x^4}{4} + \dfrac{x^5}{5} - \dfrac{x^6}{6}$

ii $\ln(1-x) = -x - \dfrac{x^2}{2} - \dfrac{x^3}{3} - \dfrac{x^4}{4} - \dfrac{x^5}{5} - \dfrac{x^6}{6}$

b $\ln\left(\dfrac{1+x}{1-x}\right) = \ln(1+x) - \ln(1-x)$

$= 2\left(x + \dfrac{x^3}{3} + \dfrac{x^5}{5} + \dfrac{x^7}{7} + \dfrac{x^9}{9} + \dfrac{x^{11}}{11}\right)$

c i 0·4046875 ii 0·405465108

d Second method

e i $x = \frac{2}{7}$

ii 0·588 (3 dp)

Exercise 10.7

1 a $\sum_{n=0}^{\infty} 4^n \frac{x^n}{n!}$ b $\sum_{n=0}^{\infty} (-1)^n \frac{x^n}{n!}$

c $\sum_{n=0}^{\infty} \left(\frac{1}{2}\right)^n \frac{x^n}{n!}$ d $\sum_{n=0}^{\infty} 3^n e \frac{x^n}{n!}$

e $\sum_{n=0}^{\infty} (-2)^n e \frac{x^n}{n!}$ f $\sum_{n=0}^{\infty} \frac{x^{2n}}{n!}$

2 a $\sum_{n=0}^{\infty} (-1)^n \frac{(3x)^{2n+1}}{(2n+1)!}$ b $\sum_{n=0}^{\infty} (-1)^n \frac{(-2x)^{2n+1}}{(2n+1)!}$

c $\sum_{n=0}^{\infty} (-1)^n \frac{\left(\frac{x}{2}\right)^{2n+1}}{(2n+1)!}$ d $\sum_{n=0}^{\infty} (-1)^n \frac{(x^2)^{2n+1}}{(2n+1)!}$

3 a $\sum_{n=0}^{\infty} (-1)^n \frac{(4x)^{2n}}{(2n)!}$ b $\sum_{n=0}^{\infty} (-1)^n \frac{(-3x)^{2n}}{(2n)!}$

c $\sum_{n=0}^{\infty} (-1)^n \frac{\left(\frac{x}{4}\right)^{2n}}{(2n)!}$ d $\sum_{n=0}^{\infty} (-1)^n \frac{x^{4n}}{(2n)!}$

4 a $\sum_{n=0}^{\infty} (-1)^n \frac{x^{2n}}{(2n)!}$

b $\frac{\sqrt{3}}{2} \sum_{n=0}^{\infty} (-1)^n \frac{(2x)^{2n+1}}{(2n+1)!} + \frac{1}{2} \sum_{n=0}^{\infty} (-1)^n \frac{(2x)^{2n}}{(2n)!}$

$= \sum_{n=0}^{\infty} \frac{(-1)^n (2x)^{2n}}{2(2n)!} \left[\frac{2\sqrt{3}x}{2n+1} + 1\right]$

c $\sum_{n=0}^{\infty} (-1)^n \frac{(3x)^{2n+1}}{(2n+1)!}$

d $-\sum_{n=0}^{\infty} (-1)^n \frac{(2x)^{2n+1}}{(2n+1)!} = \sum_{n=0}^{\infty} (-1)^{n+1} \frac{(2x)^{2n+1}}{(2n+1)!}$

e $\frac{1}{\sqrt{2}} \sum_{n=0}^{\infty} (-1)^n \frac{(3x)^{2n}}{(2n)!} - \frac{1}{\sqrt{2}} \sum_{n=0}^{\infty} (-1)^n \frac{(3x)^{2n+1}}{(2n+1)!}$

$= \sum_{n=0}^{\infty} \frac{(-1)^n (3x)^{2n}}{\sqrt{2}(2n)!} \left[1 - \frac{3x}{2n+1}\right]$

f $\frac{1}{2} \sum_{n=0}^{\infty} (-1)^n \frac{x^{2n}}{(2n)!} + \frac{\sqrt{3}}{2} \sum_{n=0}^{\infty} (-1)^n \frac{x^{2n+1}}{(2n+1)!}$

$= \sum_{n=0}^{\infty} \frac{(-1)^n x^{2n}}{2(2n)!} \left[1 + \frac{\sqrt{3}x}{2n+1}\right]$

5 a $\frac{1}{2} + \frac{1}{2} \sum_{n=0}^{\infty} (-1)^n \frac{(2x)^{2n}}{(2n)!}$ b $\frac{1}{2} - \frac{1}{2} \sum_{n=0}^{\infty} (-1)^n \frac{(2x)^{2n}}{(2n)!}$

6 a $\tan(3x) = (3x) + \frac{1}{3}(3x)^3 + \frac{2}{15}(3x)^5 + \frac{17}{315}(3x)^7 + \frac{62}{2835}(3x)^9 + \ldots$

b $\tan(-x) = (-x) + \frac{1}{3}(-x)^3 + \frac{2}{15}(-x)^5 + \frac{17}{315}(-x)^7 + \frac{62}{2835}(-x)^9 + \ldots$

c $\tan\left(\frac{x}{2}\right) = \left(\frac{x}{2}\right) + \frac{1}{3}\left(\frac{x}{2}\right)^3 + \frac{2}{15}\left(\frac{x}{2}\right)^5 + \frac{17}{315}\left(\frac{x}{2}\right)^7 + \frac{62}{2835}\left(\frac{x}{2}\right)^9 + \ldots$

7 a i $\tan^{-1}(3x) = (3x) - \frac{1}{3}(3x)^3 + \frac{1}{5}(3x)^5 - \frac{1}{7}(3x)^7 + \frac{1}{9}(3x)^9 + \ldots$

ii $\tan^{-1}(-x) = (-x) - \frac{1}{3}(-x)^3 + \frac{1}{5}(-x)^5 - \frac{1}{7}(-x)^7 + \frac{1}{9}(-x)^9 + \ldots$

iii $\tan^{-1}\left(\frac{x}{2}\right) = \left(\frac{x}{2}\right) - \frac{1}{3}\left(\frac{x}{2}\right)^3 + \frac{1}{5}\left(\frac{x}{2}\right)^5 - \frac{1}{7}\left(\frac{x}{2}\right)^7 + \frac{1}{9}\left(\frac{x}{2}\right)^9 + \ldots$

b $\pi = 4\left[(1) - \frac{1}{3}(1)^3 + \frac{1}{5}(1)^5 - \frac{1}{7}(1)^7 + \frac{1}{9}(1)^9 + \ldots\right]$

$= 4\left(1 - \frac{1}{3} + \frac{1}{5} - \frac{1}{7} + \frac{1}{9} - \ldots\right)$

The value of π is trapped between successive partial sums. By the 100th term we have 3·13 and 101th term 3·15.

8 a $\ln 3 + \frac{x}{3} - \frac{1}{2}\left(\frac{x}{3}\right)^2 + \frac{1}{3}\left(\frac{x}{3}\right)^3 - \frac{1}{4}\left(\frac{x}{3}\right)^4 + \ldots; -3 < x < 3$

b i $\ln 4 + \frac{x}{4} - \frac{1}{2}\left(\frac{x}{4}\right)^2 + \frac{1}{3}\left(\frac{x}{4}\right)^3 - \frac{1}{4}\left(\frac{x}{4}\right)^4 + \ldots; -4 < x < 4$

ii $\ln 2 + \frac{3x}{2} - \frac{1}{2}\left(\frac{3x}{2}\right)^2 + \frac{1}{3}\left(\frac{3x}{2}\right)^3 - \frac{1}{4}\left(\frac{3x}{2}\right)^4 + \ldots; -\frac{2}{3} < x < \frac{2}{3}$

iii $x^2 - \frac{x^4}{2} + \frac{x^6}{3} - \frac{x^8}{4} + \frac{x^{10}}{5} - \ldots; -1 < x < 1$

9 a $x + x^2 + \frac{x^3}{3} - \frac{x^5}{30} - \frac{x^6}{90}$

b i $1 + x - \frac{x^3}{3} - \frac{x^4}{6} - \frac{x^5}{30}$

ii $x + \frac{x^2}{2} + \frac{x^3}{3} + \frac{3x^5}{40} - \frac{7x^6}{144}$

Review 10

1 a $2 + 5 + 10 + 17 + 26 + 37 = 97$

b $\frac{1}{2} + \frac{1}{3} + \frac{1}{4} + \frac{1}{5} + \frac{1}{6} = 1\frac{9}{20}$

c $2\frac{1}{2} + 3\frac{1}{3} + 4\frac{1}{4} + 5\frac{1}{5} = 15\frac{17}{60}$

d $2 + 6 + 12 + 20 + 30 = 70$

2 a $\sum_{r=1}^{7} 3r + 1$ b $\sum_{r=1}^{20} 6r - 3$

c $\sum_{r=1}^{99} r(r+1)$ d $\sum_{r=1}^{50} \frac{1}{2r-1}$

e $\sum_{r=1}^{29} \frac{1}{(r+1)(r+2)}$

3 a 1, 3, 6, 10, 15 b $T_n = \frac{1}{2}n(n+1)$

c i $\sum_{r=1}^{n} \frac{1}{2}r(r+1)$

ii $\frac{1}{12}n(n+1)(2n+1) + \frac{1}{4}n(n+1)$

$= \frac{1}{6}n(n+1)(n+2)$

d 171 700

4 a $\frac{1}{6}n(n+1)(2n+1) - \frac{1}{2}n(n+1) - 1$ b 429

5 $\sqrt{n}$

6 $\sum_{r=2}^{n} \frac{1}{r^2-1} = \frac{1}{2}\sum_{r=2}^{n} \frac{1}{r-1} - \frac{1}{2}\sum_{r=2}^{n} \frac{1}{r+1}$

$= \frac{1}{2}\left(\frac{1}{1} + \frac{1}{2} - \frac{1}{n} - \frac{1}{n+1}\right) = \frac{3n^2 - n - 2}{4n(n+1)}$

$= \frac{(n-1)(3n+2)}{4n(n+1)}$

7 True for $n = 1$. Assume true for $n = k$: $\sum_{r=1}^{k} \frac{1}{4r(r+1)}$

$= \frac{k}{4(k+1)}$

Consider $n = k + 1$:

$\sum_{r=1}^{k+1} \frac{1}{4r(r+1)} = \sum_{r=1}^{k} \frac{1}{4r(r+1)} + \frac{1}{4(k+1)(k+1+1)}$

$= \frac{k}{4(k+1)} + \frac{1}{4(k+1)(k+1+1)}$

$= \frac{k^2+2k+1}{4(k+1)(k+2)} = \frac{(k+1)^2}{4(k+1)(k+2)}$

$= \frac{(k+1)}{4(k+1+1)}$ Hence result.

8 a $\cos x = 1 - \frac{x^2}{2!} + \frac{x^4}{4!} - \frac{x^6}{6!} + \frac{x^8}{8!}$

b $\ln(1+x) = x - \frac{x^2}{2} + \frac{x^3}{3} - \frac{x^4}{4} + \frac{x^5}{5}$

c $\sin x - \cos x = -1 + x + \frac{x^2}{2!} - \frac{x^3}{3!} - \frac{x^4}{4!}$

9 a $x\cos x = x - \frac{x^3}{2!} + \frac{x^5}{4!} - \frac{x^7}{6!}$

b $(1+x)^{\frac{1}{3}} = 1 + \frac{1}{3}x + \frac{\frac{1}{3}\left(\frac{1}{3}-1\right)}{2!}x^2 + \frac{\frac{1}{3}\left(\frac{1}{3}-1\right)\left(\frac{1}{3}-2\right)}{3!}x^3$

10 0·479

11 a $\sum_{r=0}^{\infty} \frac{(-1)^r(2x)^{2r}}{2(2r)!}\left[\sqrt{3} + \frac{2x}{2r+1}\right]$ b $e^2\left(\sum_{r=0}^{\infty} \frac{3^r x^r}{r!}\right)$

Chapter 11

Exercise 11.1

1 a i $\dot{x} = 6t + 1; \ddot{x} = 6$ ii 19 ms^{-1}; 6 ms^{-2}

b i $\dot{x} = \frac{2}{(t+1)^2}; \ddot{x} = \frac{-4}{(t+1)^3}$ ii $\frac{1}{8}$ ms^{-1}; $-\frac{1}{16}$ ms^{-2}

c i $\dot{x} = \frac{5}{2(5t+1)^{\frac{1}{2}}}; \ddot{x} = \frac{-25}{4(5t+1)^{\frac{3}{2}}}$

ii $\frac{5}{8}$ ms^{-1}; $-\frac{25}{256}$ ms^{-2}

d i $\dot{x} = 1 - e^{3-t}; \ddot{x} = e^{3-t}$ ii 0 ms^{-1}; 1 ms^{-2}

e i $\dot{x} = \frac{\sqrt{2}\pi}{6}\cos\left(\frac{\pi t}{12}\right); \ddot{x} = -\frac{\sqrt{2}\pi^2}{72}\sin\left(\frac{\pi t}{12}\right)$

ii $\frac{\pi}{6}$ ms^{-1}; $-\frac{\pi^2}{72}$ ms^{-2}

f i $\dot{x} = 1 - t^{-2}; \ddot{x} = 2t^{-3}$ ii $\frac{8}{9}$ ms^{-1}; $\frac{2}{27}$ ms^{-2}

2 a 2700 m; -6 ms^{-2} b 109 m; -12 ms^{-2}

c 21 m; 1·2 ms^{-2} d 5 m; -45 ms^{-2}

e 16 m; 1 ms^{-2} f $-0{\cdot}614$ m; -2 ms^{-2}

3 a $x(t) = t^3 + t + 3$ b 18 ms^{-1}

c i min $t^2 = 0$, so min $v = 1$ ii 192 m

4 a i $v = -\frac{3}{2}\cos 2t + \frac{3}{2}$ ii $x = -\frac{3}{4}\sin 2t + \frac{3}{2}t + 1$

b $x = \left(\frac{1}{4} + \frac{3\pi}{8}\right)$ m; $v = \frac{3}{2}$ ms^{-1}; $a = 3$ ms^{-2}

5 a $x = t^2 - \sin t \Rightarrow v = 2t - \cos t \Rightarrow a = 2 + \sin t$;
since $-1 \leqslant \sin t \leqslant 1 \Rightarrow 1 \leqslant 2 + \sin t \leqslant 3$
That is, acceleration always positive.

b $v > 0 \Rightarrow 2t - \cos t > 0$.
Trial and improvement gives $t > 0{\cdot}45$

6 a -10 ms^{-2} b i 500 m ii 10 sec

c i 0 sec and 20 sec ii -100 ms^{-1}

7 a 810 m b 135 ms^{-1}

c i 22·5 ms^{-2} ii 11·25 ms^{-2} iii 7·5 ms^{-2}

8 a Verification b Verification

c $\frac{5\pi}{6}$ ms^{-1}, 0 ms^{-2}

d Not quite, solving $v = a$ gives $t = 6.98$ (to 3 sf)

e $x_{max} \Rightarrow \sin\left(\frac{\pi t}{12}\right) = 1 \Rightarrow a = -\frac{5\pi^2}{72} \approx -0{\cdot}69$ ms^{-2}

9 a i 6 m ii 9 m

b $v = \frac{\pi}{6}$ ms^{-1} $a = 0$ ms^{-2} c 72 sec

d $v = \frac{\pi}{6}$ ms^{-1}

e $-\left(\frac{\pi}{36}\right)^2 = -0{\cdot}008$ ms^{-2}

10 a 0·524 ms^{-1} b i 5 am, 11 am

ii $-0{\cdot}548$ ms^{-2}, 0·548 ms^{-2}

11 a $v = v_0 - gt$ b $t = 0; t = \frac{2v_0}{g}$

c $t_{max} = \frac{v_0}{g}$ d $s_{max} = \frac{{v_0}^2}{2g}$

12 a $V = \frac{1}{2}kt + \frac{1}{4}k\sin 2t + 5$ b 49·1 m

13 a 14 m/s b $196\frac{2}{3}$ m

c Same

14 a 2·19 m/s b 1·39 m

Exercise 11.2

Answers given to 3 sf.

1 a Speed 10·5 m/s direction 0·641 radians to x-direction

b $\sqrt{37}$

2 a 26 m b 11·8 m c 67·0 m/s

3 a i $\frac{dy}{dx} = \frac{t+2}{t+3}$ ii $t > 0 \Rightarrow \frac{dy}{dx} > 0$

b 0·724 m

c $|v(1)| = 0{\cdot}417$ ms^{-1}; 0·644 radians

d $|a(0)| = 0{\cdot}274$ ms^{-1}; 3·560 radians

4 a $x = 68{\cdot}0, y = 1496, s = 1498$ m

b 158 ms^{-1}, direction 1·54 radians

c 9·18 ms^{-2}, direction 1·57 radians

5 a $\dot{x} = 6t - 6$; $\dot{y} = 3t^2 - 3$

b $x = 3t^2 - 6t$; $y = t^3 - 3t$

c i $t = 1$ ii $(-3, -2)$; acceleration $8{\cdot}49\ \text{ms}^{-2}$, direction 0·785 rads.

6 a 5 m b 37·5 min

c i $|v| = \sqrt{\left(\frac{65\pi}{15}\right)^2 \left[\sin^2\left(\frac{\pi t}{15} - \frac{\pi}{2}\right) + \cos^2\left(\frac{\pi t}{15} - \frac{\pi}{2}\right)\right]}$

$= \frac{65\pi}{15} \approx 13{\cdot}6$ m/min

ii $v(10) = \begin{pmatrix} -6{\cdot}81 \\ 11{\cdot}8 \end{pmatrix}$; mag $13{\cdot}6\ \text{ms}^{-1}$, dirn 2·09 radians

d Magnitude $2{\cdot}85\ \text{ms}^{-2}$; direction 4·71 radians

7 a $x = 4\sin\left(\frac{\pi}{180}t\right)$; $y = -3\cos\left(\frac{\pi}{180}t\right)$

b i $(-2, 2{\cdot}60)$

ii $v = \begin{pmatrix} -0{\cdot}0605 \\ -0{\cdot}0262 \end{pmatrix}$; $|v| = 0{\cdot}0659\ ms^{-1}$; dir = 3·55 rads

c $|a| = \frac{\pi^2\sqrt{43}}{64800} = 9{\cdot}99 \times 10^{-4}\ \text{ms}^{-2}$; dir = 5·37 rads

8 a i $x = \frac{e^t + e^{-t}}{2} + c_1$; $y = \frac{e^t - e^{-t}}{2} + c_2$ ii $(1, 0)$

b i $\sqrt{\frac{e^{2t} + e^{-2t}}{2}}$ ii $\frac{e^{2t} + 1}{e^{2t} - 1}$

c $\begin{pmatrix} 74{\cdot}2 \\ 74{\cdot}2 \end{pmatrix}$

9 a $(1, 0)$ b $\begin{pmatrix} 1{\cdot}15 \\ -1{\cdot}75 \end{pmatrix}$

10 a In both cases the angle is $\tan^{-1}(-1)$ and in same quadrant.

b Expand both and use $\sin^2 t + \cos^2 t = 1$

c i $x + y = 2$ ii sketch of $y = 2 - x$

Exercise 11.3

1 a i 1440 kg/m³ ii 30 m³/h iii 850 kg/bag iv £0·05/kg

b i 0·694 litres ii 2 minutes iii 0·0012 bags iv 20 kg

c i $\frac{dw}{dt} = \frac{dw}{dv} \times \frac{dv}{dt} = 43200$ kg/h

ii $\frac{dP}{dt} = \frac{dP}{dw} \times \frac{dw}{dv} \times \frac{dv}{dt} = £2160$/h

2 300π cm²/s

3 a i $\frac{\pi}{2}\cos\left(\frac{\pi t}{30}\right)$ ii $-\frac{\pi}{2}\sin\left(\frac{\pi t}{30}\right)$ iii $-\tan\left(\frac{\pi t}{30}\right)$

b 2 m/unit x

4 a $\frac{-2x}{3\sqrt{9 - x^2}}$ b $-11{\cdot}3$

5 a i $y = \frac{x}{3}$ ii $\frac{1}{3}$ b $\frac{2}{3}$ m/s

6 a i $v = x^3$ ii $\frac{dv}{dx} = 3x^2$ b 0·324 cm³/min

7 a i $100\ln(1{\cdot}04) . 1{\cdot}04^T$ ii $4\pi r^2$

b i 0·325 mm/degree ii 8·16 mm3/min

8 a $\frac{dk}{dt} = t + 1$ [rpm] b $\frac{dk}{dt} = 15 \Rightarrow t = 14$

c i 60 mm/rev ii 80 mm/rev

9 -3 newton/m² per second.

10 a $\frac{dT}{dh} = -\left(\frac{9{\cdot}8}{1000}\right)$ °C/m $\Rightarrow$

$\frac{dT}{dt} = -\left(\frac{9{\cdot}8}{1000}\right)(10t + 150)$°C/hour

$= -\left(\frac{9{\cdot}8}{60\,000}\right)(10t + 150)$ °C/min

[t measured in hours]

b $-\left(\frac{9{\cdot}8}{60\,000}\right)(20 + 150) = -0{\cdot}0278$ °C/min

11 a i $h = 5r \Rightarrow \frac{dh}{dr} = 5$ ii $V = \frac{1}{3}\pi r^2 h$ iii $V = \frac{5}{3}\pi r^3$

iv $\frac{dV}{dr} = 5\pi r^2$

b 0·199 m/min c 3·98 m/min

12 a 12 m/min b $1\frac{1}{3}$ m/min

13 a $\theta = 2\sin^{-1}\left(\frac{D}{4}\right)$

b i 0·125 radians per sec ii 7·16°/sec

c 14·6 cm/sec

14 a 6·4 km/min

b Note $y^2 - x^2 = k \Rightarrow 2y\frac{dy}{dx} - 2x = 0 \Rightarrow \frac{dy}{dx} = \frac{x}{y}$

This simplifies the finding of $\frac{d\theta}{dx}$ leading to $\frac{d\theta}{dt} = 3{\cdot}07$ radians per min.

Exercise 11.4

1 0·955 radians

2 a $t = \frac{1}{\sqrt{e}}$ b $V_{max} = \frac{k}{2e}$

3 Max speed of 6 m/min at $t = 0$, π i.e. (0, 4) and (0, −4)

4 a Use $\sin\theta = \frac{500 - 6t}{D}$; $\cos\theta = \frac{8t}{D}$

b 400 m

5 a $\frac{60}{v}$ hours b $\frac{720}{v}$ pounds

c $\frac{90v}{169} + \frac{720}{v}$ d 52 miles per hour

6 a $y_A = d\sin\theta$; $x_B = d\cos\theta$

b i Use the smaller triangle. ii $d = \frac{3}{\sin\theta} + \frac{9}{\cos\theta}$

c $3 + 9\tan\theta + \frac{3}{\tan\theta} + 9$

d $y - 3 = -\frac{1}{\sqrt{3}}(x - 9)$

7 12·5 m

8 a $x = 5$ b 30 cm

9 a $h = \frac{228}{r^2}$

b $= 30\left(\pi R^2 + \frac{456\pi}{R}\right) + 20\pi R$

c Radius 6 cm; height $6\frac{1}{3}$ cm

10 Using similar triangles: $h_{cyl} = h - h\frac{r_{cyl}}{r}$; substitute into volume of cylinder and find $\frac{dV_{cyl}}{dr_{cyl}}$ leading to $r_{cyl} = \frac{2}{3}r$ and $h_{cyl} = \frac{1}{3}h$

$V_{max} = \frac{4}{27}\pi r^2 h = \frac{4}{27}\pi h^3 \tan^2 a$

11 a Maximum $y = 0.25$ when $t = \frac{\pi}{6}, \frac{5\pi}{6}, x = \frac{3\sqrt{3}}{8}, -\frac{3\sqrt{3}}{8}$

b Maximum $x = 1$ when $t = 0$ or $2\pi, y = 0$.

12 a $\frac{\dot{y}}{y} = -0.2 \ln 2 + \frac{2 \cos 2t}{\sin 2t}$

b $t = 0.751, y = 0.899; t = 3.892, y = 0.582;$ $t = 7.034, y = 0.376$

13 $6\frac{2}{3}$ cm

14 a $h^2 = x^2 + y^2$

b Minimum at $x = 5$, giving $h = 5\sqrt{2}$

Review 11

1 a 9 cm b 4 cm/s

c A constant 2 cm/s^2

2 a i $x = \frac{9}{\pi} \sin \frac{\pi t}{3} + 0.02$ ii 2.50 m

b 2.72 ms^{-2}

3 a 11.75 m

b i $\dot{x} = 2; \dot{y} = 25 - 10t$

ii 15.1 ms^{-1}; 1.44 radians to x-direction

c 2.5 sec

d i $t = 5$ sec ii 25.1 ms^{-1}.

4 a $(r, 0)$

b i 31.4 ms^{-1} ii $\begin{pmatrix} 10.7 \\ -29.5 \end{pmatrix}$; 5.06 radians [290°]

c $\begin{pmatrix} 140 \\ 117 \end{pmatrix}$; magnitude 183 ms^{-2}; 0.698 radians [40°]

5 a 42 m/min b 15.0 km/min

c i 47.1 km/min ii 1680 km^2/min

6 a i 8.95 degs/hr ii −55.9 km/degree iii 500 km/h

b Diminishing at 22 500 000 km^2/h

7 a $x = 7.28, y = 3.64$

b The minimum area field would be a circle of radius x; $y = 0$.

8 The shorter sides are both 10 cm long.

Chapter 12

Exercise 12.1

1 a $5 + 5i$ b $2 + 11i$ c $6 + 3i$
d $6 + 8i$ e $17 + 16i$ f $3 + 4i$
g $2 + 11i$ h $-38 + 41i$ i $-3 - 4i$
j $-1 - 3i$ k $1 + 3i$ l $-3 - 4i$

2 a $4 + 5i$ b 10 c 2
d $7 - i$ e $7 - 24i$ f $2 - 10i$
g $6 + 2i$ h $2 + 16i$ i $30 - 10i$

3 a $-1 \pm i$ b $-2 \pm 3i$ c $3 \pm 2i$
d $1 \pm 2i$ e $2 \pm i$ f $-3 \pm 3i$

4 For roots $p \pm qi$: sum $= 2p$ and product $= p^2 + q^2$

5 $a + b = 10$ and $ab = 40 \Rightarrow a^2 - 10a + 40 = 0 \Rightarrow$ $a = 5 \pm \sqrt{15}t$

6 a i 10 ii 13 iii 5 b All answers are real.

c $a^2 + b^2 \in \mathrm{R}$

7 a $i^1 = i, i^2 = -1, i^3 = -i, i^4 = 1, i^5 = i, i^6 = -1, i^7 = -i,$ $i^8 = 1, i^9 = i, i^{10} = -1, i^{11} = -i, i^{12} = 1$

b i $i^{4n-1} = -i$ ii $i^{4n+1} = i$ iii $i^{4n+2} = -1$
iv $i^{4n} = 1$ v $i^{4n+3} = -i$

8 a $a = 8, b = 6$ b $a = 5, b = 12$

c $a = 2, b = 11$

Exercise 12.2

1 a $2 - 2i$ b $2 - i$ c $1 + i$
d $1 - i$ e $1.6 - 3.2i$ f $1.7 + 0.9i$

2 a $-i$ b $0.5 - 0.5i$ c $0.25 - 0.25i$
d $0.3 - 0.1i$ e $0.2 + 0.1i$

3 a $3 - 2i$ b $3 - 3i$ c $2 - 5i$
d $-1.5 - 3.5i$ e $-0.2 - 1.6i$ f $0.36 - 0.48i$

4 a $-3 + 2i$ and $3 - 2i$ b $-4 + i$ and $4 - i$
c $-1 + 5i$ and $1 - 5i$

5 a $-2 + i$ and $2 - i$ b $-5 + 2i$ and $5 - 2i$
c $4 + 5i$ and $-4 - 5i$

6 a i $2 - 3i$ ii $\frac{2}{13} + \frac{3}{13}i$
iii $-\frac{5}{13} + \frac{12}{13}i$ iv $-\frac{5}{13} - \frac{12}{13}i$
v $-\frac{10}{13}$ vi $\frac{24}{13}i$

b i $a - bi$ ii $\frac{a}{a^2 + b^2} + \frac{b}{a^2 + b^2}i$
iii $\frac{a^2 - b^2}{a^2 + b^2} + \frac{2ab}{a^2 + b^2}i$ iv $\frac{a^2 - b^2}{a^2 + b^2} - \frac{2ab}{a^2 + b^2}i$
v $2\left(\frac{a^2 - b^2}{a^2 + b^2}\right)$ vi $\frac{4ab}{a^2 + b^2}i$

7 a $z = a + ib \Rightarrow \bar{z} = a - ib \Rightarrow \frac{1}{2}(z + \bar{z}) = a = \Re(z)$

b $\frac{1}{2i}(z - \bar{z}) = b = \mathrm{I}(z)$

8 a i $\overline{z_1} = a - bi$ ii $\overline{z_2} = x - yi$ iii $(a + x) - (b + y)i$

b $\overline{z_1} + \overline{z_2} = \overline{z_1 + z_2}$

c i $\overline{z_1} - \overline{z_2} = \overline{z_1 - z_2}$ ii $\overline{z_1} \times \overline{z_2} = \overline{z_1 \times z_2}$
iii $\overline{z_1} \div \overline{z_2} = \overline{z_1 \div z_2}$

Exercise 12.3

1 a $z = i \Rightarrow |z| = 1$ and $\arg z = \frac{\pi}{2}$

b $z = -1 \Rightarrow |z| = 1$ and $\arg z = \pi$

c $z = -i \Rightarrow |z| = 1$ and $\arg z = -\frac{\pi}{2}$

2 Diagrams showing:

a i (3, 4) and (3, −4) ii (2, 3) and (2, −3)
iii (5, 1) and (5, −1)

b Reflection in x-axis.

3 a Diagram showing (1, 1); $|z| = \sqrt{2}$; $\arg z = \frac{\pi}{4}$

b Diagram showing (2, 3); $|z| = \sqrt{13}$; $\arg z = 0{\cdot}983$ (3 sf)

c Diagram showing (3, 2); $|z| = \sqrt{13}$; $\arg z = 0{\cdot}588$ (3 sf)

d Diagram showing (6, 0); $|z| = 6$; $\arg z = 0$

e Diagram showing (0, 3); $|z| = 3$; $\arg z = \frac{\pi}{2}$

f Diagram showing $(-4, -3)$; $|z| = 5$; $\arg z = -2{\cdot}50$ (3 sf)

g Diagram showing $(-1, 2)$; $|z| = \sqrt{5}$; $\arg z = 2{\cdot}03$ (3 sf)

h Diagram showing $(2, -3)$; $|z| = \sqrt{13}$; $\arg z = -0{\cdot}983$ (3 sf)

i Diagram showing $(4, -1)$; $|z| = \sqrt{17}$; $\arg z = -0{\cdot}245$ (3 sf)

4 a i $\frac{1}{2} - \frac{1}{2}i$ ii $|z| = \frac{1}{\sqrt{2}}$; $\arg z = -\frac{\pi}{4}$

b i $\frac{1}{10} - \frac{3}{10}i$ ii $|z| = \frac{1}{\sqrt{10}}$; $\arg z = -1{\cdot}25$

c i $6 + 2i$ ii $|z| = 2\sqrt{10}$; $\arg z = 0{\cdot}322$

5 a i $|z| = \sqrt{149}$; $\arg z = 0{\cdot}611$

ii $|z^2| = 149$; $\arg (z^2) = 1{\cdot}22$

iii $|z^3| = 149\sqrt{149}$; $\arg (z^3) = -1{\cdot}31$ $[= 3 \arg z - \pi]$

b $|z^n| = |z|^n$; $\arg (z^n) = n \times \arg z$ ... adjusted to bring it into $(-\pi, \pi]$

6 a $2\left(\cos \frac{\pi}{6} + i \sin \frac{\pi}{6}\right) = \sqrt{3} + i$

b $3\left(\cos \frac{\pi}{4} + i \sin \frac{\pi}{4}\right) = \frac{3}{\sqrt{2}} + i\frac{3}{\sqrt{2}}$

c $4\left(\cos \frac{\pi}{2} + i \sin \frac{\pi}{2}\right) = 4i$

d $3\left(\cos \frac{\pi}{3} + i \sin \frac{\pi}{3}\right) = \frac{3}{2} + \frac{3\sqrt{3}}{2}i$

e $2\left(\cos \frac{\pi}{4} - i \sin \frac{\pi}{4}\right) = \sqrt{2} - i\sqrt{2}$

f $1\left(\cos \frac{\pi}{6} - i \sin \frac{\pi}{6}\right) = \frac{\sqrt{3}}{2} - i\frac{1}{2}$

7 a $2(\cos 60° + i \sin 60°)$ b $2(\cos 45° + i \sin 45°)$

c $4(\cos 150° + i \sin 150°)$ d $(\cos 180° + i \sin 180°)$

e $3(\cos 90° + i \sin 90°)$ f $8(\cos 120° - i \sin 120°)$

g $4(\cos 150° - i \sin 150°)$ h $2(\cos 135° - i \sin 135°)$

i $2(\cos 120° - i \sin 120°)$

8 Diagrams to illustrate: a (5, 5) b (5, 5) c $(5, -5)$

d $(-5, 1)$ e $(-1, 1)$ f $(-1, -1)$

g $(-2, 3)$ h $(-5, 1)$ i (1, 1)

Exercise 12.4

1 a i $x^2 + y^2 = 25$ ii Circle centre (0, 0); radius 5

b i $(x - 3)^2 + y^2 = 4$ ii Circle centre (3, 0); radius 2

c i $(x + 1)^2 + y^2 = 16$

ii Circle centre $(-1, 0)$; radius 4

d i $x^2 + (y + 1)^2 = 9$

ii Circle centre $(0, -1)$; radius 3

e i $x^2 + (y - 2)^2 = 9$ ii Circle centre (0, 2); radius 3

f i $(x + 1)^2 + (y + 2)^2 = 9$

ii Circle centre $(-1, -2)$; radius 3

g i $x^2 + \left(y + \frac{3}{2}\right)^2 = \frac{25}{4}$

ii Circle centre $\left(0, -\frac{3}{2}\right)$; radius $\frac{5}{2}$

h i $x^2 + \left(y - \frac{1}{3}\right)^2 = \frac{25}{9}$

ii Circle centre $\left(0, \frac{1}{3}\right)$; radius $\frac{5}{3}$

i i $(x + 1)^2 + \left(y - \frac{2}{3}\right)^2 = \frac{16}{9}$

ii Circle centre $\left(-1, \frac{2}{3}\right)$; radius $\frac{4}{3}$

j i $y = \frac{1}{\sqrt{3}}x$

ii Straight line through (0, 0) gradient $\frac{1}{\sqrt{3}}$

k i $y = x$

ii Straight line through (0, 0) gradient 1

l i $y = -\sqrt{3}x$

ii Straight line through (0, 0) gradient $-\sqrt{3}$

m i $y = 1{\cdot}56x$ (to 3 sf)

ii Straight line through (0, 0) gradient tan 1

n i $y = 0{\cdot}414x$ (to 3 sf)

ii Straight line through (0, 0) gradient $\tan\left(\frac{\pi}{8}\right)$

o i $y = -\sqrt{3}x$

ii Straight line through (0, 0) gradient $-\sqrt{3}$

2 a Circle centre $(a, 0)$; radius b

b Circle centre $(0, a)$; radius b

c Circle centre (b, a); radius c

3 a $x = y$ b $y = 2x - \frac{3}{2}$

c $y = \frac{3}{2}x - \frac{5}{4}$ d $y = \frac{a}{b}x - \frac{(a^2 - b^2)}{2b}$

4 a

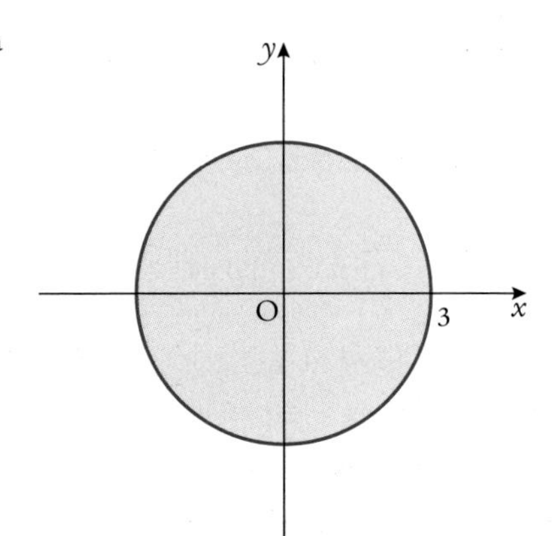

b

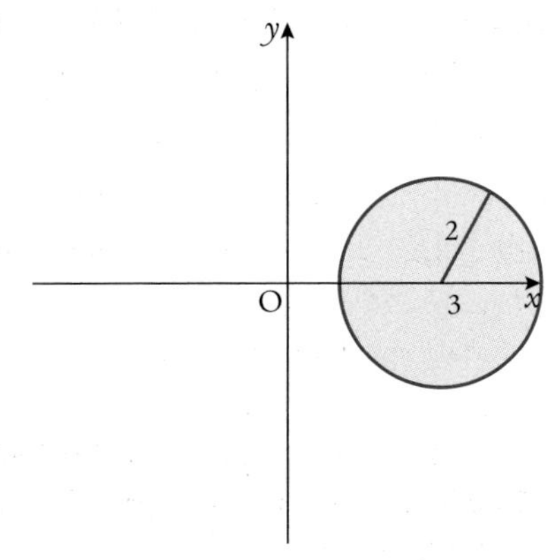

c

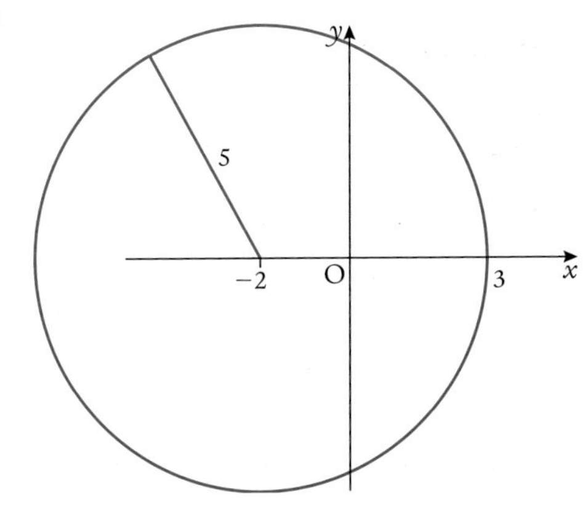

In order to save space in the answers, for the rest of this chapter an abbreviation cis is used as follows.

$a \text{ cis } x = a(\cos x + i \sin x)$

$3 \text{ cis } \frac{\pi}{4} = 3\left(\cos \frac{\pi}{4} + i \sin \frac{\pi}{4}\right)$

$4 \text{ cis } (-20°) = 4(\cos(-20°) + i \sin (-20°))$
$= 4(\cos (20°) - i \sin (20°))$

Exercise 12.5

1 a $12 \text{ cis } \frac{5\pi}{6}$ b $10 \text{ cis } \frac{5\pi}{12}$ c $8 \text{ cis } 0$
d $2 \text{ cis } \left(-\frac{5\pi}{6}\right)$ e $10 \text{ cis } \left(-\frac{\pi}{30}\right)$ f $2 \text{ cis } \left(\frac{\pi}{6}\right)$
g $\frac{5}{2} \text{ cis } \left(\frac{\pi}{8}\right)$ h $3 \text{ cis } \left(\frac{\pi}{3}\right)$ i $4 \text{ cis } \left(\frac{\pi}{7}\right)$

2 a 5 cis 0·927; 1·41 cis 0·785;
Product: 7·07 cis 1·71; Quotient: 3·54 cis 0·142
b 3·61 cis 0·983; 3·16 cis (−0·322);
Product: 11·4 cis 0·661; Quotient: 1·14 cis 1·30
c 1·41 cis (−0·785); 1·41 cis (−2.36);
Product: 2 cis 3.142; Quotient: 1 cis (1·57)
d 4·12 cis (−0·245); 2·83 cis (−0·785);
Product: 11·7 cis (−1·03); Quotient: 1·46 cis (0·540)

3 $z^2 = r^2 \text{ cis } \frac{2\pi}{3}; z^3 = r^3 \text{ cis } \pi; z^4 = r^4 \text{ cis } \left(-\frac{2\pi}{3}\right);$
$z^5 = r^5 \text{ cis } \left(-\frac{\pi}{3}\right); z^6 = r^6 \text{ cis } 0; z^7 = r^7 \text{ cis } \frac{\pi}{3}$

4 i $z^2 = r^2 \text{ cis } \pi; z^3 = r^3 \text{ cis } \left(-\frac{\pi}{2}\right); z^4 = r^4 \text{ cis } 0;$
$z^5 = r^5 \text{ cis } \frac{\pi}{2}; z^6 = r^6 \text{ cis } \pi; z^7 = r^7 \text{ cis } \left(-\frac{\pi}{2}\right)$
ii $z^2 = r^2 \text{ cis } \left(-\frac{2\pi}{3}\right); z^3 = r^3 \text{ cis } 0; z^4 = r^4 \text{ cis } \left(\frac{2\pi}{3}\right);$
$z^5 = r^5 \text{ cis } \left(-\frac{2\pi}{3}\right); z^6 = r^6 \text{ cis } 0; z^7 = r^7 \text{ cis } \frac{2\pi}{3}$
iii $z^2 = r^2 \text{ cis } \left(-\frac{\pi}{2}\right); z^3 = r^3 \text{ cis } \frac{\pi}{4}; z^4 = r^4 \text{ cis } \pi;$
$z^5 = r^5 \text{ cis } \left(-\frac{\pi}{4}\right); z^6 = r^6 \text{ cis } \left(\frac{\pi}{2}\right); z^7 = r^7 \text{ cis } \left(-\frac{3\pi}{4}\right)$
iv $z^2 = r^2 \text{ cis } 2\theta; z^3 = r^3 \text{ cis } 3\theta; z^4 = r^4 \text{ cis } 4\theta;$
$z^5 = r^5 \text{ cis } 5\theta; z^6 = r^6 \text{ cis } 6\theta; z^7 = r^7 \text{ cis } 7\theta$

5 a $-527 - 336i$
b $625[\cos(-2{\cdot}57) + i \sin(-2{\cdot}57)] = -527 - 336i$
c Method 2 would be more efficient especially when dealing with large powers.

Exercise 12.6

1 a i $8 + 13{\cdot}9i$ ii $-887 + 512i$
iii $524\,288 - 908\,093i$
b i $-8i$ ii $-8 - 13{\cdot}9i$ iii $-128 + 221{\cdot}7i$
c i $-2 + 2i$ ii -8i iii -64

2 a $27 \text{ cis } \frac{3\pi}{5}$ b $256 \text{ cis } \left(-\frac{2\pi}{3}\right)$
c $\text{cis } 0 = 1$ d $\text{cis } \frac{4\pi}{7}$

3 a $-46 + 9i$ b $-1121 + 404i$
c $-119 - 120i$ d $1024 + 1024i$

4 a cis 40° b cis (−165°)
c cis 5° d cis 170°
e cis 20° f cis (−6°)
g cis 120° h cis 175°
i cis 100° j cis 24°
k cis 90° l cis 88°

5 a i $\cos^2\theta + 2 \sin\theta \cos\theta\, i - \sin^2\theta$
ii $\cos 2\theta + i \sin 2\theta$
b i $\cos 2\theta = \cos^2\theta - \sin^2\theta$
ii $\sin 2\theta = 2 \sin\theta \cos\theta$

6 a i $\cos^3\theta + 3\cos^2\theta \sin\theta\, i - 3\cos\theta \sin^2\theta - \sin^3\theta\, i$
ii $\cos 3\theta + i \sin 3\theta$
b i $\cos 3\theta = \cos^3\theta - 3\cos\theta \sin^2\theta$
ii $\cos 3\theta = 4\cos^3\theta - 3\cos\theta$
c $\sin 3\theta = 3\sin\theta - 4\sin^3\theta$
d $\sin^3\theta = \frac{1}{4}(3\sin\theta - \sin 3\theta)$

7 a i $\cos 4\theta = 8\cos^4\theta - 8\cos^2\theta + 1$
ii $\sin 4\theta = 4\cos^3\theta \sin\theta - 4\cos\theta \sin^3\theta$
iii $\cos^4\theta = \frac{1}{8}(\cos 4\theta + 8\cos^2\theta - 1)$
b i $\cos 5\theta = 16\cos^5\theta - 20\cos^3\theta + 5\cos\theta$
ii $\sin 5\theta = 5\sin\theta - 20\sin^3\theta + 16\sin^5\theta$
iii $\cos^5\theta = \frac{1}{16}(\cos 5\theta - 5\cos\theta + 20\cos^3\theta)$

8 a i $\text{cis}\left(-\frac{11\pi}{3}\right)$ ii $\text{cis}\left(-\frac{5\pi}{3}\right)$
iii $\text{cis}\left(\frac{\pi}{3}\right)$ iv $\text{cis}\left(\frac{7\pi}{3}\right)$
b i $\frac{\pi}{3}, \frac{\pi}{3}, \frac{\pi}{3}, \frac{\pi}{3}$ ii One distinct answer
c i $\frac{\pi}{6}, -\frac{5\pi}{6}, \frac{\pi}{6}, -\frac{5\pi}{6}$ ii $\text{cis}\left(\frac{\pi}{6}\right), \text{cis}\left(-\frac{5\pi}{6}\right)$
iii

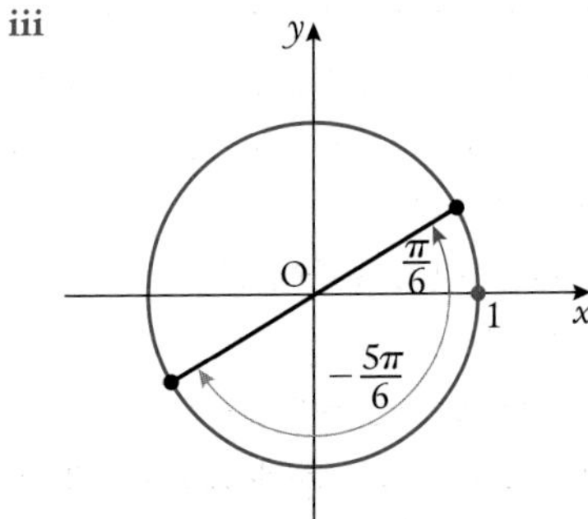

9 a Verifications

b i $\frac{11\pi}{12}, -\frac{5\pi}{12}, \frac{\pi}{4}, \frac{11\pi}{12}, -\frac{5\pi}{12}$

ii $\text{cis}\left(\frac{11\pi}{12}\right), \text{cis}\left(-\frac{5\pi}{12}\right), \text{cis}\left(\frac{\pi}{4}\right)$

iii

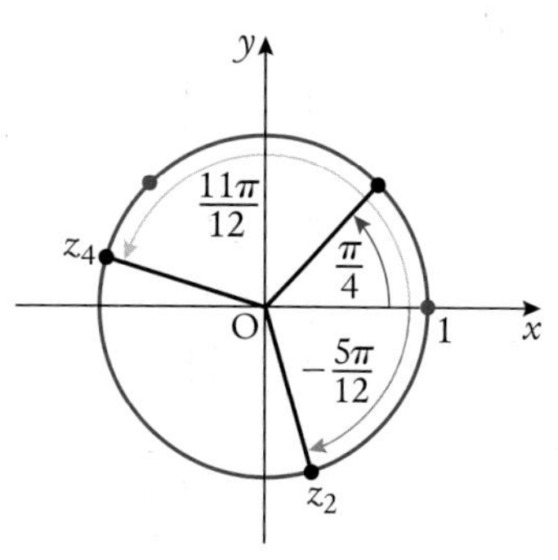

Exercise 12.7

1 a $2\,\text{cis}\left(\frac{\pi}{12} + \frac{2k\pi}{3}\right), k = 0, 1, 2$

b $\text{cis}\left(\frac{\pi}{20} + \frac{2k\pi}{4}\right), k = 0, 1, 2, 3$

c $2\,\text{cis}\left(\frac{\pi}{35} + \frac{2k\pi}{5}\right), k = 0, 1, 2, 3, 4$

d $4\,\text{cis}\left(\frac{2\pi}{9} + \frac{2k\pi}{3}\right), k = 0, 1, 2$

e $2\,\text{cis}\left(-\frac{\pi}{35} + \frac{2k\pi}{5}\right), k = 0, 1, 2, 3, 4$

f $4\,\text{cis}\left(-\frac{2\pi}{9} + \frac{2k\pi}{3}\right), k = 0, 1, 2$

g $2^{\frac{3}{8}}\,\text{cis}\left(-\frac{3\pi}{16} + \frac{2k\pi}{4}\right), k = 0, 1, 2, 3$

h $6^{\frac{1}{5}}\,\text{cis}\left(\frac{2\pi}{15} + \frac{2k\pi}{5}\right), k = 0, 1, 2, 3, 4$

i $8^{\frac{1}{8}}\,\text{cis}\left(\frac{3\pi}{16} + \frac{2k\pi}{4}\right), k = 0, 1, 2, 3$

j $6^{\frac{1}{5}}\,\text{cis}\left(-\frac{2\pi}{15} + \frac{2k\pi}{5}\right), k = 0, 1, 2, 3, 4$

2 a $\text{cis}\left(\frac{2k\pi}{3}\right), k = 0, 1, 2$

b $\text{cis}\left(\frac{2k\pi}{4}\right), k = 0, 1, 2, 3$

c $\text{cis}\left(\frac{2k\pi}{6}\right), k = 0, 1, 2, 3, 4, 5$

d $3\,\text{cis}\left(\frac{2k\pi}{4}\right), k = 0, 1, 2, 3$

e i $\text{cis}\left(\frac{\pi + 2k\pi}{5}\right), k = 0, 1, 2, 3, 4$

ii $\text{cis}\left(\frac{\pi}{10} + \frac{2k\pi}{5}\right), k = 0, 1, 2, 3, 4$

iii $\text{cis}\left(-\frac{\pi}{10} + \frac{2k\pi}{5}\right)$

f i $4\,\text{cis}\left(\frac{\pi}{3} + \frac{2k\pi}{3}\right)$ **ii** $5\,\text{cis}\left(\frac{\pi}{8} + \frac{2k\pi}{4}\right)$

iii $\frac{1}{2}\,\text{cis}\left(-\frac{\pi}{10} + \frac{2k\pi}{5}\right)$

Exercise 12.8

1 a $1 \pm 3i$ **b** $2 \pm i$ **c** $3 \pm 4i$

d $2 \pm 0{\cdot}5i$ **e** $-0{\cdot}5 \pm 0{\cdot}5i$ **f** $-0{\cdot}4 \pm 1{\cdot}2i$

2 a $\pm i$ **b** $-1 \pm 2i$ **c** $-2 \pm 5i$

d $-2 \pm i$ **e** $-0{\cdot}5 \pm 1{\cdot}5i$ **f** $-3 \pm 2i$

3 a $3, -2 \pm i$ **b** $4, 1 \pm 2i$

c $-2{\cdot}5, \pm 2i$ **d** $-1{\cdot}5, -1 \pm 3i$

e $1, \pm 1{\cdot}5i$ **f** $-2{\cdot}5, -2 \pm 3i$

4 $(z + 2)(z - 1), z^2 - 2z + 2$

5 $(z - 2)(z - 1), z^2 - 2z + 5$

6 a $2 - i, -1 \pm i$ **b** $3 - 2i, 1 \pm 2i$

c $1 - 3i, -1, 0{\cdot}5$

7 a $4 \pm i, \pm 2$ **b** $2 \pm 3i, \frac{2}{3}, \frac{1}{2}$

c $4 \pm 2i, 5, -0{\cdot}5$

8 a $-2 \pm i, -1 \pm i, -1$

Review 12

1 a $8 - 8i$ **b** $2 - 16i$

c $63 - 16i$ **d** $5 + 12i$

e $-1{\cdot}32 - 2{\cdot}24i$ **f** $3 - 2i$ or $-3 + 2i$

g 3

2 $a = 2, b = 1$

3 $13(\cos 67{\cdot}4° + i \sin 67{\cdot}4°)$

4 $3{\cdot}54, -81{\cdot}9°$ (3 sf)

5

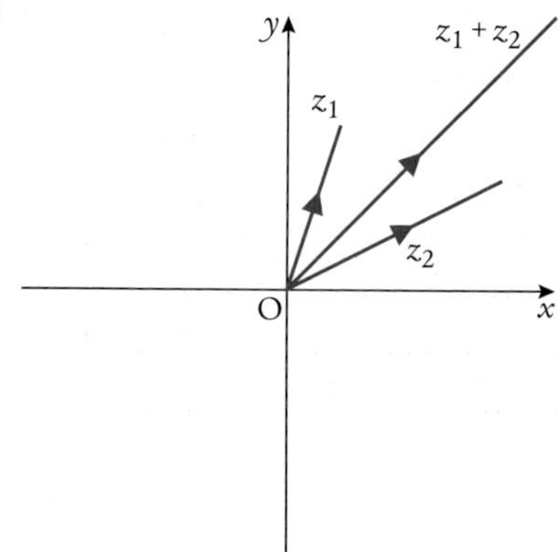

6 a $(x + 1)^2 + y^2 = 25$

b

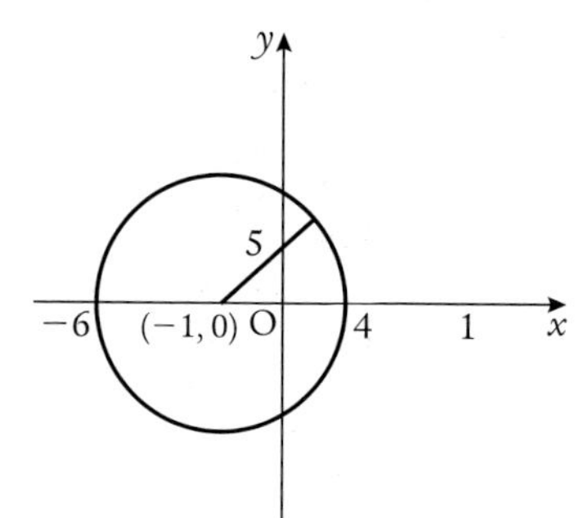

7 a $6\,\text{cis}\left(\frac{\pi}{2}\right)$ **b** $\frac{2}{3}\,\text{cis}\left(\frac{\pi}{6}\right)$

c $8\,\text{cis}\,(\pi)$

8 a $256\,\text{cis}\,(-120°)$ **b** $-128 - 221{\cdot}7i$

9 a i $\cos^5\theta + 5i\cos^4\theta\sin\theta - 10\cos^3\theta\sin^2\theta - 10i\cos^2\theta\sin^3\theta + 5\cos\theta\sin^4\theta + i\sin^5\theta$

ii $\cos 5\theta + i\sin 5\theta$

b $\sin 5\theta = 5\sin\theta - 20\sin^3\theta + 16\sin^5\theta$

10 a $z = 5\,\text{cis}\left(\frac{\pi}{12} + \frac{2k\pi}{3}\right); k = 0, 1, 2$

b 3 radials each 5 units long, 120° apart. First radial at 15°.

11 $\text{cis}\left(\frac{2k\pi}{5}\right), k = 0, 1, 2, 3, 4$

5 radials each 1 unit long, 72° apart. First radial at 0°.

12 $(z+2), (z-1), z^2 - 2z + 17$

13 $2 \pm 3i, 1 \pm 2i$

Chapter 13

Exercise 13.1

1 a 4 b 3 c 2×2

d 3×1 e $\begin{pmatrix}2\\0\end{pmatrix}$ f $(1\ 0\ 3)$

g 1 h -1 i -1

j i 3 ii 0 iii 6 iv 1 v -4 vi 0

2 a 2×2 b 3×1 c 2×3

d 3×4 e 1×3 f 3×3

3 a 3 b 3 c 5

4

	a	b	c	d	e	f
x	2	15	1	4	1	2
y	12	7	−2	3	2	−3

5 a Proof, $x + y = 1$

b i $x = 3, y = 1$ ii $x = 2, y = -1$

iii No solutions iv $x = 3, y = 1$

6 a $\begin{pmatrix}7\\1\end{pmatrix}$ b $\begin{pmatrix}5\\1\end{pmatrix}$ c $\begin{pmatrix}q\\p\end{pmatrix}$

d $(5x\ \ -2y)$ e $(2k+4\ \ 7k+1)$

f $\begin{pmatrix}5 & 7\\4 & 8\\7 & 8\end{pmatrix}$ g $\begin{pmatrix}1 & 5\\4 & 6\\13 & -3\end{pmatrix}$

h $\begin{pmatrix}5 & 5 & 1\\-1 & 1 & 10\end{pmatrix}$ i $\begin{pmatrix}6 & 1 & 5\\3 & 0 & 0\\-2 & 3 & -4\end{pmatrix}$

j $\begin{pmatrix}0 & 0 & 0\\0 & 0 & 0\\0 & 0 & 0\end{pmatrix}$ k $\begin{pmatrix}2\\-1\end{pmatrix}$

l $\begin{pmatrix}6\\-8\end{pmatrix}$ m $\begin{pmatrix}b\\-a\end{pmatrix}$

n $(5a\ \ 3b)$ o $(-3m\ \ -n)$

p $\begin{pmatrix}4 & 1\\-2 & -5\\-5 & 4\end{pmatrix}$ q $\begin{pmatrix}5 & 1\\-3 & 3\\-1 & 3\end{pmatrix}$

r $\begin{pmatrix}5 & -20 & -30\\15 & -15 & -5\end{pmatrix}$ s $\begin{pmatrix}3 & -9 & -3\\12 & -6 & 0\\15 & 3 & 9\end{pmatrix}$

t $\begin{pmatrix}6 & 11 & -4\\-9 & -4 & -6\\13 & 3 & 9\end{pmatrix}$

7 a $\begin{pmatrix}3 & 6\\-1 & 2\end{pmatrix}$ b $\begin{pmatrix}-2 & 1\\-1 & -2\end{pmatrix}$

c $\begin{pmatrix}1 & 5\\2 & -1\end{pmatrix}$ d $\begin{pmatrix}5 & 4\\5 & 10\end{pmatrix}$

e $\begin{pmatrix}1 & 0 & 0\\-1 & 1 & -2\end{pmatrix}$ f $\begin{pmatrix}3 & 4\\7 & 6\\14 & 15\end{pmatrix}$

8 a $\begin{pmatrix}-2 & 0 & -5\\18 & 8 & 5\end{pmatrix}$ b $\begin{pmatrix}7 & -4 & 4\\-5 & -1 & 6\end{pmatrix}$

c $\begin{pmatrix}13 & 0 & 8\\-19 & -3 & 6\end{pmatrix}$ d $\begin{pmatrix}10 & 2 & 2\\0 & 6 & 10\end{pmatrix}$

9 a $\begin{pmatrix}2 & -1\\0 & 3\end{pmatrix}$ b $\begin{pmatrix}2 & 1\\-2 & 1\end{pmatrix}$

c $\begin{pmatrix}5 & 4 & \frac{7}{2}\\6 & -\frac{5}{2} & \frac{3}{2}\end{pmatrix}$

10 a i $\begin{pmatrix}3 & -7\\4 & 9\\1 & 5\end{pmatrix}$ ii $\begin{pmatrix}3 & -4 & 7\\-6 & 7 & 3\\0 & 1 & -2\end{pmatrix}$

iii $\begin{pmatrix}2 & -1\\-1 & 2\end{pmatrix}$ iv $\begin{pmatrix}0 & -1 & 5\\1 & 0 & -2\\-5 & 2 & 0\end{pmatrix}$

b iii Symmetric iv Skew-symmetric

Exercise 13.2

1 a i $\begin{pmatrix}a_{11}+b_{11} & a_{12}+b_{12}\\a_{21}+b_{21} & a_{22}+b_{22}\end{pmatrix}$ ii $\begin{pmatrix}b_{11}+a_{11} & b_{12}+a_{12}\\b_{21}+a_{21} & b_{22}+a_{22}\end{pmatrix}$

b $A + B = B + A$: commutative

c Yes

d i $\begin{pmatrix}a_{11}-b_{11} & a_{12}-b_{12}\\a_{21}-b_{21} & a_{22}-b_{22}\end{pmatrix}$ ii $\begin{pmatrix}b_{11}-a_{11} & b_{12}-a_{12}\\b_{21}-a_{21} & b_{22}-a_{22}\end{pmatrix}$

e $A - B \neq B - A$: non-commutative

2 a i, ii $\begin{pmatrix}a_{11}+b_{11}+c_{11} & a_{12}+b_{12}+c_{12}\\a_{21}+b_{21}+c_{21} & a_{22}+b_{22}+c_{22}\end{pmatrix}$

iii $\begin{pmatrix}a_{11}-b_{11}-c_{11} & a_{12}-b_{12}-c_{12}\\a_{21}-b_{21}-c_{21} & a_{22}-b_{22}-c_{22}\end{pmatrix}$

iv $\begin{pmatrix}a_{11}-b_{11}+c_{11} & a_{12}-b_{12}+c_{12}\\a_{21}-b_{21}+c_{21} & a_{22}-b_{22}+c_{22}\end{pmatrix}$

b Addition is associative; subtraction is not.

3 a i $\begin{pmatrix}xa_{11} & xa_{12}\\xa_{21} & xa_{22}\end{pmatrix}$ ii $\begin{pmatrix}xb_{11} & xb_{12}\\xb_{21} & xb_{22}\end{pmatrix}$

iii & iv $\begin{pmatrix}xa_{11}+xb_{11} & xa_{12}+xb_{12}\\xa_{21}+xb_{21} & xa_{22}+xb_{22}\end{pmatrix}$

b Scalar multiplication is distributive over addition.

4 a i ii iii $\begin{pmatrix} a_{11} & a_{12} \\ a_{21} & a_{22} \end{pmatrix}$ iv $\begin{pmatrix} -a_{11} & -a_{12} \\ -a_{21} & -a_{22} \end{pmatrix}$

b O is the identity element for addition; subtraction is non-commutative.

c The 2×2 zero matrix results.

5 a $\begin{pmatrix} a_{11}+b_{11} & a_{12}+b_{12} \\ a_{21}+b_{21} & a_{22}+b_{22} \end{pmatrix}$

b $\begin{pmatrix} a_{11} & a_{21} \\ a_{12} & a_{22} \end{pmatrix}$ **c** $\begin{pmatrix} b_{11} & b_{21} \\ b_{12} & b_{22} \end{pmatrix}$

d, e $\begin{pmatrix} a_{11}+b_{11} & a_{12}+b_{12} \\ a_{21}+b_{21} & a_{22}+b_{22} \end{pmatrix}$

f $\begin{pmatrix} a_{11} & a_{12} \\ a_{21} & a_{22} \end{pmatrix}$ **g** $\begin{pmatrix} b_{11} & b_{12} \\ b_{21} & b_{22} \end{pmatrix}$

h $\begin{pmatrix} ka_{11} & ka_{12} \\ ka_{21} & ka_{22} \end{pmatrix}$ **i** $\begin{pmatrix} kb_{11} & kb_{21} \\ kb_{12} & kb_{22} \end{pmatrix}$

6 a $\begin{pmatrix} 1 & -2 & 1 \\ -4 & 3 & 0 \\ 7 & 2 & -6 \end{pmatrix}$

b i $\begin{pmatrix} 2 & -6 & 8 \\ -6 & 6 & 2 \\ 8 & 2 & -12 \end{pmatrix}$ ii $\begin{pmatrix} 0 & -2 & 6 \\ 2 & 0 & 2 \\ -6 & -2 & 0 \end{pmatrix}$

c i $A + A'$ symmetric; $A - A'$ skew-symmetric
ii Yes

d $A = \frac{1}{2}(A + A') + \frac{1}{2}(A - A')$

Exercise 13.3

1 a (5) **b** (4) **c** (10)
d (1) **e** (−5) **f** (64)
g $(2x + 3y)$ **h** $(2x + 3y - 4z)$

2 a $\begin{pmatrix} 4 \\ 11 \end{pmatrix}$ **b** $\begin{pmatrix} -1 \\ 2 \end{pmatrix}$ **c** $\begin{pmatrix} -5 \\ -5 \end{pmatrix}$

d $\begin{pmatrix} 5 \\ 2 \end{pmatrix}$ **e** $\begin{pmatrix} 8 \\ -5 \end{pmatrix}$ **f** $\begin{pmatrix} -11 \\ 27 \end{pmatrix}$

g $\begin{pmatrix} 2x+3y \\ 5y-x \end{pmatrix}$ **h** $\begin{pmatrix} 2p-q \\ 3p+7q \end{pmatrix}$ **i** $\begin{pmatrix} 6 & -4 \\ 0 & 1 \end{pmatrix}$

j $\begin{pmatrix} 0 & -4 \\ 1 & -6 \end{pmatrix}$ **k** $\begin{pmatrix} 8 \\ 9 \end{pmatrix}$ **l** $\begin{pmatrix} 2 & 3 \\ -2 & 4 \end{pmatrix}$

m $\begin{pmatrix} 2 \\ 0 \\ 8 \end{pmatrix}$ **n** $\begin{pmatrix} 0 \\ 5 \\ 3 \end{pmatrix}$ **o** $\begin{pmatrix} 0 & 3 \\ 5 & 2 \\ 3 & 11 \end{pmatrix}$

p $\begin{pmatrix} p \\ q \\ r \end{pmatrix}$

3 a $\begin{pmatrix} 1 \\ 0 \end{pmatrix}$ **b** $\begin{pmatrix} 0 \\ 1 \end{pmatrix}$ **c** $\begin{pmatrix} 1 & 0 \\ 0 & 1 \end{pmatrix}$

4 a $\begin{pmatrix} -1 & 4 \\ -2 & -1 \end{pmatrix}$ **b** $\begin{pmatrix} -5 & 2 \\ -1 & -5 \end{pmatrix}$

5 a $\begin{pmatrix} 1 & 5 \\ 5 & 4 \end{pmatrix}$ **b** $\begin{pmatrix} 4 & 5 \\ 7 & -7 \end{pmatrix}$ **c** $\begin{pmatrix} 5 & -2 \\ 16 & -4 \end{pmatrix}$

d $\begin{pmatrix} -1 & 3 \\ 1 & 7 \end{pmatrix}$ **e** $\begin{pmatrix} 1 & 3 \\ 2 & 7 \end{pmatrix}$ **f** $\begin{pmatrix} a+3c & b+3d \\ 2a-c & 2b-d \end{pmatrix}$

Exercise 13.4

1 a i $\begin{pmatrix} -1 & 4 \\ -2 & 2 \end{pmatrix}$ ii $\begin{pmatrix} 2 & 8 \\ -1 & -1 \end{pmatrix}$

b i $\begin{pmatrix} 6 & 2 \\ 2 & -2 \end{pmatrix}$ ii $\begin{pmatrix} 6 & 2 \\ 2 & -2 \end{pmatrix}$

c i $\begin{pmatrix} 12 & -2 \\ 3 & -8 \end{pmatrix}$ ii $\begin{pmatrix} 10 & -10 \\ -3 & -6 \end{pmatrix}$

d i $\begin{pmatrix} -1 & 0 \\ 0 & -1 \end{pmatrix}$ ii $\begin{pmatrix} -1 & 0 \\ 0 & -1 \end{pmatrix}$

2 a No **b** No **c** Yes

3 a $\begin{pmatrix} 5 & 4 \\ -1 & 1 \end{pmatrix}$ **b** $\begin{pmatrix} 6 & 3 \\ -3 & 0 \end{pmatrix}$ **c** Proof

4 a i, ii $\begin{pmatrix} 2 & 3 \\ -5 & 6 \end{pmatrix}$ **b** i, ii $\begin{pmatrix} 4 & 0 \\ 5 & -1 \end{pmatrix}$ **c** i, ii $\begin{pmatrix} a_{11} & a_{12} \\ a_{21} & a_{22} \end{pmatrix}$

5 a Proof **b** $\begin{pmatrix} 1 & 0 & 0 & 0 \\ 0 & 1 & 0 & 0 \\ 0 & 0 & 1 & 0 \\ 0 & 0 & 0 & 1 \end{pmatrix}$

6 a i $\begin{pmatrix} 5 & 17 \\ 1 & 6 \end{pmatrix}$ ii $\begin{pmatrix} 146 & 46 \\ 50 & 17 \end{pmatrix}$ iii $\begin{pmatrix} 46 & 12 \\ 50 & 17 \end{pmatrix}$ iv $\begin{pmatrix} 146 & 46 \\ 50 & 17 \end{pmatrix}$

b Matrix multiplication is associative: $A(BC) = (AB)C$

c Proof

7 a i $\begin{pmatrix} 3 & 4 \\ 1 & 5 \end{pmatrix}$ ii $\begin{pmatrix} 1 & 1 \\ -2 & 3 \end{pmatrix}$ iii $\begin{pmatrix} 4 & -3 \\ 9 & 7 \end{pmatrix}$ iv $\begin{pmatrix} 4 & 9 \\ -3 & 7 \end{pmatrix}$

v $\begin{pmatrix} 4 & 9 \\ -3 & 7 \end{pmatrix}$ vi $\begin{pmatrix} -5 & 15 \\ -9 & 16 \end{pmatrix}$ **b** $(AB)' = B'A'$

c Proof

8 a Proof **b** Proof

Exercise 13.5

1 a $\begin{pmatrix} 22 & 19 \\ 14 & 11 \end{pmatrix}$ **b** $\begin{pmatrix} 41 & 22 & 19 \\ 41 & 27 & 19 \end{pmatrix}$ **c** $\begin{pmatrix} 2 & -3 & -3 \\ 4 & -2 & -4 \\ 0 & 2 & 0 \end{pmatrix}$

2 a $\begin{pmatrix} 20 & 29 & 7 \\ 8 & 15 & 8 \\ 31 & 40 & 11 \end{pmatrix}$ **b** $\begin{pmatrix} 13 & 14 & 20 \\ 1 & -4 & -8 \\ 5 & -2 & -3 \end{pmatrix}$ **c** $\begin{pmatrix} 27 & 31 & 6 \\ 12 & 14 & 1 \\ 61 & 70 & 56 \end{pmatrix}$

d $\begin{pmatrix} -2 & 12 & 5 \\ 2 & -2 & -1 \\ -4 & 1 & -9 \end{pmatrix}$ **e** $\begin{pmatrix} -14 & 25 & -18 \\ 6 & -3 & 8 \\ 10 & -30 & -13 \end{pmatrix}$

f $\begin{pmatrix} 33 & 43 & 27 \\ 9 & 11 & 0 \\ 36 & 38 & 8 \end{pmatrix}$

3 a Proof **b** Yes
4 All false
5 True; proof
6 a Proof **b** $A^3 = 10I + 9A$
7 a Proof **b** Proof
8 a Proof **b** $B^3 = 9B - 28I$
9 a Proof **b** $B^2 = 4B + 5I$
c $B^3 = 21B + 20I$; $B^4 = 104B + 105I$; $B^5 = 521B + 520I$
10 $p = 3$; $q = -17$
11 $p = a_{12}a_{21} - a_{11}a_{22}$; $q = a_{11} + a_{22}$

12 a $8 \; 4 \; 6$ b $a+b \;\; 2b \;\; 3b$

c Proof d $\begin{pmatrix} 22 & 20 & 30 \\ 20 & 13 & 18 \\ 10 & 6 & 10 \end{pmatrix}$

13 a $F^2 = \begin{pmatrix} 3 & 2 & 1 \\ 2 & 2 & 1 \\ 1 & 1 & 1 \end{pmatrix}; F^3 = \begin{pmatrix} 6 & 5 & 3 \\ 5 & 4 & 2 \\ 3 & 2 & 1 \end{pmatrix}; a = 2, b = 1, c = -1$

14 Proof

15 a Proof

b $KL = J, LJ = K, KJ = L, LK = -J, JL = -K$

16 Proof

Exercise 13.6

1 a 14 b 0 c -11 d 7
e 14 f -1 g -5 h 1

2 a 4 b 7 c ± 4 d $-2, 0{\cdot}5$
e $2, -5$ f 270 g $\frac{1}{2}$

3 a i $\begin{pmatrix} 1 & 1 \\ 3 & 2 \end{pmatrix}\begin{pmatrix} x \\ y \end{pmatrix} = \begin{pmatrix} 1 \\ 4 \end{pmatrix}$ ii $|A| = -1 \Rightarrow \exists$ a solution

b i $\begin{pmatrix} 4 & 1 \\ 8 & 2 \end{pmatrix}\begin{pmatrix} x \\ y \end{pmatrix} = \begin{pmatrix} 2 \\ 3 \end{pmatrix}$ ii No solution

c i $\begin{pmatrix} 5 & -2 \\ 10 & -4 \end{pmatrix}\begin{pmatrix} x \\ y \end{pmatrix} = \begin{pmatrix} 2 \\ 1 \end{pmatrix}$ ii No solution

d i $\begin{pmatrix} 5 & -1 \\ 3 & -2 \end{pmatrix}\begin{pmatrix} x \\ y \end{pmatrix} = \begin{pmatrix} 1 \\ 0 \end{pmatrix}$ ii $|A| = -7 \Rightarrow \exists$ a solution

4 a 6 b -5 c ± 6 d No k

Exercise 13.7

1 $\begin{pmatrix} 2 & -1 \\ -3 & 2 \end{pmatrix}$

2 $\begin{pmatrix} \frac{3}{2} & -1 \\ -\frac{5}{2} & 2 \end{pmatrix}$

3 a No inverse b $\begin{pmatrix} -3 & 4 \\ 4 & -5 \end{pmatrix}$ c No inverse

d $-\frac{1}{2}\begin{pmatrix} 3 & 2 \\ 7 & 4 \end{pmatrix}$ e $\begin{pmatrix} 3 & -2 \\ -13 & 9 \end{pmatrix}$

f $\begin{pmatrix} 3 & -2 \\ -7 & 5 \end{pmatrix}$ g $\begin{pmatrix} 3 & 11 \\ 1 & 4 \end{pmatrix}$ h $\begin{pmatrix} -11 & -4 \\ -8 & -3 \end{pmatrix}$

i $\frac{1}{2}\begin{pmatrix} 3 & -1 \\ -7 & 3 \end{pmatrix}$ j $\frac{1}{7}\begin{pmatrix} 3 & -1 \\ -5 & 4 \end{pmatrix}$ k $\begin{pmatrix} -3 & 5 \\ 2 & -3 \end{pmatrix}$

l $\frac{1}{4}\begin{pmatrix} -5 & 8 \\ 3 & -4 \end{pmatrix}$ m No inverse n $\frac{1}{15}\begin{pmatrix} 1 & 2 \\ -6 & 3 \end{pmatrix}$

o $\frac{1}{11}\begin{pmatrix} 4 & -3 \\ 1 & 2 \end{pmatrix}$ p No inverse q $\begin{pmatrix} -\frac{1}{2} & \frac{3}{2} \\ 0 & -\frac{1}{2} \end{pmatrix}$

r $\frac{1}{3}\begin{pmatrix} 3 & 4 \\ 3 & 5 \end{pmatrix}$ s $\frac{1}{12}\begin{pmatrix} -2 & 6 \\ -1 & -3 \end{pmatrix}$ t $-\frac{1}{7}\begin{pmatrix} 1 & 5 \\ 2 & 3 \end{pmatrix}$

4 a $\begin{pmatrix} 2 & 8 \\ 0 & 1 \end{pmatrix}$ b $\begin{pmatrix} 13 & 11 \\ -12 & -10 \end{pmatrix}$ c $\begin{pmatrix} 1 & -3 \\ -1 & 4 \end{pmatrix}$

d $\begin{pmatrix} -2 & -\frac{5}{2} \\ 1 & 1 \end{pmatrix}$ e $\begin{pmatrix} \frac{1}{2} & -4 \\ 0 & 1 \end{pmatrix}$ f $\begin{pmatrix} -5 & -\frac{11}{2} \\ 6 & \frac{13}{2} \end{pmatrix}$

g $\begin{pmatrix} \frac{1}{2} & -4 \\ 0 & 1 \end{pmatrix}$ h $\begin{pmatrix} -5 & -\frac{11}{2} \\ 6 & \frac{13}{2} \end{pmatrix}$

5 a Proof b Proof c Proof

6 a i ii iii iv I

b In general $(AB)^{-1} = B^{-1}A^{-1}$ and $(BA)^{-1} = A^{-1}B^{-1}$

7 a $\frac{1}{a}\begin{pmatrix} 2 & 1 \\ 1 & 1 \end{pmatrix}$ b $\frac{1}{2x}\begin{pmatrix} 4 & -5 \\ -2 & 3 \end{pmatrix}$

c $\frac{1}{t^3}\begin{pmatrix} t^2 & -t^3 \\ -2 & 3t \end{pmatrix}$ d $\begin{pmatrix} \cos\theta & \sin\theta \\ -\sin\theta & \cos\theta \end{pmatrix}$

e $\begin{pmatrix} 1+x & -x \\ x & 1-x \end{pmatrix}$ f $\begin{pmatrix} a & -1-a \\ 1-a & a \end{pmatrix}$

8 a 4 b 1 c ± 2 d $-5, 6$

9 a–g Proofs

10 a Proof b i ii Proofs

11 a i $\begin{pmatrix} 2 & 1 \\ 3 & 2 \end{pmatrix}\begin{pmatrix} x \\ y \end{pmatrix} = \begin{pmatrix} 9 \\ 6 \end{pmatrix}$ ii $\begin{pmatrix} 2 & -1 \\ -3 & 2 \end{pmatrix}$

iii $(x, y) = (2, 5)$

b i $\begin{pmatrix} 4 & -3 \\ 1 & 1 \end{pmatrix}\begin{pmatrix} x \\ y \end{pmatrix} = \begin{pmatrix} 11 \\ 1 \end{pmatrix}$ ii $\frac{1}{7}\begin{pmatrix} 1 & 3 \\ -1 & 4 \end{pmatrix}$

iii $(x, y) = (2, -1)$

c i $\begin{pmatrix} 5 & 4 \\ 4 & -3 \end{pmatrix}\begin{pmatrix} x \\ y \end{pmatrix} = \begin{pmatrix} 10 \\ 39 \end{pmatrix}$ ii $-\frac{1}{31}\begin{pmatrix} -3 & -4 \\ -4 & 5 \end{pmatrix}$

iii $(x, y) = (6, -5)$

d i $\begin{pmatrix} 7 & 4 \\ 3 & 2 \end{pmatrix}\begin{pmatrix} x \\ y \end{pmatrix} = \begin{pmatrix} -1 \\ 1 \end{pmatrix}$ ii $\frac{1}{2}\begin{pmatrix} 2 & -4 \\ -3 & 7 \end{pmatrix}$

iii $(x, y) = (-3, 5)$

e i $\begin{pmatrix} 11 & 4 \\ 2 & 1 \end{pmatrix}\begin{pmatrix} x \\ y \end{pmatrix} = \begin{pmatrix} 17 \\ 5 \end{pmatrix}$ ii $\frac{1}{3}\begin{pmatrix} 1 & -4 \\ -2 & 11 \end{pmatrix}$

iii $(x, y) = (-1, 7)$

f i $\begin{pmatrix} 5 & -2 \\ 3 & -2 \end{pmatrix}\begin{pmatrix} x \\ y \end{pmatrix} = \begin{pmatrix} 34 \\ 18 \end{pmatrix}$ ii $-\frac{1}{4}\begin{pmatrix} -2 & 2 \\ -3 & 5 \end{pmatrix}$

iii $(x, y) = (8, 3)$

12 a $\begin{pmatrix} -1 \\ 2 \end{pmatrix}$ b $\begin{pmatrix} 4 \\ -5 \end{pmatrix}$

c $\begin{pmatrix} -2 \\ 3 \end{pmatrix}$ d $\begin{pmatrix} -4 \\ 11 \end{pmatrix}$

Exercise 13.8

1 a, b Proofs

2 Proof

3 $\begin{pmatrix} 1 & 0 \\ 0 & 1 \end{pmatrix}$ and $\begin{pmatrix} -1 & 0 \\ 0 & -1 \end{pmatrix}$

4 $\begin{pmatrix} 1 & 0 \\ 0 & 1 \end{pmatrix}, \begin{pmatrix} -1 & 0 \\ 0 & -1 \end{pmatrix}, \begin{pmatrix} 0 & -1 \\ 1 & 0 \end{pmatrix}$ and $\begin{pmatrix} 0 & 1 \\ -1 & 0 \end{pmatrix}$

5 a $\begin{pmatrix} -3 & 1 \\ \frac{13}{2} & -2 \end{pmatrix}$ b Proof

6 a $\begin{pmatrix} -3 & 1 \\ 10 & 3 \end{pmatrix}$ b $\begin{pmatrix} 19 & 8 \\ 11 & 5 \end{pmatrix}$

c $\begin{pmatrix} 2 & \frac{9}{4} \\ 1 & -\frac{3}{2} \end{pmatrix}$ d $\begin{pmatrix} 1 & 2 \\ 0 & -1 \end{pmatrix}$

e $\begin{pmatrix} 2 & 1 \\ -1 & 3 \end{pmatrix}$ f $\begin{pmatrix} 1 & 4 \\ -2 & 5 \end{pmatrix}$

7 a $\begin{pmatrix} 2 & 8 \\ -1 & 1 \end{pmatrix}$ b $\begin{pmatrix} 1 & 5 \\ 4 & 9 \end{pmatrix}$

c $\begin{pmatrix} 2 & 3 \\ 4 & 1 \end{pmatrix}$ d $\begin{pmatrix} 6 & -9 \\ 4 & -3 \end{pmatrix}$

8 $-3, 6$

9 $-2, 7$

10 a $\begin{pmatrix} a_{11}b_{11} + a_{12}b_{21} & a_{11}b_{12} + a_{12}b_{22} \\ a_{21}b_{11} + a_{22}b_{21} & a_{21}b_{12} + a_{22}b_{22} \end{pmatrix}$ b Proof

c $|AA'| = |A|\,|A'| = |A|^2$
$= |I| = 1$

11 Proof

12 Right-hand side of equation in each case:

a $A^{-1}B$ b CA^{-1} c $A^{-1}DA^{-1}$

d $C - B - A$ e $A^{-1}(C - B)$ f $(E - D)A^{-1}$

g $A^{-1}(G - F)A^{-1}$ h $A^{-1}CB^{-1}$

i $B^{-1}A^{-1}D$ or $(AB)^{-1}D$

j $EB^{-1}A^{-1}$ or $E(AB)^{-1}$

k $B^{-1}A^{-1}DC^{-1}$ or $(AB)^{-1}DC^{-1}$

l $A^{-1}EC^{-1}B^{-1}$ or $A^{-1}E(BC)^{-1}$

13 $A = \begin{pmatrix} -\frac{4}{5} & -\frac{3}{5} \\ \frac{3}{5} & -\frac{4}{5} \end{pmatrix}$

14 Hint: show that $b = -c$ and $a = d$

15 a–g Proofs

Exercise 13.9

1 a i -9 ii 17 iii -5 b i -9 ii 17 iii -5
c i 7 ii 11 iii -1

2 a i -7 ii -8 iii -10
b i -8 ii 11 iii 2 c $\begin{pmatrix} -8 & 10 & -8 \\ -7 & 11 & -10 \\ 2 & -4 & 2 \end{pmatrix}$

3 a i $ei - fh$ ii $bf - ec$ iii $ah - bg$
b i $dh - eg$ ii $ai - cg$ iii $cd - af$

4 a -19 b -74 c 2 d 0

5 a $-(2a + 3b + 29c)$ b $10r + 8q - p$
c $8m - 5k + 9n$ d 0

6 a $abc + 2fgh - bg^2 - af^2 - ch^2$ b 0

7 a $\begin{pmatrix} a & d & g \\ b & e & h \\ c & f & i \end{pmatrix}$ b i, ii $aei + bfg + cdh - gec - afh - bdi$

c $|A| = |A^T|$

8 a i -2 ii -8 b i 4 ii 36
c -152 d -1998
e i 2 ii $2a^3$ f $|xA| = x^n\,|A|$

Exercise 13.10

1 a $(1, 4)$ b $(7, 6)$ c $(-11, 2)$

2 a $A'(1, 1), B'(3, 2), C'(4, -1)$
b $A'(-1, 1), B'(-2, 3), C'(1, 4)$
c $A'(1, -1), B'(2, -3), C'(-1, -4)$
d $A'(-1, -1), B'(-2, -3), C'(1, -4)$
e $A'(2, 2), B'(4, 6), C'(-2, 8)$
f $A'\left(\frac{1}{2}, \frac{1}{2}\right), B'\left(1, \frac{3}{2}\right), C'\left(-\frac{1}{2}, 2\right)$

3 a $\begin{pmatrix} 2 & 1 \\ -2 & 1 \end{pmatrix}$ b $\begin{pmatrix} 3 & -4 \\ 2 & 3 \end{pmatrix}$ c $\begin{pmatrix} 5 & 3 \\ 3 & -2 \end{pmatrix}$

d $\begin{pmatrix} 1 & 1 \\ 1 & -1 \end{pmatrix}$ e $\begin{pmatrix} 0 & -1 \\ -1 & 0 \end{pmatrix}$

4 a $(a, b) \to (2a + b, a - 2b)$ b $(a, b) \to (3a, a + 4b)$
c $(a, b) \to (b, a)$ d $(a, b) \to (0, b)$
e $(a, b) \to (a, a)$ f $(a, b) \to (0, 0)$

5 a i $A'(1, 0), B'(0, -1)$ ii $\begin{pmatrix} 1 & 0 \\ 0 & -1 \end{pmatrix}$

b i $\begin{pmatrix} -1 & 0 \\ 0 & 1 \end{pmatrix}$ ii $\begin{pmatrix} 0 & 1 \\ 1 & 0 \end{pmatrix}$ iii $\begin{pmatrix} -1 & 0 \\ 0 & -1 \end{pmatrix}$

iv $\begin{pmatrix} -1 & 0 \\ 0 & -1 \end{pmatrix}$ v $\begin{pmatrix} 0 & -1 \\ 1 & 0 \end{pmatrix}$ vi $\begin{pmatrix} \frac{\sqrt{3}}{2} & -\frac{1}{2} \\ \frac{1}{2} & \frac{\sqrt{3}}{2} \end{pmatrix}$

6 a Half-turn about the origin.
b Reflection in $y = -x$.
c Clockwise quarter-turn about the origin.
d 360° rotation or the identity transformation.
e Mapping of plane onto the line $y = x$.
f Mapping of plane onto the origin.

7 a Reduction b Identity
c Enlargement
d Reflection in origin and reduction.
e Mapping to origin.
f Reflection in origin and enlargement.
g Reflection in origin.

Exercise 13.11

1 a $x + y = 0$ b $x + 2y = 0$
c $x + y = 0$ d $3x + 5y = 0$
e $x + 2y = 0$

2 a $y = 2x^2 + 2x$ b $7x - 4y + 5 = 0$
c $4x^2 - 4xy + y^2 + x - y + 1 = 0$
d $x + y = 10$

3 a $\begin{pmatrix} 0 & 1 \\ 1 & 0 \end{pmatrix}$
b $P'(0, 1), Q'(0, 2), R'(1, 2), S'(1, 1)$
c i 1 ii 1 d -1

4 a i $K'(0, 0), L'(18, 0), M'(24, 18)$
ii 18 units², 162 units², 9 iii 9

b i P′(4, 3), Q′(16, 9), R′(16, 14), S′(4, 8)
ii 15 units^2, 60 units^2, 4 iii 4

c Increase in area by a scale factor of 16; determinant = 16

5 a 27π units^2 b $|M| = 1 \Rightarrow$ Same area

6 a Images collinear b $y = 2x$

7 a $3y = 2x$ b $y = 0$
c $x = 0$ d $y = x$

8 a $\begin{pmatrix} -1 & 0 \\ 0 & -1 \end{pmatrix}$ b $\begin{pmatrix} 0 & -1 \\ 1 & 0 \end{pmatrix}$
c $\begin{pmatrix} 0 & 1 \\ -1 & 0 \end{pmatrix}$ d $\begin{pmatrix} 1 & 0 \\ 0 & 1 \end{pmatrix}$
e $\begin{pmatrix} 5 & 0 \\ 0 & 5 \end{pmatrix}$ f $\begin{pmatrix} \frac{1}{2} & 0 \\ 0 & \frac{1}{2} \end{pmatrix}$

9 a i $z \to \bar{z}$ ii $z \to -z$ iii $z \to -\bar{z}$
iv $z \to i\bar{z}$ v $z \to -i\bar{z}$ vi $z \to iz$

b $\begin{pmatrix} \frac{1}{2} & -\frac{\sqrt{3}}{2} \\ \frac{\sqrt{3}}{2} & \frac{1}{2} \end{pmatrix}$

c $1 + 2i, 1 + 4i, 3 - i, 2 - 3; \frac{1}{\sqrt{2}}(1 + i)$

d i $z \to z(\cos \alpha° + i \sin \alpha°); \alpha° = \tan^{-1} \frac{4}{3}$
ii $z \to z(\cos \beta° + i \sin \beta°); \beta° = \tan^{-1} \frac{12}{5}$
iii $z \to 5z(\cos \alpha° + i \sin \alpha°); \alpha° = \tan^{-1} \frac{4}{3}$

Exercise 13.12

1 a i $\begin{pmatrix} 1 & 0 \\ 0 & -1 \end{pmatrix}$ ii $\begin{pmatrix} -1 & 0 \\ 0 & 1 \end{pmatrix}$
iii $\begin{pmatrix} -1 & 0 \\ 0 & -1 \end{pmatrix}$ iv $\begin{pmatrix} -1 & 0 \\ 0 & -1 \end{pmatrix}$

b i $(-a, -b)$ ii $(-a, -b)$ c No

2 a i ii Half-turn about the origin.
b i, ii $(-a, -b)$
c i $\begin{pmatrix} 0 & 1 \\ 1 & 0 \end{pmatrix}$ ii $\begin{pmatrix} 0 & -1 \\ -1 & 0 \end{pmatrix}$ iii $\begin{pmatrix} -1 & 0 \\ 0 & -1 \end{pmatrix}$
iv $\begin{pmatrix} -1 & 0 \\ 0 & -1 \end{pmatrix}$
d O′(0, 0), P′(−6, 0), Q′(−3, −5)

3 a i $\begin{pmatrix} 0 & -1 \\ 1 & 0 \end{pmatrix}$ ii $\begin{pmatrix} 0 & 1 \\ -1 & 0 \end{pmatrix}$
b $FG = -GF$ (Quarter-turn in opposite direction)

4 a i $\begin{pmatrix} \cos A° & -\sin A° \\ \sin A° & \cos A° \end{pmatrix}$ ii $\begin{pmatrix} \cos B° & -\sin B° \\ \sin B° & \cos B° \end{pmatrix}$
iii $\begin{pmatrix} \cos (A+B)° & -\sin (A+B)° \\ \sin (A+B)° & \cos (A+B)° \end{pmatrix}$
b $\cos (A + B) = \cos A \cos B - \sin A \sin B$
$\sin (A + B) = \sin A \cos B + \cos A \sin B$
(The composition of two rotations is a rotation.)

5 a $a - ib$ b $-a + ib$
c $-a - ib$ d $-a - ib$

6 a $\begin{pmatrix} 0 & 1 \\ 1 & 0 \end{pmatrix}$ b $y = (2 + \sqrt{3})x$

Review 13

1 a $\begin{pmatrix} 11 & -3 \\ 6 & 19 \end{pmatrix}$ b $\begin{pmatrix} 1-k & 2 \\ 4 & 3-k \end{pmatrix}$

2 a $\begin{pmatrix} 7 & -2 & 8 \\ 6 & 6 & -5 \\ 7 & -2 & 14 \end{pmatrix}$ b $\begin{pmatrix} 4 & 3 & 0 \\ 9 & 4 & 12 \\ 3 & -6 & 7 \end{pmatrix}$

3 $\begin{pmatrix} 1 & 4 & -1 \\ 4 & 2 & 0 \\ -1 & 0 & 3 \end{pmatrix}$

4 $\begin{pmatrix} 0 & -2 & 1 \\ 2 & 0 & -3 \\ -1 & 3 & 0 \end{pmatrix}$

5 a −5 b 23

6 a $\frac{1}{14}\begin{pmatrix} 4 & 2 \\ -1 & 3 \end{pmatrix}$

7 a Proof b Proof

8 a i $\begin{pmatrix} -1 & 0 \\ 0 & -1 \end{pmatrix}$ ii $\begin{pmatrix} 1 & 0 \\ 0 & -1 \end{pmatrix}$ iii $\begin{pmatrix} -1 & 0 \\ 0 & 1 \end{pmatrix}$
b Show that $MM^T = I = M^TM$ c Proof

9 a $\begin{pmatrix} 3 & -1 \\ 4 & 2 \end{pmatrix}$ b (9, 32)

10 a b Proofs

Chapter 14

Exercise 14.1

1 a $x = 1; y = 4$ b $x = -\frac{1}{3}; y = 3\frac{2}{9}$
c Redundant: $(x, 3 - 4x)$ d Inconsistent
e $x = 2; y = -1$ f $x = 0; y = 2$

2 a Consistent: $x = 3, y = 1$ b Not consistent
c Not consistent
d Consistent: $x = -1, y = -1$

3 Redundant: $\left(x, 1\frac{2}{3} - \frac{2}{3}x\right)$

4 a Let £x = cost of cola; £y = cost of tea:
1 $x + 3y = 3{\cdot}6$; 2 $2x + 2y = 4$; 3 $3x + 2y = 5$
b $x = 1{\cdot}20, y = 0{\cdot}80$ c Not consistent.

Exercise 14.2

1 a i $\begin{pmatrix} 1 & 2 \\ 3 & -1 \end{pmatrix}\begin{pmatrix} x \\ y \end{pmatrix} = \begin{pmatrix} 4 \\ 5 \end{pmatrix}$ ii $\left(\begin{array}{cc|c} 1 & 2 & 4 \\ 3 & -1 & 5 \end{array}\right)$

b i $\begin{pmatrix} 2 & 4 \\ 1 & -2 \end{pmatrix}\begin{pmatrix} x \\ y \end{pmatrix} = \begin{pmatrix} 8 \\ -4 \end{pmatrix}$ ii $\left(\begin{array}{cc|c} 2 & 4 & 8 \\ 1 & -2 & -4 \end{array}\right)$

c i $\begin{pmatrix} 3 & -2 \\ 1 & -1 \end{pmatrix}\begin{pmatrix} x \\ y \end{pmatrix} = \begin{pmatrix} 7 \\ 2 \end{pmatrix}$ ii $\left(\begin{array}{cc|c} 3 & -2 & 7 \\ 1 & -1 & 2 \end{array}\right)$

d i $\begin{pmatrix} 3 & 0 \\ 4 & 1 \end{pmatrix}\begin{pmatrix} x \\ y \end{pmatrix} = \begin{pmatrix} -6 \\ -7 \end{pmatrix}$ ii $\left(\begin{array}{cc|c} 3 & 0 & -6 \\ 4 & 1 & -7 \end{array}\right)$

e i $\begin{pmatrix} 0.5 & 2 \\ 1 & -1.5 \end{pmatrix}\begin{pmatrix} x \\ y \end{pmatrix} = \begin{pmatrix} 3 \\ -5 \end{pmatrix}$ ii $\left(\begin{array}{cc|c} 0.5 & 2 & 3 \\ 1 & -1.5 & -5 \end{array}\right)$

f i $\begin{pmatrix} 0.4 & 0.6 \\ 0.1 & -0.2 \end{pmatrix}\begin{pmatrix} x \\ y \end{pmatrix} = \begin{pmatrix} 0.2 \\ 0.4 \end{pmatrix}$ ii $\left(\begin{array}{cc|c} 0.4 & 0.6 & 0.2 \\ 0.1 & -0.2 & 0.4 \end{array}\right)$

2 a $2x + 4y = 42$, $x + 5 = 57$ b $y = 5$, $2x - y = 4$

c $4x + y = 5$, $3x = 3$ d $3x = 5$, $4y = 3$

Exercise 14.3

1 a $\left(\begin{array}{cc|c} 2 & 1 & 6 \\ 1 & -1 & 1 \end{array}\right); \left(\begin{array}{cc|c} 1 & 0.5 & 3 \\ 0 & -1.5 & -2 \end{array}\right); x = 2\frac{1}{3}, y = 1\frac{1}{3}$

b $\left(\begin{array}{cc|c} 2 & 3 & -1 \\ 1 & -2 & -4 \end{array}\right); \left(\begin{array}{cc|c} 1 & 1.5 & -0.5 \\ 0 & -3.5 & -3.5 \end{array}\right); x = -2, y = 1$

c $\left(\begin{array}{cc|c} 4 & -3 & 22 \\ 2 & 5 & -2 \end{array}\right); \left(\begin{array}{cc|c} 1 & -0.75 & 5.5 \\ 0 & 6.5 & -13 \end{array}\right); x = 4, y = -2$

d $\left(\begin{array}{cc|c} 2 & -1 & -1 \\ 3 & -5 & -4 \end{array}\right); \left(\begin{array}{cc|c} 1 & -0.5 & -0.5 \\ 0 & -3.5 & -2.5 \end{array}\right); x = -\frac{1}{7}, y = \frac{5}{7}$

2 a $\left(\begin{array}{cc|c} 3 & -5 & -8 \\ 2 & -1 & -3 \end{array}\right); \left(\begin{array}{cc|c} 1 & 0 & -1 \\ 0 & 1 & 1 \end{array}\right); x = -1, y = 1$

b $\left(\begin{array}{cc|c} 4 & 7 & 5 \\ 3 & -4 & 13 \end{array}\right); \left(\begin{array}{cc|c} 1 & 0 & 3 \\ 0 & 1 & -1 \end{array}\right); x = 3, y = -1$

c $\left(\begin{array}{cc|c} 2 & -5 & -4 \\ 5 & -2 & -10 \end{array}\right); \left(\begin{array}{cc|c} 1 & 0 & -2 \\ 0 & 1 & 0 \end{array}\right); x = -2, y = 0$

d $\left(\begin{array}{cc|c} 6 & -4 & -36 \\ 9 & 2 & -6 \end{array}\right); \left(\begin{array}{cc|c} 1 & 0 & -2 \\ 0 & 1 & 6 \end{array}\right); x = -2, y = 6$

3 a $\left(\begin{array}{cc|c} 2 & -1 & 1 \\ 6 & -3 & 3 \end{array}\right); \left(\begin{array}{cc|c} 1 & -0.5 & 0.5 \\ 0 & 0 & 0 \end{array}\right);$

b $\left(\begin{array}{cc|c} 1 & 3 & 7 \\ 4 & 12 & 28 \end{array}\right); \left(\begin{array}{cc|c} 1 & 3 & 7 \\ 0 & 0 & 0 \end{array}\right);$

iii When redundancy exists a row of zeros occurs.

4 a $\left(\begin{array}{cc|c} 3 & -2 & 1 \\ 6 & -4 & 3 \end{array}\right); \left(\begin{array}{cc|c} 1 & -\frac{2}{3} & \frac{1}{3} \\ 0 & 0 & 1 \end{array}\right);$ b $\left(\begin{array}{cc|c} 4 & 2 & 5 \\ 2 & 1 & 3 \end{array}\right); \left(\begin{array}{cc|c} 1 & \frac{1}{2} & 1\frac{1}{4} \\ 0 & 0 & \frac{1}{2} \end{array}\right);$

iii When inconsistency exists a row implying "nothing = something" occurs.

5 a $a - b = 9; 4a - 16b = 12$

b $\left(\begin{array}{cc|c} 1 & -1 & 9 \\ 4 & -16 & 12 \end{array}\right); \left(\begin{array}{cc|c} 1 & 0 & 11 \\ 0 & 1 & 2 \end{array}\right); a = 11, b = 2$ c 5.5 units

6 a $\left(\begin{array}{cc|c} 3 & 1 & 10 \\ 5 & -2 & -9 \end{array}\right); \left(\begin{array}{cc|c} 1 & 0 & 1 \\ 0 & 1 & 7 \end{array}\right); x = 1, y = 7$

b i $\left(\begin{array}{cc|c} 3 & 1 & 10 \\ 9 & 3 & 30 \end{array}\right); \left(\begin{array}{cc|c} 1 & \frac{1}{3} & 3\frac{1}{3} \\ 0 & 0 & 0 \end{array}\right)$; Redundant

ii $\left(\begin{array}{cc|c} 3 & 1 & 10 \\ 6 & 2 & 21 \end{array}\right); \left(\begin{array}{cc|c} 1 & \frac{1}{3} & 3\frac{1}{3} \\ 0 & 0 & 1 \end{array}\right)$; Inconsistent

c i If each equation represents a line, redundancy occurs when the equations represent the same line and

ii inconsistency when they represent parallel lines.

Exercise 14.4

1 a $\left(\begin{array}{ccc|c} 1 & 2 & 1 & 8 \\ 3 & 1 & -2 & -1 \\ 1 & 5 & -1 & 8 \end{array}\right); \left(\begin{array}{ccc|c} 1 & 2 & 1 & 8 \\ 0 & 1 & 1 & 5 \\ 0 & 0 & 1 & 3 \end{array}\right); x = 1, y = 2, z = 3$

b $\left(\begin{array}{ccc|c} 2 & 3 & -1 & -1 \\ 1 & -3 & -2 & 4 \\ 5 & 1 & 3 & 4 \end{array}\right); \left(\begin{array}{ccc|c} 1 & 1\frac{1}{2} & -\frac{1}{2} & -\frac{1}{2} \\ 0 & 1 & \frac{1}{3} & -1 \\ 0 & 0 & 1 & 0 \end{array}\right); x = 1, y = -1, z = 0$

c $\left(\begin{array}{ccc|c} 3 & 1 & 0 & 5 \\ 1 & 2 & -3 & -12 \\ 1 & 0 & 2 & 10 \end{array}\right); \left(\begin{array}{ccc|c} 1 & \frac{1}{3} & 0 & 1\frac{2}{3} \\ 0 & 1 & -1\frac{4}{5} & -8\frac{1}{5} \\ 0 & 0 & 1 & 4 \end{array}\right); x = 2, y = -1, z = 4$

d $\left(\begin{array}{ccc|c} 3 & -4 & 1 & 24 \\ 1 & -2 & -2 & 7 \\ 1 & 1 & 1 & 4 \end{array}\right); \left(\begin{array}{ccc|c} 1 & -1\frac{1}{3} & \frac{1}{3} & 8 \\ 0 & 1 & 3\frac{1}{2} & 1\frac{1}{2} \\ 0 & 0 & 1 & 1 \end{array}\right); x = 5, y = -2, z = 1$

e $\left(\begin{array}{ccc|c} 4 & 2 & 1 & 3 \\ 1 & 3 & 5 & 3 \\ 2 & 0 & 3 & 5 \end{array}\right); \left(\begin{array}{ccc|c} 1 & \frac{1}{2} & \frac{1}{4} & \frac{3}{4} \\ 0 & 1 & 1\frac{9}{10} & \frac{9}{10} \\ 0 & 0 & 1 & 1 \end{array}\right); x = 1, y = -1, z = 1$

f $\left(\begin{array}{ccc|c} 1 & 1 & 5 & 0 \\ 4 & 1 & -6 & -17 \\ 1 & -1 & -1 & 0 \end{array}\right); \left(\begin{array}{ccc|c} 1 & 1 & 5 & 0 \\ 0 & 1 & 8\frac{2}{3} & 5\frac{2}{3} \\ 0 & 0 & 1 & 1 \end{array}\right); x = -2, y = -3, z = 1$

2 a $a + b + c = 2, 4a + 2b + c = 7, 9a + 3b + c = 14$

b $a = 1, b = 2, c = -1$

c $y = x^2 + 2x - 1$

3 a $-4g - 2f + c = -5, -2g + 4f + c = -5,$ $12g + 6f + c = -45$

b $g = 3, f = 1, c = -15; x^2 + y^2 - 6x + 2y - 15 = 0$

c $r = 5$

4 a $s + c + g = 185, 3s + 4c + 2g = 460,$ $2s + 3c + 2g = 375; s = 80, c = 5, g = 100$

b After 1 hour there are 5 seconds of GO phase left.

Exercise 14.5

1 a $\left(\begin{array}{ccc|c} 1 & 2 & 1 & 4 \\ 2 & -1 & -1 & 0 \\ 3 & 2 & 1 & 6 \end{array}\right); \left(\begin{array}{ccc|c} 1 & 0 & 0 & 1 \\ 0 & 1 & 0 & 1 \\ 0 & 0 & 1 & 1 \end{array}\right); x = 1, y = 1, z = 1$

b $\left(\begin{array}{ccc|c} 5 & -2 & 1 & 10 \\ 3 & -4 & -1 & 10 \\ 1 & -2 & -2 & 3 \end{array}\right); \left(\begin{array}{ccc|c} 1 & 0 & 0 & 1 \\ 0 & 1 & 0 & -2 \\ 0 & 0 & 1 & 1 \end{array}\right); x = 1, y = -2, z = 1$

c $\left(\begin{array}{ccc|c} 7 & -2 & 3 & -13 \\ 1 & 4 & 3 & 11 \\ 1 & 2 & 1 & 5 \end{array}\right); \left(\begin{array}{ccc|c} 1 & 0 & 0 & -1 \\ 0 & 1 & 0 & 3 \\ 0 & 0 & 1 & 0 \end{array}\right); x = -1, y = 3, z = 0$

d $\left(\begin{array}{ccc|c} 4 & 3 & -2 & 16 \\ 1 & -2 & -3 & -9 \\ 3 & -5 & -2 & -4 \end{array}\right); \left(\begin{array}{ccc|c} 1 & 0 & 0 & 4 \\ 0 & 1 & 0 & 2 \\ 0 & 0 & 1 & 3 \end{array}\right); x = 4, y = 2, z = 3$

e $x = 5, y = 1, z = 1$

f $x = 2, y = -3, z = 2$

2 a/b $\left(\begin{array}{ccc|c} 1 & 1 & -1 & -3 \\ 1 & 2 & -4 & -28 \\ 1 & -1 & -1 & -13 \end{array}\right); \left(\begin{array}{ccc|c} 1 & 0 & 0 & 2 \\ 0 & 1 & 0 & 5 \\ 0 & 0 & 1 & 10 \end{array}\right); a = 2, b = 5, c = 10$

c $y = 2 + 5x - 10x^2$

Exercise 14.6

1 a $x, \frac{25-16x}{9}, \frac{x-10}{9}$ b $x=1, y=2, z=-1$
c Inconsistent: no solutions.
d $x=3, y=1, z=-1$
e Inconsistent: no solutions f $x, \frac{17x+33}{8}, \frac{-11x-3}{8}$

2 $k=0$

3 $k=9$

4 a $d=-9$ and $e \neq 1$ b $d=-9$ and $e=1$
c $d \neq -9$

Exercise 14.7

1 a 1, 1, 2, 1 b 1, 2, 0, −1
c 1, 5, 6, 2 d 1, 3, 5, 1

2 a $a=\frac{1}{2}, b=\frac{1}{2}, c=0; S_n=\frac{1}{2}n^2+\frac{1}{2}n$
b $a=\frac{1}{3}, b=\frac{1}{2}, c=\frac{1}{6}, d=0; S_n=\frac{1}{3}n^3+\frac{1}{2}n^2+\frac{1}{6}n$
c $a=\frac{1}{4}, b=\frac{1}{2}, c=\frac{1}{4}, d=0; S_n=\frac{1}{4}n^4+\frac{1}{2}n^3+\frac{1}{4}n^2$

3 a $\left(\begin{array}{ccc|c} 0.500 & 0.866 & 1 & 11.0 \\ 0.985 & -0.174 & 1 & 8.26 \\ 0.866 & -0.500 & 1 & 6.60 \end{array}\right)$
b $a=2.96, b=4.01, c=6.05; y=3\sin x+4\cos x+6$
c $1<y<11$

Exercise 14.8

1 a i [11.5, 12.5) ii 0.5 iii 4%
b i [24.5, 25.5) ii 0.5 iii 2%
c i [45.5, 46.5) ii 0.5 iii 1%
d i [2.35, 2.45) ii 0.05 iii 2%
e i [7.65, 7.75) ii 0.05 iii 0.6%
f i [9.05, 9.15) ii 0.05 iii 0.5%
g i [0.445, 0.455) ii 0.005 iii 1%
h i [0.355, 0.365) ii 0.005 iii 1%
i i [0.025, 0.035) ii 0.005 iii 17%

2 a i Sum: 35 ± 1; diff: 21 ± 1 ii 1 iii 3%, 5%
b i Sum: 155 ± 1; diff: 1 ± 1 ii 1 iii 0.6%, 100%
c i Sum: 12.7 ± 0.1; diff: 0.1 ± 0.1
ii 0.1 iii 0.8%, 100%
d i Sum: 0.84 ± 0.01; diff: 0.78 ± 0.01
ii 0.01 iii 1%, 1%
e i Sum: 2.25 ± 0.01; diff: 0.25 ± 0.01
ii 0.01 iii 0.4%, 4%
f i Sum: 0.021 ± 0.001; diff: 0.001 ± 1
ii 0.001 iii 5%, 100%

3 a 46 ± 1 b 2.3 ± 0.1
c 1 ± 1 d 85 ± 1
e 2 ± 1 f 0.1 ± 0.1

Exercise 14.9

1 a i

	34.5	35	35.5
16.5	(3, 1.5)	(2.17, 2)	(1.33, 2.5)
17	(4.83, 0.5)	(4, 1)	(3.17, 1.5)
17.5	(6.67, −0.5)	(5.83, 0)	(5, 0.5)

ii/iii $1.33 \leqslant x \leqslant 6.67$ $x=4 \pm 2.76$ (67%);
$-0.5 \leqslant y \leqslant 2.5$ $y=1 \pm 1.5$ (150%)
iv Ill-conditioned

b i

	3.5	4	4.5
12.5	(0.77, 1.95)	(1.05, 1.91)	(1.32, 1.86)
13	(0.73, 2.05)	(1, 2)	(1.27, 1.95)
13.5	(0.68, 2.14)	(0.95, 2.09)	(1.23, 2.05)

ii/iii $0.68 \leqslant x \leqslant 1.32$ $x=1 \pm 0.32$ (32%);
$1.86 \leqslant y \leqslant 2.14$ $y=2 \pm 0.14$ (7%)
iv Poor, but not ill-conditioned.

c i

	18.5	19	19.5
25.5	(2.5, 2)	(0.5, 5.5)	(−1.5, 9)
26	(4, −0.5)	(2, 3)	(0, 6.5)
26.5	(5.5, −3)	(3.5, 0.5)	(1.5, 4)

ii/iii $-1.5 \leqslant x \leqslant 5.5$ $x=2 \pm 3.5$ (175%);
$-3 \leqslant y \leqslant 9$ $y=3 \pm 6$ (200%)
iv Ill-conditioned.

2 a No b Yes
c Yes d Yes

3 a $10x+10y=1700, 10x+11y=1790$
b $x=80, y=90$
c Using 1700.5 and 1789.5 (81.05, 89);
using 1699.5 and 1790.5 (78.95, 91);
$x=80 \pm 1.05, y=90 \pm 1$ (1% error)

4 Ill-conditioned. At least $x=8 \pm 11, y=4 \pm 1.5, z=7 \pm 9$

5 Solution 0, 0, 1, −1.
Using 2, 1, 1, 1 instead gives (1, −1, −1, 1)

Exercise 14.10

1 a $\begin{pmatrix} -1 & 2 & -2 \\ 3 & -6 & 7 \\ 1 & -1 & 1 \end{pmatrix}$ b $\begin{pmatrix} -2 & 1 & 2 \\ 1 & -1 & 0 \\ 1 & 0 & -1 \end{pmatrix}$

c $\begin{pmatrix} 3 & -1 & -1 \\ 0 & -2 & -1 \\ -2 & -1 & 0 \end{pmatrix}$ d $\begin{pmatrix} -1 & -6 & 4 \\ 2 & 11 & -7 \\ 0 & 2 & -1 \end{pmatrix}$

e $\begin{pmatrix} -11 & 16 & 10 \\ 9 & -13 & -8 \\ -17 & 25 & 15 \end{pmatrix}$ f $\begin{pmatrix} -1 & 0 & 1 \\ 2 & 1 & -1 \\ -3 & -1 & 1 \end{pmatrix}$

2 a $\begin{pmatrix}0&0&1\\1&0&0\\0&1&0\end{pmatrix}$ b $\begin{pmatrix}0&0&1\\0&1&0\\1&0&0\end{pmatrix}$

c $\begin{pmatrix}1&-1&-2\\0&-1&-1\\0&0&1\end{pmatrix}$ d $\frac{1}{4}\begin{pmatrix}4&0&0\\-12&4&0\\1&-1&1\end{pmatrix}$

e $\begin{pmatrix}1&-3&7\\0&1&-4\\0&0&1\end{pmatrix}$ f $\begin{pmatrix}1&0&0\\-2&1&0\\5&-4&1\end{pmatrix}$

g $\frac{1}{24}\begin{pmatrix}10&-4&2\\13&2&-7\\-32&8&8\end{pmatrix}$ h $\frac{1}{18}\begin{pmatrix}1&6&7\\3&0&3\\7&6&-5\end{pmatrix}$

3 a $(x, y, z) = (5, -1, 3)$, b $(x, y, z) = (4, 0{\cdot}5, 1)$
c $(x, y, z) = (3, -1, 2)$

4 $(3, 2)$

5 a $(1, -1, 2)$ b $(2, 1, 3)$

6 $\begin{pmatrix}1&-6&3&4\\0&-3&2&2\\-1&8&-4&-5\\0&6&-3&-4\end{pmatrix}$

Review 14

1 $x = 1, y = -1$

2 a $\begin{pmatrix}2&1&1\\3&2&-1\\1&-1&0\end{pmatrix}\begin{pmatrix}x\\y\\z\end{pmatrix} = \begin{pmatrix}2\\6\\0\end{pmatrix}$; $\left(\begin{array}{ccc|c}2&1&1&2\\3&2&-1&6\\1&-1&0&0\end{array}\right)$;

$\left(\begin{array}{ccc|c}1&\frac{1}{2}&\frac{1}{2}&1\\0&1&-5&6\\0&0&1&-1\end{array}\right)$ $x = 1$, $y = 1$, $z = -1$

3 $x = 5, y = -1, z = -3$

4 a $9a + b + 3c = 7; a + b - c = 7; a + 4b + c = 15$
b $a = 1, b = 4, c = -2$
c $x^2 + 4y^2 - 2x - 8y + 1 = 0$

5 a/b $x = 4, y = 1, z = -3$

6 a $p = 1$ and $q \neq \frac{4}{3}$ b $p = 1$ and $q = \frac{4}{3}$

7 i Ill-conditioned.

8 a $\begin{pmatrix}0{\cdot}5&0&0{\cdot}5\\1{\cdot}25&-0{\cdot}5&-0{\cdot}25\\-0{\cdot}75&0{\cdot}5&-0{\cdot}25\end{pmatrix}$

b $\begin{pmatrix}0{\cdot}5&-0{\cdot}5&0\\0{\cdot}25&1{\cdot}25&-0{\cdot}5\\-0{\cdot}375&0{\cdot}125&0{\cdot}25\end{pmatrix}$

Chapter 15

Exercise 15.1

1 Proof; 2:3 2 Proof; 2:3

3 a $\begin{pmatrix}8\\8\\0\end{pmatrix}$ b $\begin{pmatrix}9\\10\\3\end{pmatrix}$ c $\begin{pmatrix}4\\3\\3\end{pmatrix}$ d $\begin{pmatrix}-2\\-6\\0\end{pmatrix}$

e $\begin{pmatrix}-2\\1\\3\end{pmatrix}$ f $\begin{pmatrix}3\\8\\3\end{pmatrix}$

g $\begin{pmatrix}7\\6\\-3\end{pmatrix}$ h $\begin{pmatrix}4\\4\\0\end{pmatrix}$

4 a $\begin{pmatrix}11\\13\\11\end{pmatrix}$ b $\begin{pmatrix}17\\-11\\-1\end{pmatrix}$ c $\begin{pmatrix}10\\0\\-16\end{pmatrix}$

5 a i $W\left(\frac{1}{2}, \frac{5}{2}, 2\right)$ ii $X\left(\frac{1}{2}, \frac{5}{2}, 2\right)$ iii $Y\left(\frac{1}{2}, \frac{5}{2}, 2\right)$
b Proof

6 a $(8, 2, 1)$ b $(3, 4, 7)$ c $(0, -7, 5)$

7 a $85{\cdot}75°$ b $84{\cdot}2°$

8 $81{\cdot}0°$

9 $\frac{2}{3}$

10 a Use scalar product equals zero. b 7

11 21

12 Verification

Exercise 15.2

1 a

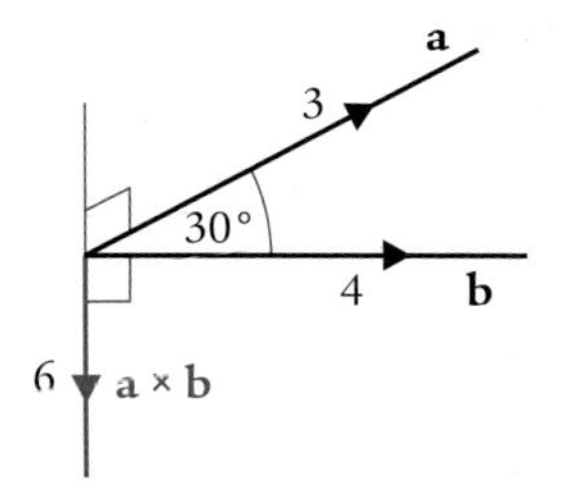

b

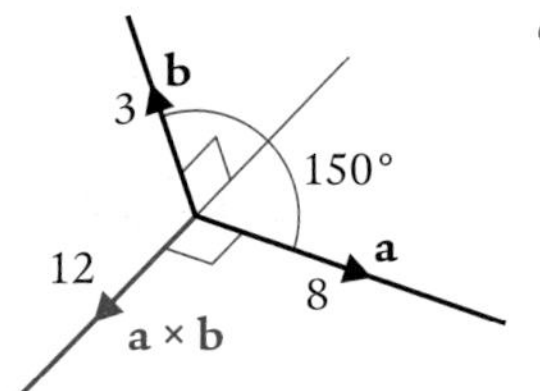

c

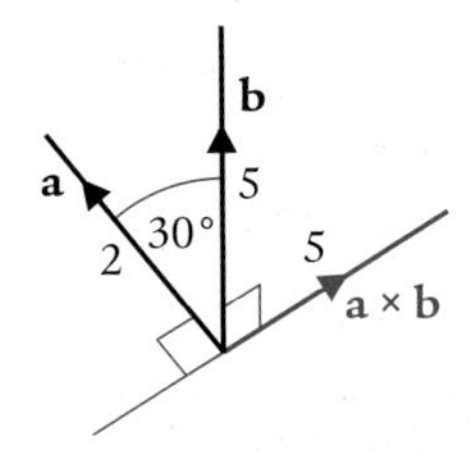

d

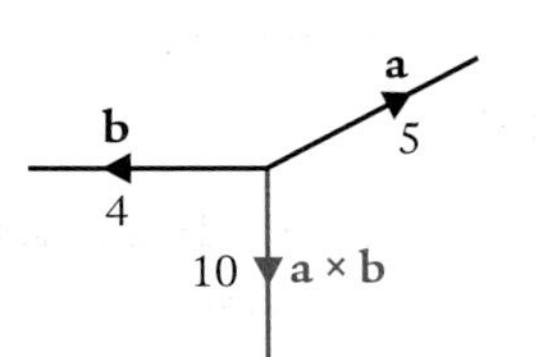

e

7.5 a × b
$5/\sqrt{2}$
b
$\sqrt{6}$
120°
a

f

b $\sqrt{8}$
45°
7
a
14 a × b

2 a $\frac{63}{65}$ b $\frac{16}{65}$ c $16\mathbf{k}$

3 a $56\mathbf{j}$ b $-48\mathbf{i}$ c $-64\mathbf{k}$

d $32\mathbf{i}$

4 Proof 5 Proof 6 Proof

7 Proof 8 $\frac{1}{2}\mathbf{b}\times\mathbf{c}$ 9 Proof

10 Proof 11 Proof

Exercise 15.3

1 a 1 b $3\sqrt{6}$

c $18\sqrt{3}$ d $\sqrt{6122}$

2 a $\begin{pmatrix}7\\-5\\-3\end{pmatrix}$ b $\begin{pmatrix}-6\\-6\\21\end{pmatrix}$

c $\begin{pmatrix}-11\\-27\\23\end{pmatrix}$ d $\begin{pmatrix}-11\\32\\26\end{pmatrix}$

3 a $3\mathbf{b}\times\mathbf{a}$ b $\begin{pmatrix}9\\-9\\-18\end{pmatrix}$

4 Verification, both equal $\begin{pmatrix}6\\-3\\3\end{pmatrix}$

5 Verification $\begin{pmatrix}-10\\7\\-16\end{pmatrix}\neq\begin{pmatrix}5\\0\\-5\end{pmatrix}$

6 a 45 b 90 c −45

7 a $\frac{1}{2}\sqrt{581}$ units^2 b $\frac{1}{2}\sqrt{230}$ units^2

8 a $-1/\sqrt{2}\mathbf{j}-1/\sqrt{2}\mathbf{k}$

b $\frac{4}{3}\sqrt{10}\mathbf{i}+\frac{5}{3}\sqrt{10}\mathbf{j}+\frac{7}{3}\sqrt{10}\mathbf{k}$ c $-\mathbf{k}$

9 a i $\frac{6}{\sqrt{85}}$ ii $\frac{2\sqrt{2}}{3}$ iii $\frac{\sqrt{6}}{3}$

b $-\frac{1}{3}$ and proof

10 Proof

11 a $\frac{\sqrt{29}}{2}$ units^2 b $4\sqrt{3}$ units^2

12 Proof

Exercise 15.4

1 Verification, both equal 53.

2 a 0 b **r** and **p** are parallel

c i $\begin{pmatrix}12\\-16\\-22\end{pmatrix}$ ii $\begin{pmatrix}-76\\-46\\-8\end{pmatrix}$

3 a −30 b −20

c 40

4 55 units^3 5 $4a^3$ units^3

6 1 7 2

8 a 1 b $\mathbf{j}.(\mathbf{k}\times\mathbf{i}), \mathbf{k}.(\mathbf{i}\times\mathbf{j})$

c $\mathbf{i}.\mathbf{k}\times\mathbf{j},\ \mathbf{j}.\mathbf{i}\times\mathbf{k},\ \mathbf{k}.\mathbf{j}\times\mathbf{i}$

Exercise 15.5

1 a $2x+3y+z=12$ b $5x+4y-3z=17$

c $2x-3y+z+1=0$

d $4x-6y-7z+101=0$

2 a $z=4$ b $2x-5y+2z=18$

c $3x-3y+5z=18$ d $8x-2y+z+59=0$

3 a $2\mathbf{i}-\mathbf{j}+4\mathbf{k}$ $2x-y+4z=1$

b i $x+9y+4z=11$ ii $7x-6y-z=0$

iii $6x-5y+6z=15$

4 a $3x-4y+5z=0$ b $x+y=3$

c $10x+y-14z+9=0$ d $x+y+z=a$

5 a $16x+31y+13z=27$ no b $2x+z=3$ yes

c $4x+4y-3z=0$ Yes

6 a $3x+4y+7z=36$

b $48x+21y-52z=75$

c $33x+48y-77z=-619$

7 A4 = A2 − A1 and fill right; A5 = A3 − A2 and fill right; A6 = B4*C5 − B5*C4

B6 = A5*C4 − A4*C5; C6 = A4*B5 − A5*B4;

C7 = A1*A6 + B1*B6 + C1*C6

8 a $z=0$ b $y=0$

c $x=0$ d $x=y$

9 Proof

10 a $\frac{\pm1}{\sqrt{398}}(-9\mathbf{i}-11\mathbf{j}+14\mathbf{k})$ b $\frac{\pm1}{\sqrt{83}}(-3\mathbf{i}+7\mathbf{j}+5\mathbf{k})$

11 $x-y-z+1=0$

12 Proof

Exercise 15.6

1 $\frac{7}{11}$ 2 82.45°

3 78.66° 4 51.28°

Exercise 15.7

[Remember that the vector equation of a plane is not unique – only a *possible* answer is given]

1 a $\mathbf{r}=(2-2t+u)\mathbf{i}+(1+2t-u)\mathbf{j}+(2-3t+2u)\mathbf{k}$

b $\mathbf{r}=(-3+5t+6u)\mathbf{i}+(2-3t-u)\mathbf{j}+(1+t-5u)\mathbf{k}$

c $\mathbf{r}=(4-t+u)\mathbf{i}+(2-t)\mathbf{j}+(1-3t+3u)\mathbf{k}$

2 $\mathbf{r}=(1+2t+u)\mathbf{i}+(1+t-u)\mathbf{j}+(1+2u)\mathbf{k}$

3 a $\mathbf{r}=(1+t+u)\mathbf{i}+(1+4t)\mathbf{j}+(1+t-u)\mathbf{k}$

b $\mathbf{r}=(3+t+u)\mathbf{i}+(-1+t+2u)\mathbf{j}+(4+u)\mathbf{k}$

c $\mathbf{r}=(1+t+u)\mathbf{i}+(3-t-2u)\mathbf{j}+(-4-2t-u)\mathbf{k}$

4 a $2x+3y-4z=10$ b $3x-2y+5z=6$

c $4x+3y-7z=3$

a $\mathbf{r} = (1 - 2t + u)\mathbf{i} + (t - 2u)\mathbf{j} + (1 + 2t)\mathbf{k}$

b $\mathbf{r} = (1 + 2t + 4u)\mathbf{i} + (1 + 5t + u)\mathbf{j} + (1 - 3u)\mathbf{k}$

c $\mathbf{r} = (2 + t + 3u)\mathbf{i} + (2 - t)\mathbf{j} + (1 - t + 2u)\mathbf{k}$

6 a Verification, $t = 3$ $u = -1$ b Proof

7 a Verification, $t = -0.2$ $u = 2.6$ b Proof

8 a Proof e.g. $\underline{WZ} = 5\underline{WX} + \underline{WY}$

b $\mathbf{r} = (2 + 5t - 9u)\mathbf{i} + (-1 - 2t + 8u)\mathbf{j} + (3 - 6t + 17u)\mathbf{k}$

c $14x - 31y + 22z = 125$

9 Proof

10 Verification

11 Verification, both have normal $2\mathbf{i} - \mathbf{j} - 3\mathbf{k}$

12 They lie on the line through the point (3, 2, 7) parallel to $4\mathbf{i} + 5\mathbf{j} + 3\mathbf{k}$

Exercise 15.8

[The equations of a line are not unique. A *possible* answer is given in each case. Equivalent answers will have a similar direction vector and a point which satisfies the other equations.]

1 a $\frac{x-1}{2} = \frac{y+2}{1} = \frac{z-3}{-1}$ b $\frac{x+1}{1} = \frac{y-2}{-1} = \frac{z+2}{1}$

c $\frac{x-4}{3} = \frac{y-2}{1} = \frac{z+1}{3}$

2 a $x = 2t + 5, y = -3, z = t - 1$

b $\frac{x}{1} = \frac{y}{-1} = \frac{z}{2}$ c $x = 0, y = 0, z = t$

3 a $\frac{x}{1} = \frac{y-1}{-1} = \frac{z-3}{7}$ b $\frac{x-5}{1} = \frac{y+1}{3} = \frac{z}{-7}$

c $\frac{x-3}{3} = \frac{y-11}{-12} = \frac{z+2}{2}$

d $\frac{x-2}{1} = \frac{y-1}{6} = \frac{z}{10}$ e $\frac{x}{1} = \frac{y}{2} = \frac{z}{3}$

f $x = a(t + 1), y = -at, z = 0$

4 Verification

5 Verification

6 AB: $\frac{x-2}{1} = \frac{y+1}{2} = \frac{z-3}{1}$

BC: $\frac{x-4}{7} = \frac{y-3}{1} = \frac{z-5}{4}$

AC: $\frac{x+3}{5} = \frac{y-2}{-3} = \frac{z-1}{2}$

Exercise 15.9

1 a $\mathbf{r} = (1 - t)\mathbf{a} + t\mathbf{b}$ b $\mathbf{r} = (1 - u)\mathbf{a} + u\mathbf{b}$

c $\mathbf{r} = (1 - 2s)\mathbf{a} + s\mathbf{b} + s\mathbf{c}$ d $\mathbf{r} = \mathbf{a} + k(\mathbf{c} - \mathbf{b})$

2 a $\mathbf{r} = (1 + t)\mathbf{i} + (1 - 2t)\mathbf{j} - \mathbf{k}$

b $\mathbf{r} = (3t - 1)\mathbf{i} + (2 + t)\mathbf{j} - t\mathbf{k}$

c $\mathbf{r} = (2 + 3t)\mathbf{i} + (2 - t)\mathbf{j} + (1 - t)\mathbf{k}$

d $\mathbf{r} = (2t + 2)\mathbf{i} + (t + 1)\mathbf{j} + (3t - 1)\mathbf{k}$

3 a $\mathbf{r} = t\mathbf{a}$ b $\mathbf{r} = (1 - t)\mathbf{a} + 2t\mathbf{b}$

c $\mathbf{r} = \mathbf{a} + t\mathbf{b}$ d $\mathbf{r} = (1 + t)\mathbf{a} + (2 - t)\mathbf{b}$

4 $-\mathbf{i} + 6\mathbf{j}$

5 $\frac{1}{3}(2\mathbf{c} - \mathbf{b})$

6 a $\mathbf{r} = t(\mathbf{c} - \mathbf{b})$ b $\mathbf{r} = \mathbf{c} + u\mathbf{b}$

c $\mathbf{r} = \frac{1}{2}\mathbf{c} + v\mathbf{b}$

d $\mathbf{r} = w\mathbf{c} + (1 - 2w)\mathbf{b}$ e $\mathbf{r} = (1 + k)\mathbf{c} - 2k\mathbf{b}$

Exercise 15.10

1 a $(2, 1, -1)$ 13·8° b $(7, -3, 0)$ 19·4°

c $\left(0, 9, \frac{5}{3}\right)$ 12·1° d $(3, 2, 4)$ 42·8°

e $(-3, 2, 0)$ 54·5° f $(-1, 4, 7)$ 24·5°

g $(4, 0, 3)$ 15·8° h $(-5, 5, 0)$ 13·1°

2 Proof, show that the direction vector of the line is perpendicular to the normal vector to the plane.

3 Proof (as Q2)

4 Proof (as Q2 but also show that "the" point on the line lies in the plane)

5 Proof (at $(2, -1, 5)$)

6 Proof (at $(4, 3, 0)$)

Exercise 15.11

1 a i Proof ii $(-1, -2, -5)$ iii 69·8°

iv $16x + 22y + z + 55 = 0$

b i Proof ii $(7, 3, -2)$ iii 11·0°

iv $x + 3y + z = 14$

2 a Proof b i $(-2, -4, 1)$ ii 60·6°

c $x - 13y - 19z + 35 = 0$

3 a $(5, -3, 0)$ b 177·2° c $x + 2y + 1 = 0$

Exercise 15.12

1 a $\frac{x+5}{2} = \frac{y-2}{-1} = \frac{z}{1}$ b $\frac{x}{2} = \frac{y-9}{-2} = \frac{z+5}{3}$

2 a e.g. $(5, 0, -1)$ b $3\mathbf{i} + 4\mathbf{j} + 2\mathbf{k}$

c $\frac{x-5}{3} = \frac{y}{4} = \frac{z+1}{2}$

3 a $x = 65t + \frac{21}{2}, y = 1, z = 26t$ or $x = 5t + \frac{21}{2}, y = 1, z = 2t$

b i 21·8° ii 68·2°

Exercise 15.13

1 a In the single point $\left(\frac{13}{5}, \frac{1}{5}, 0\right)$

b In the line $\frac{13-5x}{11} = \frac{1-5y}{2} = \frac{z}{1}$

c In three parallel lines

$\frac{5x-7}{5} = \frac{5y-11}{5} = \frac{z}{-1}$, $\frac{x-1}{1} = \frac{y-2}{1} = \frac{z}{-1}$, $\frac{5x-6}{5} = \frac{5y-13}{5} = \frac{z}{-1}$

d In three parallel lines

$\frac{x}{1}=\frac{3y-1}{-6}=\frac{z}{1}, \frac{2x-1}{2}=\frac{y}{-2}=\frac{z}{1},$
$\frac{x-2}{1}=\frac{3y+4}{-6}=\frac{z}{1}$

2 a Three coincident planes

b Three parallel planes

c The single point $\left(\frac{2}{5}, -\frac{3}{5}, 0\right)$

d The single point $\left(\frac{1}{2}, \frac{1}{2}, \frac{1}{2}\right)$

Review 15

1 $\frac{7}{25}$ 14**k**

2 $5\mathbf{i}+8\mathbf{j}-6\mathbf{k}$

3 110

4 $2x-2y+3z=14$

5 76·1°

6 $\mathbf{r}=\begin{pmatrix}2\\1\\-4\end{pmatrix}+\begin{pmatrix}3-2\\-2-1\\5+4\end{pmatrix}t+\begin{pmatrix}-4-2\\1-1\\2+4\end{pmatrix}u$
$=\begin{pmatrix}2\\1\\-4\end{pmatrix}+\begin{pmatrix}1\\-3\\9\end{pmatrix}t+\begin{pmatrix}-6\\0\\6\end{pmatrix}u$

7 a $\frac{x-2}{2}=\frac{y-1}{4}=\frac{z-1}{5}$

b $\frac{x-2}{1}=\frac{y-1}{-19}=\frac{z-1}{-11}$

8 $\mathbf{r}=(1+t)\mathbf{i}-(2+5t)\mathbf{j}+(1-t)\mathbf{k}$

9 a $(2, 1, -3)$ b 2·2°

10 a Proof, $(-1, -2, -4)$

b $23x-y-8z=11$

11 a $\frac{x}{1}=\frac{y+40}{12}=\frac{z+16}{7}$ b 81·8°

12 The second and third planes are parallel; the first plane intersects them in the parallel lines
$\frac{x+2}{-1}=\frac{y-3}{2}=\frac{z}{1}$ and $\frac{x-1.5}{-1}=\frac{y+0.5}{2}=\frac{z}{1}$

Chapter 16

Exercise 16.1

1 a Only in the case where $x=2k_1+1$ and $y=2k_2+1$ does the product xy take the form $2m+1$. In every other case it takes the form $2m$.

b x^2+x is *always* even.

2 a $a\,|\,b \Rightarrow b=ak, k\in W \Rightarrow bc=akc=a(kc)\Rightarrow a\,|\,bc$

b $a\,|\,b\Rightarrow b=ak_1, a\,|\,c\Rightarrow c=ak_2, k_1, k_2\in W\Rightarrow b+c$
$=a(k_1+k_2)\Rightarrow a\,|\,b+c$

3 a $4x^2=-12xy-9y^2=3(-4xy-3y^2)\Rightarrow 3\,|\,4x^2$
Since 3 does not divide 4 then it must divide x^2.

b A similar argument gives 4 divides $9y^2$, and hence y^2.

c Factorise: $(2x+3y)^2=0\Rightarrow y=-\frac{2}{3}x$.
Integer solutions: $(3, -2), (6, -4), (9, -6)$

4 a $b=2k\Rightarrow 10a+b=2(5a+k)\Rightarrow$ even

b $a-2b=3k\Rightarrow a=3k+2b$
$\Rightarrow n=10a+b=10(3k+2b)+b=30k+21b$
$=3(10k+7b)\Rightarrow 3\,|\,n$

c $a-5b=3k\Rightarrow a=3k+5b$ etc.

d $a-2b=7k\Rightarrow a=7k+2b$ etc.

e $a-5b=17k\Rightarrow a=17k+5b$

f $b=5k\Rightarrow n=10a+5k=5(2a+k)$

g $a-kb=5m\Rightarrow a=5m+kb\Rightarrow$
$n=10a+b=10(5m+kb)+b=5[10m+2kb]+b$
So unless b is divisible by 5, n is not.

5 $1000a+100b+10c+d=(999+1)a+(99+1)b+(9+1)c+d=9(111a+11b+c)+(a+b+c+d)$.
Hence result.

6 $10^{2n}=100^n=(99+1)^n=99k+1=11m+1$
$10^{2n+1}=10^{2n}\,.\,10=(11m+1)\,.\,10=110m+11-1$
$=11n-1$
So $10000a+1000b+100c+10d+e$
$=(11m_1+1)a+(11m_2-1)b+(11m_3+1)c$
$+(11m_4-1)d+e$
$=(11m_1a+11m_2b+11m_3c+11m_4d)$
$+(a-b+c-d+e)$ Hence result.

7 a $2^n-1=(2m)^2\Rightarrow 2^n-1=2\,.\,2m^2\Rightarrow$ odd = even
$2^n-1=(2m+1)^2\Rightarrow 2^n-1=4m^2+4m+1\Rightarrow$
$2^{n-1}=2m^2+2m+1\Rightarrow$ odd = even

b Similar to a but consider $(2m+1)^n$ for $n\geqslant 3$ using its binomial expansion.

8 a i, ii, iii $x^3-x=(x-1)x(x+1)$. Three consecutive numbers. Hence one provides a factor of 2 to the product and one provide a factor of 3. Thus there is a factor of 6.

b From above we know x^3-x can be divided by 2, 3 and 6. We know 12 can be similarly divided. So x^3-x+12 can be divided by 2, 3, 6.

Exercise 16.2

1 a i $2^3\,.\,5^2\,.\,7$ ii $3^2\,.\,5\,.\,11^2$
iii $2^2\,.\,5\,.\,7\,.\,13^2$ iv $2^4\,.\,3^2\,.\,7^2$

b i 24 ii 18 iii 36
iv 45 [Add 1 to each power and multiply results.]

2 a $108=2^2\times3^3$: 1, 2, 3, 4, 6, 9, 12, 18, 27, 36, 54, 108.

b $3528=2^3\times3^2\times7^2$: 1, 2, 3, 4, 6, 7, 8, 9, 12, 14, 18, 21, 24, 28, 36, 42, 49, 56, 63, 72, 84, 98, 126, 147, 168, 196, 252, 294, 392, 441, 504, 588, 882, 1176, 1764, 3528.

c $10\,241=7^2\times11\times19$: 1, 7, 11, 19, 49, 133, 209, 539, 931, 1463, 10 241.

3 a i $2^2\,.\,3^1=12$ ii $2^2\,.\,3^2\,.\,5\,.\,7=1260$
iii $2^4\,.\,3\,.\,5\,.\,7=1680$

b $2^4\,.\,3^2=144$; $2^2\,.\,3^4=324$

4 a $n!$ is divisible by all integers up to n. So $n!+2$ is divisible by 2, $n!+3$ is divisible by 3

b $n! + n$ is divisible by n.
c This generates $(n - 1)$ composites.

5 a $\sqrt{7} = \frac{m}{n} \Rightarrow 7n^2 = m^2$: LHS has odd number of prime factors; RHS has even.
b $\sqrt{p} = \frac{m}{n} \Rightarrow pn^2 = m^2$: LHS has odd number of prime factors; RHS has even.

6 a 37 b 0, 1, 40, 112, 117, 225, 232, ...

7 5

8 a 73 b 0, 1, 9, 104, 190, ...

9 $6^x = 2^x 3^x$; $21^y = 3^y 7^y$
By unique factorization theorem $6^x \neq 21^y$

10 $\log_{10} 5 = \frac{m}{n} \Rightarrow 5 = 10^{\frac{m}{n}} \Rightarrow 5^n = 10^m \Rightarrow 5^n = 2^m . 5^m$
$\Rightarrow 5^{n-m} = 2^m$
By unique factorization theorem $5^{n-m} \neq 2^m$

Exercise 16.3

1 a 37 b 1 c 97
d 42 e 70 f 107
g 41 h 12 i 2
j 181 k 36 l 17017

2 a 12 b 6

3 a 37 b 84

4 a $ab = mG \times nG = mnG \times G = LG \Rightarrow L = \frac{ab}{G} = \frac{ab}{(a, b)}$
b i 778 141 ii 5796 iii 44 460 iv 5 359 794
v 5200 vi 1914

5 3780 cm

6 10 220 days

Exercise 16.4

1 15; 5 . 345 − 6 . 285 = 15

2 53; 2 . 318 − 1 . 583 = 53

3 a 38 b 5 . 1558 − 6 . 1292

4 a GCD = 1 b 59 . 763 − 68 . 662
c 398 . 1178 − 317 . 1479

5 $a = 20, b = -19$

6 $x = -28, y = 291$

7 a $s = 309, t = -482, u = -257, v = 329$
b $a = -16, b = 11, c = -143, d = 114$
c $a = 3, b = 11, c = -10$

8 a $a = -1, b = 1, c = 3, d = -2$
b $a = -7, b = 7, c = 21, d = -14$
c $a = -1, b = 3, c = -1; -n . 2 + 3n . 3 - n . 5 = 2n$

9 a $5n \times 5 - 2n \times 12 = n$: five 5p coins on one pan and two £2 coins on other weighs 1 gram.
b 21 pennies on one side and 23 5p coins on other weighs 1 centigram.

Exercise 16.5

1 a 466 b 511 c 54 d 18 455

2 a 111111_2 b 11031_4
c eee_{12} d 2224_5
e 265_7 f 11125_6

3 a i D_{16} ii 9_{16} iii $D9_{16}$
b i F_{16} ii 8_{16} iii $F8_{16}$
c i C_{16} ii B_{16} iii CB_{16}
d i 4_{16} ii 3_{16} iii 43_{16}
e Group the *bits* into fours and convert.

4 a i 29 ii 9 iii 22
b Units digit records card 1 etc, a 1 means the card is selected, a zero means it is not. Add the top left hand number of the selected cards.
c The card holds the numbers 32 to 63 with 32 in the top left position.
d Top left numbers would be 1, 3, 9, 27, 81. Certain numbers would appear twice on the cards e.g. 8 would appear twice on the '1' card and twice on the '3' card. The victim would have to declare whether the card appeared once or twice. Alternatively, let certain cards be duplicates.

5 a 1, 3, 9, 27 b Base 3 is being exploited.

6 $110_2 = 6$; $20_3 = 6$; $12_4 = 6$; $11_5 = 6$ So $10_6 = 6$, $6_7 = 6$, $6_8 = 6$ etc.

7 a i 1131_4 ii 1634_8 iii 100010_2
b i 527_9 ii 101_2 iii 3314_5
c i 1201_3 ii 1254_7 iii 10101_2
d i 31_4 ii 14_7 iii 111_2

Review 16

1 Unique factorization theorem gives $2 \mid n^4 \Rightarrow n^4 = 2^4 k^4 \Rightarrow n^2 = 2 . 2 . k^2$
Also $2 \mid n^2 \Rightarrow n^2 = 2m \Rightarrow (n^2)^2 = 2 . 2 . m^2 \Rightarrow 2 \mid n^4$

2 True for $n = 1$: If true for $n = k$ then $3^{2k} + 7 = 8m \Rightarrow 3^{2k} = 8m - 7$
Consider $n = k + 1$: $3^{2(k+1)} + 7 = 3^{2k} . 9 + 7$
$= (8m - 7) . 9 + 7 = 8 . 9m - 8 . 7 = 8(9m - 7)$

3 $a - 9b = 13m \Rightarrow a = 13m + 9b \Rightarrow$
$10a + b = 130m + 90b + b = 13(10m + 7b)$

4 $\sqrt{5} = \frac{m}{n} \Rightarrow 5n^2 = m^2 \Rightarrow$ Odd number of factors = even number, of factors. which is impossible given unique factorization theorem.

5 6

6 320 . 251 − 123 . 653

7 211

8 22133_4